GOOD HOUSEKEEPING

Special Diet Cookbook

GOOD HOUSEKEEPING

Special Diet Cookbook

(Originally published as
Good Housekeeping Cookbook for Calorie Watchers)

Plus Recipes for 7 Special Diets

REVISED BY CHRISTINE M. BABIGIAN

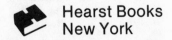

Hearst Books
New York

GOOD HOUSEKEEPING MAGAZINE

Editor in Chief JOHN MACK CARTER

GOOD HOUSEKEEPING INSTITUTE NUTRITION & DIET CENTER

Nutritionist CHRISTINE M. BABIGIAN

Photographer JAMES VILES

Notice to Reader: Before embarking on any diet in this book, we strongly recommend that you consult your doctor. The proper and safe application of information and recipes provided is the responsibility of and undertaken at the sole risk of the reader.

Library of Congress Cataloging in Publication Data

Good housekeeping special diet cookbook.

Originally published: New York. 1971.
Includes index.
1. Low-calorie diet—Recipes. 2. Diet therapy.
3. Cookery for the sick.   I. Babigian, Christine M.
II. Title.   III. Title: Special diet cookbook.
RM222.2.S33 1982   641.5'635   82-1012
ISBN 0-87851-061-3   AACR2
ISBN 0-87851-863-X (pbk.)

10 9 8 7 6 5 4 3 2

MANUFACTURED IN THE UNITED STATES OF AMERICA

Contents

How to Use This Book

This cookbook offers you a variety of sensible, nutritiously sound diets that answer your special needs. It gives weight watchers a wide choice of diet plans that insure pleasurable eating. It also outlines seven therapeutic diets tailored to specific health problems.

All good diets share several objectives. Whether a reducing or therapeutic diet, health considerations come first. In fact, it never hurts to check with your doctor *before* starting a new diet. Second, a good diet offers variety, eliminating any boring regimen. And the proper diet teaches new eating habits that make dieting easier.

Nutritional safety is all-important for a good diet program. The weight loss a crash diet produces may be paid for with a long-term loss of health. Always get your doctor's approval before beginning a diet with the object of losing more than ten pounds. Taking into account your health, age, weight and normal activity, he will recommend the proper calorie level to be maintained. Usually this works out to around 1200 calories for a woman, and 1800 for a man—about two-thirds the intake of nondieters. At this level, most people lose at the rate of one to two pounds a week.

They lose, that is, if they stay on their diet. The trouble is that many diets, including the fad variety, are so monotonous that it takes a saint to stick to them. There is nothing more boring than a diet that is limited to only a few foods—one, for example, that forbids you bread for a sandwich or catchup for a hamburger. That may seem extreme, but these and similar restrictions are a common feature of many fad diets.

In contrast, the diets in this book all include foods from each of the Basic-Four food groups essential for good health, and the recipes—over 600 of them—provide such a variety of taste-pleasing dishes that there will be little temptation to indulge in calorie-laden substitutes. All the recipes are the product of the Good Housekeeping Institute's test kitchens, and have been evaluated for flavor, appearance and reliability. Then, for each, the caloric content has been calculated.

To make matters simple for the cook who must provide for a family member's special needs, at the end of each recipe, instructions for adapting it to fit the most important therapeutic diets are given, wherever possible. In addition, beginning on page 242, general information and 173 more recipes are provided for these special diets.

Diet plans and recipes are not all that is needed for successful weight reduction. Psychological factors are important too, as is a basic understanding of what is involved in losing weight. In this book you will find the fruit of Good Housekeeping's long experience in answering the questions of those with weight problems and in providing them with the necessary support to undertake a successful weight-reduction program. Exercises to help use up calories and to tighten too-long-relaxed muscles provide additional help toward a more shapely future. Finally, the Appendix includes a complete calorie chart, as well as charts showing the iron, sodium, protein, fat, cholesterol and carbohydrate content of a number of selected foods.

A Doctor Talks Sense About Diet

BY DR. WALTER E. O'DONNELL

A well-known specialist in internal medicine, Dr. O'Donnell has helped thousands of women shed extra pounds, to the benefit of both their health and their looks. Drawing on his sympathetic understanding of their problems, he puts the problem of losing weight into a humane and sensible perspective.

Almost everybody agrees that being fat is bad for you. Fat people generally don't live as long as those of normal weight, and they look, feel and act older than their years in the meantime. Let's say you're in your twenties, thirties, or forties—younger women usually haven't begun to care, older ones have given up. You're in the doctor's office for a "checkup" because you always feel tired. Or you want to start on a weight-reduction program. So now settle back and lend an ear as we take it step by step.

Step One: Let's get a few things straight

You Can Lose. Most would-be weight losers are licked before they start—consciously or not, they are willing to go through the motions of a weight-reduction program, but mostly to prove the futility of the whole thing ("At least I tried."). Psychologically or emotionally, maybe some people *won't* lose. But that's a different thing.

Calories Do Count. It's really very simple, a matter of a person's intake versus output. If the number of calories you take in averages more than the number of calories your body uses, you will gain weight. If calories-in average less than calories-out, you will lose weight. If there is a balance between need and expenditure, your weight will remain unchanged. Nothing very complicated about that, but many patients refuse to accept it.

There's No Quick Way. There's no lack of "crash diets" or two-week tickets to a "slender, youthful figure." But if you are lugging around twenty to forty extra pounds, you'd better count on having to stick to the strict part of your diet for two to six months. Then you must find your ideal calorie intake and settle down for the long haul.

There's No Easy Way. There's no way to "sugarcoat" an effective diet. It's strong medicine, and there's no sense in denying it. "Take pounds off the easy way" is an invitation to frustration and failure.

3

There's No New Way. So-called "revolutionary" diets, exciting "research breakthroughs" and weight loss programs "based on an entirely new principle" are nonsensical come-ons.

Dieting Is Not a Part-Time Thing. It's not something you can set aside on birthdays or holidays or when you go out to eat. It's a full-time, twenty-four-hours-a-day, seven-days-a-week thing. Sorry to sound so uncompromising, but you *do* want to lose, don't you?

All Men (and Women) Are Not Created Equal—Biologically, That Is. "Well, if it's calories like you say, how about my friend Gladys. She can eat *anything* and *everything*, and she's as skinny as a rail!" exclaims a patient defiantly. You might as well face the fact now—if you haven't already—that there *are* people like that. It isn't fair, I suppose, and we don't understand why it should be so. But it is. Just don't use it as a reason why *you* can't lose weight. Losing may be harder for you, but you can do it.

No Pill or Shot Will Take Off Weight. People usually ask me, "What can I *take* to lose weight?" (They seldom say "What can I *do?*")I always tell them bluntly, "There's no medication that will take an ounce of flesh off you. There *are* pills and capsules that will help you control your appetite and combat the 'all-gone' feeling that goes with dieting. But that's all they can do."

It's Up to You. Friends can kid you, families can urge you and doctors can advise and help you—but in the final analysis it's up to you. Dieting is a lonely business and that's one reason why so few stick to it. Let's move on to Step Two.

Step Two:
Now answer
a few questions

What Did You Weigh When You Got Married?

This question usually brings color to the cheeks of women and embarrassed smiles to the faces of men. It reminds them that they weren't born fat, and it often provides some kind of mark to shoot at. (See page 319 for height-weight charts).

What Does Your Family Look Like?

Patients leap at this question because it seems to provide an out. "Oh, weight runs in my family," they exclaim excitedly. "My father weighs two hundred and thirty pounds, and my mother— And you should see my sisters!" I admit that the family glands *could* be the cause of all this avoirdupois. But I point out that the more likely cause is the family appetite—seconds on desserts also "run in families."

What Do You Look Like?

This calls for a degree of candor and self-inspection that many women can't muster. Go look in a full-length mirror. I don't know of any more effective instrument of motivation. Especially if you undress and coldly appraise yourself, front, side *and* rear. Next step: Look at some old pictures of yourself taken in your thin days. I would say compare these with some recent photos, but if you run true to form there isn't a single post-inflation picture of you (especially a full-length one) in the house. Right? Then get a snapshot taken for comparison sake.

Why Do You Eat So Much?

This is, of course, a loaded question, the sort of when-did-you-stop-beating-your-wife query which provokes patients into spasms of self-righteous denial. They launch into a pitiful description of the few non-caloric morsels which made up their breakfast. They forget or don't mention the fact that weight-conscious people invariably starve themselves during the day or two before their doctor's appointment. Also passed over is the fact that very few obese people ever eat any breakfast to speak of.

When they see my face, they may retreat a bit. "Well," they say brightly—and hopefully—"I guess it's not that I eat so much. I just eat the wrong things." This is progress on two counts: They have admitted the fact that it's eating that has made them fat, and they have accepted the idea of calorie counting.

What Are Your Eating Habits?

Most overweight people eat little or no breakfast. It's a point of pride with them and usually the jumping-off place for their tale of mystification as to why the scales are groaning under their weight. They lose sight of the fact that the no-breakfast ritual merely sets the stage for all-day nibbling or, when coupled with a skimpy lunch, a really ravenous assault on a calorie-laden evening meal. Calorie consumption per minute for overweight individuals appears to reach its peak between 7 P.M. and 11 P.M.—prime TV (and snack) time.

Discover what leads you to eat impulsively. You may remember times when someone or something upset you. Then you ate to alleviate your stress. However, eating is *not* a panacea. Try identifying the feelings or thoughts that accompany your sudden urge to eat. Whenever you're about to be overwhelmed with the need to eat, try doing something else for 15 minutes. Perhaps you can use this relaxation exercise: Breathe in deeply, and hold for 10 seconds; then let your breath out slowly. Repeat until you feel relaxed.

Before you begin to diet, keep a written record of what you eat each day and how many calories each item contains. Note also the time and place you eat, with whom you eat, how you feel, and whether you are hungry. This makes you more aware of the types of situations that cause you to overeat.

Why Do You Want To Lose Weight?

Would-be weight losers have usually been overweight for months or years. Why the big push to lose just now? The answers are always interesting and often provide an index of how successful the dieter is likely to be. A tubby woman in her forties comes steaming into the office. It seems she was at a party the night before and was mistaken for her husband's mother! Or was introduced through an error as Mrs. Hempstead—"who's sixty if she's a day." Class reunions also have a remarkable effect in resurrecting lost will power. A woman may shrug off her children's remarks, smile away her husband's reproaches and rationalize her own excuses. But when it comes to facing a jury of her peers who will coldly appraise "how Mary looks" five, ten or twenty years since graduation, that's a different story.

Do You Really Want To Lose Weight?

When I ask patients this question, they exclaim, "What? Why of course I do! Would I be here if I didn't?" Then I confront them with the hard question: How badly do they want to lose? Badly enough to face weeks, even months, of self-denial and self-discipline? Badly enough to be merely merry while all the others are eating and drinking too? Badly enough to endure those lonely seesaw battles in which you're sure *nothing* is so important as having that cake or candy? If you can't answer yes, better turn back now. Otherwise, you won't lose weight, but you will gain a guilt complex.

Step Three: Next go see your doctor

Many overweight people skip this step. Of course, it *is* possible to lose weight without your doctor's supervision. Nevertheless, consulting a doctor is still a good idea. Even more important from my point of view, it's a test of your sincerity. If you're willing to spend the time, trouble and money, your chances of success already take a leap forward.

The Checkup. A basic medical examination is the same for the obese patient as for anyone else. It includes a good history of the patient's family background and health, a thorough physical examination and a few laboratory tests. The special questions the doctor asks himself in the case of the obese patient are: (1) Is this the usual story of too many calories? Or is this one of those rare cases in which there are glandular or other factors at work? (2) Is it safe to prescribe appetite-suppressing drugs or other medication to this patient? Or does the presence of coronary disease, etc., make this hazardous? (3) Are there any special precautions which should be observed in the diet prescribed or the rate at which this patient is encouraged to lose? For example, does she have diabetes or other problems which might make unduly restrictive diets or too-rapid loss unwise?

Diets. Don't expect any magic diets. There aren't any. It's calories that count—remember? My main reliance is on reeducating the patient through the use of the calorie diary. More about this shortly.

Drugs. Some physicians will give pills to curb the appetite or calm the nerves of would-be weight losers. But that's all. In truth, there's nothing else to give. The most potent agents must be supplied by the patient—motivation, willpower, determination.

Follow-up. Better than anyone else, the physician can play the dual role of benevolent enforcer and objective observer. He will feel free to say things that nobody else would dare to, and is unlikely to be taken in by implausible self-justifications. My advice is: Go see your doctor at not longer than two-week intervals.

Step Four: Now the diet

I have one not-too-successful weight loser who paraphrases Mark Twain's comment on smoking: "Oh, going on a diet is easy; I've done it hundreds of times." And so it is. It's sticking to the diet that's hard.

Take the Long View. Once you've made your decision, stick to it. Don't redecide at every encounter with food or drink. If you do, there's bound to be at least one time when your willpower will be at a low ebb. Result: A decision in favor of "just-this-once-won't hurt." That first exception to the rule makes every subsequent one just

that much easier, and pretty soon your diet will be a memory.

Keep a Calorie Diary. Now comes the most fascinating insight into the psychology of overweight people. At the doctor's—or anybody else's—merest hint, they will buy and take twenty-five dollars' worth of pills weekly, lay out hundreds of dollars for an exercise machine, struggle through hours of complicated gymnastics in solitary misery or in classes, and travel all over in search of dietetic foods. But will they keep a calorie diary? Something that costs them almost nothing, takes only a few minutes a day—and practically ensures the success of their diet? No.

"It's very simple," I say. "All it takes is a little book with calorie values, a notebook and a pencil—and about five minutes of your time each day. Remember, I'm going to ask to see it next time." Two weeks later I ask for the calorie diary—and get only excuses. Patients, I find, don't like to be their own policemen. Keeping a calorie diary reduces a weight-program to cold hard figures that make it almost impossible to deceive oneself. But faithfully keeping a calorie diary increases a patient's chances of losing weight about tenfold, in my experience. (Use the calorie guide on pages 322-336 to make counting easier.)

How Many Calories?

There is no precise answer to this question because people vary in their ability to tolerate diets. Assuming the dieter is basically healthy and will remain under medical supervision, it really comes down to this: Should she try to lose fast or slowly?

Ideally, a slow, deliberate approach is best. Those who lose pounds this way are more likely to keep them off. Realistically, people are people and they want to see results or they'll soon quit. Most of my patients therefore go on an 800-calorie-per-day program.* I let them make up that total out of almost anything, within reason, they

---

*Dr. O'Donnell keep close tabs on his patients. For dieters not under medical supervision, the Good Housekeeping Bureau recommends a minimum of 1200 calories per day.—ED.

want. If they follow orders and keep a diary, I get a chance to see what they are eating and can put a diet back in balance if it gets too wild.

I am for a loss of about two pounds per week or a little less than ten pounds per calendar month. Motivation stays pretty well nourished at this rate of loss, I find.

At this point many a despairing patient wails, "You mean I've got to eat like *this* for the rest of my life! It's not worth it!" Which brings us to the distinction between a *weight-losing* diet and a *weight-maintenance* diet. I hasten to emphasize the fact that the beginning dieter is getting less food than she really needs so that she will lose weight. As soon as she has gotten down to a good figure, she can gradually increase her calorie allowance to a no-gain, no-loss level. This is obviously considerably above the skimpy rations of her diet.

Exercise?

I have nothing against exercise, but it's hard to imagine a more inefficient way to lose weight. But as a means of streamlining and redistributing body tissue, while losing or as a means of diversion (to keep you away from the table), exercise is great. (See pages 54—64.)

Eating Techniques. Sometimes a poor loser with a long string of diet flops in the past will finally succeed because somebody thought to emphasize such reminders as: Eat slowly and savor each bite; chew your food well; don't eat while nervous or tense; divide your daily allowance into small frequent meals; after eating, get up from the table immediately and busy yourself doing something; line up projects to do and places to go in the evening so you won't just salivate in front of the television set; and, of course, don't keep *any* snack items in the house (for more suggestions, see page 34).

Gimmicks. Many a diet has been snatched from oblivion by the use of an imaginative gimmick. One rotund woman had copies made of her most embarrassing photograph and posted these on her kitchen cabinets and on the refrigerator door—as a stern reminder of what she is fighting for. A bet

that will cost her dearly (or pay off handsomely) is the way another dieter kept herself honest. And, of course, one of the time-honored ways to lick any problem is to organize; get together with a group of fellow weight watchers in a sort of personal anti-calorie crusade. Like Alcoholics Anonymous and similar emotionally linked groups, such an approach can be very effective. Whether organized formally in the manner of TOPS (Take Off Pounds Safely) or Weight Watchers, Inc., or loosely as an off-shoot of the bridge or bowling club, it exploits the in-union-there-is-strength (and willpower) and misery-loves-company streak present in all of us.

Step Five: Don't kid yourself

I've already mentioned this business of kidding yourself—or rationalization, to put it on a loftier plane. Underlying it is the very human desire to find a face-saving way to get out of doing what we know we should do. It's probably overstating the case to say that weight losers harbor a subconscious desire to fail. Most simply want to be exempted from having to try. There are infinite variations on the theme, but here are a few of the ones I hear over and over.

• "I gave up smoking and I just couldn't control my appetite."

• "We were invited out and I just couldn't hurt Mary's feelings by refusing food."

• "We went on vacation and there wasn't much to do but eat and sleep."

• "I got sick and you know you have to keep your strength up."

• "I lost twenty pounds and nobody even noticed it. It's not worth it."

The examples could go on and on. They all have three things in common: They are all partially true; they all could be resolved with just a little foresight or willpower; and they are all substitutes for the real reason for failure.

Now you know my recommended five steps toward becoming a good loser. Will you let them work for you?

Choosing a Diet

There are good diets, bad diets and diets so disastrous that if followed for any length of time they can ruin your health and destroy your looks. To choose a diet that's right for you, you should have an understanding of the rules of good nutrition, as well as insight into your own emotional makeup.

Despite efforts by the country's leading nutritionists to demonstrate both the folly and hazards of fad diets, their popularity continues to grow. An estimated one out of three Americans are overweight to some degree, and nearly all, at one time or another, have tried to lose excess pounds by following "miracle" reducing plans.

Although miracle diets differ in the kinds and amounts of food recommended, they have one thing in common which endears them to weight-conscious Americans: they all promise a swift, easy, painless method of weight reduction.

If followed according to directions, fad diets often work—that is, they do result in weight loss. But the loss is hardly ever permanent, because the diets seldom provide directions for maintaining it through good eating habits. Within a few months the weight is regained and the dieter is not a bit better off than when he started.

THE FOLLY OF FAD DIETS

A more serious drawback to fad diets is that they can be dangerous to health, particularly if followed for too long a period. Nutritionists agree that there is no way to take off excess pounds safely and keep them off except by counting calories—and by following the basic rules of good nutrition. This, of course, requires discipline and strong motivation.

Calorically, foods are divided into three categories: protein, carbohydrate and fat. Along with minerals, vitamins and water, these make up the nutrients essential for proper functioning of the body. Between 30 and 35 percent of the calories in the normal American diet should come from fats and 50 percent from carbohydrates. The remainder—12 to 15 percent—are derived from protein sources. These ratios vary from individual to individual and from day to day.

But fad diets, by their nature, are consistently out of nutritional balance. By far the most common type is the diet that is high in protein and low in carbohydrate. If it emphasizes meat, as most do, then it is also high in fat, particularly saturated fat. Normally, carbohydrates supply half of the body's energy needs. The general theory behind a diet that restricts foods with a high carbohydrate content, primarily sugar and starches, without reducing the total number of calories, is that the body will be forced to use its own adipose (fatty) tissue for energy. Initial weight reduction on these high protein regimes is due to a loss of water. If the diet is continued, any subsequent loss is probably due to decreased caloric intake, because the dieter gets bored with so limited a choice of food and stops eating as much. Even filet mignon, day after day, becomes monotonous.

There are also medical objections to a high-protein, low-carbohydrate diet, particularly if followed for any length of time. For one thing, protein foods must be broken down by the kidneys before they are excreted. When more protein is eaten than is normally required, the overloading puts an extra strain on the kidneys.

The liver also has to do more work. Glucose, a common blood sugar needed for brain and muscle functions, is obtained from carbohydrates. When carbohydrate intake is restricted, certain body tissues (primarily the liver) have to work overtime to manufacture it from protein.

A lack of carbohydrate can lead to a condition called ketosis, since carbohydrate is needed for fat to be oxidized (burnt up). The absence of sufficient carbohydrates leads to the buildup of ketones (compounds formed by the oxidation process). In ketosis the dieter's metabolism begins to resemble that of a diabetic. In essence, sugar is not metabolized properly.

Perhaps the most immediate danger to health from high-protein diets, however, is the increase in blood cholesterol which may result from eating too much animal fat in meat. Arteriosclerosis, a thickening of the arterial walls which can lead to heart attacks, is associated with a rise in the blood's cholesterol level. Many physicians advise consuming moderate amounts of fat and cholesterol to reduce the risk of heart disease.

The five diets that follow are all high in protein, low in carbohydrates. All have attracted avid followers during the past decade. Yet all are nutritionally unsound, particularly for people with existing kidney or heart disease or liver trouble.

High-protein, low-carbohydrate diets

The Doctor's Quick Weight-Loss Diet	This is commonly called the Stillman Diet after its creator, Dr. Irwin Maxwell Stillman, a Brooklyn, N.Y., internist. Dr. Stillman has also advocated a low-protein diet, but his original diet consisted primarily of lean meats, poultry, fish, seafood, eggs, skimmed milk, cheese—all you can eat—and eight glasses of water a day. With no discernible source of carbohydrate, this diet could be dangerous for a person in poor health.
Calories Don't Count	This is an example of a fad diet that not only didn't work, but which resulted in a successful Federal court action against its originator, Dr. Herman Taller, a New York City obstetrician. Published in 1960, this high-protein, high-fat diet featured unlimited quantities of meat (including such high fat items as bacon and sausage), poultry and fish. The plan eliminated sugars and starches. Only vegetables containing minute amounts of carbohydrates were recommended. Dr. Taller stipulated that the dieter also take one safflower-oil capsule daily because he claimed "unsaturated fats . . . soften your body fat and help it out of your system." Taller was convicted in 1967 of mail fraud and violation of the Food, Drug and Cosmetic Act.
The Scarsdale Diet	This high-protein plan developed by the late Herman Tarnower, a New York obstetrician, is another variation of the eat-all-the-protein-you-want approach. Poultry, fish, eggs, beef, and lamb can be eaten in unlimited amounts. Fruits and vegetables are restricted. The diet is very rigid, allowing the dieter few decisions to make about food choices. The promised weight loss is a pound a day, but many people have lost 20 or more in two weeks. Tarnower recommended that his diet not be followed for more than 14 days.
The Dr. Atkins Super Energy Diet	Dr. Robert Atkins devised this diet for anyone who wants to lose weight or suffers from fatigue. The diet lets you eat all you want of foods that contain no carbohydrates (steak, chicken, fish, etc.), along with limited amounts of low-carbohydrate foods, such as salad greens and certain vegetables. Atkins bans sugar and all-purpose flours, claiming that they cause fatigue, depression and anxiety. For those who do not experience super energy, a supplement containing 24 vitamins and minerals is recommended in doses up to 100 times in excess of the body's normal needs. Atkins' diet has received strong criticism from the American Medical and American Heart Associations because of the potential risk of consuming a diet so high in saturated fat.

A diet high in carbohydrate and low in protein also creates nutritional imbalance. These diets usually emphasize grains, such as rice, and fruit. They also limit protein intake to far below the recommended dietary allownce of 44 grams for women and 56 grams for men. Protein, found in every living cell, is needed for growth and to build and repair worn-out tissues. During the digestive process, protein is broken down into small units called amino acids, which are required by various tissues. When there is too little protein intake, the body suffers from negative nitrogen balance. This simply means that the body loses more protein than it takes in, and that the body's own protein stores in the form of muscle tissue have to be used to make up for it. But excess weight is usually fat tissue,and this is what you want to lose—not lean muscle tissue.

High-carbo-hydrate, low-protein diets

Judy Mazel, the creator of this diet, claims you can lose weight and stay slim while eating your favorite foods and following her "conscious combining technique." According to Mazel, different enzymes digest different kinds of foods. When you don't combine foods properly, the enzymes inhibit digestion and undigested foods get "stuck" and turn into fat. The six-week weight-loss diet stresses eating unlimited amounts of fruit for the first 11 days. Eventually some vegetables, meat and fish are introduced. All foods must be eaten separately or combined correctly to allow proper digestion. For example, proteins can be eaten with other proteins or fats, but not with carbohydrates. The diet provides little protein and too many carbohydrates. Often the excessive amount of fruit causes diarrhea, which prompts dehydration and interfers with the absorption of nutrients. The Beverly Hills Diet is not based on true scientific facts. The *Journal of the American Medical Association* reported that the diet can lead to serious illness and even death.

The Beverly Hills Diet

Supposedly a Zen Buddhist diet, the Macrobiotic Diet regime is adopted frequently by young people seeking spiritual awakening. At first, rice is coupled with fruit, vegetables and chicken. Then, as a higher stage of enlightenment is reached, the diet is limited to only rice. This diet can be extremely dangerous, because those who follow it mistakenly believe that brown rice contains healing qualities that guarantee freedom from age, tension and illness. People have starved to death on this diet.

The Macrobiotic Diet

Usually used for several days to begin a diet, total fasting from solid food has been extended by some people to a week or even

Starvation diets

ten days. The idea was popularized after reports of high weight loss in obese people who were hospitalized under a doctor's care during the starvation period. But active people who attempt this often run into difficulties functioning on a day-to-day level. Although fasting does take weight off, it doesn't solve the reducing problem. After the fast is over, the dieter continues to eat the same way as before.

Six diets that really work	The best way to lose weight successfully—and keep it off—is by developing good eating habits. Eat balanced meals, choosing foods daily from the Basic-Four Groups (see page 37). The recommended servings in each group provide 1200 to 1400 calories daily. For women on a reducing schedule, 1200 calories a day is suggested; for men, 1800. Weight loss should average one to two pounds a week. Since it is not practical to fit a woman's full iron requirement (18 milligrams daily) within the 1200-calorie limit, ask your physician to recommend an iron supplement. Men won't need this supplement, and the diets will otherwise meet nutrient needs. A hint for all dieters: Use only whole-grain or enriched breads, crackers, rice or pastas.

Any of the six diets that follow on pages 13 through 29 will meet your nutritional needs, yet each has a special theme to suit your lifestyle and make dieting easier. Need a diet for the entire family or one that really drives home the principles of good menu planning? Use the Basic-Four Reducing Diet. Hate rabbit food and tiny portions? Try I Can't Believe It's a Diet. Nibble constantly? The Six-Meals-a-Day Reducing Diet was meant for you. "Need" cocktails and snacks? Follow the Eat-for-a-Treat Diet. Are you a busy lady—juggling family, job and social life? The Active Woman's Diet lets you eat meals out and entertain. An on-again-off-again dieter? Plan to diet only four days a week on the Wisconsin Diet.

I CAN'T BELIEVE IT'S A DIET

If you want a reducing diet that offers hearty fare for your healthy appetite, this diet plan lets you have generous servings of meat, hefty sandwiches, hearty main-dish casseroles. For women, a sensible 1200 calories a day is recommended; men can have 1800 calories (including two snacks). For boys and girls 7 to 12 and teenage girls, use the basic 1200-calorie diet and add two glasses of skimmed milk. For teenage boys, use "for men" portions, adding two glasses of skimmed milk.

Choose a meal plan from each category every day.

BREAKFAST

(300 calories for women, 400 for men)

1. **Juice, eggs, toast, milk**
   4-ounce glass orange or grapefruit juice
   1 soft- or hard-cooked, poached or scrambled (no added fat) egg
   1 slice toast, 1 teaspoon butter or margarine*
   8-ounce glass skimmed milk
   Coffee or tea**
   For men: Add extra slice toast

2. **Juice, cereal and fruit, milk**
   4-ounce glass orange or grapefruit juice
   1 cup ready-to-eat or 3/4 cup cooked cereal and 1/2 sliced banana or 1/2 cup fresh or unsweetened frozen strawberries
   8-ounce glass skimmed milk
   For men: Have 8-ounce glass juice and extra half serving of cereal

3. **Fruit, pancakes, milk**
   1/2 cup fresh or unsweetened canned orange or grapefruit sections or fruit cocktail
   2 4-inch pancakes (made from mix using skimmed milk) with 1 tablespoon maple syrup
   8-ounce glass skimmed milk
   For men: Have 3 pancakes

LUNCH

(450 calories for women, 500 for men)

1. **Soup, sandwich, salad, milk**
   1 cup soup: beef, chicken or turkey noodle; tomato; onion; vegetable beef or vegetarian vegetable

   Sandwich on bread, toast or large roll with reduced-calorie mayonnaise and lettuce, filled with 2 slices lean beef, chicken, turkey or ham or 1/4 cup flaked tuna or salmon
   Large tossed salad with reduced-calorie dressing or celery, carrot and pickle sticks.

   8-ounce glass skimmed milk
   For men: Add extra slice of meat to sandwich.

2. **Soup, main-dish salad, bread, milk**
   1 cup soup, beef or chicken bouillon or consommé
   1/2 cup egg, tuna, salmon, shrimp, or crab salad prepared with reduced-calorie mayonnaise and lettuce, celery and tomatoes as garnish.
   1 slice bread or toast, 1 teaspoon butter or margarine
   For men: Have 3/4 cup salad

3. **Cottage cheese or yogurt, bread, fruit**
   8-ounce container creamed cottage cheese or vanilla yogurt
   1 cup fresh fruit cocktail or dietetic-packed canned fruit
   8 saltine squares or Melba rounds (1 teaspoon butter or margarine)
   For men: Add large tossed salad with reduced-calorie dressing

4. **Omelet, toast, milk**
   2-egg plain, onion or mushroom omelet (use non-stick finish skillet)
   2 slices toast or 1 toasted English muffin or 1 large roll (do not butter)
   8-ounce glass skimmed milk
   For men: Bread or roll with 1 teaspoon butter or margarine

5. **Hamburger on roll or toast, salad, milk**
   1 4-ounce hamburger served on hamburger or hard roll, or on toast with catchup, mustard, lettuce and tomato or onion, as desired
   Small serving coleslaw or tossed salad with reduced-calorie dressing
   8-ounce glass skimmed milk

* Use whole-grain or enriched breads and crackers wherever possible.
**Have coffee or tea with any meal. Use no more than 1 teaspoon sugar; save part of milk to use as "cream."

For men: Add small apple, peach or tangerine

6. **Frankfurter on roll, sauerkraut, fruit, milk**

   1 grilled or boiled frankfurter with mustard, catchup, or relish as desired, on toasted frankfurter roll

   3/4 cup sauerkraut

   1 serving fruit from list at right, below

   8-ounce glass skimmed milk

   For men: add 3/4 cup tomato, noodle, or vegetable beef soup

DINNER

(450 calories for women, 600 for men)

1. **Meat, vegetable, salad, potatoes, or bread, fruit**

   1/4 pound (weigh uncooked) lean beef, veal, lamb, pork or liver—panbroiled, or braised in tomato juice or water

   2 servings vegetables from list at right, below—one cooked and one as salad with reduced-calorie dressing

   1/2 cup mashed or baked potato or 1 slice bread, 1 small roll, muffin or biscuit (all lightly buttered)

   1 serving fruit from list at right, below

   For men: Have 1/3 pound meat

2. **Fish, potatoes or pasta, vegetable, salad, fruit**

   1/3 pound (weigh uncooked) cod, flounder, haddock, halibut, sole or any seafood, brushed with a little oil and broiled or poached in chicken bouillon or white wine

   3/4 cup rice, noodles or diced potatoes or 1 small baked potato (1 teaspoon butter or margarine)

   2 servings vegetables from list at right, below—one cooked and one as salad with reduced-calorie dressing

   1 serving fruit from list at right, below

   For men: Have 1/2 pound fish or seafood; add 1 slice bread with 1 teaspoon butter or margarine or extra serving potatoes

3. **Chicken, potatoes or pasta, salad, dessert, fruit as snack**

   1 chicken breast (about 1/3 pound), broiled, baked or braised with pineapple juice, bouillon or white wine

   1 serving vegetable from list at right, below—cooked or as salad with reduced-calorie dressing

1/2 cup rice, noodles, or diced potatoes or 1 small baked potato (1 teaspoon butter or margarine)

1 serving any dessert with up to 150 calories from pages 210 to 241

1 serving fruit from list below as snack

For men: Have 1 whole chicken breast (about 3/4 pound)

4. **Casserole, vegetable, potatoes or pasta, salad, fruit**

   1 serving any 200 to 250 calorie main dish from pages 81 to 171

   2 servings vegetables from list below—one cooked and one as salad with reduced-calorie dressing

   1/2 cup mashed or boiled potatoes (no butter or margarine), rice or pasta

   1 serving fruit from list below

   For men: Have 1 1/2 servings main dish

SNACKS FOR MEN ONLY:

Have any two of the following:

1 toasted English muffin with 1 teaspoon butter or margarine	1 1/2 ounces raisins
25 to 30 peanuts	1 cup plain low-fat yogurt with 1 small fresh fruit, cut in pieces
1 medium cantaloupe	2 medium apples, peaches or oranges
12-ounce bottle beer	1 medium slice angel food or sponge cake
1 small cocktail	
5 saltines spread with 1 tablespoon peanut butter	1/2 cup ice milk or sherbet
1 1/2 slices whole-grain bread, toasted, with 1 teaspoon butter or margarine	3 cups popcorn with 1 tablespoon butter or margarine

FRUIT AND VEGETABLE CHOICES

Vegetables: Asparagus, broccoli, Brussels sprouts, cabbage, carrots, cauliflower, celery, green beans, greens, Italian beans, okra, sauerkraut, spinach or tomatoes

Fruits: 1 small fresh peach or apple; 1/2 fresh pear or banana; 2 fresh apricots or plums; 1 cup fresh grapes, cherries, berries or melon cubes; 1/2 cup dietetic-packed canned or frozen fruit.

SIX-MEALS-A-DAY REDUCING DIET

Dieting on six meals a day is a marvelously appealing idea to those who are confirmed nibblers. Although the plan might not be feasible during the week, it does make sense as a weekend diet. Follow one of the other 1200- or 1800-calorie diets for the five working days and then "splurge" on the weekend with the Six-Meals-a-Day Diet.

This reducing plan allows for three regular meals a day plus three sizable snacks. It is a model of flexibility. The easy-to-fix menu ideas are divided into six mealtime sections: breakfast, midmorning, lunch, midafternoon, dinner and midevening. You choose one item from each group each day, from the foods that suit your preferences and schedule. A woman can switch any lunch with any dinner (each is 300 calories), or vary the order of the 150-calorie meals (breakfast and three snacks).

The diet is planned, of course, to provide the nutrients you need. (See note on iron, page 12.) And eating many small meals throughout the day will quell hunger pangs, keep your blood-sugar and energy levels primed for action.

BREAKFAST—150 CALORIES

1/2 cup fruit juice (orange, pineapple, grapefruit, frozen grape or apple); 1 slice white, rye or whole wheat toast with 1 teaspoon butter or margarine

1/2 cup unsweetened orange or grapefruit sections; 1/3 cup cottage cheese

1/2 cup fruit juice (see list above); 1 cup puffed rice or wheat with 1/2 cup skimmed milk

1 cup beef, chicken or vegetable bouillon; 1 slice (1 ounce) Cheddar, Swiss, etc., cheese; 4 saltine squares

1 cup puffed or flaked cereal; 1/2 cup fruit juice (see list above) as "milk"

1 hard-cooked or poached egg; 1 slice toast with 1 teaspoon butter or margarine

BUTTERMILK PANCAKE COINS (see recipe, page 207) with 2 tablespoons applesauce

MIDMORNING—150 CALORIES

2 graham crackers; 1 cup skimmed milk or buttermilk

4 small whole-grain crackers; 1 tablespoon peanut butter

1 small banana; 1/3 cup cottage cheese

fruit juice (see list under breakfast); 1 muffin with 1 teaspoon butter or margarine

1 slice (1 ounce) lean boiled ham; 1 slice toast and lettuce

1 slice lightly buttered raisin toast with 1 teaspoon butter or margarine; 1/2 cup orange juice

1 thinly sliced hard-cooked egg; 4 saltine squares

LUNCH—300 CALORIES

roast-beef sandwich (2 slices bread, 1 ounce lean roast beef, reduced-calorie mayonnaise and lettuce); 1 cup skimmed milk or buttermilk; carrot and celery sticks

1 serving (3/4 cup) beef noodle soup; 2 saltine squares; 1/2 cup cottage cheese; 1/2 cup drained canned apricot halves

1/2 cup shrimp, tuna, crab or lobster salad (use reduced-calorie French dressing); tomato, celery, or lettuce; 1 small hard roll or 1 slice toast; 1 cup skimmed milk or buttermilk

OYSTER STEW (recipe, page 105); 10 oyster crackers; tossed salad with reduced-calorie dressing; 1/2 cup drained peach slices

bacon, lettuce, and tomato sandwich (2 slices toast, 2 strips crisp bacon, lettuce, tomato, 1 tablespoon reduced-calorie mayonnaise); 1/2 cup skimmed milk or buttermilk

8 ounces (1 container) fruited yogurt; 2 saltine squares or 2 Melba rounds or 1/2 slice bread

1 cup (made with skimmed milk) cream of tomato or New England clam chowder soup; 2 scrambled eggs; 1 slice unbuttered toast

MIDAFTERNOON—150 CALORIES

1 serving cream of chicken, mushroom or celery soup prepared with skimmed milk; 2 rye crackers

1 cup fresh strawberries, raspberries or blueberries; 1/4 cup reduced-calorie sour cream made by blending cottage cheese until smooth

1 plain or blueberry muffin with 1 teaspoon butter or margarine; 1/2 cup skimmed milk or buttermilk

2 saltine squares; 1 slice (1 ounce) Cheddar, Swiss, etc., cheese

1 8-ounce container plain yogurt

1/3 cantaloupe filled with 1/3 cup vanilla ice milk

1 slice American, Cheddar or Swiss cheese; 1 small apple or orange

DINNER—300 CALORIES

1/2 cup tomato juice; two broiled, lean loin lamb chops; 1/2 cup broccoli; 1/2 cup carrots; lettuce wedge with 1 tablespoon reduced-calorie Thousand Island dressing

2 grilled frankfurters (catchup or mustard to taste); 1/2 cup sauerkraut

HERB'S FAVORITE FLOUNDER (recipe, page 92); 1/2 cup mashed summer squash; 1/2 cup mixed vegetables; 1/2 cup applesauce

beef consommé; 4 ounces (raw weight) pan-broiled chicken or beef livers; 1/2 cup peas; thinly sliced cauliflowerettes with 1 tablespoon reduced-calorie dressing

BACON-STUFFED BURGERS (recipe, page 142); 6 asparagus spears; tomato and cucumber salad and 1 tablespoon reduced-calorie French dressing

CHICKEN KABOBS ITALIANO (recipe, page 130); 1/3 cup rice; tossed salad with reduced-calorie dressing

3 ounces (cooked) lean roast beef; ONIONS WITH A ZEST (recipe, page 182); 1/2 cup green beans; relish tray of carrots, celery, pickle slices

MIDEVENING—150 CALORIES

1/2 cup pudding made with skimmed milk

2 small homemade chocolate chip or sandwich-type cookies; black coffee or tea

1 1/2 cups popcorn with 2 teaspoons butter or margarine, salt to taste

1 cup plain yogurt

SHERBET SHAKE (recipe, page 70)

1/2 cup ice milk

watermelon—1 slice, 6 inches in diameter and 1 1/2 inches thick

BREAKFAST—200 CALORIES

$1/2$ cup fruit juice (orange, pineapple, grapefruit, frozen grape or apple); $11/2$ slices lightly buttered white, rye or whole-wheat toast with 1 teaspoon butter or margarine

$1/2$ cup unsweetened orange or grapefruit sections; $3/4$ cup cottage cheese

$1/2$ cup fruit juice (see list above); 1 cup puffed rice or wheat; $1/2$ cup skimmed milk

1 cup beef, chicken or vegetable bouillon; $11/2$ slices ($11/2$ ounces) Cheddar, Swiss, etc., cheese; 4 saltines

$1/2$ cup fruit juice (see list above): 1 soft- or hard-cooked or poached egg; 1 slice toast with 1 teaspoon butter or margarine

$1/2$ cup unsweetened orange or grapefruit sections; BUTTERMILK PANCAKE COINS (see recipe, page 207) with 2 tablespoons applesauce

$1/2$ cup fruit juice (see list above); $3/4$ cup cooked farina or oatmeal; $1/2$ cup skimmed milk

MIDMORNING—200 CALORIES

4 whole grain crackers; 1 slice (1 ounce) Cheddar, Swiss, etc., cheese

5 graham crackers; 1 cup skimmed milk or buttermilk

4 small whole grain crackers; 2 tablespoons peanut butter

1 large banana; $1/2$ cup cottage cheese

fruit juice (see list under breakfast);

1 English muffin with 1 teaspoon butter or margarine; 2 slices (2 ounces) lean boiled ham; 1 slice toast with 1 teaspoon butter or margarine; lettuce; $11/2$ slices raisin toast with 1 teaspoon butter or margarine; $1/2$ cup orange juice

LUNCH—400 CALORIES

roast-beef sandwich (2 slices bread, 2 ounces lean roast beef, reduced-calorie mayonnaise and lettuce); 1 cup skimmed milk or buttermilk;

carrot and celery sticks; $1/2$ cup water packed or fresh pears

1 serving ($3/4$ cup) beef-noodle soup; 3 saltine squares; $1/2$ cup cottage cheese; $1/2$ cup drained canned apricot halves; 1 cup skimmed milk or buttermilk

1 cup shrimp, tuna, crab or lobster salad (use reduced-calorie French dressing); tomato, celery or lettuce; 1 small lightly buttered hard roll; 1 cup skimmed milk or buttermilk

OYSTER STEW (see recipe, page 105); 20 oyster crackers; tossed salad with reduced-calorie dressing; 1 cup canned peach slices, drained

bacon, lettuce and tomato sandwich (2 slices toast, 2 strips crisp bacon, lettuce, tomato, 1 tablespoon reduced-calorie mayonnaise); 1 cup skimmed milk or buttermilk; 1 small apple

8 ounces (1 container) fruited yogurt; 1 medium roll with 1 teaspoon butter or margarine

1 serving ($3/4$ cup) tomato or Manhattan clam-chowder soup; 2 scrambled eggs; 1 slice lightly buttered toast with 1 teaspoon butter or margarine; 1 cup skimmed milk or buttermilk

MIDAFTERNOON—200 CALORIES

$11/2$ cup serving cream-of-chicken, mushroom or celery soup prepared with skimmed milk; 2 rye crackers

1 cup fresh strawberries, raspberries or blueberries; $1/2$ cup reduced-calorie sour cream made by blending cottage cheese until smooth

1 plain or blueberry muffin with 1 teaspoon butter or margarine; 1 cup skimmed milk or buttermilk

1 8-ounce container coffee or vanilla yogurt

watermelon—1 slice, 6 inches in diameter and 2-inches thick

2 thinly sliced hard-cooked eggs; 3 saltine squares

$1/2$ cantaloupe filled with $2/3$ cup vanilla ice milk

DINNER—600 CALORIES

$1/2$ cup tomato juice; 2 broiled lean

loin lamb chops; $3/4$ cup chopped broccoli; $3/4$ cup carrots; 1 slice lightly buttered rye bread with 1 teaspoon butter or margarine; lettuce wedge with 1 tablespoon Thousand Island dressing; $1/2$ cup canned peaches, drained

2 grilled frankfurters (catchup or mustard to taste) on frankfurter rolls; $2/3$ cup sauerkraut; $1/2$ cup flavored gelatin

HERB'S FAVORITE FLOUNDER (see recipe, page 92); $1/2$ cup mashed potatoes; $1/2$ cup mixed vegetables; tossed salad with 1 tablespoon French dressing; $3/4$ cup applesauce

beef consommé; 6 ounces (raw weight) panbroiled chicken or beef livers; $1/2$ cup peas; thinly sliced cauliflowerettes with 1 tablespoon Italian dressing; small bunch fresh grapes

BACON-STUFFED BURGERS (see recipe, page 142); 6 asparagus spears; tomato and cucumber salad with 1 tablespoon French dressing; $1/2$ cup bananas in orange juice

CHICKEN KABOBS ITALIANO (see recipe, page 130); $3/4$ cup rice; tossed salad with 1 tablespoon French dressing

4 ounces (cooked) lean roast beef; ONIONS WITH A ZEST (see recipe, page 182); $1/2$ cup green beans; relish tray of carrots, celery and pickle slices; thin slice sponge cake

MIDEVENING—200 CALORIES

1 cup grape juice

16 cashew nuts

3 small homemade chocolate chip or sandwich-type cookies; black coffee or tea

2 cups popcorn with 1 tablespoon butter or margarine and salt to taste (try garlic salt for an interesting change)

$11/2$ ounces Cheddar cheese; 3 whole grain crackers

1 cup flavored gelatin

$2/3$ cup ice milk (any flavor)

BASIC-FOUR REDUCING DIET

The Basic-Four Reducing Diet provides 1200 calories a day for women and 1800 for men—the most practical (easiest to maintain) calorie levels for long-term reducing. There are literally hundreds of everyday foods to choose from, so you can fit the diet to your budget and special food preferences of your family.

Listed on the next page are your food choices, each with its recommended portion. Also, there is a list of diet "extras"—those foods which often make meals (and snacks) more appetizing.

Your Diet Plan, below, lists total servings allowed from each group each day. The menu outline with it suggests a practical way to distribute the servings among three meals. This is, of course, simply a guide, not a rigid menu plan. As long as you include the number of servings listed for each group in Your Diet Plan, you will get all you need nutritionally (see note on iron, page 12) and also reduce. Before you start, check the Suggested Menus and the Helpful Tips opposite.

YOUR DIET PLAN

FOOD GROUPS		WOMEN	MEN
For the day	**Calories:**	**1200**	**1800**
		servings	
meat and protein-rich foods		2	3
fruits and vegetables			
fruits		3	5
vegetables		2 to 4	2 to 4
breads, cereals, pastas, some vegetables		4	6
milk and milk products		2	2
extras		3	6
For each meal:			
BREAKFAST			
fruit		1	1
bread, cereals, etc.		1	2
milk and milk products		1	1
extras		1	2
LUNCH OR SUPPER			
meat and protein-rich foods		1	1
vegetables		1 to 2	1 to 2
breads, cereals, etc.		2	2
fruit		1	2
milk and milk products		1	1
extras		1	2
DINNER			
meat and protein-rich foods		1	2
vegetables		1 to 2	1 to 2
bread, cereals, etc.		1	2
fruit		1	2
extras		1	2

At each meal, if you wish: coffee or tea with little or no sugar, with milk rather than cream.

SUGGESTED MENUS

*(portion sizes may be adjusted
for either men or women)*

1

Breakfast: Orange juice, cornflakes, skimmed milk
Lunch: Hamburger on toasted roll with pickle relish, coleslaw, apple, yogurt
Dinner: Baked fish fillets with lemon sauce, greens, broiled tomatoes, buttered muffin, cinnamon-topped pineapple chunks

2

Breakfast: Half grapefruit, poached egg, toast with cream cheese, skimmed milk
Lunch: Grilled ham sandwich, tossed salad with reduced-calorie dressing, fresh-fruit cup, skimmed milk
Dinner: Pot roast of beef with gravy (see note in Helpful Tips), oven-roasted potatoes, Brussels sprouts, apricots and a cookie

3

Breakfast: Fresh-fruit cup with cottage cheese, 1/2 buttered toasted English muffin
Lunch: Tuna salad, pickle and celery slices, hard roll, pears, skimmed milk
Dinner: Roast leg of lamb with natural gravy, herbed rice, Italian beans, peach halves on lettuce with blue-cheese dressing, for salad and dessert

4

Breakfast: Pineapple-grapefruit juice, oatmeal, 1 teaspoon butter or margarine, skimmed milk
Lunch: Chili con carne, tossed salad with reduced-calorie French dressing, bananas with sour cream, skimmed milk
Dinner: Roast chicken with gravy (see note in Helpful Tips), baked potatoes, chopped spinach, cucumbers in oil-and-vinegar dressing, canned peaches

5

Breakfast: Orange juice, puffed wheat, 1/2 cup skimmed milk
Lunch: Chicken-salad sandwich, celery sticks, tangerine, skimmed milk
Dinner: Grilled beef cubed steaks, red cabbage, corn, tossed salad, reduced-calorie dressing, chocolate pudding (see last suggestion under Helpful Tips)

HELPFUL TIPS

•Roast, broil or braise meat. Panbroiling is fine, but don't add fat unless you count it toward "extras."
•Trim extra fat from meats before you cook them.
•Four ounces of raw meat (without bone) will yield about 3 ounces of cooked meat.
•For gravies, slightly thicken canned chicken or beef broth with cornstarch. Season to taste with garlic, onion or celery salt or other herbs and spices.
•Have milk at any meal or as a snack—it's not essential to have it at breakfast or lunch.
•"Extras" can be saved from one meal to another, but remember to keep tabs on the total for the day.
•You can count all cheeses (except cream cheese) as a serving of either Meat and Protein-Rich Foods or Milk and Milk Products in order to gain the necessary number of servings daily in each category.
•Make puddings with skimmed milk. Count a 1/2-cup serving as 1/2 cup milk and an "extra."

MEAT AND PROTEIN-RICH FOODS

Cheese
cottage,* farmer's, pot or ricotta, 1/2 cup
American, Cheddar, Edam, Swiss, etc.,† 3 ounces
Eggs (2 medium)
Fish and shellfish
cooked bass,* bluefish, cod,* flounder,* haddock,* halibut, herring (plain), lobster,* mackerel, ocean perch, sole,* swordfish, trout, etc., 3 ounces
medium shrimp, 6
medium clams or oysters,* 10
crab,* salmon or tuna, 3/4 cup flaked, drained
Meat
cooked beef, game meats,* lamb, liver (all kinds),* pork, rabbit* or veal,* 3 ounces
boiled ham or lean luncheon meat,† 3 ounces
frankfurters,† 3 small
Peanut butter (1/3 cup†)
Poultry
cooked chicken,* Cornish hens, duck,† goose† or turkey, 3 ounces

BREADS, CEREALS, PASTAS, SOME VEGETABLES

Breads
rye, white and whole-wheat, 1 slice
matzoh, 1 piece
raisin, 1 slice*

Cereals
flaked or puffed ready-to-eat, 3/4 cup
cooked, 1/2 cup

Crackers
graham, 2 small
oyster, 1/2 cup
round, 5 2-inch
rye, 3 double crackers
saltines, 4 2-inch
soda, 3 small

Pastas
cooked macaroni, spaghetti, 1/2 cup
cooked egg noodles, 1/2 cup

Quick breads
biscuits, 1 average*
corn bread, 1 1/2-inch cube*
English muffins, 1/2 muffin
griddlecakes, 1 4-inch cake*
muffins, 1 average*
waffles, 1 4-inch waffle*

Rice
cooked white, 1/2 cup
cooked wild, 1/2 cup

Rolls
large hamburger, hot dog, etc., 1/2 roll

Vegetables
beans, baked, 1/4 cup
beans, cooked dried, 1/3 cup
beets, 1 cup
carrots, 1 cup
corn, 1/3 cup
onions, raw, 1 cup
peas, green, 1 cup
potatoes, white, baked, 1 small
potatoes, white, mashed, 1/2 cup
potatoes, sweet, baked, 1/4 cup
rutabagas, 1 cup
turnips, 1 cup
winter squash, 1 cup

*Count as 1 serving of Bread and 1 serving of Extras.

FRUITS AND VEGETABLES

Fruits, fresh or water packed canned or frozen*
apple, 1 small
apple juice, 1/3 cup
applesauce, 1/2 cup
apricots, 2 medium
banana, 1/2 small
berries, 2/3 to 1 cup
cantaloupe, 1/4 small
cherries, 10 large
dates, 2 small
figs, fresh, 2 large
grapefruit, 1/2 small
grapefruit juice, 1/2 cup
grape juice, 1/4 cup
grapes, 12 medium
honeydew, 1/8 small
mango, 1/2 small
orange, 1 small
orange juice, 1/2 cup
papaya, 1/3 medium
peach, 1 medium
pear, 1 small
pineapple, cubed, 1/2 cup
pineapple juice, 1/3 cup
plums or prunes, 2 medium
raisins, 2 tablespoons
tangerine, 1 large
tangerine juice, 1/2 cup
watermelon, cubed, 1 cup

*If desired, occasionally substitute 1 serving regular, canned or frozen fruit for 2 servings of raw or water packed (or in juice) fruit.

Vegetables—use them freely on diet, served unbuttered or with low-calorie dressing

asparagus	lettuce
broccoli	mushrooms
Brussels	okra
sprouts	peppers
cabbage	radishes
cauliflower	romaine
celery	sauerkraut
cucumbers	spinach
endive	summer
escarole	squash
green beans	tomato juice
greens	tomatoes
Italian beans	wax beans
kale	zucchini

MILK AND MILK PRODUCTS

Buttermilk, 1 cup
Cheese, American, Cheddar, etc., 1 ounce
Cottage cheese (creamed), 1/2 cup
Evaporated skimmed milk (undiluted), 1/2 cup
Nonfat dry milk powder, 1/3 cup
Skimmed milk, 1 cup
Yogurt, plain, 1 cup

THE EXTRAS

almonds, 5 medium
avocado, 1/8
butter, 1 teaspoon
cream, heavy, 1 tablespoon
cream, light, 2 tablespoons
cream, sour, 2 tablespoons
cream cheese, 1 tablespoon
hard candy, 2 medium
jam, scant tablespoon
jelly, scant tablespoon
margarine, 1 teaspoon
mayonnaise, 1 teaspoon
olives, 5 small
peanuts, 6 to 8
pecans, 5 medium
pickles, 3 dill
plain popcorn, 2/3 cup
salad dressing, 2 teaspoons
sponge cake, 1 very thin slice
sugar, 1 tablespoon
syrups, scant tablespoon

The Active Woman's Diet

For today's woman-on-the-go, here is a week's worth of menus geared for quick breakfasts, order-out lunches and at-home dinners. Plus there are tips that tell you how to eat out anytime and still stay slim.

The best thing about this diet is that you never feel restricted. You select a wide range of foods you like from seven food groups, and there's a daily 100-calorie bonus built right into the plan, to be used for any food you want. Save the bonus for an end-of-the-day splurge, carry it over until the next day or borrow your bonus from the following day in case you're invited out unexpectedly. For an accurate measure of how much you're losing, weigh yourself, once a week, on the same scale at the same time of day (weight fluctuates from day to day). To keep weight off forever, try to shed a modest 1 to 2 pounds per week. If you lose a large amount of weight in a short time, chances are you'll gain it back quickly.

Don't forget to exercise. It burns extra calories, tones muscles and relieves stress, so you'll look slimmer and healthier. When you exercise while dieting, you lose more fatty tissue and less muscle tissue. Walking, one of the easiest and most effective ways to exercise, burns from 5 to 8 calories per minute, depending upon your pace.

How do you eat out on the plan? Fast foods are fine to include from time to time. The smallest hamburger equals 2 bread-group servings and 1 protein-rich food. Half of a 10-inch pizza counts as 2 from the bread, 1 from the vegetable and 1 from the milk group, plus 1 protein-rich food. Restaurant and coffee-shop sandwiches, made with an average amount of meat (ask the waitress not to overload your sandwich), equal 2 bread-group servings and 1 protein-rich food. Because you're allowed only 1 tablespoon of butter or margarine a day, ask for grilled cheese sandwiches, scrambled eggs and omelets prepared without extra fat on the grill. If you order a hamburger, ask for the roll served on the side, so that extra fat drains onto the plate. Beware of coffee-shop "diet plates." A "Slim Line" special, for instance, consisting of a jumbo steakburger, cottage cheese, peach halves and melba toast, totaled 560 calories. "Lo Cal" lunch—chopped steak, cottage cheese, lettuce and tomato and melba toast—contained 635 calories.

Soup and salad bars are especially good for dieters. The average bowl of soup, containing vegetables, noodles or pasta, plus a small amount of meat, counts as 1 serving from the bread group. A recent study shows that soup, eaten 3 to 4 times a week, can keep down your calorie intake. According to Dr. Henry A. Jordan, author of *Eating Is Okay,* soup encourages good eating habits because it must be eaten slowly with a utensil while sitting at a table. And it is filling too. By comparison, foods that can be gulped down by the handful while you're watching TV or reading are rarely satisfying. Eat as much salad as you like, provided it's topped only with lemon wedges, vinegar and spices. (For the number of extra calories in salad dressing, see below.) Wherever you eat, be careful not to add calories with extra dressings, sauces and condiments. As you'll see from the list of low-calorie foods below, the extras—we've added two tablespoons in each case—make a big difference.

- 1 cup lettuce, 20 calories; with Italian dressing, 175 calories.
- 1 cup green beans, 20 calories; with margarine 220 calories.
- 4 broccoli spears, 20 calories; with Hollandaise sauce, 190 calories.

- 3 ounces broiled fish, 90 calories; with tartar sauce, 240 calories.
- 1 medium baked potato, 100 calories; with sour cream, 150 calories or with butter, 300 calories.
- Turkey sandwich, 250 calories; with mayonnaise, 450 calories.

DAILY DIET GUIDELINES

Protein-rich foods   2 servings, about 150 calories each. One serving = 3 ounces cooked lean meat; 4 ounces cooked poultry, fish or shellfish; 2 eggs; 2 ounces cheese; 1/3 cup cottage cheese; 6 ounces cooked legumes (dried peas, beans).

Milk, milk products   2 servings, 80 to 100 calories each. One serving = 1 cup skimmed milk; 1 cup buttermilk; 1/2 cup plain yogurt; 1 ounce cheese.

Breads, cereals, pasta, starchy vegetables   4 servings, 50 to 100 calories each. One serving = 1 slice bread (whole wheat, rye or white); 1/2 English muffin or bun; 1 small hard roll; 6 soda crackers; 2/3 cup pasta, noodles; 1/2 cup rice, hot cereal, peas, beets, squash; 1 ounce cold cereal; 1 cup Brussels sprouts; 1 medium potato.

Note: Cereals should be iron-fortified to provide adequate iron in the diet. If not, use an iron or balanced iron-and-vitamin supplement.

Fruits   2 servings, about 50 calories each. One serving = 1/2 cup unsweetened juice or canned fruit; 1 medium fresh fruit; 1/2 banana; 1/2 melon.

Fats   1 serving, about 100 calories. One serving = 1 tablespoon butter, margarine, vegetable oil, mayonnaise.

Vegetables   As desired—except those listed in bread group. Asparagus, bean sprouts, broccoli, cabbage, carrots, cauliflower, celery, cucumber, eggplant, green or wax beans, salad greens, tomatoes, zucchini.

Daily extras   1 teaspoon jelly or jam, 1 tablespoon catchup.

Bonus   Any food totaling to approximately 100 calories.

Unlimited   Bouillon, unflavored gelatin, lemon, lime, spices, herbs, mustard, coffee, tea.

EAT-FOR-A-TREAT DIET

If desserts and snacks are your dieting downfall, this diet may be the one for you. With it, you can have the choicest treats and *still* lose up to two pounds a week! Follow the daily menu patterns that allow 1000 calories for women, 1400 for men. Then choose treats totaling up to 200 calories (women) or 400 calories (men). The Snacker's Guide gives you just an idea of the possibilities, listing some of the traditional low-calorie snacks as well as rich once-in-a-while ones we all crave from time to time (or every day). Also included to help you fill the snacking quota: a dozen 200-calorie snacks—all permissible. And don't overlook the diet-defying recipes starting on page 65.

FOR HER:
1000 CALORIES
PLUS 200 CALORIES
OF SNACKS

FOR HIM:
1400 CALORIES
PLUS 400 CALORIES
OF SNACKS

BREAKFAST

1/2 cup citrus fruit or juice
AND
1 egg and 1 slice toast* with 1 teaspoon butter or margarine
OR
1 cup cooked or 1 1/2 cups ready-to-eat cereal
AND
1/2 glass skimmed milk
Any Meal: coffee or tea, black or with milk and up to 1 teaspoon sugar

1 cup fruit juice
AND
2 eggs plus 1 slice toast*
OR
1 cup cooked or 1 1/2 cups ready-to-eat cereal
AND
1/2 glass skimmed milk
AND
see left

LUNCH OR SUPPER

2 ounces lean meat or 1 medium serving poultry or fish; 1 serving these vegetables: asparagus, broccoli, Brussels sprouts, cabbage, carrots, cauliflower, celery, green beans, sauerkraut, spinach or tomatoes. (Serve hot, unbuttered, or as salads, using reduced-calorie dressing); 1 serving of the following: 1/2 cup potatoes, rice or noodles, 1 slice bread, or 1 small roll
OR
1 sandwich; 1 sliced egg or 1 slice poultry, lean beef or ham; 2 slices bread; reduced-calorie dressing; greens
AND
2 fresh apricots or plums; or 1 cup grapes, cherries, berries, or melon; or 1 fresh pear, peach or apple (or water- or juice-pack canned fruit)
AND
1/2 glass skimmed milk

3-ounce serving meat or large serving poultry or fish; see left for vegetable servings

OR
same as left, but use 2 sliced eggs or 2 slices meat

AND
see left

AND
1 glass skimmed milk

DINNER

3 ounces lean meat or a medium serving fish or poultry; 1 serving each vegetables and "starchy" foods—see lunch list
OR
1 serving low-calorie main dish from recipes, pages 81ff.; 1 serving vegetables—see lunch list

AND
1/2 cup gelatin dessert or pudding made with skimmed milk; or 1 thin slice angel-food or sponge cake; or 1 serving fruit from lunch list
AND
1 glass skimmed milk

4 ounces meat or generous serving fish or poultry; see lunch list for vegetable servings

OR
same as left plus 1/2 slice bread with 1 teaspoon butter or margarine

AND
see left

AND
see left

PLUS THE SNACKS

200 calories for snacks

400 calories for snacks

*Use only enriched breads, rice and pasta at all meals.

SNACKERS' GUIDE

CANDY, NIBBLERS, NUTS

almonds (12)	85
Brazil nuts (2)	55
candy bar, average	295
caramel, plain (1)	40
cheese (1 oz.)	
American	105
Camembert	85
Cheddar, process	115
cream	105
Parmesan	50
Roquefort or blue	105
Swiss	105
chewing gum (1 stick)	10
chocolate cremes (1)	50
chocolate mint patty	35
chocolate (1 oz.)	
semisweet	145
sweet	145
chocolate syrup	
(1 tbsp.)	50
coconut (¼ cup)	110
dates, pitted (¼ cup)	125
fondant (1 oz.)	105
fudge (1″ square)	75
gum drops (1 small)	10
hard candy (1 large)	35
milk chocolate (1 oz.)	145
peanut brittle (1 oz.)	120
peanuts (8 to 10)	55
pecans (9 medium)	70
pickles	
dill (1 medium)	10
sour (1 large)	15
sweet (1 small)	20
popcorn, plain (1 cup)	40
potato chips (10)	115
pretzels (5 3⅛″-long	
sticks)	10
pumpkin seeds	
shelled (1 tbsp.)	60
unshelled (¼ cup)	60
sunflower seeds	
shelled (1 tbsp.)	45
sunflower seeds	
unshelled (¼ cup)	45
walnuts (1 tbsp.)	50

BEVERAGES*

apple juice	120
bouillon	5
buttermilk	90
chocolate milk drink	190
cider	120
cocoa	245
cola drinks	
(6-oz. bottle)	70
cranberry juice	160
ginger ale	85
grape juice	170
grapefruit juice	100
lemonade	110
milk, whole	160
skimmed	90
orange juice	110
prune juice	200
tomato juice	50

RAW VEGETABLES, ½- to 1-CUP SERVINGS 25 CALORIES EACH

cabbage (Chinese, green, red, Savoy, etc.), cauliflower, celery, chicory, cucumbers, endive, escarole, lettuce (Bibb, Boston, iceberg, etc.), mushrooms, okra, green pepper, radishes, romaine, spinach tomatoes, watercress

BREADS, CRACKERS OR PASTRIES

bagel (1 large)	165
biscuits (1 medium)	90
bread (1 slice)	
Boston brown	100
cracked wheat	65
Melba toast	15
rye	60
white	70
whole wheat	65
crackers	
graham (4 small)	110
oyster (10 crackers)	45
round (1 average)	15
saltine (2″ square)	10
soda (2½″ square)	25
whole rye (1)	20
Danish pastry (1)	275
doughnut, plain (1)	125
jelly (1)	185
English muffin (1)	145
French toast (1 slice)	140
griddle cake (4″)	110
hot cross bun (1)	185
matzoh (1 plain)	120
muffins (2½″ diameter)	
blueberry	140
bran	100
corn	125
plain	120
popover (1 medium)	120
rolls, plain	
1 small	85
1 medium	115
1 large	175
waffle (7″ square)	205
zwieback (1)	30

CAKES, COOKIES, PIES

cakes	
angel-food (2″	
wedge)	110
chiffon (1/16)	215
cupcake, unfrosted	90
fruitcake (1/30 of	
8″ loaf)	55
poundcake (½″	
slice)	140
sponge cake (1/12)	195
cookies	
brownies (2″ square)	85
chocolate chip	50
fig bar (1 square)	50
gingersnap (1 small)	30
oatmeal (1 large)	65
sugar (1 large)	80
sugar wafer (1 small)	25
pies (1/7 of 9″ pie)	
coconut custard	285
lemon meringue	305
pumpkin	275

FRUITS*
75-CALORIE SERVINGS

4 small apricots or plums
1 small banana or pear
1 medium apple or orange
2 small peaches or tangerines
¾ cup blackberries, blueberries, cherries or grapes
1 cup pineapple chunks, red raspberries, or sliced strawberries
3 tbsps. raisins
2 cups cubed cantaloupe or watermelon

OTHER DESSERTS

apple brown betty	
(½-cup serving)	175
baked apple (1)	130
coffee cake (2″ × 3″)	250
frozen desserts (½ cup)	
frozen custard	125
ice cream	165
ice milk	100
sherbet	130
gelatin dessert (½ cup)	70
puddings (½ cup)	
butterscotch	140
chocolate	175
custard (baked)	150
junket	50
rice (¾ cup)	225

---

*8-oz. glass

*Fresh, water- or juice-pack canned, or unsweetened frozen fruits

12 SNACKS OF 200 CALORIES EACH FOR EAT-FOR-A-TREAT DIET

- 3/4 cup sherbet or 1/2 cup ice cream (any flavor)
- 3 cups coffee or tea, each with 1 tablespoon light cream and 2 teaspoons sugar
- 2-inch wedge angel-food or sponge cake with 3/4-cup serving fresh, unsweetened or water-pack canned fruit
- 1 cup puffed or flaked cereal with 8-ounce glass skimmed milk and 1 teaspoon sugar
- 1 slice bread or toast with 1 teaspoon butter or margarine and 1/2 cup cottage cheese
- 1/2 cup pudding made with skimmed milk and 1 fresh peach, pear, apple or small banana
- 1 1/2 ounces cheese and three 2-inch-square saltines
- 1 cup canned vegetable, noodle, minestrone or tomato soup and 3/4 cup oyster crackers
- 1 English muffin, large muffin or crescent roll with 1 teaspoon butter or margarine
- 1 fresh pear, peach, apple or small banana and 1 cup oyster crackers
- 1 soft- or hard-cooked egg and 1 slice lightly buttered and jellied toast
- 1 serving any 150-calorie dessert from low-calorie dessert recipes (pages 210-241) plus coffee with sugar and light cream

WISCONSIN DIET

Is dieting every day much too painful even to *think* about? Consider this plan! You diet Mondays and Tuesdays, Thursdays and Fridays, on 1200 calories for women, 1800 for men. On Wednesdays and over those weekends when dieting is difficult, merely hold the calorie line with a maintenance diet—2000 calories for women (1850 if you're over 40), 2800 calories for men (2600 for those over 45). As you'll see, maintenance days allow you enough calories for surprisingly hearty fare. You'll lose only one pound a week, but at that rate it will take less than three months to lose 10 pounds! Given here: a week of sample menus for inspiration. Figures in parentheses indicate portions for men. See the Basic-Four Diet for more menu ideas.

A WEEK OF DIET MENUS TO GUIDE YOU

MONDAY—A LOW-CALORIE DAY
1200 CALORIES (HERS)　1800 (HIS)

BREAKFAST
4-ounce glass orange juice	(6-ounce glass)
2 poached eggs	(same)
½ toasted English muffin	(whole muffin)
Coffee (black) or tea (with lemon)*	

LUNCH
1 cup beef bouillon	(same)
Cheese sandwich on rye (1 slice cheese, 1 tea- spoon dressing, 2 slices bread and a generous amount of lettuce)	(same, but 2 slices cheese, 1 tablespoon dressing)
½ cup raspberry sherbet	(¾ cup sherbet)

DINNER
4 1-ounce meatballs (made with round of beef)	(6 meatballs)
⅓ cup each: okra, corn	(½ cup each)
Kosher pickle sticks	(same)
1 fresh pear	(same)
4-ounce glass buttermilk	(8-ounce glass)

TUESDAY—A LOW-CALORIE DAY
1200 CALORIES (HERS)　1800 (HIS)

BREAKFAST
4-ounce glass grapefruit juice	(8-ounce glass)
¾ cup hot oatmeal	(1 cup cereal)
1 tablespoon each: honey, raisins	(same)
4-ounce glass skimmed milk	(8-ounce glass)

LUNCH
Chicken-salad platter (½ cup cubed chicken, 2 tablespoons salad dressing, seasonings and lettuce)	(same, but ¾ cup chicken)
1 slice whole-wheat bread	(same)
Crisp Chinese celery sticks	(same)
2 whole apricots (fresh or dietetic-pack canned)	(same)
4-ounce glass skimmed milk	(8 ounces whole milk)

DINNER
2 pan-broiled frankfurters (catchup or mustard)	(3 frankfurters)
1 large hard roll, 1 teaspoon butter or margarine	
½ cup peas	(¾ cup)
½ cup fresh pineapple chunks (tossed with ½ cup yogurt)	(¾ cup pineapple)
4-ounce glass skimmed milk	(whole milk)

*Any meal; Hold-the-Line days, light on milk, sugar if desired

WEDNESDAY—A HOLD-THE-LINE DAY
2000 CALORIES (HERS)　2800 (HIS)

BREAKFAST
4-ounce glass orange juice	(same)
2 slices French toast	(3 slices)
(1 tablespoon maple syrup)	(2 tablespoons syrup)

LUNCH
Glass tomato juice	(same)
Medium hamburger (on toasted roll)	(2 hamburgers) (on two rolls)
Carrot and celery sticks	(same)
½ cup rice pudding	(1 cup serving)

DINNER
1 cup minestrone soup	(same)
1 cup macaroni and cheese	(1½ cups)
Large cucumber/tomato salad (1 tablespoon Italian dressing)	(same) (same)
½ cantaloupe	(same)

SNACKS
200 calories for snacks*	(200 calories for snacks)*

THURSDAY—A LOW-CALORIE DAY
1200 CALORIES (HERS)　1800 (HIS)

BREAKFAST
4-ounce glass tomato juice (Worcestershire and lemon juice)	(8-ounce glass)
1-egg fluffy onion omelet	(2-egg omelet)
1 slice jellied toast	(1½ slices)
4-ounce glass skimmed milk	(8 ounces whole milk)

LUNCH
3 ounces pan-broiled minute steak (served on toast)	(5 ounces)
½ cup each: zucchini, carrots	(same)
Medium tossed salad (reduced-calorie dressing)	(same)
½ cup rennet custard pudding (made with skimmed milk)	(same)

DINNER
Boned chicken breast, small (sautéed and seasoned)	(same)
½ cup noodles (with poppy seeds)	(same)
½ cup stewed celery	(¾ cup)
One small biscuit (unbuttered)	(2 biscuits) (lightly buttered)
One small apple	(same)
8-ounce glass skimmed milk	(8 ounces whole milk)

*See page 26 for snack suggestions.

FRIDAY—A LOW-CALORIE DAY
1200 CALORIES (HERS)   **1800 (HIS)**

BREAKFAST
4-ounce glass pineapple   (6-ounce glass)
  juice
1 cup ready-to-eat oat cereal (same)
  (2 teaspoons sugar)   (same)
8-ounce glass skimmed milk   (whole milk)

LUNCH
Fruit-salad bowl
  (1/2 cup cottage cheese,   (same, but 1 cup
  1 cup mixed fresh fruit,   cottage cheese,
  lettuce cup)   1 1/2 cups fruit)
3 slices Melba toast   (4 slices)

DINNER
4-ounces pan-fried halibut   (6 ounces)
1/2 cup each: tomatoes,   (3/4 cup each)
  peas
1 medium hard roll   (same)
  (unbuttered)
Tossed salad   (same)
  reduced-calorie dressing   (same)
1/2 cup orange sections   (1 cup sections)
8-ounce glass skimmed milk   (same)

SATURDAY—A HOLD-THE-LINE DAY
2000 CALORIES (HERS)   **2800 (HIS)**

BREAKFAST
4-ounce glass grapefruit   (same)
  juice
2 4-inch waffles (2   (3 waffles)
  tablespoons maple syrup)   (3 tablespoons syrup)
4-ounce glass milk   (same)

LUNCH
Shrimp creole   (1 1/2 servings)
  (1/2 cup serving on rice)
Tossed salad (1 tablespoon   (same)
  cheese dressing)   (2 tablespoons)
1/2 cup baked custard   (same)

DINNER
1 medium serving meat loaf   (2 servings)
1/2 cup each: chopped broc-   (same)
  coli, mashed potatoes
Lettuce, shredded (with   (same)
  chili sauce)   (same)
1 1/2 inch wedge angel-food   (same)
  cake (topped with rasp-   (same)
  berry sauce)
8-ounce glass whole milk   (same)

SNACKS
200 calories for snacks*   (200 calories for
                        snacks*)

*See page 26 for snack suggestions.

SUNDAY—A HOLD-THE-LINE DAY
2000 CALORIES (HERS)   **2800 (HIS)**

BREAKFAST
8-ounce glass tomato juice (same)
1 fried egg   (2 fried eggs)
1 slice rye toast   (2 slices toast)
  1 teaspoon butter or marga-
  rine
8-ounce glass whole milk   (same)

LUNCH
1 cup cream of tomato soup (same)
Bacon, lettuce and tomato   (same)
  sandwich
  (2 strips crisp bacon, 1
  tablespoon dressing, 2
  slices bread, lettuce and
  tomato)
Chilled fruit cocktail   (same)

DINNER
Broiled steak (about   (same)
  5 ounces boned meat)
1/2 cup sautéed mushrooms   (same)
1/2 cup buttered spinach   (same)
Small baked potato (2   (medium potato)
  tablespoons sour cream)   (3 tablespoons)
Tiny brownie   2 brownies)

SNACKS
200 calories for snacks*   (200   calories   for
                  snacks*)

*See page 26 for snack suggestions

THE MOST COMMONLY ASKED QUESTIONS ABOUT DIETING

Over the years, the Good Housekeeping Institute has received thousands of inquiries about all aspects of dieting. Here is a sampling of questions most frequently asked about low-calorie diets.

Q. *How can I estimate the number of calories I need daily?*
A. Multiply your desirable weight (obtained from the height-weight charts on pages 323-324) by eighteen for a man and by fifteen for a woman. This is approximately the number of calories used daily by a moderately active adult. You may need about a fourth more calories if you are *very* active; a fourth less if you are less active. If you are over fifty-five, subtract another 300 calories for women and 400 calories for men.

Q. *Is overeating the only major cause of overweight?*
A. It's by far the dominant one. Obesity can be caused by any one or a combination of inherited, emotional or environmental factors. This largest class includes obesity due to overeating, inactivity, or a combination of the two. The other, much smaller, group involves some abnormality in the metabolism. (Remember, it's easier to blame metabolism than lack of willpower!)

Q. *Is hunger different from appetite?*
A. Yes. True hunger is a sensation that signifies the body's actual need for food. It may be a gnawing in the stomach, definite pain or faintness—feelings that are not only unpleasant but agonizing. Appetite is simply a healthy, normal desire for food. Although largely controlled by habit, it can be stimulated by the sight or smell of attractive food.

Q. *How can it be true that worry and nervous tension make some people lose weight, while others gain?*
A. People react in different ways to mental stress. In some, worry or fear creates what almost amounts to an aversion to food, which often is reflected physically by a "lump in the throat" that makes it seem impossible to swallow. Such people will, of course, lose weight. Others, however, find actual relief from their cares through eating, and may find particular pleasure in extremely rich foods which are associated with their childhood memories. These are the ones who gain.

Q. *Is it true that some foods "burn up" faster than others?*
A. The rate at which food is digested or absorbed in no way affects its calorie value. If total caloric intake exceeds your expenditure of energy, you'll gain weight. But foods do differ in satiety value—that is, how full they make you feel. It's important that you feel satisfied during a reducing diet. Include protein and some fat, two nutrients with "staying power." (Remember, though, that fat is the most concentrated source of calories, so it should be used in moderation.) To supply bulk, supplement protein and fat-rich foods with salads, vegetables and fruits.

Q. *When I lose weight, what happens to fat? How does the body get rid of it?*
A. When you take in too much fuel (calories), the body converts it into fatty deposits (those bulges you hate to see showing). If you need more fuel than your food is giving at any particular time, the body burns or uses up the excess fat that has been stored in "fatter" times. When you lose weight, the body is forced to use this stored fuel. The burned fuel becomes energy, carbon dioxide which you breathe out, and water eliminated in perspiration and urine.

Q. *Is it true that people over forty should cut down on the calories and protein in their diet?*
A. Men and women over forty tend to eat less than they once did (a natural compensation for a slower metabolic rate, perhaps less activity). This is good, since those in this age bracket *should* cut calories—by a regulated diet, if necessary. They should *not*, however, reduce their daily intake of protein—at least two servings of meat, fish or poultry, and two glasses of milk, should be included in meals each day.

Q. *When I diet, I can lose several pounds the first week or so, but then I always hit a plateau and get discouraged. What's wrong?*
A. A number of things can prevent weight loss, even on a diet that is followed faithfully. You should know, first of all, that a change in the rate of loss is common. Try to accept the plateau as a natural thing. Wait a week or so and you'll start losing again. Changes in the natural water balance of the body will slow the rate of loss temporarily. It is quite usual to lose several pounds of water in the first weeks. Losing fat—the important part of a diet—comes more slowly. If you've been dieting for some time now, are you counting calories as carefully as you did at first? Many dieters fail to count all the foods they eat during a day, or underestimate the size of servings. Get out your scales and measuring cups and start checking serving sizes more carefully. Calculate calories in your homemade dishes; don't just take average values from a calorie chart.

Q. *Can it possibly be true that it takes only an extra 100 calories a day to gain 10 pounds in one year?*
A. If you eat 100 extra calories every day, you'll gain 1 pound every 35 days—or over 10 pounds in one year. But look at the other side! If you eat 100 fewer calories every day, you'll *lose* 1 pound every 35 days. Actually, most of us eat according to the a-little-bit-more-today, a-little-bit-less-tomorrow pattern, and so maintain our present weight without calorie counting.

Q. *I thought the quickest way to lose weight was to eliminate liquids and salt from the diet. Why do you always recommend lots of liquids and allow salt on your reducing diets?*
A. For long-lasting weight reductions, you must lose *fatty* tissue, not water. Everyone has to have a generous amount of water daily to preserve the body's water balance and thus maintain health. The average adult needs 2½ quarts of water each day from the natural water in foods plus beverages. Any limitation of water intake should be only under strict medical supervision. It

is true that salt intake helps to regulate the amount of water in the tissues. By cutting down on salt (sodium, to be precise), a few pounds of water will be excreted. But remember you want to lose fat, not water. Low-calorie diets are restricted at best. To eliminate salt and make food less palatable is asking too much of the average dieter.

Q. *Can anything besides retention of fluids cause a gain in weight of 3 to 4 pounds in two days, when elimination is normal? Is fluid retention a danger signal?*
A. To answer the first part of your question, we know of no other explanation for such a rapid gain. About 3500 extra calories are required to produce a gain of 1 pound. This means that 10,500 extra calories must be eaten to gain 3 pounds and 14,000 to gain 4 pounds. For example, an individual who has a maintenance calorie requirement of 2000 per day would have to eat from 7250 to 9000 calories per day to gain 3 or 4 pounds in two days. Eating this large amount of food is just about a practical impossibility.

Retention of fluid is not always a danger signal. Normally, the amount of fluid held in the body tissues is regulated largely by the salt content of the diet. A liberal salt-user will retain more fluid, which the body needs under these conditions to maintain a proper balance.

The sharp drop in weight which may occur during the first days of a reducing diet is often due to fluid loss, especially if the diet emphasizes foods which are low in sodium and restricts use of salt both in cooking and at the table. Also, a temporary rise in weight due to fluid retention often precedes menstruation. Any continuing increase of weight in an individual who is not overeating or overusing salt should be brought to a physician's attention.

Q. *When you overeat, how long does it take before you start to put on weight?*
A. Excess calories are not converted into excess pounds overnight. In fact, it's impossible to gauge when your weight will go up after overeating because weight gain is also affected by the energy you expend and how much extra fluid you are retaining. If you eat 300 extra calories today, but use an

extra 300 for energy while exercising over the next few days, there will be no change in body fat (excess calories are stored as fat) and your weight will remain the same. But if over the next week you eat an extra 500 calories every day, and your level of exercise remains fairly consistent, you'll probably gain a pound. (One pound of body fat represents 3500 stored calories.)

Q. *In your diet plans you list as interchangeable a fresh, medium-size peach, pear, apple and small banana. According to my calorie chart, a peach contains 46 calories; a pear, 95; an apple, 76; a small banana, 79. How can they be substituted for one another?*
A. You're talking about a precise figuring of calories that often isn't practical on an average reducing diet. It's better to allow a dieter a wide choice of foods within a total daily calorie amount. That is why the calorie values for the four fruits you mentioned are averaged to an interchangeable 75 calories in menu calculations. On the assumption that a dieter will eat all four fruits equally often, the higher-calorie pear will balance out the low-calorie peach.

Q. *What are the calories for salt, pepper, herbs, spices, extracts, baking powder, baking soda, etc.?*
A. Since the calories in these items are miniscule, they wouldn't alter calorie totals enough to warrant including them in the average chart, or in your calorie count.

Q. *Are "starchy" and "carbohydrate" synonymous?*
A. No, they're not. All starches are carbohydrates, but not all carbohydrates are starch. Carbohydrate is a general term (like protein, fat, vitamin and mineral) which identifies one class of food components. Several types of carbohydrates include fruit sugars, "regular" sugar, and the more complex starches, dextrins and cellulose.

Q. *Does honey have fewer calories than sugar? Can I substitute it for sugar in recipes?*

A. One cup of honey has 990 calories; a cup of granulated sugar has 770. If you'd like to substitute honey for sugar occasionally, you can do it successfully in recipes for puddings or fruit-pie fillings, or as a sweetener for fruit and beverages. For each cup of sugar in a recipe, use $3/4$ to 1 cup of honey and decrease the liquid in the recipe by $1/4$ cup.

Q. *Is it true that all carbohydrates are fattening, and that starches especially should be avoided by dieters?*
A. Carbohydrates are no more and no less "fattening" than protein or fats when used in a balanced diet. Sugars, starches and protein contain the same 4 calories per gram; fats contain 9.

Calories are simply units of energy used by the body. As long as the total number you take in is less than the number you require for energy, you will not gain weight, whatever type of food you eat.

Q. *It seems that more and more cheeses are labeled "part skim." Does that mean they're lower in calories and cholesterol than other natural cheeses?*
A. Fat content of cheeses determines whether it will be "high" or "low" in calories and cholesterol. Since skim milk is lower in fat than whole milk, part-skim cheeses are lower both in calories and in cholesterol content. But in most cases only a small percentage of whole milk has been replaced with skim, so per 1-ounce serving, the cheese will contain almost the same number of calories and fat as the regular kind. Check the nutritional panel on the label. Be aware that 1 to 3 percent salt is added to most cheeses during curing, and because skim milk is naturally higher in sodium than whole milk, skim-milk cheeses have the highest percentage of sodium.

Q. *Most weight-reducing diets stress the importance of exercise as part of a total program. Does it help you lose weight faster?*
A. Any physical activity—walking, calisthenics, dancing, swimming—is an essential

part of a weight-reducing plan. It burns extra calories, helps keep you in top physical condition *and* diverts your attention from eating. After exercising, you feel great and *less hungry.*

Another big reason to exercise while dieting is to minimize loss of "lean body mass"—that is, muscle tissue. When you reduce your calorie intake, the body looks for calories to burn for energy and will take them from muscle tissue as well as from fat. But exercising while cutting calories increases the ratio of fat loss to muscle-tissue loss.

Q. *Do the packaged nonfat dry milks have all the same nutrients as regular liquid skimmed milk and whole milk? How do they compare in terms of calories?*
A. The nonfat dry milks contain all the protein, carbohydrate and minerals that are in regular skimmed milk and whole milk. Fat and fat-soluble vitamins (A and E) have been removed from this dry skimmed milk, but the rest of the vitamin content remains similar to whole milk. Most liquid skimmed milks and many nonfat dry milks now on the market have been refortified with vitamins A and D. Unmodified liquid skimmed milk and nonfat dry milk have essentially the same vitamin content. Modified skimmed milks have extra nonfat milk solids added to give more "body." Brands vary, but most contain 130 to 140 calories per glass. Dry milk reliquefied according to directions contains 90 calories per glass. But many homemakers make their own modified skimmed milk by adding extra dry milk. The flavor is better, the drink richer in nutrients.

Q. *There seem to be so many different kinds of margarine. Can you tell me what the difference is among them and how each should be used? And how do they differ in calories?*
A. *Regular margarine* is a mixture of partially hydrogenated vegetable fats and oils that have been churned with milk, colored, and fortified with vitamins A and D to give a butter-like consistency and flavor. The hydrogenation process changes liquid (poly-

unsaturated) fats into solid (saturated) fats. Regular margarine, which comes in sticks, can be used in recipes that call for butter or margarine.

Special margarines are processed so that they contain more polyunsaturated fat than regular margarines. In the ingredients list on these margarine packages, liquid oil (corn, safflower, etc.) is listed first. These margarines are recommended·for diets rich in polyunsaturated fats. Stick margarines of this type can be used as you would regular margarines. Soft (tub) margarines in this special-margarine category can be used like other margarines (see below).

Soft margarines have been specially processed to be spreadable at refrigerator temperatures. They come in tubs, rather than as sticks. Many, but not all, of the soft margarines are also special margarines. They can be used successfully in most recipes. For baking, it is safer to use recipes developed especially for soft margarines.

Whipped margarines are regular margarines that have been whipped with air to increase their volume by about 50 percent. On a weight basis (pound for pound), they are the equivalent of regular margarine. On a volume basis (tablespoon for tablespoon), however, they're not comparable to regular margarine because of the incorporated air. They can be used in cooking and baking on an equal weight basis, but not on a volume basis.

Imitation margarines do not contain as much fat as is required by Federal regulations for regular margarines—they have about half the fat and calories of regular margarines. Because they contain less fat and more water than regular margarine, they should not be used for making baked goods.

Almost all the different types of margarine come both salted and unsalted. If a recipe specifies unsalted (sweet) margarine, by all means use it.

Q. *Why do the figures in various calorie books differ so much?*
A. Differences in a food's age, maturity,

variety, water content, and the season it was grown can cause variations of as much as 10 percent. In a food such as bologna, depending on the proportions of fat, meat and starchy filler in a particular brand, the difference can go as high as 100 percent. In homemade baked goods and prepared dishes—apple dumplings, spaghetti sauce, etc.—the only way to get even a workable approximation is to calculate the calories yourself by adding the number in the individual ingredients and dividing by the number of servings. One word of advice: When calorie books differ, take the highest figure or at least an average figure. If you always take the lowest one, you'll only be cheating yourself.

Q. *Can alcohol be used by the body like food to supply calories? Does all the alcohol evaporate when wine, beer, etc. is used in cooking, and if so, does this eliminate all the calories?*
A. The body can and does use the calories from alcohol. A gram of pure alcohol provides about seven calories. In "hard" liquors, this amounts to 100 to 125 calories per 1½ ounce jigger, depending on the proof of the liquor.

The alcohol in wines and liquors does evaporate in cooking and boiling, and the calorie count is significantly reduced. In a dry wine, the number of calories is essentially lowered to zero. A sweet wine, however, contains sugar. When you cook with this, you lose the alcohol, but you're left

with the sugar content, which does not boil off. The amount of sugar and, therefore, the remaining calorie content vary from one sweet wine to another.

Q. *How much difference does it make in calories when you drain syrup from canned fruit? Does the drained fruit have the same number of calories as fresh?*
A. Canned fruit absorbs a significant amount of sugar, so it's higher in calories than fresh even when drained. The degree of difference dpends on the concentration of the syrup—light, medium, heavy, extra heavy—and the type of fruit. Draining does eliminate the calories you would get if you served some syrup with the fruit. This can mean 25 to 100 calories per serving.

Q. *Do the dietetic chocolate candies made with non-nutritive sweetener contain fewer calories than regular chocolate candy?*
A. Regular chocolate candy has about 145 calories per ounce. "Dietetic" chocolate, sweetened with nonnutritive sweetener, has between 100 and 150 calories per ounce. In many cases, the "dietetic" chocolates contain dilutants (often nonfat dry-milk solids) to decrease the fat and calorie content. These chocolates usually list the caloric value on the label as calories per 100 grams. When you check to see whether their caloric savings are really worthwhile, remember that regular chocolate candy ranges from 475 to 530 per 100 grams.

DIETING IS A STATE OF MIND

1. Pick a good diet plan. Make sure you select one that not only is well-balanced but includes foods you like. There's no need to eliminate high-calorie favorites if you know how to fit them in.
2. Set formal goals. Make a chart, like the one at right, on graph paper. On the left, starting at the bottom, enter your desired weight, then mark off each pound until your current weight is reached. Along the base line, fill in the number of weeks it should take to reach your goal. Expect a jagged

chart; weight loss is never smooth from week to week. So don't get discouraged.

3. Throw out all fattening treats (or give them away). The fewer temptations you have around, the easier it is to resist "just one."

4. Keep busy. If you tend to nibble while you watch television, occupy your hands with knitting or crossword puzzles.

5. Perk up the table and diet fare with a colorful centerpiece, tangy relishes.

6. Take small bites and eat slowly. You will think you are eating more and your stomach will have more time to signal when you are full.

7. Avoid lunch and dinner invitations for the first few weeks.

8. Trade secrets with a dieting friend. While you wouldn't bore non-dieters with your dieting woes, it is helpful to talk to a kindred spirit. For more moral support, have tea or broth with her daily.

9. Mark milestones. When you have lost 5 or 10 pounds, get a new girdle to make yourself more shapely.

10. Have snapshots taken to show how you look in a tight dress or a bathing suit.

11. Make or buy a new dress or get out an old favorite that is a size or two too small. It will give you incentive to reach your goal.

12. Stamp out boredom. Plan a whole list of odd jobs. Do one every time you want a snack.

13. Study overweight people on the bus or street. Vow you'll never have hips, thighs or arms that heavy.

14. Walk away from the refrigerator when hunger pangs strike. A restful walk or casual bicycle ride will take you far from snack foods.

15. Schedule a fifteen-minute exercise session for the same time daily, preferably before you eat.

16. Get eight hours' sleep. You will have more willpower if you are well rested.

17. Weigh yourself only once or twice a week so you can see a definite change each time.

TIPS ON LOW-CALORIE COOKING

1. Panbroil meats in a skillet with a non-stick finish so you won't have to add fat.

2. Serve the hearty vegetables. Beets, carrots, peas, onions, winter squash and turnips have only 40 calories each per 1/2-cup serving.

3. For a hot cereal that is ready in a minute in pre-measured portions, try instant cream of wheat or oatmeal.

4. Trim all fat from pork chops and they will have the same calories as lean beef. Panbroil or braise with beef bouillon.

5. By draining the oil from canned tuna, you will cut its calories by one-third. Or use water-packed tuna, which has less than half the calories of oil-packed.

6. For cream sauces and sautéing foods, use half the usual amount of fat and substitute skimmed for whole milk.

7. For drinking, puddings, sauces, etc., use reliquefied nonfat dry milk in place of higher-calorie whole milk.

8. Bouillon makes a fine clear gravy for meats and has practically no calories.

9. Season with herbs or spices instead of butter or margarine. Rosemary, thyme, poultry seasoning and sage all add marvelous flavor but no calories to main courses, vegetables and pastas.

10. Start meals with filling, low-calorie appetizers: clear broths or soups, spiced fruit or vegetable juices.

11. Buy frozen unsweetened berries, loose in plastic bags, so you can take out only the amount needed. (Once thawed, syrup forms.) Buy frozen vegetables that way too.

12. When buying canned fruits, try pineapple packed in juice (not syrup) or unsweetened applesauce. Or drain heavy syrup from sugar-pack fruits and replace with unsweetened fruit juice.

13. Beware of hot breads. They contain more calories per serving than regular bread.

Planning Meals

There are many different needs to meet in preparing food. But with a Basic-Four Food Chart as your guide, you can easily plan meals that will tempt the appetites and insure the well-being of every member of the family, from baby to grandparent.

Planning and preparing attractive, nutritionally balanced meals for everyone can be a complex responsibility. A woman must keep in mind her own dietary needs, particularly during pregnancy, as well as develop healthy eating habits in her children while they're small and see that they get extra vitamins during teenage years. Men and women watching their waistlines need to adjust their diets according to their activity levels, while older family members must compensate for declining appetites. Considering the diversity of dietary situations, it is remarkable that a simple outline, The Basic-Four Food Guide, can satisfy everyone's needs.

The Basic-Four

The Basic-Four refers to a classification of foods into four major categories: Milk and Dairy Products; Meat, Fish and Poultry; Fruits and Vegetables; Bread and Cereals. To make sure that you are serving well-balanced meals that provide all the necessary nutrients, plan your daily menus to include at least the number of servings shown in each category. In most cases you will be serving more than the minimum, since most family members will need more than the 1200 to 1400 calories supplied by the basic outline. Complete your menus with extra servings from the basic food groups. Use the Keep-Trim Guide on pages 38 and 39 to keep a continuing eye on calories by selecting relatively low-calorie foods from each group. The menus on pages 40 and 41 give a week of easy-to-fix meal ideas.

THE BASIC-FOUR FOOD GROUPS

THE FOOD GROUPS	THE SERVING SIZES	THE NUTRIENTS THEY SUPPLY
Meat and protein-rich goods: 2 servings of meats, fish, poultry, eggs or cheese, dried beans, peas, nuts, etc., may be substituted for the meats.	one serving equals: 3 ounces lean, cooked meat, fish or poultry 2 eggs 3 slices (ounces) cheese 1 cup cooked beans 4 tablespoons peanut butter	Meats and meat alternatives provide protein, iron, niacin and the other B vitamins.
Fruits and vegetables: 4 servings of fruits and vegetables. Be certain to include one serving of citrus fruit or tomatoes and one of dark-green or leafy vegetables daily.	one serving equals: 1/2 cup canned or cooked fruit 1 fresh peach, pear, etc. 1 cup fresh berries or cherries 1/2 cup cooked vegetables 1 cup uncooked leafy vegetables	Fruits and vegetables supply vitamins A and C plus the other vitamins, minerals and fiber.
Breads, cereals and pasta: 4 servings of enriched, fortified, or whole-grain cereals and breads.	one serving equals: 1 slice bread 1 small biscuit, muffin or roll 1/2 cup potatoes, pasta or rice 3/4 to 1 cup flaked or puffed cereals 1/2 cup cooked cereals	Cereals and breads are important sources of carbohydrates and of the B vitamins as well as supplemental amounts of protein and iron.
Milk and milk products: 2 servings of milk and other dairy foods for adults; 3 to 4 servings for children; 4 or more servings for teens.	one serving equals: 8-ounce glass of skimmed or whole milk 1 ounce (1 slice) cheese 1/2-cup cottage cheese	Milk contributes significant amounts of calcium, protein and riboflavin as well as vitamins A and D and the B vitamins.

	All You Can Eat, Anytime You Like	Great Big Servings (even seconds)
MEAT AND PROTEIN-RICH FOODS		
FRUITS AND VEGETABLES	tomato or vegetable juices vegetables (unbuttered): asparagus, broccoli, cabbage, cauliflower, celery, cucumbers, endive, escarole, green beans, greens, Italian beans, kale, kohlrabi, lettuce, mushrooms, okra, peppers, radishes, romaine, sauerkraut, spinach, summer squash, tomatoes and wax beans	fruit or fruit juices (fresh, unsweetened frozen, packed in water or fruit juice): apples, berries, cherries, grapefruit, grapes, melons, oranges, peaches, pineapple and tangerines soups—except cream soups and chowders vegetables (unbuttered): Brussels sprouts, carrots, green peas, onions and rutabagas
BREADS AND CEREALS		Melba toast rye wafers
MILK AND MILK PRODUCTS		skimmed milk: regular or reliquefied dry milk, evaporated skimmed milk, modified skimmed milk or buttermilk yogurt: plain
SUPPLEMENTAL FOODS	coffee or tea—no sugar and no cream consommé or bouillon gelatin desserts—artificially sweetened only salad dressings—reduced calorie only seasoners, relishes: catchup, chili sauce, etc. soft-drinks—artificially sweetened only; plain soda water	olives; ripe or stuffed

THE BASIC FOUR FOOD GROUPS

Generous Portions	Average Amounts	Take It Easy On These
cheese: cottage, farmer, pot and ricotta eggs: baked, coddled, poached, soft- or hard-cooked fish and shellfish (except breaded or fried): bass, cod, flounder, haddock, ocean perch, sardines (drained), shellfish (any kind), tuna (well drained or in water), or broth packs and white fish poultry (except breaded or fried): chicken, Cornish hens and turkey	cheese: any not in Generous Portions eggs: fried, scrambled and omelets fish (except breaded or fried): bluefish, halibut, mackerel, salmon and swordfish meats (except breaded, fried): lean, well-trimmed cuts of beef, ham, lamb, pork and veal crisp bacon, canned meats, cold cuts, corned beef, frankfurters, rabbit and variety meats (liver, etc.) poultry: duckling and goose	fried and breaded meats, fish and poultry untrimmed or fatty meats
fruits (fresh or packed in water, fruit juice or light syrup): bananas and pears fruit drinks and nectars fruit juices: grape, prune and cranberry vegetables (unbuttered): beets, corn, limas, parsnips, pumpkin and winter squash	fruits; regular canned, dried, sweetened frozen or stewed	fried and breaded vegetables
	bread, crackers or rolls: any type cereals: ready-to-eat and cooked dried beans: peas, lentils or limas macaroni, spaghetti, noodles, etc. pancakes and waffles potatoes: white or sweet quick breads: biscuits, muffins, etc. rice: plain or seasoned	pies and pastries pizza snack foods; chips, pretzels and similar items
milk: regular whole and evaporated yogurt: plain	cream soups and chowders custard: baked and sauce milk drinks puddings: regular or instant	eggnog ice cream and frozen custard malted milk drinks
gelatin desserts: regular (plain or fruited) and fruit whips popcorn, unbuttered	angel food or sponge cake candy: hard, jelly beans and marshmallows honey and molasses jams, jellies, marmalades, etc. salad dressings: regular sherbets, ices, ice milks soft drinks: regular syrups: maple, corn, etc.	butter or margarine cakes: not in Average Amounts candy: not in Average Amounts cookies creams: light, heavy, commercial sour nuts and nut butters sauces and gravies—rich ones

A WEEK OF MENUS FOR THE FAMILY

Each day's menus contain all the Basic-Four foods. By adjusting the serving sizes, you can serve these meals to the whole family without exceeding anyone's calorie quota. (One normal serving equals 3 ounces cooked meat, $1/2$ cup fruits and vegetables, 1 slice bread and 1 8-ounce glass milk.)

1

BREAKFAST
pineapple juice
cornflakes
rye toast
milk

LUNCH
split pea soup with croutons
chicken- or tuna-filled omelet
zucchini coins
peach slices
buttermilk

DINNER
sautéed minute or veal steaks (with onion gravy)
Italian green beans
Farmland Pepper Hash (see recipe page 200)
homemade cornbread
fresh fruit compote

2

BREAKFAST
orange juice
pancakes or waffles (with applesauce and cinnamon)
cocoa

LUNCH
panbroiled hamburger
enriched rice with parsley
sliced radishes (with French dressing)
fruit-flavored gelatin
milk

DINNER
Broiled Mackerel Platter (see recipe, page 81) (with broccoli and tomatoes)
pear half with cottage cheese (on lettuce)
enriched hard rolls
angel-food cake (glazed with chocolate syrup)
milk

3

BREAKFAST
orange sections
puffed rice
oatmeal-bread toast
milk

LUNCH
beef bouillon
Swiss cheese sandwich on rye
tomato wedges and cucumber slices
raspberry sherbet

DINNER
roast pork
Green Beans Italian (see recipe, page 191)
corn niblets
lettuce wedges (with French dressing)
broiled grapefruit halves
milk

4

BREAKFAST
tomato juice
baked eggs on toast
bacon
milk

LUNCH
fruit-salad bowl (with fresh or canned fruit, cottage cheese and sherbet)
Crisp Crusts (see recipe, page 207)

DINNER
Lamb-and-Carrot Meatballs (see recipe, page 157)
sautéed green-pepper strips
curried enriched rice
strawberries and sour cream (fresh or frozen berries)

5

BREAKFAST
  grapefruit sections
  oatmeal with honey and raisins
  milk

LUNCH
  corned-beef hash and poached eggs (on
    toast)
  canned baby carrots
  banana slices and vanilla wafers
  milk

DINNER
  vegetable soup (with enriched saltines)
  London broil
  baked potato (with yogurt and chives)
  Herbed Tomato Salad (see recipe, page 195)
  pineapple chunks

6

BREAKFAST
  tangerine slices
  fluffy onion omelet
  whole-wheat toast slices
  milk

LUNCH
  chicken livers and mushrooms (broiled on
    skewers)
  enriched noodles
  lettuce wedges (with French dressing)

  canned fruit cocktail (drain syrup, then add
    orange juice)
  milk

DINNER
  Skillet Pineapple Chicken (see recipe, page
    113)
  peas and onion slices
  buttered parslied potatoes
  baked cup custard

7

BREAKFAST
  orange juice
  toasted English muffin
  Canadian bacon
  milk

LUNCH
  tuna-salad platter
  celery and carrot strips
  enriched refrigerated biscuits (with jam and
    jelly)
  fresh grapes or apples
  milk

DINNER
  meatloaf with mushroom gravy
  mashed potatoes
  spinach with nutmeg
  Blueberry Cottage Pudding (see recipe, page
    220)

DIET DURING PREGNANCY

Meal planning during pregnancy is no more complicated than at any other time, despite all the old wives' tales. Meals should be chosen from the Basic-Four food groups, plus an extra two glasses of milk each day to provide the additional protein and calcium needed by the developing baby. (The Basic-Four already calls for two glasses of milk; the extra two make up the one-quart requirement for pregnant women.)

The questions and answers that follow cover all the essential points a pregnant woman needs to know about her diet.

Q. *Does diet during pregnancy really make a difference in the baby's and mother's health?*
A. There is no question that it does. Nutritionists have found that mothers with the best diets have fewer difficulties during pregnancy, fewer premature births and healthier babies. During pregnancy the mother must supply the food necessary for her own body plus the nutrients needed by the developing baby. Quite literally she eats for both.

Q. *What foods should the mother-to-be eat?*
A. The Basic-Four Food Groups chart on page 37 gives the fundamentals for meal planning, but remember to include an extra two glasses of milk each day. The menu suggestions on pages 40-41 provide about 1800 calories; add two glasses of skimmed milk, 1–2 ounces of meat, fish or poultry and supplementary choices of fruits, vegetables and bread. About 2300 calories are recommended for pregnant women. Go over this diet with your doctor; he may change it to fit your special requirements.

Q. *Is a quart of milk a day still the cornerstone of a pregnancy diet?*
A. Yes, it is. You need abundant amounts of calcium and riboflavin (a B vitamin) as well as protein, and milk is an excellent source of all three. If weight is a problem, cut the calories in half by using skimmed milk or nonfat dry milk. Practically all fresh liquid skimmed milks are fortified with Vitamins A and

D. Also consider evaporated milk or evaporated skimmed milk. Use them in custards, in place of egg in meat loaf, and cream sauces, etc. One-half cup undiluted evaporated milk is the equivalent to 1 cup of regular milk.

Q. *How about the filled milks, imitation milks, and coffee lighteners as a substitute for regular milk?*
A. We don't recommend them. Filled milk is basically skimmed milk with another fat substituted for the butterfat, but it is sometimes difficult to tell it from imitation milk. Imitation milk is a synthetic; many brands do not contain as much protein, calcium or vitamins as regular milk. Coffee lighteners are also poor substitutes; some brands are actually recommended for low-calcium diets.

Q. *Is the calcium and protein found in the cream part of milk?*
A. No, it's the skimmed milk part that is rich in these nutrients. The butterfat (cream) does "carry" Vitamins A and D, but most commercial skimmed milks have been refortified with these vitamins.

Q. *What if you don't like milk or are allergic to it?*
A. If it is a case of dislike, use milk to prepare puddings or creamed soups. Yogurt, cottage cheese, or hard cheeses are also fine substitutes for milk. Allergies are another problem. If your doctor approves, try goat's milk. It is available in most large cities and in dried form. Otherwise, your physician will probably recommend calcium in tablet

or capsule form. And you will need to eat extra servings of other protein-rich foods to compensate for the protein in the milk.

Q. *Why is so much emphasis placed on meat, fish and poultry in the pregnancy diet outline?*
A. Protein is the answer again. These foods plus milk and eggs are the best source of high-quality protein. Each day a pregnant woman needs about 74 grams of protein as compared with 44 grams for the average woman. In terms of food, a quart of milk and 6 ounces of cooked meat plus the added protein found in bread, potatoes, and cerals provides approximately 74 grams of protein.

Q. *Are there any other ways of getting protein?*
A. Yes, there are. Protein comes from both animal and vegetable sources. The rich animal sources are listed above, but dried beans, peas, and lentils as well as breads, cereals, and nuts are also good sources. However, the protein from animal sources can be utilized more completely by the body. Therefore, physicians recommend that at least half the protein in the diet come from animal sources. If you have bean-based main dishes, include cheese or meat in the dish. Or use milk or cheese in the same meal.

Q. *Is a Vitamin D supplement necessary?*
A. No, it is not. Assuming you have the quart of milk a day, you will be getting all the Vitamin D you need. In fact, Vitamin D as a supplement is discouraged in pregnancy diets and vitamin supplements are generally limited to 400 I.U. in one day's dosage.

Q. *How about Vitamin A?*
A. The daily quart of milk, butter or margarine, one egg, and a serving of yellow or dark-green leaf vegetables plus the lesser amounts found in other foods will provide the recommended amount of Vitamin A in the diet.

Q. *How much Vitamin C is recommended?*
A. During pregnancy, the recommended allowance is increased to 80 milligrams a day. A 6-ounce serving of orange or grapefruit juice plus the recommended amounts of other fruits and vegetables will easily provide this amount.

Q. *What about the B vitamins—thiamine (B₁), riboflavin (B₂), niacin, B₆, B₁₂?*
A. These vitamins are supplied in many foods—milk, meat, fish and poultry, wholegrain or enriched breads and cereals and many vegetables.

Q. *Is additional iron needed in a pregnancy diet?*
A. Generous amounts of iron (18 milligrams a day) are needed by all young women. Actual needs are not increased during pregnancy, since loss through menstrual flow is eliminated, but the body adapts itself to absorb more of the iron ingested. The basic recommended diet will provide all the needed iron, providing a conscious effort is made to eat iron-rich foods daily and include one serving of liver weekly. If liver is not a favorite, try some of the more subtle forms like chopped chicken liver or liver mixed with beef to make hamburger or meat loaf. In addition to liver, eat other iron-rich foods—oysters, clams, dark-green leafy vegetables, eggs, dried peas or beans, dried fruits,and even mushrooms.

Q. *Should salt be used?*
A. You definitely should not go on a salt-free (low-sodium) diet unless your physician recommends it. If you find swelling of the fingers, eyelids, or ankles, consult your physician immediately. During the last months of pregnancy, swelling of the ankles often occurs because of pressure of the growing baby. But let your doctor decide if this swelling is a problem which should be treated.

Q. *What about iodized salt?*
A. Iodine is important in the maternal diet and should have continued use during preg-

nancy. Use iodized salt unless your physician forbids it.

Q. *Should tea, coffee and alcohol be avoided?*
A. Tea and coffee should be drunk in moderation. The Surgeon General of the United States advises pregnant women not to drink alcoholic beverages. Even moderate drinking can be harmful to the unborn child. Women who drink heavily during pregnancy risk bearing a child with Fetal Alcohol Syndrome, which is characterized by a variety of birth defects.

Q. *How much water should be drunk daily?*
A. The recommended amount of total liquid is six to eight glasses during the first half of pregnancy. The natural water found in food plus four to six glasses of water, soda, tea, etc. will provide adequate amounts of liquid. This may decrease during the later stages of your pregnancy, but your physician must be the one to decide.

Q. *What about smoking?*
A. It is now known that cigarette smoking will retard fetal growth. Physicians strongly recommend that smokers, especially heavy smokers, cut down the number of cigarettes during pregnancy or, if possible, quit smoking altogether.

Q. *Do those passions for pickles, chilis, ice cream, watermelon, and other exotic foods that pregnant women are famous for mean that their diet is deficient in some way?*
A. Nutritionists have not found any relationship between these passions (technically called pica) and actual nutrient needs. Many physicians now feel it is caused by a combination of folklore suggesting the thought and a subconscious desire for sympathy.

Q. *Are there any foods to be avoided during pregnancy?*
A. None other than those foods that habitually disagree with the woman because of difficulty in digestion or, perhaps, an allergy.

Q. *How much weight should a pregnant woman gain?*

A. If her weight was normal at the beginning of pregnancy, her physician will probably recommend a total gain of 25 to 30 pounds. This allows for the baby's weight, and fluid that surrounds him, the placenta and enlarged uterus, and a small weight gain by the mother.

Q. *What if she was underweight before pregnancy?*
A. The doctor should decide, but most would recommend that she try to bring her weight to normal and then gain the additional 25 to 30 pounds.

Q. *What if she was overweight before pregnancy?*
A. Again the doctor must be the one to prescribe a diet, but it is possible to get all the needed nutrients during pregnancy and still not gain weight.

Q. *If weight gain turns out to be too rapid, should a pregnant woman go on a reducing diet?*
A. Only if it is recommended by her physician. If this excessive gain occurs over weeks or months, he will probably recommend using skimmed milk, lean cuts of meat and fish and poultry, and avoiding cakes, pastries, etc. to cut down on calories. If the weight gain is sudden—in a day or two—the physician should be contacted immediately. This type of weight gain is due to water retention and might indicate the beginning of toxemia.

Q. *Don't many women lose weight during the early months?*
A. Yes, they do. Morning sickness can lead to a general distaste for food. Eat too little and you will lose weight.

Q. *Can anything be done about morning sickness?*
A. Yes. As a first step, keep crackers by the bed and have one or two before getting up. Cut down on smoking. Move slowly when first getting up. If these precautions don't reduce the symptoms, ask your physician for help—there are a number of methods nowadays, that can help control morning sickness.

MEALS FOR YOUNG CHILDREN

From the time a child is born until he is twelve months of age, his diet is controlled by the pediatrician. Follow the doctor's advice—he knows your child's needs. But after this medical supervision is relaxed, you may be unsure about just what to do.

Use the meal plan on page 46 and the ideas that follow as guidelines. The family budget and food preferences will determine variations. Remember that children need the same type of food as adults; only the amounts differ. Everyone needs meat, fish, poultry, eggs and cheese; fruits and vegetables; whole-grain or enriched cereals, breads and pastas; and milk and milk products. If your child has special problems, such as an allergy, your doctor will suggest substitutions for these basic groups.

Appetites do vary from child to child and time to time. As his rate of growth slows after the first year, the child will actually eat less, in proportion to his size, than he did as an infant.

• When the child is not hungry do not force him to eat. Let him wait for the next meal. Forcing food can cause weight problems.

• Choose snacks from the basic foods. Save sweets for dessert.

• Keep portions small and make seconds available.

• Introduce each new food in small quantities and don't make a fuss if the child won't eat it. Try it again in a few weeks.

• Serve in miniature: milk in small glasses or cups; quarter slices of bread and toast; carrots cut into baby-bite-size pieces.

• Encourage the child to feed himself. And accept the spilled food and egg on the bib—it's all part of learning.

• When the child has several teeth, start him on foods that require chewing. If he is limited to pureed food, he may later be slow to accept solid food.

• Allow time to play quietly before meals.

• Avoid distractions during the meal.

• Silverware suited to the child's use should be small enough to handle, yet enough like the adult type so transition comes easily.

• Meals should be served attractively and, of course, in such a way as to encourage good table manners within the child's understanding.

• Give the child water to drink when he wakes up in the morning and, if constipation is a problem, prune juice or other fruit juice just before breakfast. Limiting liquids at supper and before bedtime make it easier for the child to remain dry through the night.

• Use milk in cream soups, puddings, cocoa, and other foods as well as for drinking. If getting enough milk into the child is a real problem, add nonfat dry-milk powder to mashed potatoes or cooked cereals. Make up double-strength nonfat dry milk to be used in puddings and soups.

FOOD FOR CHILDREN ONE TO FIVE

Food	Include Each Day	Average Serving for Each Age		
		1 year	2 to 3 years	4 to 5 years
Meat, fish poultry, cottage cheese	1 to 4 level tablespoons	1 tablespoon	2 to 3 tablespoons	4 tablespoons (about 2 ounces)
Eggs	1 egg	1 egg	1 egg	1 egg
Cooked vegetables (mostly green or yellow)	1 to 2 servings	2 tablespoons	3 tablespoons	3 to 4 tablespoons
Potatoes (white or sweet)	1 serving	2 tablespoons	3 tablespoons	4 tablespoons
Raw vegetables	1 serving	a small serving, such as 1/4 medium carrot		
Fruit (include one serving citrus fruit or tomato juice daily)	2 servings	1/4 cup or 1/2 cup citrus juice	1/3 to 1/2 cup	1/3 to 1/2 cup
Enriched or whole-grain bread	1 1/2 to 3 slices	1/2 to 1 slice	1 slice	1 to 1 1/2 slices
Enriched or whole-grain cereal or pasta	1 serving	1/4 cup	1/3 cup	1/2 cup
Milk (cheese or yogurt)	3 to 4 cups or 3 servings	1/2 to 1 cup	1/2 to 1 cup	1 cup
Butter or margarine as a spread on bread or on vegetables				

MEALS FOR CHILDREN SIX TO TWELVE

During these years, emphasis should be put upon broadening the child's likes and interest in food. Serve as wide a variety of food as possible; encourage the child to accept suitable invitations to meals away from home so that he can see how other families eat. Emphasize good table manners, within the framework of pleasant, relaxed meals. While eating should be pleasant and fun, it should not be a reward for "being good." Good eating habits (and mental attitudes) formed during these years will last a life-time. By the age of six, children need almost as many calories as an adult woman. Since they still eat relatively small meals with between-meal snacks, their food intake isn't always obvious. The Basic-Four Guide is particularly helpful in planning meals for this age group.

If a child is mildly overweight, there is no need to put him on a formal diet. Such a child is usually less active than others in his age group. Encourage him to get out and play more actively. If his lack of activity appears to stem from shyness or a sense of awkwardness, discuss the problem with his teacher. She'll be able to work on it during school hours. Adjust the child's caloric level by substituting skimmed milk for whole; replacing candy, cookies and other sweets with low-calorie snacks; and cutting down on servings.

If overweight has become severe, the child should be taken for a physical examination. Follow the doctor's advice on diet, and encourage the child to play actively. Since so many parents of overweight children are heavy themselves, they should also consider their own diet. "Do as I say, not as I do" never works, and is particularly inadvisable when dealing with today's keenly aware, well-informed youngsters.

MEALS FOR TEENS

Teens are always hungry. Just to supply a seventeen-year-old young man with enough to eat can play havoc with the family food budget. If he is active in sports, he may need up to 4000 calories a day, twice what his mother eats and half again his father's food needs. For the seventeen-year-old girl, the difference is smaller—2300 to 2400 calories for a moderately active girl as compared with her mother's 2000 calories and 2700 for her father.

This actual need for more food should make it easy to assure good nutrition for teens. Studies show, however, that teens (particularly girls) are among the most poorly fed people in this country. These girls will be mothers in a few years. By that time it is important that they should have established sensible eating habits and developed strong, healthy bodies that will enable them to respond easily to the stresses and strains of pregnancy.

To plan meals for teens, start with the Basic-Four Chart on page 37, plus two extra cups of milk. This basic diet will provide 1500 to 1700 calories each day. Boys need twice that amount simply to maintain their weight. Girls need approximately 600 additional calories. These are usually made up by additional servings and by this age group's favorite food—snacks. Following are suggestions for making sure that the snacks your teenager gets carry their weight nutritionally.

Snacks are the fun part of eating

• Keep the ingredients for tasty sandwiches on hand. Rolls and lettuce, peanut butter and jelly or raisins, luncheon meats, roast beef or poultry to slice, cheeses of all kinds tempt teens to eat properly.
• A bowl of fresh fruit and nuts makes good eating as well as a decorative centerpiece.
• Have foods like carrots, cauliflower, cucumbers, and tomatoes washed and ready to eat in the refrigerator.
• Keep whole-grain or enriched crackers on hand.
• Try buttermilk; cottage cheese; Swiss, Edam or other types of hard cheese; chocolate milk; cocoa (made with milk) or canned milkshakes as a different way of serving milk.
• Make up cocoa with an extra tablespoon or two of nonfat dry-milk powder in addition to the regular milk used.
• Add extra cheese to homemade or frozen pizza.
• Make milkshakes in a blender by blending 1/2 pint ice cream, 1 cup cold milk, 1 1/3 cups nonfat dry-milk powder and 1 teaspoon to a tablespoon of flavoring like chocolate syrup, instant coffee powder, maple syrup or fruit jams, or fruit (fresh or canned). Makes 2 servings.

Eating breakfast

Often it is difficult to get teens to take time out for breakfast. They may say they dislike it, or that they are too rushed to eat. Try getting the family started 20 minutes earlier to avoid the rush atmosphere. Then proceed to make breakfast as pleasant and delicious an experience as possible.

The basic breakfast pattern consists of fruit (preferably one rich in vitamin C like a citrus fruit) or tomato juice, enriched or whole-grain bread or cereal and a protein-rich food like eggs, meat or milk. Since hot cereals come in instant form, let the teen make his own portion or prepare it the moment before breakfast. Or try convenience breakfast products like frozen waffles and premixed pancake batter which require very few cooking steps.

For the breakfast non-conformist, try some of these "unbreakfast" foods:

1. Cottage cheese on fruit, cinnamon toast
2. Scrambled-egg sandwich with catchup on a hard roll; a tangerine to eat section by section
3. Juice, buttered enriched saltines and "fortified" cocoa (see opposite page)
4. Juice and a slice or two of frozen pizza, topped with extra cheese and warmed for 10 to 15 minutes in 400°F. oven.

Finally, *don't* insist that teens always have breakfast at home. Often a trip on the school bus does unsettle the stomach. Maybe the answer is breakfast in a luncheonette, but *do* insist that the meal be a good one—not coke and a doughnut.

The woes of being underweight

Being underweight is as frustrating as being fat. Here are some suggestions to give teens who want to put on pounds.

• Be patient. It takes as much time to gain weight as it does to lose it. To gain one pound, you have to eat 3500 more calories than your body uses.

• Start with a hearty breakfast. It's been at least nine hours since the last meal and your body is ready for a meal.

• Plan on six meals a day. Lots of little meals seem less filling than only three large ones.

• Eat a variety of foods. It's the best way to get all the needed nutrients. "Fattening" foods like milkshakes may have more calories, but they are also usually more filling.

• Eat favorite foods. It's human nature to eat more of the things you enjoy.

• Make meals pleasant. A calm atmosphere and plenty of time to eat makes it easier to enjoy the extra food needed.

• Eat with a friend. Afternoon snacks are more fun if you can share them with someone. And its much more difficult to "forget" to eat if you have made a formal date for a snack.

• Don't fill up on low-calorie liquids. The stomach needs room for food. Start with the main dish rather than soup. Drink the soda after the sandwich. Eat the cake, then quench thirst with a glass of milk.

• Get plenty of exercise. Fresh air and exercise are nature's pepper-uppers.

• Get plenty of sleep. Being rested and relaxed helps the body use food more efficiently and makes life (and eating) more fun.

The woes of being overweight

Because the body's caloric needs during the teen years are so great, it's easier to lose weight than it ever will be again. Here are some suggestions to give teens who want to shed pounds.

• Pick a diet plan (like any of the six on pages 13 to 29) that fits in most closely with your current eating habits, but add an extra two glasses of skimmed milk or buttermilk. This will bring the calories up to 1400 for girls and 2000 for boys—more sensible levels for teen dieters. Don't expect to lose more than two pounds a week. But if you stick to the 1400 or 2000 calorie level, you can expect to *maintain* this rate of loss.

• Start with a good breakfast; have a reasonable lunch and a smaller dinner than usual; and then try not to eat after 8 o'clock. Keep yourself busy so that there's less temptation to snack. When you do go out with the gang, pick snacks wisely. Have sherbet, not ice cream; cole slaw, not french fries, with your hamburger; low-calorie soda or lemonade, not a milkshake. Even cheat judiciously: Have two slices of pizza, not four; plain pizza, not with extra cheese; an ice-cream soda, not a milkshake; a slice of poundcake, not pie à la mode. Keep a good calorie guide handy. (Check the difference in the numbers of calories in the items just mentioned—you'll be surprised.)

• Last but not least, get more exercise. Walk, don't ride to school. Go out for a sport, and really *work* in gym class instead of hiding in a corner. Do calisthenics at home.

Complexion care for teens

As the endocrine and hormone systems develop during the teen years, they often get out of balance and complexion problems result. Careful skin care is necessary to minimize these problems, particularly acne and blackheads. Here are tips for teens wth troublesome skin.

Most skin problems in teens are due to excessively oily skin. To remove excess oils, wash your face several times a day with soap and hot water; pat (don't rub) dry. Powder or other makeup tends to clog the pores and will aggravate pimples or blackheads. (However, blushers, which are applied more lightly and less extensively, may be used to add color.)

To remove blackheads, heat the skin with a hot damp cloth, then press out (don't pinch) the blackhead. If it doesn't come out easily, don't force it. Pinching the skin can spread the infection. If the skin condition is serious, see a physician. (Dermatologists are specialists in skin problems.) Medication can often do wonders where do-it-yourself remedies are futile and possibly harmful.

It has been found that acne is not *caused* by eating a specific food or group of foods—though in some cases a particular food might *aggravate* the condition and should be dropped from the diet temporarily. Follow your physician's advice. He may recommend that some of these foods be minimized in the diet: sugars and syrups; fats, particularly in fried foods, rich sauces and pastries.

MEALS FOR MATURE ADULTS

Caloric requirements decrease with age because of decreased activity, lean body mass (muscle tissue) and metabolic rate. By sixty-five, a moderately active man needs only 2400 calories a day; a moderately active woman, 1800. Luckily, the appetite also decreases with age, so it is less of a struggle to maintain a reasonable weight. Careful selection of food is important to insure proper nutrient intake without excessive calories. As part of the general cutback in calories, fats in the diet should be limited. Emphasize the use of lean meat or fish and poultry; cut down on butter or margarine and high-calorie desserts; use skimmed milk or buttermilk. Any of the low-calorie recipes in this book will meet these requirements.

Nutritional needs in terms of protein, vitamins and minerals don't shift with age. Degenerative changes may interfere with the body's ability to obtain nourishment. For example, there is a tendency to eat less protein, often because meat is difficult to chew when the teeth are faulty; taste buds become less effective, the sense of smell diminishes and there is a decrease in gastric secretion. These changes can make eating less pleasurable. In older people, meeting nutritional requirements is crucial because one nutritional deficiency can bring about another and another. If there are health problems requiring a therapeutic diet, eating habits must be shifted. The special diet recipes and general information (pages 242-318) in this book cover, among others, the four therapeutic diets most often needed by this age group—low-fat, low-cholesterol; low sodium; low-purine; and gallbladder diets.

In later years, families are smaller, and there is less inspiration to cook. The first big adjustment is to get used to planning, buying and preparing foods for one or two and not four or five. Once that adjustment has been made, it soon becomes evident that in an age of freezers, instant mixes and convenience-food products, it is comparatively easy to cook attractive, nutritious, filling meals on a smaller scale. In any case, the following suggestions should prove helpful:
• Prepare in quantity and freeze. For example: Buy hamburger in 1-pound lots; divide into patties; wrap individually and freeze. Let thaw overnight in refrigerator and the meat will be

ready to cook the next day. Or cook while still frozen, but allow at least double the cooking time.

• The same principle can be applied to casserole dishes. Prepare for four to six servings; divide into individual 1-cup to 1-pint servings; freeze. Thaw before rewarming for best results. Most dishes are hot after 30 minutes in a 350°F. oven. Remember to undercook main dishes slightly if they are to be frozen, since the food will be further cooked when it is reheated.

• Try commercial frozen main dishes—lasagna, stuffed peppers, Swiss steak, and so on. Keep a supply of favorites on hand.

• Use products that are frozen individually rather than in chunks, making it easier to separate just the amount needed: e.g., frozen veal steaks, minute steaks, shrimp, fish steaks, frozen vegetables in plastic bags.

• Buy bread in half-pound loaves and freeze what you don't immediately need. It will keep up to three months. Also, look for refrigerated biscuits packed five to a can. They must be cooked all at once, but warm extras for a second meal. There are also frozen brown-and serve rolls. Rewrap unheated rolls tightly after opening the package and the remainder will stay fresh for later meals.

• Avail yourself of the myriad of individually packaged products on supermarket shelves. Although they may seem less economical than larger sizes, remember that you save nothing on food you throw away. Try *tuna and salmon* in 3$^1/_4$-ounce cans (individual servings); *ready-to-eat and instant cooked cereals* in individual serving packets; *fruit juices* in one-serving 6- or 6$^1/_2$-ounce cans; *single-layer cake mixes; instant breakfast* in ready-to-serve single portions; *fresh fruit* (what could be more portion-controlled than a banana, apple or orange?). Also, buy butter by the half- or quarter-pound; eggs by the half-dozen; chicken in parts; small jars of instant coffee. (Flavor deteriorates if coffee is kept too long.)

• Take advantage of other convenience foods. For example, *sauce and gravy mixes* can be made up a quarter at a time. Just measure total mix, stir well, then use only one quarter; adjust other ingredients proportionately. Prepare according to directions. Do the same thing with *dried-soup mixes* or with *gelatin-dessert mix*. (Remember to seal leftovers carefully—the mixes lump if exposed to air.) *Dry coffee lighteners* keep indefinitely on the pantry shelf. The frozen lighteners last several weeks in the refrigerator and can be used on cereals as well as in beverages. *Refrigerator cookies* can be baked a few at a time or as you need them. *Pasteurized process cheese* can be spread on toast or used as "instant" sauce for vegetables or meat. *Instant nonfat dry milk* can be used as is in cooking, reliquefied as needed—even one glass at a time—for drinking.

• Buy some small equipment: 7-inch skillets, $1/2$- to 1-quart saucepans, 1-quart casseroles, a small coffeemaker. If you broil food often, purchase a counter-top broiler. It's easier to clean than an oven broiler.

• Blended vegetables can be eaten as a puree, added to soups or stews, or baked topped with an egg or some cheese.

• Wheat germ can boost vitamin B and iron in the diet. Sprinkle it over yogurt, cottage cheese, ricotta cheese or ice cream. It also adds texture to pancake batter, meatloaf or scrambled eggs.

• Breakfast cereals are well fortified and can be a good source of nutrients. The bran cereals are excellent sources of fiber. Cereal is eaten along with milk, and this will incorporate calcium, protein and other nutrients into the diet. Try adding cereal to yogurt for a change.

Shaping Up with Exercise

Regular exercise is essential for good posture, suppleness, strength and vitality. Those are reasons enough to include it in a slimming program. But it also has more direct benefits, in terms of shaping you up while it helps trim you down.

The importance of exercise

Whether it takes the form of calisthenics or walking, bowling, cycling or swimming, exercise should be done regularly and vigorously for best results. Walk a mile in twenty minutes; swim, don't float; bowl alone, not in a group of six; and exercise at least three times a week in addition to your regular activities.

Is exercise an efficient way to lose weight? The answer is obvious in the chart below, which gives the number of calories used up by some common exercises. An hour of vigorous walking uses fewer than 300 calories—not enough to get rid of a tenth of a pound. On the other hand, if you keep it up for a year, you could lose 10 pounds. So, on a long term basis, exercise *can* be effective.

Moreover, a reducing diet is most effective when combined with exercise. As the fat melts away, firm up the muscles with spot exercises. Physical-fitness expert Nicholas Kounovsky has developed sets of exercises anyone can follow. Illustrated on the following pages, they include Plan I for general muscle tone; Plan II, spot exercises for hips, waistline, etc; Plan III for the practiced exerciser who wants to keep trim. Finally, there are exercises specifically recommended for new mothers and middle-aged adults, along with a rundown on aerobic exercise.

CALORIES USED UP BY ACTIVITIES

Exercise	Calories Used Up per minute	Minutes to Use Up to 100 Calories
Bicycling, fast	8.9	11
Bicycling, slow	2.9	34
Dancing,slow	4.4	23
Ping-pong	5.1	20
Running	8.1	12
Skating	4.1	24
Swimming, rapid	9.2	11
Walking, slow	2.3	43
Walking, rapid	3.9	25
Reclining	.1	100

TIPS ON DOING EXERCISES

• Check with your doctor before starting an exercise program.

• Read and carefully follow directions for exercises. Be sure to breathe as suggested.

• Never force yourself. If an exercise cannot be completed without straining, do part of it and gradually work into the rest.

• Start by doing each exercise three times; work up to six. If an exercise specifies an alternate leg, do each leg six times.

• Wait at least an hour and a half after eating before you exercise. Remember, too, if you can exercise at the same time each day, it's more likely to become a habit.

The Kounovsky method of teaching physical fitness emphasizes six factors: endurance, suppleness, equilibrium, strength, speed and coordination. Plan I is a series of simple yet challenging exercises to develop these factors. Start gently at first, improve gradually. Work up from three to six times for each exercise. Be sure to read the Tips on Doing Exercises above, before you start.

PLAN I: BASIC DAILY EXERCISES FOR EVERYONE

FOR ENDURANCE
(the body's ability to resist fatigue):

1. Assume a squatting position with fingertips braced on floor, weight on toes, head straight. Exhale.

2. Straighten up and raise left knee, bending arms over head with palms together. Inhale. Resume original position and alternate knees.

FOR COORDINATION
(the body's ability to move smoothly and accurately):

1. With weight on right leg, simultaneously lift left leg and raise right arm out to side, left arm straight up.

2. Lunge on left leg to side, reversing arm positions as you do so. Breathe normally throughout. Alternate legs.

FOR STRENGTH
(the body's muscular force)

1. From a full standing position, with fingers clasped behind neck and back held straight, bend knees so weight is on toes. Inhale.

2. Straighten up. Raise left knee and try to touch right elbow with it. Exhale. Go back to first position and alternate legs.

FOR EQUILIBRIUM
(the ability to maintain balance):

1. Balance on toes of right foot for ten seconds, without moving that foot. Do same on left foot.

2. With eyes closed, balance for ten seconds on right foot, bending at waist with left leg extended. Breathe normally. Alternate legs.

FOR SUPPLENESS
(limberness and flexibility of joints):

1. From a standing position, lunge sideways with left leg. Flex arms over head to right. Inhale.

2. Bend from waist and try to touch left toes. Exhale. Repeat exercise, starting with right lunge. Stretch fully as possible.

FOR SPEED
(the rapidity of bodily movements):

1. Legs apart and straight, bend torso forward, with arms outstretched to sides. Keep head straight.

2. Swiftly twist trunk from side to side, touching floor with one hand while other arm points upward. Inhale and exhale slowly while twisting.

PLAN II: EXERCISES FOR SPECIFIC PARTS OF THE BODY

After you've mastered the exercises in Plan I, you can begin to concentrate on particular areas: waistline, chest, arms, legs, abdomen, hips or thighs. These exercises are more difficult and it is wise to go slowly. Be sure to incorporate what you have learned from Plan I. For example, if you feel you need more suppleness, you should accentuate bending movements. As in Plan I, start by doing the exercise three times and gradually work up to six.

EXERCISES FOR THE WAISTLINE

1. From a sitting position, bend knees, balance on hips, stretching arms forward, parallel to knees. Exhale.

2. Still balanced on hips, straighten legs and raise arms above head as high as possible. Inhale.

1. Lie on back with with fingers clasped behind head, left knee bent and parallel to floor. Inhale.

2. Sit up and try to touch left knee with right elbow. Exhale. Repeat with right knee, left elbow.

1. Lying on back, raise legs until vertical. With right elbow on floor, press left palm into right. Inhale.

2. Slowly lower legs to right side. Exhale. Do several times on right side; repeat for left side.

FOR CHEST, ABDOMEN, ARMS, LEGS

The pace at which you exercise is an individual matter. Extremely lively and tense people should do exercises slowly and in a relaxed manner (the way a cat stretches, for instance). There should be an awareness of the entire self. On the other hand, if a person is tired and sluggish, the pace should be brisk and have a definite rhythm. Try background music to establish a mood and set the pace you want.

1. From a standing position with legs apart, bend forward until palms are flat on the floor . . . . .

2. Move hands farther out . . .

3. "Walk" forward with hands . . . .

4. Up on toes to go sideways . . . .

5. And stretch as far as possible (be careful not to overestimate your range). Breathe regularly throughout.

FOR POSTURE (BACK, HIPS, THIGHS, NECK, UPPER ARMS AND SHOULDER GIRDLE)

1. Lie in prone position. Extend right arm out, with bent left arm back, right knee bent and up. Exhale.

2. Raise shoulders, right arm and left leg as high as possible. Keep left arm bent back for support. Inhale. Repeat with opposite leg and arm.

1. Start in standing position. Bend body from waist. With arms outstretched, head down, exhale.

2. Straighten back and raise head. Bend arms at elbows, placing hands behind neck. Inhale.

**FOR HIPS,
THIGHS AND
LOWER BACK**

1. Assume a kneeling
   position with hands
   flat on floor and head
   up. Exhale.

2. Slowly extend right
   leg to side, as straight
   as possible. Inhale.
   Return to position;
   extend left leg.

1. Start in kneeling position. Slowly extend
   left leg back and up,
   so weight is on
   hands, right knee and
   foot. Keep head up.
   Exhale.

2. Pressing with right
   foot, straighten right
   leg to raise body,
   keeping left leg high.
   Pull shoulders back.
   Inhale when up.
   Repeat with right leg
   up.

1. From standing position, place left foot forward, right leg back.

2. Wiggle hips from side to side. Repeat, changing legs.

1. Start in standing position. With feet together and knees bent, leap from side to side.

2. Keep arms outstretched as you alternate leaps from side to side, six times each.

1. From crouch, bend left leg, extend right one to side.

2. Lift hips, shift legs from side to side, keeping weight on hands.

PLAN III: SPECIAL EXERCISES FOR VITALITY AND VIGOR

This is your graduate course in exercising! After you have mastered the exercises in Plan I and those in Plan II that are applicable to any particular figure problems, add as many of these exercises as you have time for. They take a bit more practice, but, as in the case of all the exercises given, it is best to start slowly and improve gradually. Breathing should be according to intensity, but as steady as possible.

These exercises will help you gain the control that leads to graceful and assured movements. As you become more proficient at them, you will discover a paradox: The more control there is, the greater the freedom of movement.

Start from standing position. With feet together and keeping knees loosely bent, lightly jump forward (far left) and back (left). Do six times each.

Start in crouch position on toes with knees bent. Exhale. Swing legs out so body is to side. Raise right arm. Inhale. Alternate sides. (This is a difficult exercise).

EXERCISES FOR SPECIFIC GROUPS

New mothers and middle-aged adults (although this second group can mean anyone between the ages of twenty and eighty, depending on physical shape) have particular problems that often can be helped by doing specific exercises. Following are the exercises from the three plans given in this section which should be emphasized if you fall into either group.

NEW MOTHERS

Problem:

A new mother is naturally anxious to get back to the size dress she wore before pregnancy. But she usually must get rid of flabby inches in the region of the abdomen and waistline.

Exercises:

Two groups from Plan II, those for the WAIST-LINE and the ABDOMEN. The latter exercise is also good for firming the pectoral muscles.

MIDDLE-AGED ADULTS

Problem:

Decreased physical activity can result in flabbiness, stiffness, weariness, slowness, awkwardness, even lack of balance.

Exercises:

All of Plan I.
Plan II, with particular emphasis on exercises for the WAISTLINE.
Plan III: as many exercises as can be done comfortably. Progress slowly.

AEROBIC EXERCISE

Aerobic exercise not only benefits your muscles, it strengthens the cardiovascular system as well. The reason? Aerobic exercise produces a rapid, continuous blood flow through the heart—much more so than regular exercises. Exercises such as jogging, cycling, walking and jumping rope are good examples of aerobics: All four involve rhythm, repetition and motion, which improve cardiovascular fitness. The intensity and duration of these activities are important. When exercise lasts longer than 2 minutes, each heartbeat becomes more efficient at getting oxygen to the muscles, and thus performs better in producing energy. As long as you exercise, the process continues. Because aerobic exercise "works" the heart muscle, that muscle becomes stronger. The stronger heart pumps more blood per beat and therefore works more efficiently by circulating the same amount of blood with fewer beats.

Recipes for Calorie Watchers

The low-calorie recipes in this section cover everything from soup to dessert, plus hors d'oeuvres and snacks. Use them as part of a formal reducing diet (the I-Can't-Believe-It's-a-Diet and Eat-for-a-Treat Diets on pages 13-14 and 24-27 both make special allowances for these recipes) or simply to keep trim by skimming away extra calories painlessly.

Almost all these recipes can also be used for family members with special diet problems—a need to cut down on cholesterol or sodium, for example, or to eat more iron. The changes necessary to adapt a recipe to special uses are listed at the end of each. Also check the section on Special Diets, pages 242-318; it contains general information, cooking hints and additional recipes.

All the recipes have been prepared, tasted, rechecked and tasted again in the Good Housekeeping Institute test kitchens. To assure success, follow the instructions precisely and use exactly the amount of ingredients specified. This is essential in low-calorie recipes—an extra dab of butter here and a tablespoon of sugar there can add hundreds of calories to a recipe.

Calories per serving (rounded to the nearest 5 calories) are given for each recipe. They are determined by carefully dividing the yield into equal servings. You can use the same method to check the calories in other dishes. To do so, jot down the ingredients and amounts specified; then, using a calorie guide, determine the number of calories in each ingredient. Add the calories to get the recipe total; divide this total by the number of servings. Here's an example from page 218:

CUSTARD RICE PUDDING (6¹/₂-cup servings)

1 cup hot cooked rice	205 calories
2 eggs	160
¹/₃ cup granulated sugar	255
¹/₄ cup raisins	105
spices*	——
2 cups skimmed milk	180
	——
	905 total calories
	150 calories per serving

*Salt, vanilla and cinnamon contain too few calories to be included in total.

A calorie guide is provided on pages 322 to 336. You might also send for the following booklets from the U.S. Government Printing Office, Superintendent of Documents, Washington, D.C. 20402:

Nutritive Value of Foods (Home and Garden Bulletin Number 72). Available for $3.25, this booklet gives calories and other nutrient values for various foods in common serving sizes.

Composition of Foods: Raw, Processed, Prepared. Available for $7.00, this booklet lists nutrient, calorie, protein, fat, carbohydrate, vitamin and mineral values for a pound of food as purchased and for 100 grams of the same food as prepared.

APPETIZERS AND SNACKS

HOT CRABMEAT PIE (80 calories per serving)

2 3-ounce packages Neufchâtel cheese
1 6¹/2-to 7¹/2-ounce can King crab, flaked, well drained
2 tablespoons instant minced onion
1 tablespoon milk
¹/2 teaspoon prepared horseradish
¹/4 teaspoon salt
dash pepper
¹/4 cup sliced blanched almonds

About 30 minutes before serving: Preheat oven to 375°F. In medium bowl, thoroughly mix all ingredients but almonds. Spoon mixture into 8-inch pie plate; sprinkle with almonds. Bake 15 to 20 minutes. Cut into 10 wedges.

Diabetic diet: Exchanges per serving = 1 meat and 1 fat.

EASY SWEET-AND-SOUR MEATBALLS (35 calories per meatball)

¹/3 cup packed dark brown sugar
¹/4 cup lemon juice
1 tablespoon catchup
³/4 pound lean ground beef
1 egg
¹/4 cup dry bread crumbs
¹/4 teaspoon salt
dash pepper

About 30 minutes before serving: In medium saucepan, combine ¹/2 cup water, brown sugar, lemon juice and catchup; heat to boiling. Meanwhile, in medium bowl, combine round steak and remaining ingredients. Shape into about 30 small meatballs; add to boiling sauce. Cook, covered, over low heat, for about 15 minutes. Keep warm in chafing dish; serve with toothpicks. Makes about 30 appetizers.

Low-fat, low-cholesterol diet: Prepare as directed but use only white of the egg. 1 gram fat per meatball.
High-iron diet: .5 milligram iron per meatball.

CONFETTI COCKTAIL (105 calories per serving)

1¹/2 cups sauterne
2 teaspoons salt
2 pounds sea scallops, cut into quarters
1 4-ounce can pimentos
1 large green pepper, diced
¹/3 cup diced celery
¹/4 cup chopped scallions
¹/3 cup lemon juice
¹/4 teaspoon white pepper
lettuce leaves
lemon slices for garnish

Early in day or day before: In sauterne, 1 cup water and salt, simmer scallops, covered, 5 minutes; drain. In bowl, combine scallops, ¹/4 cup diced pimentos, ¹/3 cup diced green pepper, celery, scallions, lemon juice and pepper; cover; refrigerate, tossing occasionally.

About 15 minutes before serving: Cut rest of pimentos and pepper into strips. In compote or flat serving dish, arrange scallop mixture on bed of lettuce leaves; garnish with pimento, pepper strips and lemon slices. Spoon juice from scallops over them. Makes 8 first-course servings.

Diabetic diet: Exchanges per serving = 2 meat and ¹/2 vegetable.
Egg-, gluten-, milk- and wheat-free diet: Prepare as directed.
High-iron diet: 2 milligrams iron per serving.

TANGY GARLIC DIP FOR RAW VEGETABLES (195 calories per cup of dip)

1 8-ounce container plain
   yogurt
1 envelope (.7 ounces) garlic
   salad-dressing mix
cherry tomatoes, cucumber
   sticks, sliced raw turnips,
   mushroom slices, carrot
   sticks or celery strips

About 2 hours before serving: In small bowl, blend yogurt and
dressing mix. Refrigerate until serving time. Use as a dip for your
choice of vegetables. Makes 1 cup.

Low-fat, low-cholesterol diet: Negligible fat per serving.

VEGETABLE DIP (350 calories per cup)

1 cup reduced-calorie mayonnaise
2 teaspoons tarragon vinegar
1/2 teaspoon salt
1/2 teaspoon curry
1/8 teaspoon thyme leaves
dash pepper
2 teaspoons chili sauce
2 teaspoons chopped chives
2 tablespoons grated onion
raw cauliflowerettes
4- to 6-inch celery sticks
4- to 6-inch carrot sticks

About 30 minutes before serving: In small bowl, mix first 9 ingredients; refrigerate. At serving time, spoon mayonnaise mixture into
small bowl; set in center of plate, surrounded by cauliflowerettes,
celery and carrot sticks. Makes about 1 cup.

Low-fat, low-cholesterol diet: Less than 1 gram fat per "dip."

COOL CUCUMBER DIP (300 calories per recipe)

3 medium cucumbers
1 8-ounce container creamed
   cottage cheese, sieved
1 tablespoon skimmed milk or
   reliquefied nonfat dry milk
1 tablespoon minced pimento
dash cayenne
1 teaspoon salt
1/2 teaspoon pepper

About 30 minutes before serving: For dip, pare, then finely chop 1
cucumber, draining well on paper towels. In medium bowl, blend
cucumber well with remaining ingredients. Cut unpared cucumbers into sticks about 4 inches long and 1/2-inch wide. Spoon dip
into serving bowl; set on plate, surrounded by cucumber sticks,
for dunking. Makes about 1 1/2 cups.

Egg- and gluten-free diet: Prepare as directed.
Low-fat, low-cholesterol diet: Less than 1 gram fat per "dip."

PIQUANT DIP FOR SHRIMP (20 calories for each dipped shrimp)

1 8-ounce container creamed
   cottage cheese
1/2 cup chili sauce
1/2 green pepper, chopped
1 teaspoon Worcestershire
2 drops red food color
dash cayenne
2 7-ounce packages frozen
   shelled and deveined shrimp
parsley for garnish
lemon slices, radish buds, carrot curls or pimento strips

About 3 hours before serving: In electric-blender container at low
speed, blend cottage cheese, chili sauce, green pepper, Worcestershire, red food color and cayenne. Refrigerate, covered, until
serving time.

Cook shrimp as label directs; drain; refrigerate until serving
time.

To serve: Stir cheese mixture; put into small serving bowl. Decorate bowl with nest of parsley; fill with chilled shrimp. Surround
with lemon slices, radish buds, carrot curls or pimento strips.
Makes 40 to 50 shrimp or nibblers for 8 to 10.

Low-fat diet: Prepare as directed but use low-fat cottage cheese. Negligible fat per dipped shrimp. Omit recipe from low-cholesterol diet.

SPICED PINEAPPLE PICKUPS (about 5 calories per "pickup")

**2 16-ounce cans pineapple
chunks**
³/₄ cup vinegar
dash salt
6 to 8 whole cloves
2 2-inch sticks cinnamon

Day before: Drain pineapple chunks, reserving ³/₄ cup syrup. In medium saucepan, mix reserved syrup and remaining ingredients; cover; simmer 10 minutes. Stir in pineapple chunks; refrigerate.

To serve: Drain syrup and spices from pineapple. Serve chunks in bowl with toothpicks as pickups.

Egg-, gluten-, milk- and wheat-free diet: Prepare as directed.
Low-fat, low-cholesterol diet: Negligible fat per serving.
Low-sodium diet: Prepare as directed but omit salt. Negligible sodium per serving.

MARINATED CARROT STICKS (30 calories per serving)

6 medium carrots
1 garlic clove, halved
¹/₂ cup wine vinegar
**1 teaspoon dried mint leaves
(optional)**

About 3 hours before serving: Scrape carrots and cut each crosswise, then lengthwise, to make 4 pieces. Cook in salted boiling water until just tender-crisp—10 to 15 minutes. In shallow dish, mix garlic, vinegar, mint leaves and carrot sticks. Cover, refrigerate, and marinate 2 to 4 hours. Drain carrots. Makes 4 servings.

Diabetic diet: Exchanges per serving = 1 vegetable.
Egg-, gluten-, milk- and wheat-free diet: Prepare as directed.
Low-fat, low-cholesterol diet: Negligible fat per serving.
Low-purine diet: Prepare as directed.
Low-sodium diet: 15 milligrams sodium per serving.

SESAME-TOPPED STUFFED CELERY (40 calories per stick)

¹/₄ cup sesame seeds
**1 8-ounce container creamed
cottage cheese***
¹/₄ teaspoon onion salt
**3 large green celery stalks,
washed and trimmed**

About 30 minutes before serving: Preheat oven to 350°F. In small baking pan, toast sesame seeds 5 to 10 minutes, or until golden brown; cool.

Meanwhile, in blender container, at low speed, blend cottage cheese and onion salt until smooth. (Or sieve cottage cheese and onion salt until smooth.)

Use mixture to fill celery stalks; sprinkle with toasted sesame. Cut each stalk into three even lengths. Refrigerate until serving time. Makes 9 servings.

*Use a brand with a relatively soft curd—it blends better.

Diabetic diet: Exchanges per stick = 1¹/₂ vegetable, 1 meat and ¹/₂ fat.
Egg-, gluten- and wheat-free diet: Prepare as directed.
Low-purine diet: Prepare as directed.

SPICY GLAZED FRUIT (150 calories per serving)

1 large banana
3 tablespoons brown sugar
**3 tablespoons butter or marga-
rine, softened**
¹/₈ teaspoon ground cloves
¹/₈ teaspoon salt
**1 16-ounce can cling-peach
halves, drained**
**1 15¹/₂-ounce can pineapple
rings, drained**

About 20 minutes before serving: Preheat broiler if manufacturer directs. Slice banana diagonally. Combine sugar, butter or margarine, cloves and salt; spread on top of bananas, peaches and pineapple. Place peaches and pineapple on broiler rack; broil 3 or 4 minutes. Add banana slices, and broil until tinged with brown. Makes 6 servings.

Egg-, gluten-, milk- and wheat-free diet: Prepare as directed but use milk-free margarine on milk-free diet.
Low-fat, low-cholesterol diet: Prepare as directed but use margarine instead of butter. 5 grams fat per serving.
Low-purine diet: Prepare as directed.
Low-sodium diet: Prepare as directed but use unsalted butter or margarine; omit salt. 5 milligrams sodium per serving.

ORANGE-PINEAPPLE FROST (150 calories per serving)

4 cups orange juice
2 cups pineapple juice
²/₃ cup fresh lime juice
1 pint lemon or orange sherbet

Early in day: Mix orange juice with pineapple and lime juice. Refrigerate, covered.

To serve: Fill 6 iced-tea glasses with juices; add a ball of sherbet to each. Makes 6 servings.

Low-fat, low-cholesterol diet: Negligible fat per serving.
Low-fat, bland (gall bladder) diet: Prepare as directed.
Low-purine diet: Prepare as directed.
Low-sodium diet: 5 milligrams sodium per serving.

WATERMELON COOLER (40 calories per serving)

6 thin lime slices
1 14- to 16-pound watermelon
cheesecloth
3 to 4 8-ounce bottles lemon-lime soda
granulated sugar
fresh lemon juice
mint sprigs for garnish

Day before: Place lime slices in bottom of 1¹/₂ pint mixing bowl; add enough cold water to just cover; freeze until solid. Add more cold water to fill bowl; freeze.

About 30 minutes before serving: Using sharp knife, with a single lengthwise cut, slice across watermelon about one-fourth down from top. Place a double layer of cheesecloth on top of a large bowl. Using a large spoon, scoop out a few pieces of meat from larger section of watermelon onto cheesecloth, being careful to leave ¹/₂ inch of meat around the rind to form shell. Bring corners of cheesecloth together; then, holding it over bowl, squeeze out as much juice as possible. Discard pulp and seeds. Repeat this scooping and squeezing until all meat from both sections of watermelon has been turned into juice—10 to 14 cups in all. Discard smaller watermelon shell.

Using small paring knife, cut a sawtooth pattern around rim of larger watermelon shell. Also slice a piece of rind from bottom so that melon stands level. Skim air bubbles from surface of juice. Then, using measuring cup, fill watermelon shell, using 1 cup lemon-lime soda for every 4 cups of watermelon juice. For every 5 cups of this liquid, add about 3 teaspoons sugar and 1 teaspoon lemon juice, or to your taste; skim off any bubbles, if necessary. Now remove lime-decorated ice from bowl and place lime-side up, in watermelon shell. Serve garnished with mint sprigs. Makes about 20 servings.

Diabetic diet: Prepare as directed but substitute low-calorie sugar-free lemon-lime soda for regular; omit sugar. Exchanges per serving = ¹/₂ fruit.
Egg-, gluten-, milk- and wheat-free diet: Prepare as directed.
Low-fat, low-cholesterol diet: Negligible fat per serving.
Low-purine diet: Prepare as directed. Omit recipe if carbonated beverages are forbidden on diet.
Low-sodium diet: Negligible sodium per serving.

BLUSHING BUTTERMILK (70 calories per serving)

¹/₂ cup icy-cold tomato juice
¹/₂ cup cold buttermilk
lemon juice (optional)

To serve: Mix tomato juice and buttermilk; stir in dash of lemon juice, if desired. Makes 1 serving.

Bland diet: Prepare as directed.
Diabetic diet: Exchanges per serving = 1 vegetable and ¹/₂ skimmed milk.
Egg-, gluten- and wheat-free diet: Prepare as directed.
Low-fat, low-cholesterol diet: Negligible fat per serving.
Low-fat, bland (gall bladder) diet: Prepare as directed.
Low-purine diet: Prepare as directed.
Low-residue diet: Prepare as directed.

CAFÉ AU CRÉME (25 calories per serving)

¹/₂ cup evaporated milk
¹/₄ teaspoon vanilla extract
1¹/₂ tablespoons confectioners'
sugar
¹/₂ teaspoon cinammon
2 cups hot coffee
nutmeg

About 30 minutes before serving: In ice-cube tray, freeze evaporated milk, just until ice crystals form ¹/₂ inch in from edge of tray. In small bowl, combine frozen milk, vanilla, sugar and cinnamon; with electric mixer, at medium speed, beat until thick. Fill each of 8 demitasse cups one-fourth full with milk mixture; fill cups with hot coffee. Sprinkle each with nutmeg. Makes 8 servings.

Egg-, gluten- and wheat-free diet: Prepare as directed.

MULLED APPLE JUICE (60 calories per serving)

1 quart (4 cups) apple juice
1¹/₂ teaspoons whole cloves
5 small cinnamon sticks
5 whole allspice

Day before or just before serving: In medium saucepan, heat apple juice to boiling. Tie remaining ingredients in cheesecloth bag; add bag to juice; boil 5 minutes. Remove spice bag; serve hot. Makes eight ¹/₂ cup servings.

Diabetic diet: Exchanges per serving = 1 fruit.
Egg-, gluten-, milk- and wheat-free diet: Prepare as directed.
Low-fat, low-cholesterol diet: Negligible fat per serving.
Low-purine diet: Prepare as directed.
Low-sodium diet: Negligible sodium per serving.

SHERBET SHAKE (140 calories per serving)

¹/₂ cup orange sherbet
2 cups skimmed milk or re-
liquefied nonfat dry milk

A few minutes before serving: In blender container, at low speed, blend sherbet and milk until smooth. Divide between 2 large glasses.

Bland diet: Prepare as directed.
Egg-, gluten-, and wheat-free diet: Prepare as directed but use gluten-free sherbet on gluten-free diet.
Low-fat, low-cholesterol diet: Negligible fat per serving.
Low-fat, bland (gall bladder) diet: Prepare as directed.
Low-purine diet: Prepare as directed.
Low-residue diet: Prepare as directed.

PINEAPPLE BANANA SHAKE (105 calories per serving)

1¹/₂ cups buttermilk
¹/₂ cup drained pineapple
chunks
¹/₂ medium banana
nutmeg for garnish

Just before serving: In blender container, at high speed, blend first 3 ingredients until smooth. Serve sprinkled with nutmeg. Makes 2 servings.

Bland diet: Prepare as directed but substitute canned peaches for pineapple; omit nutmeg.
Diabetic diet: Prepare as directed but use pineapple packed in juice. Exchanges per serving = 1 skim milk and 1 fruit.
Egg-, gluten- and wheat-free diet: Prepare as directed.
Low-fat, low-cholesterol diet: Negligible fat per serving.
Low-fat, bland (gall bladder) diet: Prepare as directed for bland diet.
Low-purine diet: Prepare as directed.
Low-residue diet: Prepare as directed for bland diet.

NIBBLER TRAY OF LOW-CALORIE GOODIES

Shrimp and Apple Ball. Spear cooked shelled shrimp with toothpicks and stick into large apple. Serve with chili sauce for dipping. Use Shrimp and Apple Ball as centerpiece and surround with:

Curried Ripe Olives. To reduced-calorie Italian dressing, add curry to taste. Pour over drained ripe olives. Refrigerate for several hours, stirring occasionally; then drain and serve as snacks.

Herbed Tuna. Break water-packed tuna into large chunks and marinate in reduced-calorie French dressing. Garnish with snipped parsley and chopped chives.

Topped Cucumber Slices. Top cucumber slices with Neufchâtel cheese and pimento strips.

Ham Rolls. Roll thin slices of cooked ham, salami or other sliced cold meats around cooked asparagus spears or slices of apple, melon, celery, cucumber or chicken.

Stuffed Celery Stalks. Fill small celery stalks with cottage cheese seasoned with onion salt. Sprinkle with poppy seeds.

Swiss-Cheese-Pepper Squares. Toss together short, thin strips of Swiss cheese and green pepper, reduced-calorie mayonnaise, salt, pepper. Trim crusts from pumpernickel-bread slices; cut into quarters. Top with Swiss-cheese mixture.

KEEP-TRIM SANDWICH SUGGESTIONS

To make sandwiches that are lower in calories, keep these tips in mind: Use thinly sliced bread, or buy unsliced bread and slice it very thin. Don't spread the bread with anything before adding a filling; instead, choose fillings moist enough to hold bread slices together, and spread on only a thin layer. Lettuce will make sandwich fuller without adding calories; but pack lettuce separately if sandwich is to be carried to be eaten later. Season keep-trim sandwiches generously—a thin, tasty sandwich is much more satisfying than a thick, tasteless one. Pack fresh fruit, vegetable nibblers and a beverage with sandwich to round out lunch. And for a change of pace in sandwiches, try these:

COMBINE Roquefort and Neufchâtel* cheeses with a bit of minced onion or a dash of onion juice and some chopped canned mushrooms. Try it on dark bread.

TRY a combination of crumbled bacon and chopped sweet gherkins, moistening with cottage cheese "sour cream."†

MIX a bit of leftover cooked chicken with a few chopped ripe olives and just enough reduced-calorie mayonnaise‡ to moisten. Great on raisin bread.

SPARK tuna with minced celery, chopped onions, salt and a bit of cottage cheese "sour cream."† Spread on thin, thin, slices of date-nut bread.

CHOPPED canned shrimp and chopped apple make a nice salad, mixed with a bit of reduced-calorie mayonnaise‡ and curry. It's especially good on dark bread.

NEUFCHÂTEL cheese* and orange marmalade on raisin bread is a tasty quickie.

SPREAD rye or pumpernickel bread with apple butter; add thin ham slices for a flavor switch.

MIX cottage cheese with drained canned crushed pineapple and a bit of onion salt for a Hawaiian-style filling. Serve it on raisin or dark bread.

CHOP up leftover sautéed chicken livers with a few stuffed olives. It's very good on rye or pumpernickel bread.

FOR a hefty sandwich that goes easy on calories, place a slice or two of ham or beef between rye or pumpernickel along with some coleslaw made with reduced-calorie mayonnaise.‡ (Pack coleslaw separately to carry.)

THINLY sliced green pepper and ham or beef slices on dark or white bread make a delicious sandwich.

---

*Neufchâtel cheese has 32 percent fewer calories than cream cheese.

†Cottage cheese, blended smooth in electric blender with a bit of water or milk, makes a tasty, lower-calorie alternate for sour cream.

‡Salad dressing has about two-thirds the calories of regular mayonnaise. Reduced-calorie mayonnaise has about one-third the calories of regular mayonnaise.

SOUPS

POTATO SOUP LACED WITH LIME (125 calories per serving)

1 10¹/₂-ounce can condensed cream-of-potato soup
1 soup-can skimmed milk or reliquefied nonfat dry milk
1 lime

About 15 minutes before serving: Prepare soup as label directs but use skimmed milk. Cut lime in half. Squeeze juice from one half and stir into soup; slice remaining half for garnish. Makes 3 servings of a scant cup each.

Diabetic diet: Exchanges per serving = ¹/₂ bread and ¹/₂ milk.
Low-fat diet: 2 grams fat per serving. Omit recipe from low-cholesterol diet.
Low-purine diet: Prepare as directed.

POTATO SOUP WITH OREGANO (125 calories per serving)

1 10¹/₄-ounce can frozen condensed cream-of-potato soup
1 soup-can skimmed milk or reliquefied nonfat dry milk
¹/₄ teaspoon oregano leaves

About 15 minutes before serving: Prepare soup as label directs but use skimmed milk and add oregano. Serve hot or cold. Makes three ³/₄-cup servings.

Diabetic diet: Exchanges per serving = ¹/₂ milk and ¹/₂ bread.
Low-fat diet: 2 grams fat per serving. Omit recipe from low-cholesterol diet.
Low-purine diet: Prepare as directed.

APPETIZER SOUP (75 calories per serving)

2 beef-bouillon cubes
2 chicken-bouillon cubes
1 19-ounce can tomatoes
1 medium onion, chopped
¹/₂ cup thinly sliced carrots
2 stalks celery, cut into ¹/₂-inch slices
3 whole peppercorns
¹/₂ teaspoon sage leaves
¹/₄ cup shredded Parmesan cheese

About 1 hour before serving: In medium saucepan, combine 3 cups water and all remaining ingredients but cheese; cover; simmer 45 minutes. Serve sprinkled with grated Parmesan cheese. Makes 4 servings of about 1 cup each.

Diabetic diet: Prepare as directed but omit Parmesan. Exchanges per serving = 1 vegetable.
Low-fat, low-cholesterol diet: Prepare as directed but omit Parmesan. Negligible fat per serving.

SOUTH-OF-THE-BORDER CHOWDER (120 calories per serving)

1 10¹/₄-ounce can frozen condensed New England clam-chowder soup
²/₃ cup skimmed milk or reliquefied nonfat dry milk
1 beef-bouillon cube
1 cup water
few dashes Tabasco
1 4¹/₂-ounce can shrimp, drained

Several hours before serving: In medium saucepan, heat chowder, milk, bouillon, water and Tabasco to boiling. Rinse shrimp, refrigerate 8 for garnish. In electric-blender container (with lid ajar to allow hot air to escape), at low speed, blend soup with rest of shrimp until smooth. Refrigerate mixture.

To serve: Pour chowder into glass mugs; garnish each with reserved shrimp, coarsely chopped. Makes four ³/₄-cup servings.

Bland diet: Prepare as directed but omit bouillon cube and Tabasco.
Diabetic diet: Exchanges per serving = ¹/₂ bread and 1 meat.
Low-fat diet: 5 grams fat per serving. Omit recipe from low-cholesterol diet.
Low-fat, bland (gall bladder) diet: Prepare as directed for bland diet.
Low-residue diet: Prepare as directed for bland diet.

CHICKEN BROTH WITH MEATBALLS AND SPINACH (115 calories per serving)

1/2 pound lean ground beef
3/4 teaspoon salt
1/8 teaspoon pepper
2 tablespoons shredded Parmesan cheese
1 tablespoon chopped parsley
1 tablespoon packaged dried-bread crumbs
3 tablespoons water
7 to 8 cups canned chicken broth (about 4 13³/4-ounce cans)
1 10-ounce package frozen chopped spinach, thawed

About 1 hour before serving: In medium bowl, combine lean ground beef with salt, pepper, Parmesan, parsley, bread crumbs and water. With a 1/2-teaspoon measuring spoon, form into small balls. Bring chicken broth to boiling. Drop meatballs into broth and cook, uncovered, about 10 minutes. Then add spinach and continue cooking about 5 minutes, or until meatballs and spinach are tender. Makes eight 1-cup servings.

Diabetic diet: Exchanges per serving = 1 meat and 1 vegetable.
Low-fat, low-cholesterol diet: Prepare as directed but omit Parmesan. 5 grams fat per serving.
High-iron diet: 4 milligrams iron per serving.

JELLIED TOMATO BOUILLON (40 calories per serving)

2 envelopes unflavored gelatin
1 tablespoon lemon juice
4 beef-bouillon cubes
1 24-ounce can tomato juice
1/2 teaspoon grated lemon peel
1 teaspoon Worcestershire
6 onion rings

At least 3 hours before serving: In medium saucepan, stir gelatin into 1/2 cup cold water; let stand 5 minutes to soften. Stir in lemon juice, bouillon cubes, tomato juice, 2 cups water and lemon peel. Stirring occasionally, bring mixture to boiling. Stir in Worcestershire. Refrigerate until set.

To serve: Stir jellied soup, then ladle into cups. Serve immediately. Garnish with onion rings. Makes six 3/4-cup servings.

Diabetic diet: Exchanges per serving = 1 vegetable.
Low-fat, low-cholesterol diet: Negligible fat per serving.

BEEFY-FLAVORED GREEN-BEAN SOUP (15 calories per serving)

1 15¹/2-ounce can green beans
1 cup water
2 beef-bouillon cubes
salt and pepper to taste

About 15 minutes before serving: In electric-blender container, at high speed, blend green beans and their liquid until smooth. (Or press mixture through food mill.) In saucepan, heat blended green beans and remaining ingredients, stirring occasionally, for 10 minutes. Makes four 3/4-cup servings.

Diabetic diet: Exchanges per serving = 1 vegetable.
Low-fat, low-cholesterol diet: Negligible fat per serving.
Low-residue diet: Prepare as directed but omit pepper.

BEEF BROTH WITH MEATBALLS (110 calories per serving)

1/2 pound lean ground beef
3/4 teaspoon salt
1/8 teaspoon pepper
1/4 teaspoon thyme leaves
1 beaten egg
2 teaspoons flour
2 tablespoons water
2 10¹/2-ounce cans condensed beef broth

About 25 minutes before serving: In medium bowl, combine all ingredients but beef broth. With wet hands, form heaping teaspoonful of this meat mixture into small ball; repeat with rest of meat. In large saucepan, dilute beef broth as label directs; heat. Drop meatballs into boiling broth; cover; simmer 15 minutes, or until meatballs are tender. Makes six 1-cup servings.

Diabetic diet: Exchanges per serving = 1 meat.
Low-fat, low-cholesterol diet: Prepare as directed but use only white of the egg. 5 grams fat per serving.
High-iron diet: 1.5 milligrams iron per serving.

1-2-3 GAZPACHO (70 calories per serving)

1 medium cucumber
1 quart (4 cups) chilled canned
   tomato juice
1/3 cup wine vinegar
1 1/2 tablespoons salad oil
1/2 teaspoon oregano leaves
dash Tabasco
12 ice cubes

About 10 minutes before serving: Pare cucumber. Cut 6 thin slices, then dice remaining cucumber. In blender container, at high speed, blend diced cucumber and remaining ingredients except ice cubes until smooth.

To serve: Pour soup over ice cubes in chilled bowls; garnish with cucumber slices. Makes six 3/4-cup servings.

Diabetic diet: Exchanges per serving = 1 vegetable and 1/2 fat.
Egg-, gluten-, milk- and wheat-free diet: Prepare as directed.
Low-fat, low-cholesterol diet: 4 grams fat per serving.
Low-purine diet: Prepare as directed.
Low-sodium diet: Prepare as directed but substitute low-sodium tomato juice for regular and omit Tabasco. 10 milligrams sodium per serving.

STRAWBERRY-RHUBARB SOUP (115 calories per serving)

1 pint strawberries, sliced
1 pound rhubarb, chopped
1 1/4 cups orange juice
about 1/2 cup granulated sugar
1/4 cup chopped orange segments

About 3 hours before serving: In medium pan, combine strawberry slices (reserve 6 for garnish), rhubarb and orange juice; simmer 10 minutes. Stir in 1/2 cup sugar or sugar to taste; cool.

In covered electric-blender container, at low speed, blend strawberry mixture one-half at a time. (Or put berries through a food mill.) Then fold in chopped orange segments; refrigerate, covered.

To serve: Garnish soup with reserved strawberry slices. Makes 6 servings.

Egg-, gluten-, milk- and wheat-free diet: Prepare as directed.
Low-fat, low-cholesterol diet: Negligible fat per serving.
Low-purine diet: Prepare as directed.
Low-sodium diet: Negligible sodium per serving.

HOLIDAY TOMATO SOUP (115 calories per serving)

1 6-ounce can frozen orange-
   juice concentrate
3 juice-cans water
2 10 3/4-ounce cans condensed
   tomato soup

About 15 minutes before serving: In large saucepan, heat all ingredients to a gentle simmer. Serve hot or cold. Makes six 1-cup servings.

Diabetic diet: Exchanges per serving = 1 bread and 1 fruit.
Low-fat, low-cholesterol diet: 1 gram fat per serving.
Low-purine diet: Prepare as directed.

TOMMY'S TARRAGON SOUP (70 calories per serving)

1 tablespoon butter or margarine
2 tablespoons minced onion
2 tablespoons minced celery
2 cups canned tomato juice
1/2 teaspoon salt
1/2 teaspoon tarragon
1/8 teaspoon pepper
dash Tabasco

About 25 minutes before serving: In heavy saucepan over medium heat, in butter or margarine, sauté onion and celery until onion turns golden. Add remaining ingredients; bring to boiling; lower heat and simmer 5 minutes. Makes three 2/3-cup servings.

Diabetic diet: Prepare as directed but use margarine instead of butter. Exchanges per serving = 1 vegetable and 1 fat.
Low-fat, low-cholesterol diet: Prepare as directed but sauté vegetables in only 1 teaspoon margarine. 2 grams fat per serving.
Low-purine diet: Prepare as directed.

FRESH VEGETABLE SOUP (125 calories per serving)

1 quart water
1 teaspoon salt
1 cup sliced carrots
1 cup diced potatoes
1 cup diced fresh tomatoes
1 cup chopped green onions
1/2 10-ounce package frozen
   baby lima beans
1/2 pound fresh green beans, cut
   into 1-inch pieces
1/2 cup corn, scraped from cob
1 teaspoon salt
1 cup hot fluffy rice (packaged
   precooked, regular or processed kind)

About 1 hour before serving: In large kettle or Dutch oven, simmer, covered, all ingredients but corn, 1 teaspoon salt and rice for 30 minutes. After soup has simmered 30 minutes, add corn and 1 teaspoon salt. Simmer, covered, 15 minutes longer.

To serve: Spoon some rice into each bowl; ladle soup over it. Makes about six 1-cup servings.

Diabetic diet: Exchanges per serving = 1 bread and 1 vegetable.
Low-fat, low-cholesterol diet: Negligible fat per serving.
Low-purine diet: Prepare as directed.
Low-sodium diet: Prepare as directed but omit lima beans and salt; cook rice without adding salt. 15 milligrams sodium per serving.

RED CABBAGE SOUP (70 calories per serving)

2 tablespoons butter or margarine
2 medium onions, sliced
8 cups (about 1 1/2 pounds)
   shredded red cabbage
2 potatoes, sliced
1 apple, sliced
2 quarts water
1 10 1/2-ounce can condensed
   beef broth
2 1/2 teaspoons salt
1/4 to 1/2 teaspoon pepper
1/8 teaspoon thyme leaves
1/8 teaspoon garlic powder
1 small bay leaf

About 3 hours before serving: In large kettle, in butter or margarine, sauté onions until golden. Add remaining ingredients. Stir; then simmer, covered, 2 hours. In blender container (with lid ajar to allow hot air to escape), blend one-sixth of soup at low speed until creamy. Repeat until all of soup is blended. (Or press through food mill.) Makes twelve 1-cup servings.

Diabetic diet: Prepare as directed but use margarine instead of butter. Exchanges per serving = 1 vegetable and 1/2 fat.
Low-fat, low-cholesterol diet: Prepare as directed but use margarine instead of butter. 1 gram fat per serving.

WESTERN CORN CHOWDER (130 calories per serving)

1 tablespoon butter or margarine
2 tablespoons minced onion
2 tablespoons minced green
   pepper
1/2 cup thinly sliced green celery
2 tablespoons flour
1 10 1/2-ounce can condensed
   cream-of-chicken soup
2 1/2 cups skimmed milk or reliquefied nonfat dry milk
1/8 teaspoon sage leaves
dash cayenne
1 8-ounce can whole-kernel
   corn, undrained
chopped parsley for garnish

About 25 minutes before serving: In medium saucepan, in butter or margarine, sauté onion, green pepper and celery until golden. Stir in flour, then soup, then milk. Heat, stirring, to boiling. Add sage, cayenne and corn; heat to boiling. Serve garnished with parsley. Makes six 3/4-cup servings.

Diabetic diet: Prepare as directed but use margarine instead of butter. Exchanges per serving = 1 vegetable and 1/2 milk, and 1/2 fat.
Low-fat diet: Prepare as directed but use margarine instead of butter. 5 grams fat per serving. Omit recipe from low-cholesterol diet.

SHERRIED VICHYSSOISE (115 calories per serving)

2 10¼-ounce cans frozen condensed cream-of-potato soup,
  thawed
2 cups skimmed milk or reliquefied nonfat dry milk
¼ cup cooking sherry
chopped chives for garnish

About 20 minutes before serving: Prepare soup as label directs, but use skimmed milk and add cooking sherry. Garnish with chopped chives. Makes 6 servings of a scant cup each.

Diabetic diet: Exchanges per serving = ½ milk and ½ bread.
Low-fat diet: 5 grams fat per serving. Omit recipe from low-cholesterol diet.
Low-purine diet: Prepare as directed. Omit recipe if sherry is forbidden on diet.

MANHATTAN SUPPER SOUP (150 calories per serving)

½ **pound lean ground beef**
2 **cups coarsely chopped cab-**
  bage (about ¼ of a small cab-
  bage)
1 **large onion, thinly sliced**
1 **stalk green celery, sliced**
3 **carrots, cut into 1-inch slices**
1 **medium potato, cubed**
1 **tablespoon parsley flakes**
3 **ounces tomato paste (½ 6-**
  ounce can)
1 **16-ounce can tomatoes**
1 **10½-ounce can condensed**
  beef broth
2 **soup-cans water**
1 **teaspoon salt**
⅛ **to ¼ teaspoon pepper**
1½ **teaspoons granulated**
  sugar
1 **10-ounce package frozen peas**

At least 1½ hours before serving: In large kettle or Dutch oven, cook meat until it loses its red color. Add remaining ingredients except frozen peas; simmer, uncovered, 50 minutes. Add peas; cover; cook 10 minutes, or until peas are tender. Makes 8 servings of about 1 cup each.

Diabetic diet: Prepare as directed but omit sugar. Exchanges per serving = 1 meat, 1 bread and 1 vegetable.
Low-fat, low-cholesterol diet: 5 grams fat per serving.

TOMATO AND EGG SOUP (Sopa de Tomate e Ovos) (100 calories per serving)

butter or margarine
1 **large onion, thinly sliced**
2 **pounds fresh tomatoes, sliced**
salt
¼ **cup chopped parsley**
½ **teaspoon granulated sugar**
⅛ **teaspoon pepper**
2 **hard-cooked eggs, sliced**

About 1½ hours before serving: In large kettle, in 1 tablespoon butter or margarine, sauté onion until soft. Add tomatoes and 1 teaspoon salt; simmer 10 minutes. Now add 1 quart water and parsley; simmer, covered, 1 hour. Press soup through food mill, then add ½ teaspoon salt, sugar and pepper. Heat, then stir in 1 tablespoon butter or margarine. Arrange sliced eggs in bottom of soup tureen; pour in soup and serve. Makes six 1-cup servings.

Diabetic diet: Prepare as directed but omit sugar. Prepare as directed and use margarine instead of butter. Exchanges per serving = 1 vegetable and 1 fat.
Gluten-, milk- and wheat-free diet: Prepare as directed but use milk-free margarine on milk-free diet.
High-iron diet: 1.5 milligrams iron per serving.
Low-purine diet: Prepare as directed.
Low-sodium diet: Prepare as directed but use unsalted butter or margarine; omit salt. 30 milligrams sodium per serving. If eggs are also omitted, 5 milligrams sodium per serving.

ROYAL CONSOMMÉ (70 calories per serving)

2 10¹/₂-ounce cans condensed beef broth
4 peppercorns
3 whole cloves
2 bay leaves
¹/₄ teaspoon grated lemon peel
¹/₂ avocado, cut into 6 thin slices

About 10 minutes before serving: In medium saucepan, combine beef broth with 2 soup-cans water. Add peppercorns, cloves, bay leaves and lemon peel. Cover and heat to boiling; simmer 1 or 2 minutes. Strain, then float avocado slices on top. Makes six 1-cup servings.

Diabetic diet: Exchanges per serving = ¹/₂ fat.
Low-fat, low-cholesterol diet: Omit avocado. Negligible fat per serving.

HOT TOMATO SOUP VERDI (50 calories per serving)

1 46-ounce can vegetable-juice cocktail
¹/₂ cup dry sherry
1 tablespoon brown sugar
¹/₂ cup chopped green onions for garnish

About 15 minutes before serving: In large saucepan, heat vegetable juice, sherry and sugar to boiling. Serve in mugs, topped with green onions. Makes six 1-cup servings.

Diabetic diet: Prepare as directed but omit sugar; use non-nutritive sweetener equivalent to 1 tablespoon sugar. Exchanges per serving = 1 vegetable.
Low-fat, low-cholesterol diet: Negligible fat per serving.
Low-purine diet: Prepare as directed.

TOMATO SIP (40 calories per serving)

2 10¹/₂-ounce cans condensed beef bouillon
1 19-ounce can tomato juice
2 lemon slices
6 whole cloves
¹/₈ teaspoon basil
2 tablespoons dry sherry

About 15 minutes before serving: In saucepan, heat all ingredients to boiling; simmer 5 minutes; strain out spices. Serve in mugs or cups. Makes 6 servings of a scant cup each.

Diabetic diet: Exchanges per serving = 1 vegetable.
Low-fat, low-cholesterol diet: Negligible fat per serving.

POTATO-MUSHROOM SOUP (105 calories per serving)

1 cup mixed slivered carrots, celery and parsnips
3 cups cubed potatoes
salt
butter or margarine
¹/₂ pound fresh mushrooms, sliced
pepper
¹/₄ cup flour
1 garlic clove, minced
1 teaspoon marjoram leaves

About 2 hours before serving: In large kettle, combine mixed vegetables with potatoes, 2¹/₂ teaspoons salt and 2 quarts boiling water; simmer, covered, about 30 minutes. In skillet, in 1 tablespoon butter or margarine, sauté mushrooms 5 minutes; sprinkle with ¹/₈ teaspoon pepper. Add to soup and let simmer. Meanwhile, in same skillet, melt 2 tablespoons butter or margarine; stir in flour until smooth; continue stirring until mixture is light brown. Remove from heat and slowly stir in 1 cup cold water. Now pour this mixture through a strainer into soup; add garlic and marjoram. Simmer, stirring occasionally, until vegetables are tender and soup is thickened—about 45 minutes. Makes 8 servings of a scant 1¹/₂ cups each.

Diabetic diet: Prepare as directed but use margarine instead of butter. Exchanges per serving = 1 vegetable, 1 bread and 1 fat.
Egg-, gluten-, milk- and wheat-free diet: Prepare as directed but use a milk-free margarine on milk-free diet; substitute 2 tablespoons cornstarch for flour on gluten- and wheat-free diets.
Low-fat, low-cholesterol diet: Prepare as directed but use margarine instead of butter. 5 grams fat per serving.
Low-sodium diet: Prepare as directed but use unsalted butter or margarine; omit salt. 15 milligrams sodium per serving.

RANCH-STYLE VEGETABLE SOUP (170 calories per serving)

1/2 pound lean ground beef
2 medium potatoes, cubed
1 small sweet potato, cubed
3 medium carrots, cut into 1/2-inch slices
2 teaspoons salt
1 tablespoon parsley flakes
2 tablespoons barley
6 cups water
1/2 9-ounce package frozen cut green beans

About 1 hour and 15 minutes before serving: In large saucepan, cook beef, stirring constantly, until well browned. Add remaining ingredients except green beans. Cover; simmer 45 minutes. Add green beans. Simmer, uncovered, 15 minutes. Makes 6 servings of about 1 1/2 cups each.

Bland diet: Prepare as directed. Omit parsley flakes if forbidden on diet.
Diabetic diet: Exchanges per serving = 1 meat, 1 vegetable and 1 bread.
Low-fat, low-cholesterol diet: 5 grams fat per serving.
Low-fat, bland (gall bladder) diet: Prepare as directed.
Low-residue diet: Prepare as directed but omit parsley flakes.
Low-sodium diet: Prepare as directed but omit salt. 55 milligrams sodium per serving.

CHICKEN CORN SOUP (105 calories per serving)

1 10 1/2-ounce can condensed chicken-with-rice soup
1 soup-can skimmed milk or reliquefied nonfat dry milk
1 8-ounce can cream-style corn
2 tablespoons coarsely chopped parsley
1/4 teaspoon salt
generous dash thyme leaves

About 15 minutes before serving: In medium saucepan, heat all ingredients to boiling; simmer 5 minutes. Makes four 3/4-cup servings.

Diabetic diet: Exchanges per serving = 1 bread and 1/2 skim milk.
Low-fat diet: 1 gram fat per serving. Omit recipe from low-cholesterol diet.

CURRIED APPLE SOUP (90 calories per serving)

1 tablespoon salad oil
1 medium onion, chopped
3 cups chicken broth
3 tablespoons cornstarch
1 to 2 teaspoons curry
2/3 cup evaporated skimmed milk, chilled
2 apples, peeled
salt

Early in day: In large skillet, in oil, sauté onion until transparent. Add chicken broth, cornstarch, dissolved in small amount of water, and curry. Heat to boiling, stirring constantly. Cover and simmer 8 minutes. Refrigerate.

Just before serving: In blender container, at high speed, blend cold broth mixture, milk and one apple, quartered, until smooth. (Or puree mixture with food mill.) Dice remaining apple and add to soup. Salt to taste. Serve cold. Makes 6 servings.

Diabetic diet: Exchanges per serving = 1/2 fat, 1/2 fruit and 1/2 milk.
Low-fat, low-cholesterol diet: 2 grams fat per serving.

WATERCRESS VICHYSSOISE (95 calories per serving)

1 10 1/4-ounce can frozen condensed cream-of-potato soup, thawed
1 soup-can water
1/2 cup firmly packed, coarsely chopped watercress

Up to 20 minutes before serving: In blender container, at low-speed, blend all ingredients 1 minute, or until smooth. In medium saucepan, simmer mixture 5 minutes. Makes three 3/4-cup servings.

Diabetic diet: Exchanges per serving = 1 bread and 1 fat.
Low-fat diet: 5 grams fat per serving. Omit recipe from low-cholesterol diet.
Low-purine diet: Prepare as directed.

QUICK SENEGLASE (120 calories per serving)

1 cup skimmed milk or re-
liquefied nonfat dry milk
2 teaspoons curry
1 10½-ounce can condensed
cream-of-chicken soup
3 lemon slices for garnish

About 10 minutes before serving: In electric-blender container, at low speed, blend skimmed milk, curry and undiluted cream-of-chicken soup about 10 seconds, or until smooth. Garnish with lemon slices and serve cold. Makes 3 servings of a scant cup each.

Diabetic diet: Exchanges per serving = 1 milk.
Low-fat diet: 5 grams fat per serving. Omit recipe from low-cholesterol diet.

JELLIED BOUILLON (20 calories per serving)

1 envelope unflavored gelatin
3 beef-bouillon cubes
1 thin slice boiled ham (about 1
ounce), trimmed of fat
6 thin cucumber slices
¼ carrot, cut into short thin
strips
1 tablespoon lemon juice
½ teaspoon Worcestershire

Early in day: Sprinkle gelatin on ½ cup cold water to soften. In saucepan, simmer bouillon cubes in 2½ cups water until dissolved. Roll ham tightly into a pinwheel, then cut crosswise into thin slices. Meanwhile, in medium baking dish, place rolled ham, cucumber and carrot strips in a single layer. Stir gelatin, lemon juice and Worcestershire into bouillon. Pour mixture over ham and vegetables; refrigerate until consistency of soft jelly.

To serve: Spoon into chilled soup bowls. Makes 6 servings.

Diabetic diet: Prepare as directed but omit ham.
Low-fat, low-cholesterol diet: 1 gram fat per serving.

EASY MINESTRONE (120 calories per serving)

1 10¾-ounce can condensed
vegetarian-vegetable soup
1 10½-ounce can chicken-
noodle soup
1 16-ounce can kidney beans
1 garlic clove, minced
⅓ cup chopped parsley

About 15 minutes before serving: In large saucepan, simmer all ingredients with 1 soup-can water for 10 minutes. Makes 6 servings of a scant cup each.

Low-fat, low-cholesterol diet: 2 grams fat per serving.
High-iron diet: 2 milligrams iron per serving.

OXFORD CIRCLE CORN CHOWDER (130 calories per serving)

1 8¾-ounce can cream-style
corn
1 cup skimmed milk or re-
liquefied nonfat dry milk
¼ cup shredded American
cheese
chopped parsley for garnish

About 15 minutes before serving: In medium pan, combine corn, skimmed milk and cheese. Cook over low heat, stirring, until mixture just begins to bubble. Sprinkle with parsley. Makes 3 servings.

Diabetic diet: Exchanges per serving (⅔ cup) = 1 bread and ½ milk.
High-iron diet: 1 milligram iron per serving.
Low-purine diet: Prepare as directed.

BROTH WITH CHICKEN AND PEA PODS (70 calories per serving)

2 10¾-ounce cans condensed
chicken broth
1 teaspoon soy sauce
⅛ teaspoon ground ginger
1 small chicken breast, skinned
and cut into matchstick-thin
strips
1 6-ounce package frozen Chinese pea pods, thawed

In 3-quart saucepan over medium heat, heat broth, 2 soup-cans water, soy sauce and ginger to boiling. Add chicken and continue cooking 5 minutes, or until chicken is fork-tender. To serve, add pea pods and heat through. Makes 6 servings.

Diabetic diet: Exchanges per serving = 2 meat and ½ vegetable.
Low-sodium diet: Prepare as directed but substitute 3 teaspoons no salt-added, chicken-flavor bouillon for condensed chicken broth; omit soy sauce. 2 milligrams sodium per serving.
Low-fat, low-cholesterol: Prepare as directed. 2 grams fat per serving.
Egg-, gluten-, milk- and wheat-free diet: Prepare as directed but omit soy sauce.

TAVIA'S LENTIL SOUP (100 calories per serving)

¹/₂ cup dry lentils
1 quart water
1 cup canned tomatoes
1 onion, thinly sliced
1 stalk celery, thinly sliced
1 teaspoon salt
¹/₄ teaspoon garlic powder
¹/₈ teaspoon pepper

Day before or early in day: In large covered saucepan, simmer all ingredients 1 hour, or until lentils are tender. In blender container (with lid ajar to allow hot air to escape), blend soup one-quarter at a time until smooth. Or press through a food mill until smooth. Reheat and serve hot. Makes four 1-cup servings.

Diabetic diet: Exchanges per serving = 1 vegetable and 1 bread.
Low-fat, low-cholesterol diet: Negligible fat per serving.
High-iron diet: 2 milligrams iron per serving.
Low-sodium diet: Prepare as directed but substitute low-sodium canned tomatoes for regular; omit salt. 20 milligrams sodium per serving.

CHICKEN BORSCHT (145 calories per serving)

1 16-ounce can julienne beets, undrained
2 10¹/₂-ounce cans condensed beef bouillon
1 tablespoon flour
¹/₄ teaspoon pepper
1 cup cut-up cooked or canned chicken
¹/₃ cup lemon juice

About 15 minutes before serving: In large saucepan, combine beets, bouillon and 1¹/₂ cups water. Stir a small amount of this mixture into flour and pepper to form a smooth paste; stir into remaining mixture. Simmer, covered, 10 minutes, then stir in chicken and lemon juice. Makes 4 servings.

Low-fat, low-cholesterol diet: 5 grams fat per serving.

FRENCH ONION SOUP (90 calories per serving)

2 tablespoons butter or margarine
4 cups sliced onions
5 beef-bouillon cubes
¹/₄ teaspoon pepper
¹/₂ teaspoon Worcestershire
¹/₂ teaspoon bottled sauce for gravy
6 Melba-toast rounds
1 tablespoon shredded Parmesan cheese

About 45 minutes before serving: In large skillet, in butter or margarine, sauté onions until tender. Dissolve bouillon cubes in 4 cups boiling water; add to onion, pepper, Worcestershire and bottled sauce for gravy. Simmer, covered, about 30 minutes. Before serving, top each serving with a Melba-toast round and sprinkle it with Parmesan cheese. Makes 6 servings.

Low-fat diet: 5 grams fat per serving.

VEGETABLE SHRIMP SOUP (65 calories per serving)

1 small onion, thinly sliced
1 carrot, thinly sliced
1 stalk celery, thinly sliced
1 tablespoon soy sauce
¹/₂ teaspoon salt
¹/₂ teaspoon granulated sugar
1 tablespoon lemon juice
1 pound package frozen shelled and deveined shrimp
parsley for garnish

About 30 minutes before serving: In medium saucepan, combine onion, carrot, celery, soy sauce, salt and sugar, with 4 cups water. Simmer until vegetables are tender. Add lemon juice and shrimp; cook until shrimp curl and turn pink—about 5 minutes. Garnish with parsley. Makes 4 servings.

Diabetic diet: Prepare as directed but omit sugar. Exchanges per serving = 1 meat and 1 vegetable.
Low-fat diet: 1 gram fat per serving. Omit recipe from low-cholesterol diet.

FISH AND SEAFOOD

BROILED MACKEREL PLATTER (345 calories per serving)

2 1-pound fresh mackerels, fillet *
1/4 teaspoon pepper
2 10-ounce packages frozen broccoli spears
7 small mushrooms
salad oil
3 tablespoons reduced-calorie Italian dressing
1 1/2 slices day-old bread, finely crumbled
6 to 8 thin tomato slices
1 ounce shredded Cheddar or American cheese

About 25 minutes before serving: Preheat broiler 10 minutes if manufacturer directs. Sprinkle fillets with pepper. Broil, flesh side up, 4 to 5 inches from heat for 7 minutes. Meanwhile, cook broccoli as label directs. Prepare mushrooms for broiling: with sharp knife, remove 3 thin curved strips equidistantly apart, from around top of each mushroom cap; then brush lightly with salad oil.

At end of 7 minutes, carefully turn fillets over. Brush skin of each with reduced–calorie Italian dressing; sprinkle with bread crumbs. Arrange mushrooms beside fillets. Broil 3 to 5 minutes, or until fish flakes easily with fork. Meanwhile, arrange broccoli in baking dish; top with tomato slices; sprinkle cheese down center; broil just until cheese melts.

To serve: Place fish in center of platter and arrange broccoli around edges. Makes 4 servings.

Bland diet: Prepare as directed but omit pepper; brush fish with salad oil instead of Italian dressing; omit broccoli, tomatoes and cheese.
Diabetic diet: Exchanges per serving = 4 meat and 1 vegetable.
Low-fat, low-cholesterol diet: Prepare as directed but use flounder, sole or haddock fillets; omit cheese. 2 grams fat per serving.
Low-fat, bland (gall bladder) diet: Prepare as directed for bland diet.
Low-residue diet: Prepare as directed for bland diet.
Low-sodium diet: Prepare as directed but use fresh flounder fillets (4 ounces each); cook broccoli without added salt; brush fish with salad oil (not Italian dressing); use unsalted bread; omit cheese. 110 milligrams sodium per serving. (If prepared with regular bread, 155 milligrams per serving.)

*Or use two 16-ounce packages frozen cod, haddock, sole or flounder fillets; thaw for several hours so fish separates easily, then prepare as directed above. 290 calories per serving.

BAKED SWORDFISH AU GRATIN (260 calories per serving)

1 pound fresh swordfish steaks, 1/2- to 3/4-inch thick (or frozen swordfish steaks, thawed)
1/2 cup salad oil
1/2 cup sauterne
1 teaspoon parsley flakes
1/4 teaspoon thyme leaves
1 bay leaf, crumbled
6 peppercorns
1 small onion, thinly sliced
1/3 cup packaged dried-bread crumbs
1/3 cup shredded Parmesan cheese
1/4 teaspoon oregano leaves

About 2 1/2 hours before serving: Cut swordfish steaks into 4 portions. In medium baking pan, combine marinade of salad oil, sauterne, parsley, thyme, bay leaf, peppercorns and onion; lay fish on top; refrigerate at least 2 hours, occasionally spooning marinade over fish.

Preheat oven to 350°F. Combine bread crumbs, cheese and oregano. Coat fish with this mixture; place in baking dish; cover; bake 20 minutes. Uncover and bake 15 minutes longer, or until fish flakes easily with fork. If browner surface is desired, place under broiler until light brown. Makes 4 servings.

Diabetic diet: Exchanges per serving = 3 meat and 1/2 bread.

FLORENTINE FILLETS (230 calories per serving)

1 4-ounce can chopped mushrooms
salad oil
1/2 cup chopped onion
1 cup crushed saltines (about
  20)
1/4 teaspoon pepper
1/8 teaspoon sage leaves
1/8 teaspoon mace
6 4-ounce fresh sole or flounder
  fillets
salt
1 10-ounce package frozen
  chopped spinach, thawed,
  thoroughly drained
4 teaspoons lemon juice
4 medium tomatoes
reduced-calorie Italian dressing

About 40 minutes before serving: Preheat oven to 325°F. Make stuffing: Drain mushrooms, reserving juice. In skillet over medium heat, in 1 tablespoon salad oil, sauté onion and mushrooms until onion is golden. Remove from heat; stir in crushed saltines, pepper, sage, mace and 2 tablespoons reserved mushroom juice.

Sprinkle sole fillets with salt. Spread with drained spinach; sprinkle with lemon juice; top with stuffing. Roll up each fillet; secure with toothpicks. Arrange, side by side, in medium baking dish; brush with 1 tablespoon salad oil. Cut tops from tomatoes; place in pan; sprinkle with salt; brush with reduced-calorie dressing. Bake fillets and tomatoes 15 minutes, or until fish flakes easily with fork. Remove picks. Makes 6 servings.

Diabetic diet: Exchanges per serving = 3 meat, 1 vegetable, 1 bread and 1 fat.
Low-fat, low-cholesterol diet: 10 grams fat per serving.
High-iron diet: Prepare as directed and be sure to use enriched saltines. 3 milligrams iron per serving.

GREEK BAKED HALIBUT (320 calories per serving)

1/2 tablespoon salad oil
2 medium onions, thinly sliced
1 garlic clove, crushed
1/2 cup chopped parsley
1/8 teaspoon pepper
1 16-ounce can tomatoes
1 tablespoon tomato paste
  (optional)
2 chicken-bouillon cubes
3 fresh halibut steaks, cut
  about 3/4-inch thick (about 1 1/2
  pounds)
3 thin tomato slices
3 thin lemon slices

About 1 hour before serving: In large skillet over medium heat, in oil, sauté onions and garlic until golden. Add parsley, pepper, canned tomatoes, tomato paste and bouillon cubes; simmer, uncovered, 20 minutes.

Preheat oven to 350°F. Place fish steaks in medium (about 12″ by 8″ by 2″) baking dish; cover with tomato sauce; top with tomato and lemon slices. Bake 20 to 25 minutes, or until fish flakes with a fork. Makes 3 servings.

Egg-, gluten-, milk- and wheat-free diet: Prepare as directed but omit bouillon cubes.
Low-fat, low-cholesterol diet: 5 grams fat per serving.

TOMATO-TOPPED FISH FILLETS (165 calories per serving)

1 16-ounce package frozen cod,
  perch or flounder fillets,
  thawed and drained
onion salt
1/4 teaspoon pepper
2 tablespoons lemon juice
1 tablespoon melted butter or
  margarine
1 medium tomato, sliced

About 30 minutes before serving: Preheat oven to 400°F. In greased large shallow baking dish, arrange fillets. Sprinkle with 1/2 teaspoon onion salt, and pepper. Combine lemon juice and butter; pour over fish. Place tomato slices on top; sprinkle with 1/4 teaspoon onion salt. Bake 20 to 25 minutes, or until fish flakes easily when tested with a fork. Makes 3 servings.

Diabetic diet: Prepare as directed but use margarine instead of butter. Exchanges per serving = 4 meat, 1/2 vegetable, and 1 fat.
Egg-, gluten-, milk- and wheat-free diet: Prepare as directed but use milk-free margarine for milk-free diet.
Low-fat, low-cholesterol diet: Prepare as directed but use salad oil or margarine in place of butter. 5 grams fat per serving.
Low-sodium diet: Prepare as directed but use only fresh (not frozen) fish; substitute onion powder for onion salt; use unsalted butter or margarine. 120 milligrams sodium per serving.

BOSTON FISH SALAD (235 calories per serving)

1 16-ounce package frozen cod, perch or flounder fillets, thawed and drained
1 cup reduced-calorie mayonnaise
1 cup minced celery
1/2 cup grated carrot
1 tablespoon capers
2 teaspoons lemon juice
1/4 teaspoon salt
1/4 teaspoon onion salt
1 small head Boston lettuce
2 hard-cooked eggs, sliced
1 cup sliced cooked beets

About 1 hour before serving: Bake fish as label directs. In large bowl, flake fish and combine with next 7 ingredients. Refrigerate.

To serve: Line salad platter with lettuce leaves; spoon fish mixture over top. Arrange egg slices on top of fish and beets around sides of platter. Makes 4 servings.

Diabetic diet: Carefully divide salad into 4 equal individual servings. Exchanges per serving = 3 1/2 meat and 1 vegetable.
Low-fat, low-cholesterol diet: Prepare as directed but omit egg. 10 grams fat per serving.

SHRIMP PIQUANT (280 calories per serving)

2 tablespoons salad oil
1 1/2 pounds large shrimp, shelled and deveined or 1 16-ounce package frozen, shelled and deveined shrimp
1 garlic clove, minced
1/4 teaspoon ground ginger
1/8 teaspoon pepper
water
1 envelope chicken-flavor bouillon
1 tablespoon soy sauce
2 tablespoons cornstarch
2 medium green peppers, cut into 1-inch pieces
2 green onions, thinly sliced
2 1/2 cups cherry tomatoes
3 cups hot cooked rice

In 12-inch skillet over medium-high heat, in hot salad oil, cook shrimp, garlic, ginger and pepper until shrimp turn pink, about 5 minutes, stirring frequently. (If using frozen shrimp, reduce cooking time to 3 minutes.) Add 1 cup water, bouillon and soy sauce; heat to boiling. Meanwhile, in cup, combine cornstarch and 2 tablespoons water. Reduce heat to medium; add cornstarch mixture and green peppers to simmering liquid; cook, until thickened, about 5 minutes, stirring constantly. Stir in tomatoes; heat through. To serve, spoon into deep platter; sprinkle with green onions and serve.

Low-fat diet, low-cholesterol diet: Omit from low-cholesterol diet. (6 grams fat per serving.)
Diabetic diet: Exchanges per serving = 3 meat, 1 1/2 vegetable, 1 bread and 1 fat.

ALOHA FLOUNDER (220 calories per serving)

1 8 1/2-ounce can pineapple tidbits
2 carrots, sliced diagonally
1 16-ounce package frozen flounder fillets, thawed (or 3 small fresh fillets)
1 teaspoon granulated sugar
1 teaspoon cornstarch
1/2 teaspoon soy sauce
1/2 green pepper, cut into thin strips
3 slices onion, separated into rings

About 30 minutes before serving: Preheat oven to 425°F. Drain syrup from pineapple into medium pan; reserve tidbits. Add carrot slices and cook, covered, until tender-crisp—about 15 minutes.

Meanwhile, place fillets in buttered medium baking pan; bake 20 minutes. In cup, mix sugar, cornstarch and soy sauce. When carrots are almost tender, add pineapple tidbits, green pepper, onion rings and cornstarch mixture. Cook, stirring constantly, until vegetables are tender-crisp and glazed—about 5 minutes. Serve vegetables over fish. Makes 3 servings.

Diabetic diet: Prepare as directed but for regular pineapple, substitute 1 cup pineapple and juice from 1 15 3/4-ounce can pineapple packed in pineapple juice; omit sugar; carefully divide into 3 equal servings. Exchanges per serving = 4 meat, 1 1/2 vegetable and 1 fruit.
Egg-, gluten-, milk- and wheat-free diet: Prepare as directed but omit soy sauce.
Low-fat, low-cholesterol diet: 1 gram fat per serving.
Low-sodium diet: Prepare as directed but use fresh instead of frozen fish; omit soy sauce. 105 milligrams sodium per serving.

BAKED STRIPED BASS WITH CLAMS (155 calories per serving)

1 dozen hard-shelled clams
1 4-pound striped bass, dressed and boned, but with tail on
1 teaspoon salt
1/4 teaspoon basil
1/8 teaspoon pepper
1/2 cup parsley sprigs
1 medium onion, thinly sliced
2 celery stalks with leaves, chopped
1 garlic clove, halved
2 bay leaves
1/2 cup dry white wine
2 tablespoons butter or margarine, melted

About 50 minutes before serving: Preheat oven to 350°F. Scrub clams under cold running water; set aside. Sprinkle inside of fish with salt, basil and pepper. Arrange parsley and half of onion slices inside fish; place fish in large shallow baking pan or oven-proof serving dish.

Around fish, place clams, remaining onion, celery, garlic and bay leaves. Pour wine and butter or margarine over fish. Cover pan with foil and bake 40 to 50 minutes, or until fish flakes easily when tested with a fork and shells of clams are open. Discard garlic and bay leaves. Makes 8 servings.

Egg-, gluten-, milk- and wheat-free diet: Prepare as directed but use milk-free margarine on milk-free diet.
Low-fat diet: 5 grams fat per serving. Omit recipe from low-cholesterol diet.

BAKED FLOUNDER FILLETS SUPREME (300 calories per serving)

8 flounder fillets (about 2 pounds)
seasoned salt
1 medium tomato, halved
4 slices natural Swiss cheese, halved
2 tablespoons butter or margarine
1 3- or 4-ounce can sliced mushrooms, drained (reserve liquid)
2 small onions, sliced
1 1/2 tablespoons flour
chopped parsley
1 cup skimmed milk or reliquefied nonfat dry milk
6 tablespoons sherry
2 cups packaged precooked rice

About 45 minutes before serving: Sprinkle flounder fillets lightly on both sides with seasoned salt, then roll up each. Cut tomato into 8 slices. Arrange flounder rolls, seam side down, alternately with tomato and cheese slices, down center of large (about 13" by 9" by 2") baking dish. Preheat oven to 400°F. In large skillet, in butter or margarine, sauté mushrooms and onions until golden brown. Now stir in flour, 1 1/2 teaspoons seasoned salt and 1/4 cup parsley, then skimmed milk, mushroom liquid combined with enough water to make 1/2 cup, and sherry. Bring to boiling, then pour over fish. Bake 20 minutes, or until fillets are golden and easily flaked with fork. Meanwhile, prepare rice as label directs; stir in 1/2 cup parsley. When fish is done, spoon rice around sides. Makes 8 servings.

Diabetic diet: Prepare as directed but use margarine instead of butter. Carefully divide into 8 equal servings. Exchanges per serving = 3 meat, 1 vegetable, 1 bread and 1 fat.

HALIBUT STEAK WITH EGGPLANT AND TOMATO SAUCE (280 calories per serving)

2 tablespoons salad oil
1 large green pepper, cut into 1/2-inch strips
1 large onion, thinly sliced
1 1-pound eggplant, peeled, cubed
2 8-ounce cans tomato sauce
1/2 cup dry white wine
1 garlic clove, minced
1 bay leaf
2 tablespoons butter or margarine
2 tablespoons lemon juice
salt and pepper
1 2-pound halibut steak

About 30 minutes before serving: In large skillet over medium-high heat, in oil, cook green pepper and onion until tender; add eggplant, tomato sauce, wine, garlic and bay leaf; simmer 15 minutes. Meanwhile, preheat broiler if manufacturer directs. In small saucepan over low heat, melt butter or margarine with lemon juice, 1/2 teaspoon salt and 1/4 teaspoon pepper. Place fish in broiling pan and brush with butter mixture. Broil 5 minutes; turn and brush with butter mixture. Broil 5 minutes longer, or until fish flakes easily when tested with fork. Serve fish with sauce. Makes 6 servings.

Diabetic diet: Prepare as directed but use margarine instead of butter. Exchanges per serving = 1 vegetable for 2/3 cup sauce, and 1 meat for each ounce of fish and 1 fat.
Low-fat, low-cholesterol diet: Prepare as directed but use margarine instead of butter. 10 grams fat per serving.

FLOUNDER FOR A FEW (295 calories per serving)

4 carrots, cut into 1/2-inch slices
2 medium potatoes, cubed
2 medium onions, cut into thin rings
2 large celery stalks, cut into 1/2-inch slices
2 tablespoons finely chopped pimento
1/4 medium green pepper, finely chopped
1 16-ounce package frozen flounder fillets
1 teaspoon salt
1/4 teaspoon poultry seasoning
3 tablespoons flour
1 8-ounce tube refrigerated biscuits (10 biscuits)

Day before: Place carrots, potatoes, onions, celery, pimento and green pepper in large saucepan. Cut frozen fillet into 1-inch cubes. Place cubes over vegetables in saucepan; add salt and 1 cup water; cover. Bring water to boiling, then simmer 15 to 20 minutes, or until vegetables are tender-crisp. Cool; refrigerate.

About 45 minutes before serving: Preheat oven to 425°F. Heat vegetables and fish to boiling. Thoroughly drain off broth; reserve; place drained stew in 2-quart casserole. Measure 1 1/2 cups of broth, adding water if necessary. In medium saucepan, stirring constantly, slowly stir broth into poultry seasoning and flour. Cook, stirring constantly, until thickened and smooth. Pour sauce over stew. Top with biscuits. Bake 15 to 20 minutes, or until biscuits are a dark golden brown. Makes 5 servings.

Diabetic diet: Prepare as directed but divide stew among 5 individual casserole dishes, and top with 2 biscuits each; bake as directed. Exchanges per serving = 2 meat, 1 vegetable and 2 bread.
Low-fat diet: 5 grams fat per serving. Omit recipe from low-cholesterol diet.

CURRIED SWORDFISH AND RICE (265 calories per serving)

1 pound swordfish steak, cut into 4 pieces
1 teaspoon lemon juice
6 peppercorns
1 teaspoon salt
1 bay leaf
1 tablespoon salad oil
1 tablespoon minced onion
1 tablespoon cornstarch
1 teaspoon curry
2 cups cooked rice

About 30 minutes before serving: In medium skillet over high heat, heat 3 cups water to boiling; reduce heat to medium-low. Add swordfish, lemon juice, peppercorns, salt and bay leaf; simmer, covered, 10 to 15 minutes, or until fish flakes easily when tested with fork. With pancake turner, place fish on warm platter. Strain skillet liquid, reserving 1 cup. In same skillet over medium heat, in oil, cook onion until limp. In small bowl, stir reserved fish liquid into cornstarch; pour into skillet and cook until thickened, stirring frequently; blend in curry.

To serve: Pour sauce over fish and rice. Makes 4 servings.

Diabetic diet: Exchanges per serving = 3 meat and 1 bread.
Egg-, gluten-, milk- and wheat-free diet: Prepare as directed.
Low-fat, low-cholesterol diet: 10 grams fat per serving.

PERCH À LA GRECQUE (250 calories per serving)

2 tablespoons salad oil
5 medium onions, sliced
5 large tomatoes
2 garlic cloves, minced
1/2 cup chopped parsley
2 16-ounce packages frozen ocean perch fillets, thawed
1 1/2 teaspoons salt
1/4 teaspoon pepper
3 tablespoons lemon juice
2 lemons, sliced

About 1 1/2 hours before serving: Preheat oven to 375°F. In large skillet over medium heat, in oil, sauté onions until tender; add 3 tomatoes (peeled and chopped), garlic and parsley; simmer 5 minutes. Sprinkle fillets with salt and pepper and lemon juice; arrange in medium baking dish; cover with onion mixture. Slice rest of tomatoes; arrange alternately with lemon slices on perch. Bake 45 minutes. Makes 6 servings.

Diabetic diet: Exchanges per serving = 4 meat, 2 vegetable and 1 fat.
Egg-, gluten-, milk- and wheat-free diet: Prepare as directed.
Low-fat, low-cholesterol diet: 5 grams fat per serving.
Low-sodium diet: Prepare as directed but use only fresh (not frozen) perch; omit salt. 120 milligrams sodium per serving.

FILLETS SUPREME (180 calories per serving)

1 tablespoon salad oil
1 large onion, sliced
1/2 cup white wine
1/2 teaspoon paprika
1/2 teaspoon salt
1 16-ounce package frozen flounder or sole fillets, thawed

About 30 minutes before serving: In medium skillet over medium heat, in oil, cook onion until limp. Add 1/2 cup water, wine, paprika and salt. Cover and simmer 20 minutes, stirring occasionally. Add fish; simmer 6 to 9 minutes, or until fish flakes with a fork. Serve sauce over fish. Makes 3 servings.

Egg-, gluten-, milk- and wheat-free diet: Prepare as directed.
Low-fat, low-cholesterol diet: 5 grams fat per serving.
Low-sodium diet: Prepare as directed but omit salt; use only fresh (not frozen) fish fillets. 120 milligrams sodium per serving.

COD WITH SPANISH SAUCE (240 calories per serving)

1 tablespoon salad oil
1 large onion, sliced
1 16-ounce can tomatoes
1/8 teaspoon oregano leaves
salt
1 16-ounce package frozen cod fillets, thawed
pepper
1 tablespoon lemon juice
1 tablespoon butter or margarine

About 45 minutes before serving: In skillet, in oil, sauté onion until golden; stir in tomatoes, oregano and 1/2 teaspoon salt; simmer, uncovered, 30 minutes. Meanwhile, preheat oven to 350°F. Sprinkle cod with pepper and lemon juice; dot with butter or margarine. Bake 20 minutes, or until cod flakes easily when tested with a fork; top with sauce and bake 5 minutes more. Makes 3 servings.

Diabetic diet: Prepare as directed but use margarine instead of butter. Exchanges per serving = 3 meat, 1 vegetable and 1 fat.
Egg-, gluten-, milk- and wheat-free diet: Prepare as directed but use milk-free margarine on milk-free diet.
Low-fat, low-cholesterol diet: Prepare as directed but use margarine or salad oil instead of butter. 10 grams fat per serving.
Low-sodium diet: Prepare as directed but use low-sodium packed canned tomatoes; omit salt; use fresh (not frozen) fillets and unsalted butter or margarine. 100 milligrams sodium per serving.

BAKED COD WITH GRAPEFRUIT (210 calories per serving)

2 16-ounce packages frozen cod fillets, thawed
1 large grapefruit
1/2 teaspoon salt
1/8 teaspoon pepper
1 cup day-old bread crumbs
2 tablespoons butter or margarine, melted
1/4 teaspoon thyme leaves

About 40 minutes before serving: Preheat oven to 350°F. Into small bowl, section grapefruit; let stand 5 minutes to collect juice. Brush cod fillets generously with juice from grapefruit; sprinkle with salt and pepper. Place in medium (about 12" by 8") baking pan.

In small bowl, combine bread crumbs, 1 tablespoon melted butter or margarine and thyme leaves; sprinkle over fish. Arrange grapefruit sections over bread crumbs; drizzle with remaining butter. Bake 25 to 30 minutes, or until fish flakes easily when tested with a fork. Makes 6 servings.

Diabetic diet: Prepare as directed but use margarine instead of butter. Exchanges per serving = 4 meat, 1 bread and 1 fat.
Low-fat, low-cholesterol diet: Prepare as directed but use margarine instead of butter. 5 grams fat per serving.
Low-sodium diet: Prepare as directed but use fresh (not frozen) fillets; omit salt; use unsalted butter or margarine. 145 milligrams sodium per serving. If also prepared with unsalted bread, 105 milligrams sodium per serving.

HALIBUT BAKED IN FOIL (285 calories per serving)

2 fresh halibut steaks, cut 3/4-inch thick (about 1 pound)
salad oil
4 small potatoes, thinly sliced
2 medium onions, thinly sliced
2 carrots, thinly sliced
salt and pepper to taste
chopped parsley for garnish

About 50 minutes before serving: Preheat oven to 450°F. Remove skin from halibut steaks. Cut meat from bone and halve, lengthwise, to make 4 serving pieces.

For each serving: Pour 1 teaspoon salad oil in center of 18-inch square of heavy-duty foil. Top with one piece of fish, then one quarter of potatoes, onions and carrots, sprinkling each layer with salt and pepper to taste. Wrap, using double folds. Place on cookie sheet. Bake 25 minutes, or until fish flakes easily with fork. Sprinkle with parsley. Makes 4 servings.

Bland diet: Prepare as directed but omit onion, pepper and parsley.
Diabetic diet: Exchanges per serving = 3 meat, 1 vegetable and 1 bread.
Egg-, gluten-, milk- and wheat-free diet: Prepare as directed.
Low-fat, low-cholesterol diet: 5 grams fat per serving.
Low-fat, bland (gall bladder) diet: Prepare as directed but omit onion, pepper and parsley.
High-iron diet: 3 milligrams iron per serving.
Low-residue diet: Prepare as directed but omit onion, pepper and parsley.
Low-sodium diet: Prepare as directed but use only fresh (not frozen) halibut; omit salt. 80 milligrams sodium per serving.

PERCH FILLETS WITH DIABLO SAUCE (175 calories per serving)

1 16-ounce package frozen perch fillets, thawed
1 teaspoon seasoned salt
1/4 teaspoon seasoned pepper
1 slice white bread
butter or margarine
1/3 cup chili sauce
1 1/2 teaspoons lemon juice
1/2 teaspoon Worcestershire

About 25 minutes before serving: Preheat oven to 350°F. Arrange fillets in greased ovenproof shallow dish; sprinkle with seasoned salt and pepper. Spread bread with butter, and cut into cubes; sprinkle over fish. Bake 15 minutes, or until fish flakes easily when tested with fork. Meanwhile, in cup, combine chili sauce, lemon juice and Worcestershire. Serve fillets with sauce. Makes 3 servings.

Diabetic diet: Prepare as directed but use margarine instead of butter. Exchanges per serving = 3 meat and 1 vegetable.
Low-fat, low-cholesterol diet: Prepare as directed but use margarine instead of butter. 5 grams fat per serving.

MAMBO FLOUNDER (215 calories per serving)

1 16-ounce package frozen flounder fillets, thawed (or 3 small fresh fillets)
1/2 cup tomato sauce
2 tablespoons grated Parmesan cheese
1 16-ounce can small whole white potatoes, drained
1/4 teaspoon oregano leaves
1/4 teaspoon basil
chopped parsley

About 30 minutes before serving: Preheat oven to 425°F. In medium baking pan, arrange fillets in single layer. Pour tomato sauce over fish; sprinkle with cheese. Place potatoes around fish, and sprinkle seasonings and parsley over cheese and potatoes. Bake 20 minutes, or until fish flakes easily with fork. Makes 3 servings.

Diabetic diet: Exchanges per serving = 4 meat and 1 bread.
Egg-, gluten-, and wheat-free diet: Prepare as directed.
Low-fat, low-cholesterol diet: Prepare as directed but omit cheese. 1 gram fat per serving.

STUFFED FLOUNDER LORRAINE (170 calories per serving)

2 tablespoons salad oil
1/4 cup chopped celery
2 tablespoons chopped parsley
2 tablespoons minced onion
1 cup (about 1/4 pound) finely
   chopped fresh mushrooms
1 cup packaged stuffing mix
salt
6 small fresh flounder fillets
   (about 1 1/2 pounds)
paprika and chopped parsley
   for garnish

About 40 minutes before serving: Preheat oven to 350°F. In medium skillet over medium heat, in oil, sauté celery, parsley, onion and mushrooms until golden. Turn off heat; add 1/3 cup water and stuffing mix; mix thoroughly. Lightly salt each fillet on both sides. Place one-sixth stuffing mixture toward thinner end of dark side of each fillet. Roll up; place each roll, not touching, open side down, in medium (about 9-inch square) baking dish. Pour 1/3 cup water over fish. Cover; bake 10 minutes; remove cover and bake 10 to 14 minutes more, or until fish flakes easily when tested with fork. Garnish with paprika and parsley. Makes 6 servings.

Diabetic diet: Exchanges per serving = 3 meat, 1 1/2 vegetable, 1 fat, and 1/2 bread.
Low-fat, low-cholesterol diet: 5 grams fat per serving.

SOLE À LA PARISIENNE (260 calories per serving)

2 tablespoons finely minced
   onion
4 small fresh sole fillets (about
   1 1/2 pounds)
salt and pepper to taste
1/2 cup dry white wine
1 tablespoon butter or margarine
2 tablespoons flour
1/2 cup half-and-half
1/8 teaspoon nutmeg
dash pepper
1/2 cup grated Swiss cheese

About 30 minutes before serving: Preheat oven to 350°F. In range-top casserole, sprinkle onions, then top with fillets (in a single layer). Sprinkle with salt and pepper; add wine, and heat on top of range until liquid is just boiling. Then bake in oven for 10 minutes. Remove fish from oven; turn oven setting to "broil."

Drain all liquid from fish, reserving 1/2 cup. In medium sauce-pan, melt butter; stir in flour. Slowly stir in reserved cooking liquid, half-and-half, nutmeg and pepper. Cook, stirring constantly, until thickened and smooth; stir in 1/3 cup grated cheese. Pour sauce over fish; top with remaining cheese. Run under broiler until brown. Makes 4 servings.

Diabetic diet: Prepare as directed, but use margarine instead of butter; after fish has been cooked, divide it among 4 individual broiler-proof casseroles; cover with sauce and broil as directed. Exchanges per serving = 4 meat, 1/2 milk and 1 fat.
Egg-, gluten- and wheat-free diet: Prepare as directed but substitute 1 tablespoon cornstarch for flour in gluten- and wheat-free diets.

STUFFED BAKED SWORDFISH (270 calories per serving)

1 swordfish steak, cut 1-inch
   thick (about 1 1/2 pounds)
1 1/2 teaspoons salad oil
1 tiny onion, finely chopped
1/8 pound fresh mushrooms,
   finely chopped (about 4
   medium mushrooms)
1/2 large stalk green celery with
   leaves, chopped
1/2 teaspoon salt
1/8 teaspoon pepper
1/8 teaspoon poultry seasoning
1 1/2 cups fresh bread cubes
salt and pepper to taste
paprika, chopped parsley and
   lemon slices for garnish

About 45 minutes before serving: Preheat oven to 375°F. Remove skin from swordfish steak. Cut pocket in swordfish just as you would for stuffed pork chops. In skillet over medium heat, in oil, sauté onion, mushrooms and celery until onion is golden. Stir in salt, pepper, poultry seasoning and bread cubes. Use mixture to stuff swordfish. Sprinkle on both sides with salt and pepper to taste.

Place fish in large (about 13" by 9" by 2") baking dish; cover with foil or lid. Bake 20 minutes, or until fish flakes easily with fork.

To serve: Cut steak into 4 equal servings; sprinkle with paprika and parsley; top with lemon slices. Makes 4 servings.

Egg-, gluten-, milk- and wheat-free diet: Prepare as directed but substitute 1 cup cooked rice for bread cubes for gluten- and wheat-free diet; use rice with milk-free margarine for milk-free diet.
Low-fat, low-cholesterol diet: 10 grams fat per serving.
Low-sodium diet: Prepare as directed but use only fresh instead of frozen swordfish; omit salt; substitute 1 cup unsalted cooked rice for bread cubes. 145 milligrams sodium per serving.

SAUTÉED SOLE IN EGG SAUCE (Chi Tan Ch'ao Pan-Yu) (275 calories per serving)

1¼ pounds fresh sole fillets
3 eggs
1 teaspoon salt
2 tablespoons cornstarch
3 tablespoons salad oil
2 green onions (both tops and bulbs), thinly sliced crosswise
1 piece crystallized ginger, finely minced
1 tablespoon dry sherry

About 30 minutes before serving: Cut fillets, across the grain, into 2-inch-wide strips. In medium bowl, beat together eggs, salt and cornstarch. Add strips of sole and coat completely with egg mixture.

In large skillet, heat one tablespoon salad oil until sizzling. Drain excess egg mixture from sole. Taking care not to let pieces touch, add one-third of sole, one piece at a time, to skillet. Cook over high heat until fish just begins to turn white around sides and top—about 2 minutes; with spatula, turn each piece and cook one minute more. Remove pieces to warm platter.

Repeat until all fish is cooked. Stir sliced green onions, ginger, sherry and 2 tablespoons water into egg remaining in bowl. Remove skillet from heat; pour in egg-onion mixture; top with cooked sole. Cover; let stand about 2 minutes more, or until egg has set slightly. Serve immediately. Makes 4 servings.

Diabetic diet: Prepare as directed but substitute ¼ teaspoon ground ginger for crystallized ginger. Carefully divide into 4 equal servings. Exchanges per serving = 4 meat and 1 fat.
Milk- and wheat-free diet: Prepare as directed.
Low-sodium diet: Prepare as directed but use only fresh sole; omit salt. 165 milligrams sodium per serving.

CURRIED STUFFED BASS (205 calories per serving)

1½ cups water
1 6-ounce package curried-rice mix
1 2-pound dressed striped bass or other dressed whole fish
juice of 1 lime or lemon
1 teaspoon salt
pepper to taste

About 50 minutes before serving: Preheat oven to 500°F. In medium saucepan, heat water to boiling; add rice mix; cover; simmer 10 minutes. Meanwhile, sprinkle fish inside and out with lime juice, salt and pepper. Place on cookie sheet, lined with large sheet of wide foil.

Use hot rice to fill cavity of fish. Wrap fish in foil, using double folds. Bake 10 minutes, then turn down heat to 425°F. and bake 25 minutes more, or until fish flakes easily with fork. Open foil carefully and pour off excess liquid. Makes 6 servings.

Egg-, gluten-, milk- and wheat-free diet: Prepare as directed but use rice mix not containing monosodium glutamate on gluten-free diet.
Low-fat, low-cholesterol diet: 5 grams fat per serving.

FLOUNDER IN VELVET SAUCE (195 calories per serving)

2 16-ounce packages frozen flounder fillets, thawed
2 tablespoons butter or margarine
3 tablespoons flour
1½ cups skimmed milk or reliquefied nonfat dry milk
¼ teaspoon salt
¼ teaspoon white pepper
2 tablespoons shredded Parmesan cheese
paprika

About 45 minutes before serving: Preheat oven to 400°F. Place fillets in layers in medium (about 12″ by 8″ by 2″) baking dish. In small saucepan, melt butter; blend in flour; gradually add milk, stirring constantly, until mixture thickens. Stir in salt, pepper and Parmesan; pour mixture evenly over fish. Sprinkle with paprika. Bake 30 minutes, or until fish flakes easily with fork. Makes 6 servings.

Bland diet: Prepare as directed but omit pepper.
Diabetic diet: Prepare as directed but use margarine instead of butter. Carefully divide into 6 equal servings. Exchanges per servng = 3 meat, ½ milk and 1 fat.
Low-fat, bland (gall bladder) diet: Prepare as directed, but omit pepper and cheese if forbidden on diet.
Low-residue diet: Prepare as directed but omit pepper.

BAKED FISH WITH HORSERADISH SAUCE (180 calories per serving)

salt and pepper to taste
1 16-ounce package frozen fish
   fillets, partially thawed (cod,
   flounder, sole)
1/2 cup creamed cottage
   cheese*
1/2 tablespoon skimmed milk or
   reliquefied nonfat dry milk
2 tablespoons prepared horseradish
1 tablespoon lemon juice
1 tablespoon honey or granulated sugar
2 teaspoons chopped chives

About 30 minutes before serving: Preheat oven to 450°F. Salt and pepper each side of fish fillets; then place in lightly greased shallow baking dish. Tightly cover dish and bake for 15 to 20 minutes, or until fish flakes easily with fork.

Meanwhile, in electric-blender container, place cottage cheese, milk, horseradish, lemon juice and honey; at low speed, blend until smooth; stir in chives. (Or cottage cheese may be pressed through a fine sieve and mixed with other ingredients.) Serve sauce over hot fillets. Makes 3 servings.

Diabetic diet: Prepare as directed but omit honey or sugar; use nonnutritive sweetener equivalent to 1 tablespoon sugar. Top each serving fish with 3 tablespoons sauce. Exchanges per serving = 4 meat.
Egg-, gluten- and wheat-free diet: Prepare as directed.
Low-fat, low-cholesterol diet: 5 grams fat per serving.

*For smoothest sauce, use a brand of cottage cheese which has a soft curd.

FLOUNDER TURBOTS (290 calories per serving)

1 tablespoon salad oil
1/4 cup chopped onion
1/4 cup chopped celery
2 cups packaged herb-
   seasoned bread-stuffing mix
1 16-ounce package frozen
   flounder fillets, thawed
salt and pepper to taste
chopped parsley for garnish
lemon wedges for garnish

About 40 minutes before serving: In skillet over medium heat, in oil, sauté onion and celery until onion is golden. Stir in 2/3 cup water, then stuffing mix until evenly moistened.

Meanwhile, preheat oven to 350°F. Lightly oil three 1-pint ovenproof casseroles. Lightly sprinkle fillets with salt and pepper; arrange along sides and part of bottom of casseroles. Divide stuffing mix among casseroles. Cover with foil; bake 20 minutes, or until fish flakes with fork.

To serve: Turn turbots out of casseroles onto serving plates; garnish with parsley and lemon wedges. Makes 3 servings.

Diabetic diet: Exchanges per serving = 4 meat, 1 bread and 1 fat.
Low-fat, low-cholesterol diet: 5 grams fat per serving.

FISH WITH FRESH MUSHROOMS (Ikan Masak Djamur) (160 calories per serving)

1 tablespoon salad oil
1 medium onion, thinly sliced
3/4 pound fresh mushrooms,
   thinly sliced
1 pound fresh flounder fillets,
   cut crosswise into 1-inch
   slices
salt and pepper
1 tablespoon soy sauce
1 tablespoon dry sherry
1 large stalk green celery, cut
   into thin crosswise slices

About 25 minutes before serving: In large skillet over medium heat, in oil, sauté onion 1 minute. Add mushrooms and sauté, stirring constantly, 2 minutes, or until mushrooms are wilted. Spread a layer of fillet slices on mushrooms; sprinkle with pepper. Top with remaining fillet slices; season them. Add soy sauce, sherry and celery; cover; simmer 10 minutes. Makes 4 servings.

Diabetic diet: Carefully divide into 4 equal servings. Exchanges per serving = 3 meat and 1 vegetable.
Egg- and milk-free diet: Prepare as directed.
Low-fat, low-cholesterol diet: 5 grams fat per serving.
Low-sodium diet: Prepare as directed but use only fresh flounder; omit salt and soy sauce. 115 milligrams sodium per serving.

ZESTY SAUCED HADDOCK (200 calories per serving)

1 pound fresh haddock fillets
(or 1 16-ounce package frozen
haddock fillets, thawed,
drained)
salt
1/2 cup sour cream
1/8 teaspoon dry mustard
1/8 teaspoon ginger
generous dash thyme leaves
paprika for garnish
chopped parsley for garnish

About 30 minutes before serving: Preheat oven to 400°F. Lightly grease medium (about 10″ by 6″ by 2″) baking dish. Divide haddock into 3 serving pieces; sprinkle on both sides with salt; place, in single layer, in baking dish.

In small bowl, mix sour cream, mustard, ginger and thyme; spread mixture on top of fillets. Bake 20 to 25 minutes, or until fish flakes easily with a fork. Serve sprinkled with paprika and parsley. Makes 3 servings.

Bland diet: Prepare as directed but omit mustard, ginger and parsley; use ground thyme.
Diabetic diet: Prepare as directed but divide into 4 equal servings. Exchanges per serving = 3 meat and 1 fat.
Low-residue diet: Prepare as directed for bland diet.
Low-sodium diet: Prepare as directed but use only fresh haddock; omit salt. 135 milligrams sodium per serving.

CHERVIL BAKED SOLE (170 calories per serving)

2 16-ounce packages frozen fillets of sole, trimmed
1 teaspoon chervil
1 teaspoon salt
1/4 teaspoon pepper
1/4 teaspoon paprika
1 medium onion, sliced
1/2 cup skimmed milk or reliquefied nonfat dry milk
1/4 cup chicken broth
2 tablespoons butter or margarine

About 30 minutes before serving: Preheat oven to 400°F. In buttered large shallow baking dish, place fillets; sprinkle on both sides with combined chervil, salt, pepper and paprika. Separate onion into rings and place over fillets. Pour milk and broth over fish; dot with butter. Bake 20 to 25 minutes, or until fish flakes easily with fork. Makes 6 servings.

Diabetic diet: Prepare as directed but use margarine instead of butter. Carefully divide into 6 equal servings. Exchanges per serving = 3 meat and 1 fat.
Egg-, gluten- and wheat-free diet: Prepare as directed, but use homemade chicken broth for gluten- and wheat-free diets.
Low-fat, low-cholesterol diet: Prepare as directed but use salad oil or margarine instead of butter. 5 grams fat per serving.

COD CASSEROLE (Cod à la Gomes de Sa) (225 calories per serving)

1 1/2 cups water
salt
1 carrot, sliced
4 medium onions, thinly sliced
3 or 4 peppercorns
2 or 3 whole allspice
1 bay leaf
1 16-ounce package frozen cod fillets, thawed
2 tablespoons salad oil
1 garlic clove, sliced
4 medium potatoes, boiled, peeled, sliced 1/2-inch thick
1/2 teaspoon pepper
1/3 cup sliced ripe olives
1/2 cup dry white wine
3 hard-cooked eggs, shelled
1/2 cup chopped parsley

About 1 hour before serving: In large saucepan, combine water, 1 teaspoon salt, carrot, 1 sliced onion, peppercorns, allspice and bay leaf; bring to boiling. Add fish fillets and cook about 10 minutes. Drain; remove any bones; flake.

Preheat oven to 400°F. In large skillet over medium heat, in oil, sauté garlic until golden. Remove garlic; then, in same oil, sauté 3 sliced onions until tender. Add potatoes; sprinkle with 1 teaspoon salt, and pepper; add cod, olives and wine; heat about 5 minutes, stirring occasionally.

Arrange mixture in greased 2-quart casserole; bake 10 minutes. Chop 1 hard-cooked egg; cut rest into quarters. Before serving, garnish center of casserole with chopped egg, chopped parsley and egg quarters. Makes 6 servings.

Diabetic diet: Prepare as directed but divide mixture among 6 individual casseroles; bake and garnish as directed. Exchanges per serving = 2 meat, 1 vegetable, 1 bread and 1 fat.
Gluten-, milk-, and wheat-free diet: Prepare as directed.

HERB'S FAVORITE FLOUNDER (200 calories per serving)

1 tablespoon salad oil
1 onion, minced
1 16-ounce package frozen
    flounder fillets, thawed
1/2 teaspoon salt
1/4 teaspoon basil
1/4 teaspoon garlic powder
1/8 teaspoon pepper
2 medium fresh tomatoes,
    chopped

About 25 minutes before serving: In large skillet over medium heat, in oil, sauté onion until golden; lay fillets in skillet; cook, uncovered, 5 minutes. Add remaining ingredients; cover; cook, over low heat, 15 minutes, or until fish flakes easily with a fork. Makes 3 servings.

Diabetic diet: Exchanges per serving = 3 meat, 1 vegetable and 1 fat.
Egg-, gluten-, milk- and wheat-free diet: Prepare as directed.
Low-fat, low-cholesterol diet: 5 grams fat per serving.
Low-sodium diet: Prepare as directed but use fresh (not frozen) fillets; omit salt. 125 milligrams sodium per serving.

BAKED FISH À LA GRAPEFRUIT (205 calories per serving)

1 4-pound cleaned striped bass
salt
butter or margarine
1 small onion, minced
4 slices bread, crumbled
1/4 teaspoon pepper
1/2 teaspoon basil
2 tablespoons chopped parsley
1 grapefruit
parsley sprigs

About 1 hour before serving: Sprinkle bass, inside and out, with 1 teaspoon salt. Preheat oven to 400°F. In small skillet over medium heat, in 2 tablespoons butter or margarine, sauté onion until golden; stir in bread, 1/2 teaspoon salt, pepper, basil and chopped parsley. Use this bread mixture to loosely stuff fish, then fasten opening with toothpicks.

Line a large roasting pan with foil; place fish on pan. Pare and section grapefruit, squeezing any juice into a small bowl containing 2 tablespoons melted butter or margarine. Brushing fish often with this mixture, bake 45 minutes, or until fish flakes easily with a fork. Lay grapefruit sections over fish and bake 5 minutes more. Remove toothpicks; garnish with parsley sprigs.

To serve: Cut top side of fish into 4 servings, just down to backbone. Remove stuffing to serving plates, then discard backbone. Serve lower section of fish in same way. Makes 8 servings.

Egg-, gluten-, milk- and wheat-free diet: Prepare as directed but use milk-free margarine and bread on milk-free diet; use 1 cup cooked rice (in place of bread cubes) on gluten- and wheat-free diets.
Low-fat, low-cholesterol diet: Prepare as directed but use salad oil or margarine instead of butter. 10 grams fat per serving.

SALMON FROID SMITHANE (240 calories per serving)

4 1-inch-thick fresh salmon
    steaks (about 1 1/2 pounds)
1/2 cup diced celery
few parsley sprigs
1 medium onion, thinly sliced
6 peppercorns
2 bay leaves
1/2 teaspoon basil
salt
1 8-ounce container (1 cup)
    small-curd creamed cottage
    cheese
dash Tabasco
2 teaspoons white horseradish
watercress, lemon and lime
    wedges for garnish

Day before serving: In large skillet, place salmon steaks, celery, parsley, onion, peppercorns, bay leaves, basil and 1 teaspoon salt. Cover with boiling water; simmer, covered, 10 minutes, or until fish flakes easily when tested with fork. Remove from liquid; drain well. Arrange on platter; cover; refrigerate.

Just before serving: In electric-blender container, at low speed, blend cottage cheese, Tabasco, 1 teaspoon salt and horseradish until smooth. (Add a tablespoon or two of milk if needed to obtain a smooth consistency.) Spoon cottage cheese mixture into opening between "legs" of salmon steaks. Garnish with watercress and lemon and lime wedges. Makes 4 servings.

Diabetic diet: Exchanges per serving = 5 meat and 1/2 fat.
Low-fat, low-cholesterol diet: 10 grams fat per serving.

SPICY TUNA CHOWDER (260 calories per serving)

1 6¹/2- or 7-ounce can tuna,
   drained and flaked
1 small onion, sliced
1 potato, cubed
1 carrot, diced
¹/4 cup diced celery
1 16-ounce can tomatoes
¹/2 teaspoon salt
¹/4 teaspoon thyme leaves
¹/8 teaspoon pepper
chopped parsley for garnish

About 1 hour before serving: In skillet, in 1 tablespoon oil drained from tuna, sauté onion until golden. Stir in potato, carrot, celery, tomatoes, ³/4 cup water, salt, thyme and pepper; simmer, covered, 35 to 40 minutes, or until vegetables are tender. Add tuna and heat; sprinkle with parsley. Makes 2 servings.

Diabetic diet: Exchanges per serving = 3 meat, 2 vegetable and ¹/2 bread.
Egg-, gluten-, milk- and wheat-free diet: Prepare as directed but use tuna not containing monosodium glutamate on gluten-free diet.
Low-fat, low-cholesterol diet: Prepare as directed but use low-sodium packed canned tuna and tomatoes; omit salt. 70 milligrams sodium per serving.

TUNA-CURRY SOUFFLÉ (260 calories per serving)

2 tablespoons butter or margarine
2 tablespoons minced onion
1 garlic clove, minced
1 teaspoon parsley flakes
¹/4 teaspoon ginger
¹/4 teaspoon salt
1 teaspoon curry
¹/4 cup flour
1 cup skimmed milk or re-
   liquefied nonfat dry milk
1 6¹/2- or 7-ounce can tuna, well
   drained, flaked
4 eggs, separated

About 1 hour and 20 minutes before serving: Preheat oven to 325°F. Grease 2-quart casserole. In medium skillet over medium heat, in butter, sauté onion, garlic and parsley flakes until onion is lightly browned; stir in ginger, salt and curry. Make a smooth paste with flour and a bit of milk; stir in remaining milk; add mixture to sautéed onions in skillet. Stirring constantly, cook until mixture thickens; remove from heat. Stir in tuna, then egg yolks, until sauce is smooth.

In large bowl, beat egg whites until stiff peaks form. Pour sauce mixture over egg whites; gently fold together until smooth; pour into casserole. Bake 50 to 60 minutes, or until surface is brown and rebounds when lightly touched. Serve immediately. Makes 4 servings.

Bland diet: Prepare as directed but omit onion, garlic, ginger and curry.
Diabetic diet: Prepare as directed but use margarine instead of butter. Exchanges per serving = 2 meat and ¹/2 milk.
Low-fat diet: Prepare as directed but use water-packed tuna in place of regular. 10 grams fat per serving. Omit recipe from low-cholesterol diet.
Low-residue diet: Prepare as directed for bland diet.
Low-sodium diet: Prepare as directed but use unsalted butter or margarine; omit salt; use curry not containing salt; use low-sodium canned tuna. 130 milligrams sodium per serving.

TUNA-VEGETABLE RAREBIT (300 calories per serving)

1 10-ounce package frozen
   mixed vegetables
1 10¹/2-ounce can condensed
   cream-of-celery soup
¹/4 cup skimmed milk or reliquefied nonfat dry milk
2 6¹/2- or 7-ounce cans tuna,
   drained
1 cup shredded Cheddar
   cheese
¹/4 teaspoon oregano leaves
¹/4 teaspoon dry mustard
dash Tabasco
dash pepper
3 English muffins, split and
   toasted

About 30 minutes before serving: Cook mixed vegetables as label directs; drain. In large skillet over low heat, stir together mixed vegetables and remaining ingredients except English muffins; heat. Serve over the toasted muffins. Makes 6 servings.

Diabetic diet: Exchanges per serving = 3 meat, 2 bread and ¹/2 fat.
Low-purine diet: Prepare as directed but omit tuna. Makes 3 to 4 servings.

TUNA SCRAMBLE SALAD (320 calories per serving)

1 tablespoon salad oil
1 medium onion, chopped
1¹/₃ cups packaged precooked rice
1 teaspoon seasoned salt
1 10-ounce package frozen chopped spinach
2 6¹/₂- or 7-ounce cans tuna, drained, flaked
¹/₈ teaspoon seasoned pepper
¹/₂ cup shredded process Cheddar cheese

About 25 minutes before serving: In skillet, in oil, sauté onion until golden. Stir in rice, 1¹/₂ cups water and seasoned salt. Bring rice to boiling. Cover; remove from heat; let stand 10 minutes. Meanwhile, cook spinach as label directs; drain. Add to rice with tuna and seasoned pepper; toss lightly. Top with cheese. Makes 5 servings of about 1 cup each.

Diabetic diet: Exchanges per serving = 3 meat, 1 vegetable and 2 bread.
Low-fat, low-cholesterol diet: Prepare as directed but omit cheese. 10 grams fat per serving.

TEMPTING TUNA TOSS (220 calories per serving)

2 hard-cooked eggs, shelled
2 6¹/₂- or 7-ounce cans tuna, drained and flaked
¹/₄ teaspoon oregano leaves
scant ¹/₂ teaspoon onion salt
¹/₈ teaspoon garlic powder
¹/₂ cup reduced–calorie mayonnaise
4 lettuce cups

About 20 minutes before serving: In medium bowl, finely chop eggs. Toss eggs with remaining ingredients except lettuce. Serve in lettuce cups. Makes 4 servings.

Diabetic diet: Exchanges per serving = 3 meat and 1 vegetable.
Low-fat, low-cholesterol diet: 10 grams fat per serving.

CREAMED TUNA ROCKEFELLER (280 calories per serving)

1 10-ounce package frozen chopped spinach, thawed
¹/₄ cup cooked salad dressing
5 tablespoons flour
¹/₂ teaspoon salt
2 cups skimmed milk or re-liquefied nonfat dry milk
¹/₄ green pepper, minced
2 tablespoons minced onion
1 6¹/₂- or 7-ounce can tuna, thoroughly drained
¹/₂ cup grated Cheddar cheese

About 45 minutes before serving: Preheat oven to 350°F. Lightly grease 4 ovenproof 1-cup casserole dishes. Carefully press all liquid from thawed spinach, then divide it evenly among casseroles.

In medium saucepan, mix cooked salad dressing, flour and salt to form a smooth paste; slowly stir in milk until smooth; add green pepper and onion. Then, stirring constantly, heat until thickened and smooth. Divide sauce among casseroles. Break tuna into small pieces; divide among casseroles. Sprinkle cheese on tuna. Bake 20 minutes, or until cheese sauce bubbles. Makes 4 servings.

Diabetic diet: Exchanges per serving = 2 meat, 1 vegetable and 1 milk.
High-iron diet: 3 milligrams iron per serving.

TUNA-TOPPED APPLE SALAD (280 calories per serving)

1 6¹/₂- or 7-ounce can tuna, drained and flaked
¹/₃ cup reduced–calorie mayonnaise
2 stalks celery, minced
1 large red apple
lemon juice
2 lettuce leaves
paprika for garnish

About 10 minutes before serving: In small bowl, combine tuna, low-calorie mayonnaise and celery. Core apple and slice crosswise into 4 slices. Sprinkle or brush with lemon juice. Place 2 apple slices on each lettuce leaf; top with mound of tuna salad; sprinkle with paprika. Makes 2 servings.

Diabetic diet: Exchanges per serving = 3 meat, 1 vegetable and 1 fruit.
Low-fat, low-cholesterol diet: Prepare as directed but use water-packed tuna. 5 grams fat per serving.
Low-sodium diet: Prepare as directed but use low-sodium canned tuna, low-sodium mayonnaise (see recipe page 317); omit celery. 70 milligrams sodium per serving.

GOLDEN GARDEN TUNA PIE (330 calories per serving)

4 medium carrots, cut into 1-
inch pieces
1 pound (about 3 medium) potatoes, cut into large cubes
1/2 teaspoon salt
1 teaspoon celery salt
1 10-ounce package frozen peas
3 tablespoons flour
1/3 cup nonfat dry-milk powder
1 cup skimmed milk or re-
liquefied nonfat dry milk
2 61/2- or 7-ounce cans water-
packed tuna, drained, flaked
1 8-ounce tube refrigerated
crescent rolls

About 30 minutes before serving: Preheat oven to 375°F. In medium saucepan, in 1 cup water, cook carrots, potatoes, salt and celery salt, covered, 5 minutes. Add frozen peas; cover; boil 10 minutes more.

Meanwhile, in 11/2-quart casserole, mix flour and dry-milk powder. Slowly stir in skimmed milk to form a smooth paste. When vegetables are cooked, stir in flour-milk mixture; cook until thickened and smooth; stir in tuna. Return mixture to casserole. Cut crescent rolls (still rolled as they come from package) crosswise into 1/4-inch slices; use to top tuna mixture. (Bake leftover slices on cookie sheet at the same time.) Bake 12 to 15 minutes, or until golden brown. Makes 6 servings of about 1 cup each.

High-iron diet: Prepare as directed but use crescent rolls made with enriched flour. 3 milligrams iron per serving.

TUNA, SPANISH STYLE (265 calories per serving)

2 tablespoons salad oil
1 cup packaged precooked rice
1 medium onion, thinly sliced
1/3 cup chopped green pepper
1 teaspoon salt
dash cayenne
1 garlic clove, minced
1 20-ounce can tomatoes
1/2 cup tomato juice
2 4-ounce cans sliced mushrooms, undrained
1 61/2- or 7-ounce can tuna,
drained

About 50 minutes before serving: In large skillet, in oil, brown rice, stirring constantly, until golden. Add 1 cup water, then all remaining ingredients but tuna. Cook covered, over low heat, adding more water if necessary, 35 to 40 minutes. Break tuna into large pieces; place on top of rice mixture; heat, covered, 5 minutes. Makes 4 servings.

Diabetic diet: Exchanges per serving = 2 meat, 2 vegetable, 1 bread and 1 fat.
Low-fat, low-cholesterol diet: 10 grams fat per serving.
Low-sodium diet: Prepare as directed but omit salt; use low-sodium canned tomatoes, tomato juice and tuna; substitute fresh mushrooms for canned. 35 milligrams sodium per serving.

TUNA-POTATO PATTIES (260 calories per serving)

1 61/2- or 7-ounce can tuna,
drained
1 tablespoon lemon juice
instant mashed potatoes for 4
servings
1 teaspoon parsley flakes
1 tablespoon instant minced
onion
1 egg, beaten
1 teaspoon salt
1/4 teaspoon pepper
flour
2 tablespoons salad oil
1 8-ounce can tomato sauce
with cheese

About 20 minutes before serving: In medium bowl, flake tuna; sprinkle with lemon juice. Make up instant mashed potatoes as label directs but omit salt and butter and use skimmed milk; add to tuna with parsley flakes, minced onion, egg, salt and pepper; mix well. With floured hands, shape into 8 patties; coat each with flour. In medium skillet over medium heat, in oil, brown patties on both sides. Meanwhile, heat tomato sauce. Serve patties with tomato sauce. Makes 4 servings.

Bland diet: Prepare as directed but omit onion, pepper and tomato sauce with cheese.
Diabetic diet: Exchanges per serving = 2 meat, 1/2 vegetable and 1 bread.
Low-fat, low-cholesterol diet: Prepare as directed but use only white of egg; use plain tomato sauce (not tomato sauce with cheese). 10 grams fat per serving.
Low-fat, bland (gall bladder) diet: Prepare as directed but use only white of egg; omit onion, pepper and tomato sauce with cheese.
Low-residue diet: Prepare as directed for bland diet.

ZESTY TUNA BUNS (270 calories per serving)

$^2/_3$ cup evaporated skimmed milk

2 cups fresh bread cubes

2 6$^1/_2$- or 7-ounce cans tuna, drained, flaked

1 tablespoon catchup

1 tablespoon prepared mustard

1 tablespoon pickle relish

2 teaspoons lemon juice

$^1/_2$ teaspoon salt

$^1/_2$ teaspoon grated onion

$^1/_8$ teaspoon pepper

3 split hamburger buns

6 tender lettuce leaves

1 medium tomato, cut into 6 slices

About 25 minutes before serving: Preheat broiler 10 minutes if manufacturer directs. In medium bowl, combine milk and bread cubes; with fork, beat until almost smooth. Then mix in tuna, catchup, mustard, pickle relish, lemon juice, salt, grated onion and pepper.

Separate split hamburger buns. Spread tuna mixture over bun halves; broil 5 inches from heat until light golden—about 8 minutes. Then transfer to warm platter and top each with a lettuce leaf and a tomato slice. Makes 6 servings.

Diabetic diet: Prepare as directed but omit pickle relish. Exchanges per serving = 1 meat, 1 bread and $^1/_2$ milk.
Low-fat, low-cholesterol diet: 5 grams fat per serving.

TOMATO-TUNA CHOWDER (250 calories per serving)

1 tablespoon salad oil

$^1/_3$ cup chopped onion

1 garlic clove, minced

1 stalk celery, chopped

2 tablespoons minced green pepper

2 medium potatoes, diced

1 teaspoon salt

2 6$^1/_2$- or 7-ounce cans tuna, drained, flaked

1 19-ounce can tomato juice

$^1/_2$ teaspoon poultry seasoning

dash cayenne

About 30 minutes before serving: In large saucepan, in oil, sauté onion, garlic, celery and green pepper until onion is golden. Add potatoes, 2 cups water and salt; cover; boil gently 20 minutes, or until potatoes are almost tender. Add remaining ingredients; cover; boil gently 10 minutes longer. Makes 4 servings of about 2 cups each.

Diabetic diet: Exchanges per serving = 3 meat, 1 vegetable and 1 bread.
Egg-, gluten-, milk- and wheat-free diet: Prepare as directed but use tuna and tomato juice not containing monosodium glutamate on gluten-free diet.
Low-fat, low-cholesterol diet: Prepare as directed but use water-packed tuna. 10 grams fat per serving.
Low-sodium diet: Prepare as directed but omit salt; use low-sodium canned tuna and tomato juice. 75 milligrams sodium per serving.

SWEET-AND-SOUR TUNA, ORIENTAL STYLE (295 calories per serving)

1 tablespoon salad oil

1 green pepper, cut into thin strips

1 large onion, thinly sliced

1 tablespoon cornstarch

1 13-ounce can pineapple chunks

2 tablespoons granulated sugar

2 tablespoons vinegar

2 6$^1/_2$- or 7-ounce cans tuna, drained, flaked

1 teaspoon salt

$^1/_8$ teaspoon pepper

3 cups cooked rice

About 30 minutes before serving: In large skillet over medium heat, in oil, sauté green pepper strips and onion until onion is just limp. Mix in cornstarch. Add syrup drained from pineapple, then cook, stirring constantly, until thickened and smooth. Add pineapple chunks, sugar, vinegar, tuna, salt and pepper. Cook 5 minutes, stirring regularly. Serve over rice. Makes 6 servings.

Egg-, gluten-, milk- and wheat-free diet: Prepare as directed but use tuna not containing monosodium glutamate on gluten-free diet.
Low-fat, low-cholesterol diet: 10 grams fat per serving.
Low-sodium diet: Prepare as directed but use low-sodium packed tuna; omit salt; serve over unsalted rice. 65 milligrams sodium per serving.

BAKED TUNA-CHEESE CASSEROLE (300 calories per serving)

1 cup elbow macaroni
1 tablespoon butter or margarine
¼ cup finely chopped onions
¼ cup flour
½ teaspoon salt
⅛ teaspoon pepper
1 teaspoon dry mustard
2 cups skimmed milk or reliquefied nonfat dry milk
2 6½- or 7-ounce cans tuna, thoroughly drained
1 8-ounce can diced carrots, drained
½ cup grated sharp Cheddar cheese

About 45 minutes before serving: Cook macaroni as label directs, but use minimum recommended cooking time; drain. Preheat oven to 375°F. In medium saucepan over medium heat, in butter, satué onion until golden. Stir in flour, salt, pepper and mustard. Stirring constantly, slowly stir in milk until mixture is smooth and has thickened slightly. Add drained macaroni, tuna and carrots; heat to simmering. Pour mixture into 1½-quart casserole; top with grated cheese. Bake 20 minutes or until cheese browns slightly. Makes 6 servings of about 1 cup each.

Diabetic diet: Prepare as directed but use margarine instead of butter. Divide mixture among 6 individual casseroles, top with cheese; bake 15 minutes. Exchanges per serving = 2 meat, 1 bread and 1 milk.
Low-fat, low-cholesterol diet: Prepare as directed but use salad oil or margarine instead of butter; omit cheese. 10 grams fat per serving.

TIP-TOP TUNA CASSEROLE (265 calories per serving)

1 tablespoon salad oil
½ cup chopped onion
1 cup chopped green pepper
2 tablespoons flour
1 29-ounce can tomatoes (about 3½ cups)
1 tablespoon Worcestershire
1 teaspoon dry mustard
½ teaspoon salt
½ teaspoon granulated sugar
¼ teaspoon pepper
2 6½- or 7-ounce cans chunk-style tuna, drained
1 8-ounce can refrigerated buttermilk biscuits

About 45 minutes before serving: Preheat oven to 375°F. In medium saucepan, in oil, sauté onion until limp; add green pepper and continue cooking until tender—about 5 minutes. Stir in flour. Add tomatoes, Worcestershire, mustard, salt, sugar and pepper; simmer, covered, 10 minutes. Add tuna and pour into 2½-quart casserole.

For topping: Cut each biscuit into sixths. Arrange pieces on casserole with points up. Bake 25 minutes. Cover lightly with foil if biscuits brown too soon. Makes 6 servings.

Diabetic diet: Prepare as directed but omit sugar; divide mixture among 6 individual casserole dishes, then top with biscuit pieces; bake as directed. Exchanges per serving = 2 meat, 1½ bread and 1 vegetable.
Low-fat diet: 10 grams fat per serving. Omit recipe from low-cholesterol diet.

CLASSIC TUNA DINNER (335 calories per serving)

4 ounces spaghetti
1 6½- or 7-ounce can chunk-style tuna, drained
1 tablespoon parsley flakes
1 tablespoon lemon juice
2 tablespoons olive oil
salt and pepper to taste

About 15 minutes before serving: Cook spaghetti as label directs. Meanwhile, in small bowl, chop tuna finely; mix in parsley and lemon juice. In medium saucepan, heat oil and tuna mixture; simmer until bubbly and heated through. Toss spaghetti with tuna sauce. Season with salt and pepper if desired. Makes 3 servings.

Bland diet: Prepare as directed but omit pepper.
Diabetic diet: Carefully divide into 3 equal servings. Exchanges per serving = 2 meat, 2 bread and 2 fat.
Egg-, gluten-, milk- and wheat-free diet: Prepare as directed, but use bean threads or transparent noodles instead of spaghetti, and tuna not containing monosodium glutamate, for wheat- and gluten-free diets.
Low-fat, low-cholesterol diet: Prepare as directed but substitute salad oil for olive oil. 15 grams fat per serving.
Low-residue diet: Prepare as directed but omit pepper.

PALOS VERDES STEW (270 calories per serving)

1 tablespoon salad oil
1 medium onion, minced
1 cup chopped celery
3 potatoes, quartered, then
    thinly sliced
1¹/₂ teaspoons oregano leaves
1 teaspoon salt
1 24-ounce can tomato juice
1 6¹/₂- or 7-ounce can water-
    packed tuna, drained, flaked

About 35 minutes before serving: In large skillet over medium heat, in oil, sauté onion and celery until onion is golden. Add potatoes, 1 cup water, oregano and salt; cover; simmer 10 minutes, or until potatoes are almost tender. Add tomato juice and tuna; simmer 10 minutes more, or until potatoes are done. Serve in soup bowls. Makes 4 servings.

Diabetic diet: Carefully divide into 4 equal servings. Exchanges per serving = 4 meat, 1 vegetable and 1 bread.
Egg-, gluten-, milk- and wheat-free diet: Prepare as directed but use tomato juice and tuna not containing monosodium glutamate on gluten-free diets.
Low-fat, low-cholesterol diet: 5 grams fat per serving.
High-iron diet: 3.5 milligrams iron per serving.
Low-sodium diet: Prepare as directed but omit salt; use low-sodium canned tomato juice and tuna. 45 milligrams sodium per serving.

TUNA BARBECUE (225 calories per serving)

1 teaspoon butter or margarine
1 garlic clove, minced
5 stuffed olives, chopped
1 teaspoon Worcestershire
¹/₃ cup catchup
¹/₂ teaspoon dry mustard
1 6¹/₂- or 7-ounce can tuna,
    drained and flaked
4 hamburger buns, split

About 30 minutes before serving: In medium saucepan, in butter, sauté garlic until soft; add ¹/₃ cup water, olives, Worcestershire, catchup, mustard and tuna. Simmer, uncovered, 15 minutes.
    To serve: Use to fill buns. Makes 4 servings.

Low-fat, low-cholesterol diet: Prepare as directed but use margarine instead of butter; omit olives. 5 grams fat per serving.

TUNA IN A SPINACH NEST (330 calories per serving)

2 10-ounce packages frozen leaf
    spinach
1 tablespoon butter or marga-
    rine
1 green pepper, slivered
1 10¹/₂-ounce can condensed
    mushroom soup
2 pimentos, cut into strips
2 6¹/₂- or 7-ounce cans tuna,
    drained and flaked
¹/₈ teaspoon pepper
1 cup soft day-old bread crumbs

About 20 minutes before serving: Cook spinach as label directs; drain. Meanwhile, in skillet, in butter, sauté green pepper until tender. Add mushroom soup, stirring until smooth; add pimentos, tuna and pepper; simmer 5 minutes. Add bread crumbs to spinach; toss well. Spoon onto serving dish in shape of ring; spoon tuna mixture into center. Makes 4 servings.

Diabetic diet: Prepare as directed but divide spinach and tuna mixture among 4 individual casserole dishes. Exchanges per serving = 3 meat, 1 vegetable and 1 bread.
High-iron diet: 5 milligrams iron per serving.

PIQUANT SALAD (250 calories per serving)

4 medium carrots, sliced diago-
    nally
¹/₂ pound tiny white onions
1 cup white vinegar
³/₄ cup granulated sugar
1 tablespoon pickling spice
³/₄ teaspoon salt
2 medium tomatoes, sliced
2 6¹/₂- or 7-ounce cans tuna,
    drained and cut into chunks
1 8-ounce can ripe extra-large
    pitted olives, drained
6 hard-cooked eggs, halved

Day before serving: In medium saucepan, heat carrots and onions with water to cover; cover and boil 20 minutes or until tender-crisp. Meanwhile, in small saucepan, stir vinegar, 1 cup water, sugar, pickling spice and salt; heat to boiling; cool.
    Arrange tomatoes, tuna, olives and eggs in large shallow dish. Add drained carrots and onions. Pour pickling liquid over all; cover dish and refrigerate. To serve: With slotted spoon, arrange salad on salad plate. Makes 6 servings.

Diabetic diet: Prepare as directed but omit sugar; add non-nutritive equivalent to ¹/₄-cup sugar to pickling mixture. Carefully divide into 6 equal servings. Exchanges per serving = 3 meat and 1 vegetable.
Low-fat, low-cholesterol diet: Prepare as directed but omit olives and hard-cooked eggs. 5 grams fat per serving.
High-iron diet: 3 milligrams iron per serving.

CRAB-ASPARAGUS CASSEROLE (260 calories per serving)

2 tablespoons butter or margarine
1/4 cup flour
1 1/4 cups milk
seasoned salt
seasoned pepper
4 teaspoons grated Parmesan
cheese
2 6-ounce packages frozen King
crab, thawed, drained
2 15-ounce cans colossal white
asparagus spears, drained
paprika

About 1 hour before serving: Preheat oven to 375°F. In small saucepan over low heat, melt butter; stir in flour until blended smooth. Slowly add milk, stirring constantly to avoid lumps. Then add 1 teaspoon seasoned salt, 1/2 teaspoon seasoned pepper, grated cheese. Cook sauce, stirring until smooth and thickened; set aside.

Line bottom of buttered 1 1/2-quart casserole with crab; sprinkle lightly with seasoned salt and seasoned pepper, then add 6 table-spoons cheese sauce; mix lightly with fork. Arrange asparagus spears on top of crab mixture. Spoon remaining cheese sauce over asparagus, covering it entirely. Sprinkle with paprika. Bake 40 minutes, or until bubbly. Makes 4 servings.

Bland diet: Prepare as directed but omit pepper.
Diabetic diet: Prepare as directed but use margarine instead of butter. Carefully divide into 4 equal servings. Exchanges per serving = 2 meat, 1 milk, 1 vegetable and 1 fat.
Low-fat diet: Prepare as directed but use skimmed milk in place of whole. 10 grams fat per serving. Omit recipe from low-cholesterol diet.
High-iron diet: 4.5 milligrams iron per serving.
Low-residue diet: Prepare as directed but omit pepper.

TOMATO-CURRY LOBSTER TAILS (260 calories per serving)

6 large frozen rock-lobster tails
(10 ounces each)
2 tablespoons butter or margarine
1/2 cup minced onion
1 garlic clove
1/2 cup chopped green pepper
1 16-ounce can tomatoes
2 teaspoons curry
1 teaspoon salt
1 bay leaf

About 1 hour before serving: Boil lobster tails as label directs. Cut away underside membrane and remove meat from shells; cut meat into bite-size pieces and reserve shells.

In large saucepan over medium heat, in butter, cook onion, gar-lic and green pepper until onion and green pepper are tender but not brown. Add tomatoes, curry, salt and bay leaf. Cover and cook over low heat 10 minutes, stirring occasionally.

Add lobster meat and cook until heated through, about 5 min-utes.

To serve: Remove garlic and bay leaf. Fill reserved shells with lobster mixture. Makes 6 servings.

Low-fat diet: 10 grams fat per serving. Omit recipe from low-cholesterol diet.

ALASKA CRAB NEWBURG SALAD (205 calories per serving)

1 6-ounce package frozen King
crab, thawed and thoroughly
drained
1 teaspoon lemon juice
1/4 teaspoon salt
dash pepper
1/4 pound fresh mushrooms,
thinly sliced
1/4 cup reduced-calorie mayonnaise
1 tablespoon dry sherry
2 slices hot toast
paprika for garnish

About 1 1/2 hours before serving: In medium bowl, toss crab with all remaining ingredients but toast and paprika; cover; refrigerate. At serving time: Heap salad generously onto hot toast; sprinkle with paprika. Makes 2 servings.

Diabetic diet: Exchanges per serving = 3 meat and 1 bread.
Low-fat diet: 5 grams fat per serving. Omit recipe from low-cholesterol diet.

SALMON PUFF (270 calories per serving)

1 16-ounce can salmon
2 tablespoons butter or margarine
3 tablespoons flour
1 teaspoon salt
1/2 teaspoon dry mustard
1/2 teaspoon Worcestershire
1 cup skimmed milk or re-
  liquefied nonfat dry milk
4 eggs, separated

About 1 hour and 15 minutes before serving: Preheat oven to 375°F. Grease 1½-quart soufflé dish or casserole. In medium saucepan over medium heat, melt butter; stir in flour, salt, mustard and Worcestershire until blended. Slowly stir in milk and cook, stirring constantly, until thickened; cool about 10 minutes.

Beat in egg yolks, one at a time. In medium bowl, flake salmon and remove bone (do not drain); stir into egg mixture.

In large bowl, with electric mixer at high speed, beat egg whites until stiff peaks form; fold gently into mixture. Lightly pour into dish and bake 40 to 45 minutes, or until puffy and golden. Serve at once. Makes 6 servings.

Diabetic diet: Prepare as directed but use margarine instead of butter. Exchanges per serving = 2 meat, 1/2 milk and 1 fat.
High-iron diet: 3 milligrams iron per serving.

NIPPY SHRIMP (155 calories per serving)

1 tablespoon salad oil
1 pound package frozen shelled
  deveined shrimp, thawed,
  drained
2 tablespoons soy sauce
2 tablespoons vinegar
2 tablespoons catchup
2 teaspoons granulated sugar
1/2 teaspoon ginger
1/2 teaspoon garlic salt
2 scallions, chopped

About 10 minutes before serving: In medium skillet over low heat, in oil, cook shrimp 4 minutes. Add remaining ingredients; simmer 5 minutes. Makes 4 servings.

Low-fat diet: 5 grams fat per serving. Omit recipe from low-cholesterol diet.

SHRIMP BOUQUET PLATTER (285 calories per serving)

2 pounds large shrimp, shelled,
  deveined and cooked
salt
lemon juice
1 10-ounce package frozen
  peas, cooked
1½ pounds small shrimp,
  shelled, deveined and
  cooked, cut into chunks
10 hard-cooked eggs, cut into
  chunks
1/2 cup diced celery
3 medium potatoes, cooked, cut
  into chunks
1/4 cup milk
1¼ cup reduced-calorie mayonnaise
1/4 teaspoon pepper
parsley sprigs for garnish
fluted, halved lemon slices for
  garnish

Day before serving: Toss large whole shrimp with 1 teaspoon salt and 1 tablespoon lemon juice; refrigerate. Separate 1/4 cup of cooked peas; wrap; refrigerate. In large bowl, toss together cut-up shrimp, remaining peas, egg chunks, diced celery, potato chunks, milk, low-calorie mayonnaise, 2½ teaspoons salt, 1 tablespoon lemon juice, pepper.

Grease inside of 3-quart mixing bowl; line bottom with waxed paper; cover with single layer of whole shrimp. Line sides of bowl with one row of shrimp, then spoon in some potato-shrimp mixture and press level with shrimp. To sides of bowl add second row of shrimp, then spoon rest of salad into bowl and press firmly until level with shrimp circle. Refrigerate, covered. (Shrimp sizes vary, so some salad may be left over; refrigerate to serve next day.)

About 15 minutes before serving: Run spatula around inside of bowl to loosen salad; invert round platter on top of bowl; invert both; remove waxed paper. Garnish center of each shrimp with refrigerated pea; top salad with parsley sprigs; circle with fluted lemon slices. Makes 10 servings.

High-iron diet: 3.5 milligrams iron per serving.

FRAGRANT SHRIMP RAREBIT (290 calories per serving)

1 tablespoon butter or margarine
1/2 teaspoon dried dill weed
1/2 teaspoon salt
dash cayenne
2 tablespoons flour
1 1/2 cups skimmed milk or reliquefied nonfat dry milk
1 chicken-bouillon cube
1 pound fresh shrimp, shelled
   and deveined (or 1 pound
   package frozen shelled
   deveined shrimp, thawed and
   drained)
3/4 cup grated mild Cheddar
   cheese
4 slices toast, cut into triangles

About 20 minutes before serving: In medium saucepan, melt butter; stir in dill weed, salt, cayenne and flour; cook, stirring constantly, 1 minute. Slowly stir in milk; cook until thickened and
smooth. Add bouillon cube and shrimp; cook, stirring constantly,
until shrimp curl and turn pink—about 5 minutes. Remove from
heat; stir in cheese until melted. Divide cheese-shrimp mixture
among 4 individual 1-cup casseroles; serve with toast triangles.
Makes 4 servings.

Bland diet: Prepare as directed but omit dill, cayenne and bouillon
cube.
Diabetic diet: Prepare as directed but use margarine instead of butter.
Exchanges per serving = 3 meat, 1 bread and 1/2 milk.
Low-residue diet: Prepare as directed for bland diet.

DIFFERENT SHRIMP CURRY (325 calories per serving)

1/2 cup flaked coconut
1 1/2 cups uncooked long-grain
   rice
1 tablespoon salad oil
3 medium onions, thinly sliced
1 carrot, thinly sliced
1 garlic clove, minced
1 green pepper, coarsely
   chopped
1 red eating apple, thinly sliced
1 tablespoon curry
4 whole cloves
1 stick cinnamon
1 pound package frozen shelled
   deveined shrimp
2 tablespoons cornstarch

About 30 minutes before serving: In medium saucepan, heat
coconut and 2 cups water; cover and simmer 10 minutes. Drain
coconut, reserving liquid.

   Cook rice as label directs but omit butter. In large skillet over
medium heat, in oil, sauté onions, carrots and garlic until onion is
limp. Add green pepper, apple slices, liquid drained from coconut, curry, 2 teaspoons salt, cloves and cinnamon stick; cover;
simmer 3 minutes. Add frozen shrimp; cover; cook 5 to 10 minutes, or until shrimp have curled and are pink.

   Meanwhile, stir enough water into cornstarch to form a smooth
paste. Slowly stir into curry mixture; heat until smooth and thickened; remove cloves and cinnamon stick. Serve curry over rice.
Top with flaked coconut. Makes 6 servings.

Low-fat diet: Prepare as directed but omit coconut. 5 grams fat per serving. Omit recipe from low-cholesterol diet.

SHRIMP, SAILOR STYLE (245 calories per serving)

1 17-ounce can Italian tomatoes, undrained
2 tablespoons chopped parsley
2 cups sliced celery
1/4 teaspoon basil
1 teaspoon salt
1/8 teaspoon pepper
1/2 teaspoon oregano leaves
1/2 6-ounce can tomato paste
1 cup uncooked long-grain rice
1 pound package frozen shelled
   deveined shrimp

About 45 to 50 minutes before serving: In large skillet or Dutch
oven, simmer tomatoes, parsley, celery, basil, salt, pepper, oregano and tomato paste, uncovered, stirring occasionally, 30 minutes, or until celery is almost tender. Meanwhile, cook rice as
label directs but omit butter. When tomato sauce is cooked, stir in
frozen shrimp. Simmer 5 to 10 minutes, or until shrimp turn pink
and curl. Serve over rice. Makes 5 servings.

Egg-, gluten-, milk- and wheat-free diet: Prepare as directed.
Diabetic diet: Prepare as directed but serve shrimp sauce over 1/2 cup
rice. Exchanges per serving = 2 meat, 1 vegetable and 1 bread.
Low-fat diet: 1 gram fat per serving. Omit recipe from low-cholesterol
diet.

CRAB THERMIDOR (275 calories per serving)

4 slices white bread
1 tablespoon butter or margarine
1¹/₂ tablespoons flour
²/₃ cup half-and-half
¹/₂ teaspoon salt
¹/₈ teaspoon nutmeg
dash paprika
generous dash pepper (preferably white pepper)
dash garlic salt
2 tablespoons dry sherry or water
2 6-ounce packages frozen King crab, thawed, thoroughly drained (or 2 6¹/₂- to 7¹/₂-ounce cans King crab, thoroughly drained)
¹/₃ cup grated mild process Cheddar cheese

About 30 minutes before serving: Preheat oven to 350°F. Toast bread in oven until golden-brown on one side; turn; toast other side.

Meanwhile, in medium saucepan, melt butter; stir in flour. Stirring constantly, slowly add half-and-half. Cook, stirring, until thickened and smooth. Stir in salt, nutmeg, paprika, pepper, garlic salt and sherry. Add crab; heat, stirring, to simmering. Turn mixture into 1-quart ovenproof casserole; sprinkle with grated cheese. Run under broiler until cheese melts and is golden.

To serve: Cut each slice of toast into quarters. Use as a "nest" for the Crab Thermidor. Makes 4 servings.

Bland diet: Prepare as directed but omit nutmeg and pepper; use water (not sherry).
Diabetic diet: Prepare as directed but use margarine instead of butter. Exchanges per serving = 2 meat, 1 bread, ¹/₂ milk and 1 fat.
Low residue diet: Prepare as directed for bland diet.

TOMATO BAKED SHRIMP (175 calories per serving)

1 10-ounce package frozen shelled deveined shrimp
¹/₂ cup canned condensed tomato soup
2 teaspoons parsley flakes
¹/₂ teaspoon oregano leaves
¹/₄ teaspoon paprika
¹/₈ teaspoon garlic powder
1 4-ounce can mushrooms, drained

About 25 minutes before serving: Cook shrimp as label directs; drain. Meanwhile, in medium saucepan, combine undiluted tomato soup and remaining ingredients. Heat to boiling, stirring occasionally. Add shrimp to sauce. Makes 2 servings.

Diabetic diet: Exchanges per serving = 4 meat and 1 vegetable.
Low-fat diet: 2 grams fat per serving. Omit recipe from low-cholesterol diet.

CRAB-CHEESE PILAF (295 calories per serving)

2 tablespoons salad oil
1 cup chopped onion
1 cup sliced celery
¹/₄ cup diced green pepper
¹/₄ pound fresh mushrooms, sliced
¹/₂ cup thinly sliced carrots
¹/₂ teaspoon salt
1 bay leaf
1 tablespoon granulated sugar
2 16-ounce cans tomatoes
³/₄ cup packaged precooked rice
2 6¹/₂- to 7¹/₂-ounce cans King crab, thoroughly drained (or 2 6-ounce packages frozen King crab, thawed, thoroughly drained)
¹/₂ cup grated Cheddar cheese

About 45 minutes before serving: Preheat oven to 350°F. In large ovenproof skillet over medium heat, in oil, sauté onion, celery, green pepper, mushrooms and carrots until onion is golden; add salt, bay leaf, sugar and tomatoes; simmer 5 minutes. Stir rice and crab into tomato mixture; sprinkle cheese on top. Bake 20 to 25 minutes. Serve in soup bowls, if desired. Makes 5 servings of about 1 cup each.

Diabetic diet: Prepare as directed but omit sugar. Exchanges per serving = 3 meat, 2 vegetable, 1 bread and 1 fat.
Egg-, gluten-, milk- and wheat-free diet: Prepare as directed but omit cheese on milk-free diet.

SCALLOPS VINAIGRETTE (230 calories per serving)

1 pound potatoes, thinly sliced
1 pound fresh scallops (or frozen scallops, thawed)
1 cup thinly sliced green celery
2 tablespoons chopped pimento
2 tablespoons minced onion
2 tablespoons chopped parsley
1/4 cup vinegar
2 tablespoons salad oil
1 teaspoon salt
1/8 teaspoon pepper
4 lettuce cups

At least 4 hours before serving: In medium saucepan, in salted boiling water to cover, simmer potatoes 10 minutes, or until almost tender.

Meanwhile, slice scallops, across the grain, into thin disks. Add scallops to potatoes; bring water back to boiling; cover; simmer 5 minutes, or until scallops are cooked. Carefully drain off liquid and reserve (it's an excellent base for soups); let potatoes and scallops cool slightly, then cover and refrigerate.

Meanwhile, in large bowl, toss together celery, pimento, onion, parsley, vinegar, oil, salt and pepper. Cover; refrigerate.

To serve: Toss scallops and potatoes with vinaigrette dressing. Arrange on lettuce cups. Makes 4 servings.

Diabetic diet: Carefully divide into 4 equal servings. Exchanges per serving = 2 meat, 1 vegetable, 1 bread and 1 1/2 fat.
Egg-, gluten-, milk- and wheat-free diet: Prepare as directed.
Low-fat diet: 5 grams fat per serving. Omit recipe from low-cholesterol diet.

PAELLA PRONTO (325 calories per serving)

2 6-ounce packages curried-rice mix
8 scrubbed cherrystone clams in shells
3 frozen rock-lobster tails, partially thawed, cut into 1-inch pieces (about 6 ounces)
1 green pepper, cut into eighths
1 15-ounce can asparagus or hearts of artichoke, drained
4 canned pimentos, quartered

About 30 minutes before serving: In very large skillet or Dutch oven, prepare rice mix as label directs, but reduce total amount of water by 1 cup; omit butter. To rice as it cooks, add clams, lobster tails and green pepper. When seafood is done, add asparagus and pimentos. Makes 4 servings.

Egg-, gluten-, milk- and wheat-free diet: Prepare as directed. For gluten-free diet, select rice mix which does not contain monosodium glutamate.
Low-fat diet: 2 grams fat per serving. Omit recipe from low-cholesterol diet.
High-iron diet: 5 milligrams iron per serving.

BOUILLABAISSE, AMERICAN STYLE (210 calories per serving)

1 tablespoon salad oil
1 cup chopped onions
1/2 cup chopped celery
2 16-ounce cans tomatoes
1 garlic clove, minced
1 tablespoon chopped parsley
1 1/2 teaspoons seasoned salt
1/4 teaspoon thyme leaves
2 1/2 pounds striped or sea bass fillets, cut into large pieces (or 2 1/2 pounds halibut steak cut into chunks)
1 1/2 dozen clams (little necks) in shell
1 tablespoon cornstarch
1 pound fresh or frozen shrimp, shelled and deveined

About 1 hour before serving: In Dutch oven, in oil, sauté onion with celery until tender—about 5 minutes. Stir in tomatoes, garlic, parsley, seasoned salt and thyme. Simmer, covered, 10 minutes. Add bass and cook 10 minutes, or until fish flakes with fork.

Meanwhile, scrub clams under running water; place them in small kettle with 1/2 inch boiling water. Cover and steam until shells just open—about 5 minutes. Strain hot broth through cheesecloth; reserve 1 cup. Keep clams warm.

Blend cornstarch with clam juice; stir into tomato mixture; heat to boiling. Add shrimp and simmer about 5 minutes, or until shrimp have turned pink and are tender. Add reserved clams. Makes 10 servings.

Egg-, gluten-, milk- and wheat-free diet: Prepare as directed but substitute regular salt for seasoned salt.
Low-fat diet: 5 grams fat per serving. Omit recipe from low-cholesterol diet.
High-iron diet: 3.5 milligrams iron per serving.

SEAFOOD BOATS (220 calories per serving)

1 teaspoon salt
8 peppercorns
2 whole allspice
1 bay leaf
4 chicken-bouillon cubes
2 summer squash
2 zucchini
1/4 cup reduced–calorie mayonnaise
2 teaspoons granulated sugar
1/2 teaspoon prepared mustard
1/4 cup lemon juice
1 cup cooked, shelled, deveined shrimp
1 6-ounce package frozen King crab, thawed, drained
1/4 cup drained cooked peas
1/2 cup canned hearts of palm, sliced
1/4 pound fresh mushrooms, quartered
1 hard-cooked egg, chopped
curly endive
cherry tomatoes
1 lemon, cut into wedges for garnish

Early in day: In large kettle, heat 2 quarts water, salt, peppercorns, allspice, bay leaf and bouillon cubes to boiling; simmer 10 minutes.

Cut thin lengthwise slice from each squash and zucchini; scoop out some of pulp. Cook vegetables in seasoned water 10 to 15 minutes, or until tender-crisp; drain well; refrigerate.

Up to 1 hour before serving; In small bowl, combine reduced-calorie mayonnaise, sugar, mustard and lemon juice. Halve all but 4 shrimp. In medium bowl, toss halved shrimp, crab, peas, hearts of palm, mushrooms and egg with mayonnaise mixture. Fill each zucchini and squash with crab mixture; garnish with whole shrimp; arrange on platter with endive, tomatoes and lemon wedge for garnish. Makes 4 servings.

Diabetic diet: Prepare as directed but omit sugar. Exchanges per serving = 3 meat, 2 vegetable and 1 bread.
Low-fat diet: 5 grams fat per serving. Omit recipe from low-cholesterol diet.
High-iron diet: 5 milligrams iron per serving.

CRAB BISQUE (195 calories per serving)

1 10³/4-ounce can condensed tomato soup
1 11¹/4-ounce can condensed pea soup
2 cups skimmed milk or reliquefied nonfat dry milk
1 teaspoon curry
1/2 teaspoon salt
1/4 teaspoon pepper
2 6¹/2- to 7¹/2-ounce cans King crab, drained

About 15 minutes before serving: In large saucepan, mix together all ingredients but crab; simmer 5 minutes. Then add crab and simmer, over medium heat, about 10 minutes. Makes six 1-cup main-dish servings.

Diabetic diet: Exchanges per serving = 2 meat, 1/2 milk and 1 bread.
Low-fat diet: 3 grams fat per serving. Omit recipe from low-cholesterol diet.

COUNTRY SCALLOPS (290 calories per serving)

4 bacon slices, cut into small pieces
2 tablespoons diced onion
1/3 cup catchup
2 teaspoons Worcestershire
1/4 teaspoon salt
1/8 teaspoon pepper
1 16-ounce package frozen scallops, thawed, drained

About 20 minutes before serving: In medium skillet over medium heat, fry bacon pieces until limp. Drain off fat; add onion; continue cooking 5 minutes longer, or until bacon is lightly browned. Stir in catchup, Worcestershire, salt and pepper. Add scallops and cook until tender—about 5 to 8 minutes—stirring occasionally. Makes 3 servings.

High-iron diet: 4 milligrams iron per serving.

OYSTER STEW (200 calories per serving)

1 10-ounce can frozen condensed oyster stew
1 soup-can skimmed milk or
reliquefied nonfat dry milk
2 thin lemon or fresh tomato
slices for garnish
chopped parsley or dried parsley flakes for garnish

About 20 minutes before serving: Prepare stew as label directs,
but substitute skimmed milk for water.

To serve: Divide stew between 2 soup bowls; top each with
lemon or tomato slice and sprinkling of parsley. Makes two 1¼-
cup servings.

Bland diet: Prepare as directed but omit garnish.
Diabetic diet: Exchanges per serving = 1 meat, 1 bread and ½ milk.
Low-fat diet: 10 grams fat per serving. Omit recipe from low-cholesterol
diet.
Low-fat, bland (gall bladder) diet: Prepare as directed but omit garnish.
If oysters cause "gas" omit recipe.
Low-residue diet: Prepare as directed but omit garnish.

OYSTER DIABLE (190 calories per serving)

16 large shucked raw oysters (or
2 7½-ounce cans oysters)
skimmed milk or reliquefied
nonfat dry milk
2½ tablespoons flour
¾ teaspoon salt
⅛ teaspoon pepper
¼ teaspoon paprika
¼ teaspoon prepared or dry
mustard
2 tablespoons horseradish
1 teaspoon Worcestershire
2 teaspoons lemon juice
2 cups toasted ½-inch bread
squares
¾ cup chopped celery
celery leaves

About 45 minutes before serving: Preheat oven to 400°F. Drain
oysters; add enough milk to liquid to make 2 cups. In saucepan,
mix flour, salt, pepper, paprika and mustard. Gradually add liquid,
stirring until smooth. Stir in horseradish, Worcestershire and
lemon juice. Cook, stirring, over low heat, until thickened. In each
of four 12-ounce casseroles, arrange layer of bread squares;
cover with layers of celery, drained oysters and sauce. Top with
remaining bread squares. Bake 20 to 25 minutes, or until bubbling. Garnish with celery leaves. Makes 4 servings.

Diabetic diet: Exchanges per serving = 1 meat and 1 bread.
Low-fat diet: 3 grams fat per serving. Omit recipe from low-cholesterol
diet.
High-iron diet: 7 milligrams iron per serving.

SCALLOPS EN BROCHETTE (265 calories per serving)

12 small mushrooms
½ large green pepper
2 tablespoons melted butter or
margarine
2 tablespoons lemon juice
¼ teaspoon salt
dash pepper
1 pound sea scallops (about 12)
4 slices bacon
2 ounces Cheddar cheese

About 1 hour and 15 minutes before serving: Remove stems from
mushrooms. (Refrigerate stems for use in soup another day.) Cut
green pepper into 8 pieces about 1-inch square. In pie plate, combine butter, lemon juice, salt and pepper. Add scallops, mushrooms and green pepper pieces; cover; refrigerate 30 minutes,
tossing occasionally.

Preheat broiler if manufacturer directs. In medium skillet over
medium-high heat, fry bacon until light-golden but still limp; drain
on paper towels.

Run a skewer through one end of a bacon slice, then lace
bacon through a fourth of the scallops, mushrooms and green-
pepper pieces, alternating foods. Repeat with 3 more skewers.
Place skewers on broiling pan and broil 10 minutes, turning frequently.

Cut cheese into eight thin slices. When skewered food is done,
place cheese strips on top of skewers. Broil just until cheese
melts. Makes 4 servings.

Diabetic diet: Prepare as directed but use margarine instead of butter.
Exchanges per serving = 3 meat, 1 vegetable and ½ fat.
Egg-, gluten- and wheat-free diet: Prepare as directed.

CAPRICIOUS CRAB CASSEROLE (240 calories per serving)

1 6-ounce package seasoned white-and-wild-rice mix
2 tablespoons salad oil
1 large onion, finely chopped
1 large stalk green celery with leaves, chopped
1 eating apple, chopped
1 to 2 teaspoons curry
3 6-ounce packages frozen King crab, thawed, thoroughly drained (or 3 6¹/₂- to 7¹/₂-ounce cans King crab, thoroughly drained)
2 tablespoons raisins

About 1 hour before serving: Cook rice mix as label directs but omit butter and decrease cooking time to 20 minutes. (Rice will be moist.) Preheat oven to 375°F. In large skillet over medium heat, in oil, sauté onion and celery until onion is golden. Stir in apple, curry, drained crab, raisins and cooked rice. Turn into 2-quart casserole; cover; bake 20 minutes. Makes 6 one-cup servings.

Diabetic diet: Prepare as directed but divide mixture among 6 individual casseroles; bake only 15 minutes. Exchanges per serving = 2 meat, 1 bread, ¹/₂ fat and 1 fruit.
Low-fat diet: 5 grams fat per serving. Omit recipe from low-cholesterol diet.
Egg-, gluten-, milk- and wheat-free diet: Prepare as directed but use rice mix not containing monosodium glutamate, on gluten-free diet.

CRAB-MUSHROOM OMELET MINIATURES (200 calories per serving)

3 eggs
2 tablespoons flour
1 6-ounce package frozen King crab, thoroughly drained (or 1 6¹/₂- to 7¹/₂-ounce can King crab, drained)
1 cup cooked frozen peas (or 1 8-ounce can peas, thoroughly drained)
1 cup finely chopped fresh mushrooms
1 tablespoon minced onion
¹/₂ teaspoon salt
generous dash curry
2 tablespoons salad oil

About 20 minutes before serving: In medium bowl, beat eggs and flour until smooth. Mix in crab, peas, mushrooms, onion, salt and curry. In medium skillet over medium heat, in oil, drop egg mixture by heaping teaspoonfuls. Cook about 2 minutes, or until egg is lightly browned; turn, cook other side. Makes 4 servings.

Bland diet: Prepare as directed but omit onion and curry.
Diabetic diet: Exchanges per serving = 2 meat and 1 vegetable and 1¹/₂ fat.
Low-residue diet: Prepare as directed for bland diet.

LOBSTER, ITALIAN STYLE (195 calories per serving)

salt
6 8-ounce frozen rock-lobster tails
2 tablespoons olive oil
2 tablespoons minced onion
¹/₂ garlic clove, minced
1 16-ounce can whole tomatoes
1 teaspoon lemon juice
¹/₄ teaspoon oregano leaves
¹/₈ teaspoon pepper
parsley and lemon wedges for garnish

About 1 hour before serving: In 10-quart pot, heat 4 or 5 quarts water and 1 tablespoon salt to boiling. Add frozen lobster tails. When water reboils, lower heat and simmer 10 minutes. Drain lobster; then drench with cold water; drain again. With kitchen shears, cut away underside membrane. Grasp tail meat and gently pull it from shell in one piece, reserving whole shells. Dice meat.

In large skillet, in hot oil, sauté onion and garlic. Drain tomatoes and cut into pieces. Add tomatoes, ¹/₂ cup tomato liquid (use leftover tomato juice as beverage another day), lemon juice, 1 teaspoon salt, oregano and pepper; simmer 5 minutes. Add diced lobster, heating only until mixture is hot and bubbling. Fill reserved shells with mixture; garnish with parsley and lemon wedges. Makes 6 servings.

Diabetic diet: Exchanges per serving = 4 meat, 1 vegetable and 1 fat.
Egg-, gluten-, milk- and wheat-free diet: Prepare as directed.
High-iron diet: 3 milligrams iron per serving.

WHALER'S INN SHRIMP CHOWDER (250 calories per serving)

1 tablespoon butter or margarine
1/2 cup finely chopped onion
2 medium potatoes, cut into 1/2-
inch cubes
salt
1/2 10-ounce package frozen
peas
1 pound package frozen shelled
deveined shrimp, thawed
1 tablespoon flour
2 cups skimmed milk or reliquefied nonfat dry milk,
scalded
pepper
thin tomato slices for garnish

About 45 minutes before serving: In large saucepan in butter, sauté onion until golden. Add potatoes, 1 tablespoon salt and 2 cups water; bring to boiling; cover; cook 15 to 20 minutes, or until potatoes are tender. Add peas and shrimp, stirring occasionally; boil gently 5 minutes, or until shrimp are pink and cooked. Meanwhile, stir just enough water into flour to make a smooth paste. Stir in potato mixture. Stir in scalded milk, then salt and pepper to taste. Makes 4 servings of about 1 1/2 cups each.

Bland diet: Prepare as directed but omit onion, pepper and tomato slices.
Diabetic diet: Prepare as directed but use margarine instead of butter. Exchanges per serving = 2 meat, 1 bread and 1/2 milk.
Low-fat diet: 5 grams fat per serving. Omit recipe from low-cholesterol diet.
Low-fat, bland (gall bladder) diet: Prepare as directed but omit onion, pepper and tomato slices.
Low-residue diet: Prepare as directed for bland diet.

CALIFORNIA SCALLOPS (165 calories per serving)

1 pound scallops
1 tablespoon salad oil
1 garlic clove, minced
2 medium tomatoes, halved
pepper
salt
1 1/2 tablespoons lemon juice
1 tablespoon melted butter or
margarine
lemon twists for garnish
chopped parsley for garnish

About 50 minutes before serving: Let scallops stand in oil and garlic about 30 minutes. Preheat broiler 10 minutes if manufacturer directs. Meanwhile, sprinkle tomato halves with pepper and 1/2 teaspoon salt. In shallow roasting pan, arrange with scallops. Over scallops pour butter, 1/2 teaspoon salt and 1/8 teaspoon pepper. Broil about 10 minutes, turning once. Serve garnished with lemon twists and parsley. Makes 4 servings.

Diabetic diet: Prepare as directed but use margarine instead of butter. Exchanges per serving = 3 meat, 1 vegetable and 1 fat.
Egg-, gluten-, milk- and wheat-free diet: Prepare as directed but use milk-free margarine on milk-free diet.
Low-fat diet: Prepare as directed but use margarine instead of butter. 5 grams fat per serving. Omit recipe from low-cholesterol diet.

SHRIMP-AND-FLOUNDER MAYONNAISE (Mayonnaise de Camarão e Linguado) (225 calories per serving)

2/3 cup lemon juice
6 tablespoons chopped parsley
1 tablespoon granulated sugar
1 teaspoon salt
6 whole peppercorns
2 bay leaves
2 16-ounce packages frozen
flounder fillets, thawed
1/4 teaspoon seasoned salt
1 7-ounce package frozen
shelled deveined shrimp,
cooked
3 hard-cooked eggs
reduced-calorie mayonnaise
rolled anchovy fillets
romaine leaves

At least 6 hours before serving: In large skillet, bring 1/3 cup lemon juice, 1/4 cup parsley, sugar, salt, peppercorns and bay leaves to boiling. Lay fillets in mixture in skillet; cover; simmer 5 minutes. Refrigerate in skillet. Combine 1/3 cup lemon juice, 2 tablespoons parsley, seasoned salt and cooked shrimp. Refrigerate.

About 30 minutes before serving: Halve hard-cooked eggs lengthwise; top each with 1/4 teaspoon reduced–calorie mayonnaise, then a rolled anchovy. Cut up half refrigerated shrimp and toss with 1 cup finely sliced romaine and 1/4 cup low-calorie mayonnaise. Arrange fish in 6 romaine cups. Top with shrimp mixture and a dollop of reduced–calorie mayonnaise. Garnish with remaining shrimp and egg halves. Makes 6 servings.

CURRIED SHRIMP WITH HONEYDEW (210 calories per serving)

1 teaspoon salt
2 peppercorns
1 pound package frozen shelled deveined shrimp
1/2 cup reduced–calorie mayonnaise
1/4 cup sour cream
1 teaspoon curry
1 ripe medium honeydew melon
8 lettuce leaves

About 45 minutes before serving: In medium saucepan, bring 2 cups cold water to boiling; add salt, peppercorns and shrimp; cook until shrimp are pink and tender; drain; let cool slightly; then split each lengthwise. In medium bowl, combine reduced–calorie mayonnaise, sour cream and curry. Add shrimp; toss well; set aside.

Quarter honeydew melon lengthwise; remove seeds and pare each wedge; then cut across each wedge a few times, almost through melon. Arrange lettuce on serving plates; top each with melon wedge and fill with one-fourth of shrimp mixture. Makes 4 servings.

Diabetic diet: Exchanges per serving = 3 meat, 1 fruit and 1/2 fat.
High-iron diet: 3 milligrams iron per serving.

LUNCHEON SCALLOP CHOWDER (195 calories per serving)

1 teaspoon lemon juice
1/2 teaspoon salt
generous dash pepper
1/4 teaspoon celery salt
1/4 teaspoon onion salt
1 pound fresh scallops (or frozen scallops, thawed)
2 tablespoons butter or margarine
3 tablespoons flour
2 cups milk
2 cups skimmed milk or reliquefied nonfat dry milk
salt and pepper to taste
chopped parsley

About 20 minutes before serving: In medium saucepan, heat 1 cup water, lemon juice, salt, pepper, celery salt and onion salt to boiling. Add scallops (halve large ones); cover; gently boil 3 to 5 minutes, or until scallops are just cooked. Remove from heat.

Meanwhile, in large saucepan, melt butter; stir in flour. Slowly add milk and cook, stirring constantly, until mixture thickens. Add cooked scallops and cooking broth; season to taste with salt and pepper. Serve sprinkled with parsley. Makes 6 luncheon main-course servings of 1 cup each.

Bland diet: Prepare as directed but omit pepper, celery salt, onion salt and parsley.
Diabetic diet: Prepare as directed but use margarine instead of butter. Exchanges per serving = 1 meat, 1 milk and 1 fat.
Low-fat diet: Prepare as directed but use all skimmed milk. 5 grams fat per serving. Omit recipe from low-cholesterol diet.
Low-fat, bland (gall bladder) diet: Prepare as directed for bland diet.
Low-residue diet: Prepare as directed for bland diet.

SHRIMP AND TUNA GOURMET (230 calories per serving)

1 tablespoon butter or margarine
1 4-ounce can mushrooms, drained
1/3 cup chopped green onions
1 10 1/2-ounce can condensed cream-of-chicken soup
1 teaspoon Worcestershire
4 drops Tabasco
1/4 cup diced canned pimentos
1/2 cup pitted ripe olives
1 cup cooked, deveined, shelled shrimp
1 6 1/2- or 7-ounce can chunk-style tuna, drained
1/2 cup skimmed milk or reliquefied nonfat dry milk

About 30 minutes before serving: In medium skillet over medium heat, in butter, cook mushrooms and green onions, stirring occasionally, 5 minutes. Stir in undiluted soup, Worcestershire, salt and Tabasco and continue cooking, stirring occasionally, until mixture is hot and bubbly. Reduce heat to low and stir in remaining ingredients, stirring until mixture is hot. Makes 4 servings.

MARLISE'S CREAMY RING WITH CRABMEAT (220 calories per serving)

1 3-ounce package lime gelatin
1 cup reduced–calorie mayon-naise
1 8-ounce container small curd creamed cottage cheese
1 teaspoon white horseradish
³/₄ cup finely chopped peeled cucumber
¹/₄ cup chopped red onion
2 7¹/₂-ounce cans King crab, well drained and flaked (or 2 6-ounce packages frozen King crab, thawed and well drained)
¹/₂ cup reduced–calorie Italian dressing
¹/₂ head lettuce, shredded
parsley for garnish

Early in day: In medium bowl, dissolve lime gelatin in ³/₄ cup boiling water; refrigerate at least 30 minutes, stirring occasionally, or until gelatin is consistency of unbeaten egg whites. In large bowl, mix reduced–calorie mayonnaise, cottage cheese and horseradish until well blended. Stir in cucumber, onion and gelatin. Pour into 6-cup ring mold. Refrigerate until firm.

About 10 minutes before serving: Marinate crab in the reduced-calorie Italian dressing about 10 minutes. Unmold gelatin onto shredded lettuce. Stir crab to mix in dressing; place in center of ring and garnish with parsley. Makes 6 servings.

Diabetic diet: Prepare as directed but substitute 1 4-serving envelope low-calorie lemon flavor gelatin for regular. Exchanges per serving = 2 meat, 1 vegetable and ¹/₂ milk.
Low-fat, low-cholesterol diet: Prepare as directed but substitute 2 6¹/₂- or 7-ounce cans tuna (well drained and in chunks) for crab. 10 grams fat per serving.

SCALLOPS IN THE GARDEN (265 calories per serving)

2 9-ounce packages frozen cut green beans
1 cup uncooked long-grain rice
2 tablespoons butter or marga-rine
1¹/₂ pounds fresh sea scallops, split crosswise
1 teaspoon salt
¹/₈ teaspoon pepper
2 tomatoes, cut into wedges
1 tablespoon soy sauce
1 teaspoon cornstarch

About 30 minutes before serving: In separate saucepans, cook green beans and rice as labels direct but omit butter or margarine. In large skillet over medium heat, in butter, sauté scallops 8 minutes. Sprinkle with salt and pepper; toss with drained green beans and tomatoes; heat. Mix soy sauce, cornstarch and ¹/₄ cup water until smooth; stir into scallop mixture. Serve on heated platter, with a border of hot fluffy rice. Pass soy sauce. Makes 6 servings.

Bland diet: Prepare as directed but omit pepper, tomatoes and soy sauce.
Diabetic diet: Carefully divide scallop mixture into 6 equal servings (about ³/₄ cup each). Exchanges per serving = 3 meat and 1 vegetable plus 1 fat and 1 bread for each ¹/₂-cup rice used.
Egg-, gluten-, milk- and wheat-free diet: Prepare as directed but use milk-free margarine for milk-free diet; omit soy sauce on gluten- and wheat-free diet.
Low-fat diet: 5 grams fat per serving. Omit recipe from low-cholesterol diet.
Low-fat, bland (gall bladder) diet: Prepare as directed but omit pepper, tomatoes and soy sauce.
High-iron diet: 3 milligrams iron per serving.
Low-residue diet: Prepare as directed for bland diet.

SHRIMP AMANDINE (245 calories per serving)

butter or margarine
¹/₂ cup roasted slivered almonds
2¹/₂ pounds fresh medium shrimp, shelled, deveined
¹/₂ teaspoon salt
dash pepper
2 tablespoons chopped chives

About 15 minutes before serving: In medium skillet over medium heat, in 1 tablespoon butter, sauté almonds until golden; remove; drain on paper toweling. In same skillet, in 1 tablespoon butter, sauté half of shrimp, stirring constantly, a few minutes, or until they turn pink and are tender. Repeat with remaining shrimp. Sprinkle with salt and pepper.

To serve: Sprinkle shrimp with almonds and chives. Makes 6 servings.

Diabetic diet: Prepare as directed but use margarine instead of butter. Carefully divide into 6 equal servings. Exchanges per serving = 3 meat.

PACIFIC SEAFOOD IN OLIVE-RICE RING (315 calories per serving)

1 16-ounce can tomatoes
1/4 cup catchup
1 medium onion, sliced
1/8 teaspoon instant minced garlic
2 teaspoons granulated sugar
1/2 teaspoon Tabasco
2 tablespoons butter or margarine
1/4 cup flour
1 tablespoon chili powder
1/2 cup bottled clam juice
1 6-ounce package frozen King crab, thawed and drained
1 7-ounce package frozen shrimp, thawed
2 7³/4-ounce cans oysters, drained
1/2 teaspoon salt
3 cups hot fluffy rice
1/4 cup sliced stuffed olives

About 45 minutes before serving: In saucepan, simmer tomatoes with catchup, onion, garlic, sugar and Tabasco 15 minutes; strain. In same saucepan, melt butter; stir in flour and chili powder until smooth; gradually stir in bottled clam juice and strained tomato sauce; boil 5 minutes. Add crab meat, shrimp and oysters; simmer 10 minutes or until shrimp turn pink and curl. Add salt. Toss hot rice with sliced stuffed olives; arrange in ring on heated platter. Pour seafood mixture in center. Makes 6 servings.

Diabetic diet: Prepare as directed but use margarine instead of butter; omit sugar.
　To serve: Top 1/2 cup (1 bread exchange) or 1 cup (2 bread exchanges) rice with a generous cup of seafood mixture (3 meat and 1 bread exchange).
Low-fat diet: Prepare as directed but omit olives. 5 grams fat per serving. Omit recipe from low-cholesterol diet.
High-iron diet: 6 milligrams iron per serving.

SHRIMP-AND-COTTAGE-CHEESE SALAD (195 calories per serving)

1/2 pound cooked, shelled, deveined shrimp, chilled
1 8-ounce container creamed cottage cheese
1/4 cup chopped pecans
1 tablespoon minced onion
3 tablespoons reduced–calorie mayonnaise
3 tablespoons reduced–calorie French dressing
4 large lettuce cups
8 tomato wedges for garnish
parsley sprigs for garnish

Up to 30 minutes before serving: Cut shrimp into bite-size pieces. In medium bowl, mix shrimp, cottage cheese, pecans, onion, reduced–calorie mayonnaise and French dressing. Cover; refrigerate until serving time.

　To serve: Heap shrimp mixture in lettuce cups; garnish with tomatoes and parsley. Makes 4 servings.

Diabetic diet: Exchanges per serving = 2 meat, 1 vegetable, 1/2 milk and 1 fat.
Low-fat diet: 10 grams fat per serving. Omit from low-cholesterol diet.
Low-purine diet: Prepare as directed but omit shrimp. Makes 3 servings.

LOBSTER TAILS WITH SPICY RICE (235 calories per serving)

4 3-ounce frozen rock-lobster tails
melted butter or margarine
1/4 teaspoon onion salt
pepper to taste
1 tablespoon chopped parsley
3/4 cup uncooked long-grain rice
2 tablespoons minced onion
garlic salt to taste

About 30 minutes before serving: Boil frozen lobster tails as label directs. When lobster tails are cooked, cut away thin undershell; bend back tail until shell cracks. Brush with 1 tablespoon melted butter; sprinkle with onion salt and pepper.

　Meanwhile, cook rice as label directs but omit butter. Then stir in onion, 1 tablespoon butter or margarine and garlic salt to taste.

　To serve: Arrange lobster tails on serving dish; spoon rice around them. Makes 4 servings.

Diabetic diet: Prepare as directed but use margarine instead of butter. Exchanges per serving = 2 meat and 1 bread.
Egg-, gluten-, milk- and wheat-free diet: Prepare as directed but use milk-free margarine on milk-free diet.
Low-fat diet: 5 grams fat per serving. Omit recipe from low-cholesterol diet.

OVEN-BAKED CHICKEN SUPREME (250 calories per serving)

2 tablespoons butter or margarine, melted
1/4 cup flour
1 teaspoon seasoned salt
1 egg, beaten
1 tablespoon water
1/4 cup packaged dried-bread
crumbs
1/4 cup grated Parmesan cheese
2 whole chicken breasts (about
1 1/2 pounds), split, skinned
and boned

About 1 hour before serving: Preheat oven to 350°F. In each of 4 cereal bowls, place butter or margarine, mixtures of flour and seasoned salt, beaten egg and water and bread crumbs and cheese. Beginning with butter, dip chicken breasts into each of 4 bowls, consecutively, ending with crumb-cheese mixture. On rack in shallow baking dish, arrange breasts close together. Bake 45 minutes, or until chicken is tender when pierced with fork. Remove from oven; turn heat to "broil"; slip chicken under broiler for a few minutes to lightly brown crust. Makes 4 servings.

Bland diet: Prepare as directed but substitute salt for seasoned salt.
Diabetic diet: Exchanges per serving = 4 meat, 1 vegetable and 1 1/2 fat.
Low-residue diet: Prepare as directed for bland diet.

CHICKEN-AND-PEA SALAD (260 calories per serving)

4 medium tomatoes
seasoned salt
seasoned pepper
bottled reduced–calorie Italian
dressing
1/3 cup reduced–calorie mayonnaise
1 teaspoon prepared mustard
1/2 cup cooked peas
2 cups cooked chicken chunks

At least 2 hours before serving: Cut 1/4-inch slice from stem end of each tomato; scoop out pulp, reserving some. Sprinkle each tomato shell with seasoned salt, pepper and some reduced–calorie Italian dressing; refrigerate.

In medium bowl, combine reduced–calorie mayonnaise, mustard, 1/3 cup peas, and chicken; season to taste with seasoned salt and pepper; stir in 1/4 cup reserved tomato pulp. Fill drained tomato shells with chicken salad; garnish with rest of peas and cut-up tomato. Makes 4 servings.

Diabetic diet: Exchanges per serving = 3 meat and 1 vegetable.
Low-fat, low-cholesterol diet: 10 grams fat per serving.

CHICKEN-COD CHOWDER (170 calories per serving)

1 14 1/2-ounce can chicken-
noodle soup
1 10 1/2-ounce can condensed
chicken broth
1 16-ounce package frozen cod
fillets, partially thawed

About 20 minutes before serving: In medium saucepan, heat soup and undiluted broth to boiling. Meanwhile, cut cod fillets into 1-inch cubes. Add to soup and cook 10 minutes, or until fish flakes easily with fork. Makes 3 servings.

Diabetic diet: Exchanges per serving (1 cup) = 4 meat and 1/2 bread.
Low-fat, low-cholesterol diet: 2 grams fat per serving.

QUICK AVOCADO-CHICKEN SALAD (280 calories per serving)

2 cups cut-up cooked chicken
1/4 cup reduced–calorie mayonnaise
salt
1/8 teaspoon seasoned pepper
1/3 cup diced celery
3 small avocados
lemon juice
6 large pitted ripe olives, quartered
watercress for garnish

About 1 hour before serving: In medium bowl, toss together chicken, reduced–calorie mayonnaise, 1/2 teaspoon salt, seasoned pepper and celery; refrigerate, covered. Halve avocados; remove pits; brush with lemon juice; sprinkle with salt. Then fill each avocado half with chicken salad; garnish with 4 ripe olive quarters and cress. Refrigerate until served. Makes 6 servings.

Diabetic diet: Exchanges per serving = 2 meat and 4 fat.

CHICKEN OCEANIA (250 calories per serving)

1/3 cup flour
1/4 teaspoon celery salt
1/4 teaspoon garlic salt
1/4 teaspoon nutmeg
2 whole chicken breasts (about
    1 1/2 pounds), split, skinned
    and boned
2 tablespoons salad oil
2 tablespoons soy sauce
1 8 1/2-ounce can sliced pineap-
    ple

About 30 minutes before serving: Stir together flour, salt, celery salt, garlic salt and nutmeg; use to coat chicken, shaking off excess. In large skillet over medium heat, in oil, cook chicken until fork-tender—5 to 7 minutes on each side. Pour soy sauce, pineapple slices (and syrup) over chicken; stir gently to loosen any particles from bottom of skillet. Cover; simmer 10 minutes, or until gravy has thickened slightly. Top chicken with pineapple slices, then gravy. Makes 4 servings.

Diabetic diet: Prepare as directed but substitute, for sweetened pineapple, one 15 3/4-ounce can pineapple slices packed in pineapple juice. Serve 1/2 cup pineapple with chicken. Exchanges per serving = 3 meat, 1 fruit and 1 1/2 fat.
Low-fat, low-cholesterol diet: 10 grams fat per serving.

PINEAPPLE CHICKEN (275 calories per serving)

1 6-ounce can frozen pineapple-
    juice concentrate
2 whole chicken breasts (about
    1 1/2 pounds), split
salt and pepper
2 tablespoons butter or marga-
    rine

Early in day: Remove juice from freezer to thaw.

About 1 hour before serving: Season chicken with salt and pepper. In medium skillet over medium heat, in butter or margarine, brown on both sides. Drain on paper towels; wipe excess fat from pan.

Return chicken to pan; sprinkle with 1 teaspoon salt and 1/4 teaspoon pepper; add juice concentrate. Cover; cook over low heat until tender—20 to 30 minutes. Remove chicken to platter; keep warm. Cook liquid in pan to consistency of medium sauce. Pour over chicken. Makes 4 servings.

Egg-, gluten-, milk- and wheat-free diet: Prepare as directed but use milk-free margarine on milk-free diet.
Low-fat, low-cholesterol diet: Prepare as directed but use salad oil or margarine instead of butter; dieter should not eat skin of chicken. 10 grams fat per serving.
Low-sodium diet: Prepare as directed but omit salt; use unsalted butter or margarine. 80 milligrams sodium per serving.

GINGER SKILLET CHICKEN (275 calories per serving)

1 1/2 tablespoons flour
1 teaspoon salt
1 1/2 teaspoons granulated
    sugar
1 teaspoon ginger
1 3-pound broiler-fryer, cut up
2 tablespoons salad oil
1 16-ounce jar refrigerated fruit
    salad
about 1/2 cup orange juice

About 1 hour before serving: Combine flour, salt, sugar and ginger; use to coat chicken. (Reserve flour.) In large skillet over medium heat, in oil, brown chicken. Into measuring cup, drain liquid from fruit; add enough orange juice to make 1 cup. Add to chicken. (Reserve fruit.) Simmer, covered, 30 to 45 minutes, or until fork-tender.

In cup, mix leftover flour with 3 tablespoons water until smooth; stir into liquid in skillet; cook, stirring, until thickened. Add drained fruit and heat about 1 minute. Makes 6 servings.

Diabetic diet: Prepare as directed but omit sugar and use an unsweetened refrigerated fruit salad. Serve chicken with 1/2 cup fruit and juice. Exchanges per serving = 3 meat and 1 fruit.
Egg-, gluten-, milk- and wheat-free diet: Prepare as directed but coat chicken with cornstarch for gluten- and wheat-free diets.
Low-fat, low-cholesterol diet: Dieter should not eat skin of chicken. 10 grams fat per serving.
High-iron diet: 3 milligrams iron per serving.
Low-sodium diet: Prepare as directed but omit salt. 95 milligrams sodium per serving.

MUSHROOM-STUFFED ROAST CHICKEN (325 calories per serving)

3 cups day-old bread crumbs
2 tablespoons finely chopped
 parsley
1/2 medium onion, minced
1/2 teaspoon salt
pepper
1/2 pound fresh mushrooms,
 chopped
1/2 teaspoon ground thyme
melted butter or margarine
1 3-pound broiler-fryer
2 tablespoons lemon juice
3 tablespoons flour
2 cups chicken broth
1 teaspoon marjoram leaves
1/2 teaspoon salt

About 2 hours before serving: Preheat oven to 375°F. Mix crumbs, parsley, onion, salt, 1/8 teaspoon pepper, mushrooms, thyme and 2 tablespoons melted butter or margarine. Use to stuff chicken, closing openings with toothpicks.

Place chicken in baking pan; brush with mixture of 2 tablespoons melted butter or margarine and 2 tablespoons lemon juice. Bake 1 hour and 15 minutes, or until golden brown and tender. When chicken is done, remove to heated platter; remove toothpicks. From pan pour off all but 2 tablespoons fat. Place pan over medium-high heat; stir in flour, then chicken broth, marjoram, salt and 1/8 teaspoon pepper. Cook, stirring, until slightly thickened; pass in gravy boat. Makes 6 servings.

Diabetic diet: Prepare as directed but use margarine instead of butter. Exchanges per serving = 1 bread and 1 fat for 1/3 cup stuffing; 1 meat for each ounce of chicken; up to 1/4 cup gravy = 1 "free."
Low-fat, low-cholesterol diet: Prepare as directed but use salad oil or margarine instead of butter; dieter should not eat skin of chicken. 10 grams fat per serving.
High-iron diet: 4 milligrams iron per serving.

BARBECUED CHICKEN IN A SACK (300 calories per serving)

2 clean medium brown-paper
 bags
salad oil
2 3-pound broiler-fryers
1/4 cup chili sauce
1/4 cup bottled barbecue sauce
12 ears corn in husks (optional)

About 2 1/4 hours before serving: Preheat oven to 375°F. Rub paper bags, inside and out, with salad oil. Place a chicken in each bag; set, side by side, in covered roaster or shallow roasting pan. Stir chili sauce and barbecue sauce together. Pour half over each chicken, right in bags; close bags. Run ears of corn (in their husks) under cold water; place around chicken for baking at same time. Place cover on roaster (or cover shallow roasting pan with foil). Bake chickens 1 1/2 to 2 hours, or until fork-tender. Makes 12 servings.

Low-fat, low-cholesterol diet: Prepare as directed; dieter should not eat skin of chicken. 10 grams fat per serving.
High-iron diet: 3.5 milligrams iron per serving.

SKILLET PINEAPPLE CHICKEN (205 calories per serving)

3 large whole chicken breasts
 (about 2 1/2 pounds), split,
 skinned and boned
1 teaspoon salt
2 tablespoons butter or margarine
1 tablespoon instant minced
 onion
1 cup diagonally sliced celery
1 green pepper, cut into strips
1 8-ounce can pineapple tidbits
1 teaspoon soy sauce
1/2 teaspoon cinnamon
2 teaspoons cornstarch

About 35 minutes before serving: Cut each chicken-breast half into 10 to 12 crosswise strips. Sprinkle with salt. In large skillet over high heat, in butter or margarine, brown chicken strips 3 minutes, stirring constantly. Add onion, celery and green pepper; continue cooking 2 minutes. Add pineapple, soy sauce, cinnamon and 1/4 cup cold water; stir; cover; simmer 4 minutes. Blend cornstarch with 2 tablespoons cold water; stir into skillet. Cook, stirring, until thickened. Makes 6 servings.

Low-fat, low-cholesterol diet: Prepare as directed but use salad oil or margarine instead of butter. 5 grams fat per serving.

OVEN-FRIED CHICKEN (255 calories per serving)

1¹/₂ cups packaged cornflake
  crumbs
2 teaspoons seasoned salt
¹/₂ teaspoon seasoned pepper
2 eggs
4 whole chicken breasts (about
  3 pounds), split
6 tablespoons butter or margarine

Up to 1¹/₂ hours before serving: Preheat oven to 350°F. On piece of waxed paper, combine crumbs, seasoned salt and pepper. In small bowl, beat eggs with 2 tablespoons water. Dip chicken, first into egg mixture, then into crumb mixture. Meanwhile, in each of 2 shallow baking pans in oven, melt 3 tablespoons butter; in it, arrange chicken. Bake about 1 hour, or until fork-tender. Makes 8 servings.

Bland diet: Prepare as directed but omit pepper and substitute salt for seasoned salt.
Diabetic diet: Prepare as directed but use margarine instead of butter. Exchanges per serving = 4 meat, ¹/₂ bread and 2 fat.
Low-residue diet: Prepare as directed for bland diet.

CHICKEN-STUFFED ORANGES (180 calories per serving)

6 oranges
¹/₂ cup reduced–calorie mayonnaise
grated orange peel
1¹/₂ teaspoons orange juice
¹/₈ teaspoon white pepper
3 cups cooked chicken chunks
¹/₂ cup cut-up orange sections
¹/₂ cup green grapes, halved
¹/₄ to ¹/₂ teaspoon salt

About 2 hours before serving: Slice top from each orange, about one-third way down; with sharp knife, cut out orange sections from both the tops and bottoms; reserve ¹/₂ cup. Make shallow saw-toothed edge around top of each orange shell. In medium bowl, combine reduced–calorie mayonnaise, 1 teaspoon grated orange peel, orange juice and pepper. Mix in chicken, then ¹/₄ cup reserved orange sections and some grapes; add salt to taste. Heap into orange shells; garnish with remaining orange sections and grapes; sprinkle with orange peel. Refrigerate. Makes 6 servings.

Diabetic diet: Exchanges per serving = 3 meat and ¹/₂ fruit.
Low-fat, low-cholesterol diet: 5 grams fat per serving.

CHICKEN PORTUGAIS (280 calories per serving)

2 tablespoons bacon fat
4 whole chicken breasts (about
  3 pounds), split, boned and
  skinned
pinch instant minced garlic
¹/₄ cup chopped onion
2 teaspoons flour
¹/₂ cup white wine
1 10¹/₂-ounce can condensed
  beef broth
2 tomatoes
4 cups hot fluffy rice

About 25 minutes before serving: In large skillet over medium heat, in bacon fat, brown chicken breasts 2 minutes on each side. Add garlic and onion; cook 3 minutes; stir in flour, then wine and undiluted broth. Let all simmer, uncovered, 10 minutes, or until chicken is fork-tender.

Meanwhile, chop tomatoes coarsely. Add to chicken; continue boiling 5 minutes. Serve over hot fluffy rice. Makes 8 servings.

Diabetic diet: Serve chicken with ¹/₂ cup gravy over ¹/₂ cup rice. Exchanges per serving = 4 meat and 1 bread.
Low-fat, low-cholesterol diet: Prepare as directed but use salad oil (not bacon fat). 5 grams fat per serving.

CHICKEN-WATERCRESS SOUP (180 calories per serving)

1 10¹/₂-ounce can condensed
  chicken broth
¹/₂ teaspoon salt
2 tablespoons finely minced
  onion
¹/₄ cup diced celery
1¹/₂ cups cooked diced chicken
  or turkey (about ¹/₂ pound)
1 cup firmly packed coarsely
  chopped watercress
1 tablespoon cornstarch

About 15 minutes before serving: In medium saucepan, simmer chicken broth, 1 cup water, salt, onion, celery and chicken 10 minutes. Add watercress and simmer again until just wilted. Meanwhile, mix cornstarch with enough water to form a smooth paste. Stir into soup; cook a few seconds until clear and smooth. Makes 3 servings of 1 cup each.

Diabetic diet: Exchanges per serving = 4 meat.
Egg-, gluten-, milk- and wheat-free diet: Prepare as directed but use homemade chicken broth.
Low-fat, low-cholesterol diet: 5 grams fat per serving.
High-iron diet: 3 milligrams iron per serving.

SAVORY CHICKEN (300 calories per serving)

3 tablespoons flour
1 teaspoon salt
¹/₄ teaspoon paprika
3 whole chicken breasts (about 2¹/₂ pounds), split, skinned and boned
2 tablespoons salad oil
1 envelope (.6 ounces) old-fashioned French-dressing mix
1 13³/₄-ounce can chicken broth
1 medium onion, quartered
6 medium new potatoes
6 carrots
chopped parsley for garnish

About 1¹/₄ hours before serving: Combine flour, salt and paprika; use to coat chicken on all sides. In Dutch oven over medium heat, in oil, brown chicken on all sides; then sprinkle with French-dressing mix and add broth and onion.

Scrub new potatoes; cut carrots into thirds, lengthwise; add both to chicken. Simmer, covered, about 50 minutes, or until all are tender. Arrange on heated platter; then sprinkle with parsley. Spoon juices from Dutch oven over chicken and vegetables. Makes 6 servings.

Diabetic diet: Exchanges per serving = 4 meat for each half chicken breast; 1 bread for a potato; 1 vegetable for 1 carrot; up to 3 tablespoons gravy = 1 "free" exchange.
Low-fat, low-cholesterol diet: 5 grams fat per serving.

SIMMERED CHICKEN IN LEMON (255 calories per serving)

1 3-pound broiler-fryer, cut up
2 bay leaves
1 teaspoon salt
12 small white onions, peeled
1 9-ounce package frozen artichoke hearts
2 tablespoons flour
2 egg yolks
2 tablespoons lemon juice
paprika for garnish

About 1 hour and 10 minutes before serving: Place chicken in Dutch oven; add 2 cups water, bay leaves, and salt; cover; bring to boiling, then simmer 1 hour. At end of first 30 minutes, add onions; at end of next 20 minutes, add artichoke hearts; cook all until tender. Blend flour, ¹/₂ cup water, egg yolks, lemon juice; stir into liquid in Dutch oven, and cook, stirring, until thickened. Sprinkle with paprika. Makes 6 servings.

Diabetic diet: Serve 2 tablespoons gravy with each serving. Exchanges per serving = 2 vegetable; 1 meat for each ounce of cooked chicken; up to 2 tablespoons gravy = 1 "free" exchange.
High-iron diet: 4 milligrams iron per serving.

CHICKEN, HUNTER STYLE (315 calories per serving)

2 2¹/₂-pound broiler-fryers, quartered
1 teaspoon paprika
seasoned salt
¹/₄ teaspoon seasoned pepper
2 tablespoons salad oil
10 white onions, peeled
¹/₂ pound mushrooms, sliced
1 small eggplant, pared, cut into ¹/₂-inch strips
1 green pepper, cut into strips
¹/₈ teaspoon pepper
¹/₂ teaspoon thyme leaves
1 teaspoon basil
2 garlic cloves, minced
2 bay leaves
¹/₂ cup sherry
4 tomatoes, quartered

About 2¹/₂ hours before serving: Sprinkle chicken with paprika, 1¹/₄ teaspoons seasoned salt and pepper. Preheat oven to 375°F. Meanwhile, in large skillet, in oil, brown chicken on all sides. Arrange in 3-quart casserole.

In fat left in skillet, sauté onions until golden. Now add mushrooms, eggplant, green pepper, 1¹/₄ teaspoons seasoned salt, pepper, thyme, basil and garlic and sauté 2 or 3 minutes. Add to chicken in casserole with bay leaves and sherry. Bake, covered, 45 minutes. Add tomatoes and bake 20 minutes longer. Makes 8 servings.

Egg-, gluten-, milk- and wheat-free diet: Prepare as directed but for gluten-free diets use plain salt and pepper (not seasoned salt and pepper).
Low-fat, low-cholesterol diet: Prepare as directed; dieter should not eat skin of chicken. 15 grams fat per serving.
High-iron diet: 4.5 milligrams iron per serving.

PRESSURE-COOKED PIMENTO CHICKEN (300 calories per serving)

1/4 cup flour
1 tablespoon seasoned salt
1/4 teaspoon seasoned pepper
1 tablespoon paprika
1 3 1/2-pound chicken, cut up
2 tablespoons salad oil
2 4-ounce cans pimentos, drained
1 large onion, sliced
1/8 teaspoon instant minced garlic
1 bay leaf
1 stalk celery, chopped
1 teaspoon Worcestershire
1/2 cup water
2 teaspoons cornstarch

About 45 minutes before serving: Combine flour, seasoned salt, seasoned pepper and paprika; coat chicken with flour mixture. In pressure cooker, in oil, brown until golden.

Add pimentos, onion, garlic, bay leaf, celery, Worcestershire and water; close cover securely. Place pressure regulator on vent pipe as manufacturer directs; bring up to 15 pounds pressure. Cook chicken 15 minutes, then let pressure reduce of its own accord. With slotted spoon, remove chicken and vegetables to heated platter. Stir cornstarch into a little water until smooth, then stir mixture into gravy in cooker. Cook until thickened; pour some over chicken; pass rest in gravy boat. Makes 6 servings.

Low-fat, low-cholesterol diet: Prepare as directed; dieter should not eat skin of chicken. 15 grams fat per serving.
High-iron diet: 4 milligrams iron per serving.

CHICKEN BREASTS AMANDINE (265 calories per serving)

2 tablespoons butter or margarine
2 large whole chicken breasts (about 1 1/2 pounds), split, skinned and boned
1 small garlic clove, minced
1/4 cup roasted, blanched slivered almonds
1 fresh mushroom, sliced
1/2 teaspoon salt
1/4 teaspoon pepper
1 10 1/2-ounce can condensed chicken broth
1 tablespoon cornstarch
parsley sprigs for garnish

About 40 minutes before serving: In skillet over medium heat, in butter or margarine, brown chicken breasts, garlic, almonds and mushroom slices, stirring occasionally, until all are golden. Now add salt, pepper and chicken broth; simmer, covered, 30 minutes, or until chicken is tender. Then mix cornstarch with a little water; stir into liquid in skillet; cook, stirring constantly, until thickened. Garnish chicken with parsley sprigs. Makes 4 servings.

Diabetic diet: Prepare as directed but use margarine instead of butter. Carefully divide into 4 equal servings. Exchanges per serving = 4 meat, 1 vegetable and 1 1/2 fat.
Low-fat, low-cholesterol diet: Prepare as directed but use salad oil or margarine instead of butter. 10 grams fat per serving.
Low-sodium diet: Prepare as directed but use salad oil or unsalted butter or margarine; omit salt; use 1 1/4 cups unsalted chicken broth or water in place of canned broth. 70 milligrams sodium per serving.

CHICKEN WITH BUTTERMILK GRAVY (250 calories per serving)

1 tablespoon butter or margarine
1 small garlic clove
1 medium onion, chopped
4 chicken legs with thighs (about 1 1/2 pounds)
1/4 teaspoon ginger
1 1/2 teaspoons curry
1 teaspoon salt
2 tablespoons chopped almonds (optional)
2 cups buttermilk
2 tablespoons flour
paprika for garnish
dried parsley flakes for garnish

About 1 hour before serving: In large skillet, in butter or margarine, sauté garlic and onion until onion is lightly browned; remove garlic and discard. Brown chicken until golden, then remove. Add ginger, curry, salt and almonds to skillet; stir in 1 cup buttermilk; stirring constantly, bring mixture to boiling. Return chicken to skillet; cover; simmer, turning occasionally, 40 minutes, or until tender.

Remove chicken to warm platter. Stirring constantly, slowly mix remaining 1 cup of buttermilk into flour to form smooth paste; add paste to stock in skillet, still stirring constantly. Heat mixture almost to boiling—do not boil or mixture (which is never absolutely smooth) will separate.

To serve: Sprinkle chicken with paprika and garnish with parsley flakes. Pass remaining gravy. Makes 4 servings.

Diabetic diet: Prepare as directed but use margarine instead of butter; serve 1/2 cup gravy with each serving. Exchanges per serving = 3 meat and 1/2 milk.
Low-fat, low-cholesterol diet: Prepare as directed but remove skin from chicken and use margarine or salad oil instead of butter. 10 grams fat per serving.

CHICKEN ITALIANO (245 calories per serving)

1 3-pound broiler-fryer, skinned and cut up
1/2 teaspoon salt
1/8 teaspoon pepper
1 15 1/2-ounce jar spaghetti sauce with mushrooms

About 1 hour and 15 minutes before serving: Preheat oven to 350°F. In large shallow baking dish, arrange chicken pieces so they do not overlap. Sprinkle with salt and pepper. Pour tomato sauce over chicken. Bake 1 hour, or until chicken is fork-tender, basting occasionally. Makes 4 servings.

Diabetic diet: Exchanges per serving = 1 meat for each ounce cooked chicken, plus 1 vegetable for 1/2 cup sauce.
Egg- and milk-free diet: Prepare as directed but select a spaghetti sauce not containing cheese.
Low-fat, low-cholesterol diet: Prepare as directed but select spaghetti sauce not containing cheese. 10 grams fat per serving.

FORK-AND-SPOON CHICKEN CANTALOUPE SALAD (275 calories per serving)

1/2 cup bottled reduced–calorie Italian dressing
1/4 cup reduced–calorie mayonnaise
1/8 teaspoon seasoned pepper
1/3 cup diced celery
2 tablespoons sliced scallions
3 cups cut-up cooked chicken
2 cantaloupes
watercress for garnish

Early in day, or at least 2 hours before serving: In medium bowl, stir together reduced–calorie dressings, seasoned pepper, celery and scallions. Add chicken; toss well; refrigerate, covered. Halve cantaloupes; remove seeds; refrigerate, covered.

To serve: Fill cantaloupe halves with chicken salad; garnish each half with 4 sprigs of cress. Makes 4 servings.

Diabetic diet: Prepare as directed but use mixture to fill 6 small cantaloupe halves. Exchanges per serving = 3 meat and 1 fruit.
Low-fat, low-cholesterol diet: 10 grams fat per serving.

QUICK CUCUMBER BOATS (125 calories per serving)

3 cucumbers
2 9-ounce packages frozen cut green beans, cooked
chopped dill
1 to 2 tablespoons cocktail onions
2 cups julienne strips of cooked chicken breasts
reduced–calorie Italian dressing
salt

About 1 hour before serving: Cut cucumbers in half lengthwise; with pointed knife, remove and discard seeds. Scoop out cucumber shells; cut meat scooped from shells into strips. In medium bowl, toss green beans with 1 tablespoon chopped dill, cocktail onions, chicken, reduced–calorie dressing to taste and cucumber strips. Sprinkle cucumber shells lightly with salt; fill with salad mixture. Garnish with chopped dill. Refrigerate. Makes 6 servings.

Diabetic diet: Exchanges per serving = 2 meat and 1 vegetable.
Low-fat, low-cholesterol diet: 5 grams fat per serving.
High-iron diet: 3 milligrams iron per serving.

SPICY BAKED CHICKEN (205 calories per serving)

1 3-pound broiler-fryer, cut up
3/4 cup chicken broth
1 teaspoon instant minced onion
1/2 teaspoon salt
1/4 teaspoon thyme leaves
1/8 teaspoon seasoned pepper
1/8 teaspoon instant minced garlic
2 teaspoons cornstarch
1/2 cup seedless grapes

About 1 1/2 hours before serving: Preheat oven to 400°F. In shallow open roasting pan, arrange chicken pieces; pour broth over them. Combine instant minced onion, salt, thyme, seasoned pepper and instant minced garlic; sprinkle over chicken. Bake, uncovered, 1 hour, or until fork-tender, basting frequently. Transfer to warm platter. Stir cornstarch into a little water until smooth, then stir into gravy in pan. Cook until thickened; add grapes. Pass as gravy for chicken. Makes 6 servings.

Diabetic diet: Exchanges per serving = 4 meat plus 1 "free" for 1/4 cup gravy.
Low-fat, low-cholesterol diet: Prepare as directed; dieter should not eat skin of chicken. 10 grams fat per serving.
High-iron diet: 3 milligrams iron per serving.

MIRIAM'S CHICKEN (270 calories per serving)

1 3-pound broiler-fryer, cut up
salt
1/4 teaspoon pepper
2 tablespoons salad oil
2 cups diced onion
1 cup diced green pepper
1 garlic clove, minced
1 cup chopped fresh tomatoes
1/4 cup chopped parsley

About 1 hour before serving: Sprinkle chicken with 1 teaspoon salt and the pepper. In large skillet over medium heat, in oil, brown with diced onion until golden; add green pepper and garlic; sauté a few minutes longer. Stir in chopped tomatoes, parsley and 1 teaspoon salt; simmer, covered, 45 minutes or until tender, adding 1/4 to 1/2 cup water if needed. Before serving, skim off any surface fat from gravy. Makes 6 servings.

Diabetic diet: Include 1/3 cup gravy with each serving. Exchanges per serving = 1 vegetable and 1 meat for each ounce of cooked chicken.
Low-fat, low-cholesterol diet: Prepare as directed; dieter should not eat skin of chicken. 10 grams fat per serving.
High-iron diet: 3.5 milligrams iron per serving.
Low-sodium diet: Prepare as directed but omit salt. 100 milligrams sodium per serving.

CHICKEN À L'ORANGE (270 calories per serving)

2 1/2 tablespoons flour
1 teaspoon chili powder
1/2 teaspoon salt
2 whole chicken breasts (about 1 1/2 pounds), split
2 tablespoons salad oil
1 tablespoon grated orange peel
1 cup orange juice
1 teaspoon granulated sugar
1 orange, sectioned

About 1 hour before serving: Combine flour with chili powder and salt; coat chicken with mixture. In large skillet over medium heat, in oil, brown on all sides. Stir in remaining flour mixture, orange peel, orange juice and sugar; simmer, covered, 45 minutes, or until chicken is tender. Remove cover; add orange sections and heat 5 minutes. Makes 4 servings.

Diabetic diet: Prepare as directed but omit sugar. Include 1/4 cup gravy and orange slices with each serving. Exchanges per serving = 4 meat and 1 fruit.
Egg-, gluten-, milk- and wheat-free diet: Prepare as directed but flour chicken with cornstarch (not flour) for gluten- and wheat-free diets.
Low-fat, low-cholesterol diet: Prepare as directed but remove skin from chicken before preparing. 10 grams fat per serving.
Low-sodium diet: Prepare as directed but use chili powder not containing salt; omit salt. 60 milligrams sodium per serving.

BAKED BROILERS WITH CRAB (320 calories per serving)

2 2-pound broiler-fryers (back-bones removed), quartered
butter or margarine
seasoned salt
pepper and paprika
1/4 cup chili sauce
2 7 1/2-ounce cans King crab, drained (or 2 6-ounce packages frozen King crab, thawed, thoroughly drained)
3 slices bread, cubed
1 teaspoon poultry seasoning
parsley for garnish

About 1 1/4 hours before serving: Preheat oven to 375°F. Rub chicken with softened butter or margarine, then with 1 teaspoon seasoned salt, pepper and paprika. Lay, skin side up, in roasting pan; roast, uncovered, 35 minutes. In small saucepan, melt 2 tablespoons butter or margarine; stir in chili sauce; spread mixture over chicken and bake 10 minutes longer.

Meanwhile, in large bowl, flake crab; toss with bread cubes, poultry seasoning, 1 teaspoon seasoned salt and 2 tablespoons melted butter. Turn chicken skin side down; pile some crab mixture onto each piece; bake 20 minutes longer. Garnish with parsley. Makes 8 servings.

Low-fat diet: Prepare as directed; dieter should not eat skin of chicken. 15 grams fat per serving. Omit recipe from low-cholesterol diet.
High-iron diet: 3 milligrams iron per serving.

EASY CHICKEN PARTS, COMPANY STYLE (250 calories per serving)

³/₄ teaspoon salt
¹/₈ teaspoon pepper
¹/₄ teaspoon paprika
1 3-pound broiler-fryer, skinned, cut up
1 10¹/₂-ounce can condensed cream-of-chicken soup
¹/₂ cup skimmed milk or re-liquefied nonfat dry milk
1 cup chopped green pepper

About 1 hour before serving: Preheat oven to 375°F. Combine salt, pepper and paprika; sprinkle over chicken. Arrange meat-side down in large (about 13″ by 9″ by 2″) baking dish. Blend chicken soup with milk; pour over chicken. Top with chopped green pepper. Bake 45 minutes, or until fork-tender. Makes 6 servings.

Diabetic diet: Include ¹/₃ cup gravy with each serving. Exchanges per serving = ¹/₂ skim milk plus 1 meat for each ounce cooked chicken.
Low-fat diet: 5 grams fat per serving. Omit recipe from low-cholesterol diet.
High-iron diet: 3.5 milligrams iron per serving.

CHICKEN WITH WALNUTS (Hop Po Gai Ding) (300 calories per serving)

1 teaspoon granulated sugar
1 teaspoon salt
¹/₄ tablespoon soy sauce
2 tablespoons dry sherry
3 whole chicken breasts (about 2¹/₂ pounds), split, skinned and boned
cornstarch
1 egg, beaten
3 tablespoons salad oil
¹/₂ cup walnut halves
¹/₂ teaspoon ginger
2 garlic cloves, minced
2 5-ounce cans sliced bamboo shoots, drained

About 45 minutes before serving: In medium bowl, combine sugar, salt, soy sauce and sherry. Cut chicken into 1- to 1¹/₂-inch slices, then let stand in sherry mixture about 15 minutes. Remove, reserving sherry mixture. Sprinkle chicken lightly with cornstarch, then toss with beaten egg.

In skillet over medium heat, in oil, lightly toast walnuts, stirring constantly; remove; drain. To oil remaining in skillet, add ginger, garlic and chicken. Cook, stirring constantly, until chicken is well browned on all sides. Now add ³/₄ cup water and sherry mixture. Simmer, covered, until chicken is tender—about 20 minutes. Then stir in bamboo shoots and walnuts and simmer 5 minutes more. Makes 6 servings.

Diabetic diet: Prepare as directed but use margarine instead of butter. Omit sugar; carefully divide into 6 equal servings. Exchanges per serving = 4 meat and 1 fat.
Low-fat, low-cholesterol diet: Prepare as directed but omit egg. 15 grams fat per serving.

CHICKEN WITH ORANGE SAUCE (250 calories per serving)

¹/₄ cup cornstarch
salt and pepper
2 whole chicken breasts (about 1¹/₂ pounds), split and skinned
2 tablespoons salad oil
1 10¹/₂-ounce can condensed chicken broth
¹/₂ cup orange juice
¹/₂ unpeeled orange, thinly sliced
¹/₂ green pepper, chopped
¹/₄ cup finely diced pimento
¹/₄ pound medium mushrooms, quartered
¹/₄ teaspoon ginger

About 1 hour before serving: Mix cornstarch, ¹/₂ teaspoon salt and generous dash pepper; use to coat chicken. In large skillet over medium heat, in oil, brown chicken until golden. Turn, skin side up, then add remaining ingredients. Cover; simmer, stirring occasionally, 30 minutes, or until chicken is tender. Season gravy with salt and pepper to taste. Makes 4 servings.

Diabetic diet: Prepare as directed; serve ¹/₂ cup gravy with each serving. Exchanges per serving = 4 meat, 1 fruit and 1¹/₂ fat.
Low-fat, low-cholesterol diet: 10 grams fat per serving.

BAKED CHICKEN CASSEROLE (250 calories per serving)

1 cup uncooked elbow macaroni
2 cups skimmed milk or reliquefied nonfat dry milk
1/4 cup flour
2 chicken-bouillon cubes
2 cups diced cooked chicken
1/2 teaspoon marjoram leaves
dash pepper
1/4 cup chopped parsley
1/4 cup chopped onion
1 cup diced celery
5 mushrooms, thinly sliced
2 tablespoons chopped green
pepper
1 1/2 teaspoons salt
1 tablespoon chopped pimento
(optional)

About 1 hour before serving: Preheat oven to 350°F. Cook macaroni as label directs; drain. In 2-quart ovenproof saucepan, slowly
add milk to flour, stirring constantly to form a smooth paste. Add
bouillon cubes; cook on range top, still stirring constantly, until
sauce is thickened and smooth. Stir in cooked macaroni, chicken
and remaining ingredients. Bake, uncovered, 25 to 30 minutes, or
until bubbly. Makes 5 servings of about 1 cup each.

Diabetic diet: Prepare as directed but divide mixture among 5 individual casseroles; bake 20 minutes. Exchange per serving = 2 meat, 1
bread and 1/2 milk.
Low-fat, low-cholesterol diet: 5 grams fat per serving.

CHICKEN OLÉ (280 calories per serving)

1 3-pound broiler-fryer, cut up
1/4 cup flour
2 tablespoons salad oil
1/2 medium onion, chopped
1 medium tomato, chopped
1/2 cup raisins
1/4 cup sliced stuffed olives
1/2 teaspoon salt
dash pepper

About 1 1/2 hours before serving: Coat chicken with flour. In large
skillet over medium heat, in oil, brown chicken on both sides.
Remove from skillet. In same skillet, sauté onion until transparent. Add tomatoes, then browned chicken, raisins, olives, salt,
pepper and 1 cup water. Bring to boiling; reduce heat and simmer,
covered, 45 minutes, or until chicken is fork-tender. Arrange
chicken on heated large platter; pour on sauce. Makes 6 servings.

Egg-, gluten-, milk- and wheat-free diet: Prepare as directed but sprinkle chicken with cornstarch instead of flour for gluten- and wheat-free
diets.
Low-fat, low-cholesterol diet: Prepare as directed; dieter should not eat
skin of chicken. Omit recipe if olives are forbidden on diet. 10 grams fat
per serving.
High-iron diet: 3.5 milligrams iron per serving.
Low-sodium diet: Prepare as directed but omit olives and salt. 100 milligrams sodium per serving.

CHICKEN À LA KING (230 calories per serving)

1 10 1/2-ounce can condensed
chicken broth
1 10-ounce package frozen peas
1/4 chopped onion
7 tablespoons flour
1/8 teaspoon pepper
1 teaspoon salt
1 teaspoon granulated sugar
1 tablespoon butter or margarine
2 cups cut-up cooked chicken
2 canned pimentos, finely
minced
1 egg yolk
6 slices toasted rye bread, quartered

About 20 minutes before serving: In medium saucepan, heat
chicken broth to boiling; add peas and onion; cover; simmer 3
minutes. Meanwhile, in medium bowl, mix flour, pepper, salt and
sugar. Slowly stir in 1 1/2 cups water to form thin smooth paste.
Stirring constantly, stir paste into chicken broth; cook until thickened. Add butter or margarine, chicken and pimentos; cook 5 minutes. Mix a bit of sauce with egg yolk, then stir into chicken mixture. Serve immediately in individual 1-cup casseroles with toast
quarters to one side. Makes 6 servings.

Diabetic diet: Prepare as directed but omit sugar and use margarine
instead of butter. Exchanges per serving = 3 meat, 2 bread, 1 vegetable
and 1/2 fat.
Low-fat, low-cholesterol diet: Prepare as directed but use skimmed
milk in place of water; use margarine instead of butter; omit egg yolk. 5
grams fat per serving.

QUICK CAMP-STYLE CHICKEN LEGS (230 calories per serving)

1 envelope instant meat marinade
¹/₂ cup orange juice
2 tablespoons soy sauce
2 tablespoons honey
1 tablespoon lemon juice
¹/₂ teaspoon ginger
8 chicken legs with thighs
(about 4 pounds)
¹/₂ cup bottled barbecue sauce

About 1 hour before serving: In shallow baking pan, combine meat marinade with orange juice, soy sauce, honey, lemon juice and ginger. Arrange chicken in marinade; prick with fork, then let stand 10 minutes, turning a few times.

Meanwhile, preheat broiler 10 minutes if manufacturer directs. Remove chicken from marinade and place, skin side down, on broiler rack (reserve marinade). Brush with barbecue sauce, then broil, about 7 inches from heat, brushing occasionally with marinade and sauce. When chicken is almost fork-tender, turn, skin side up, and brush with rest of marinade and barbecue sauce. Continue broiling until tender when pierced with fork. Makes 8 servings.

Low-fat, low-cholesterol diet: Dieter should not eat skin of chicken. 10 grams fat per serving.
High-iron diet: 3 milligrams iron per serving.

CHICKEN IN A JIFFY (195 calories per serving)

2 large whole chicken breasts
(about 1¹/₂ pounds) split,
skinned and boned
2 tablespoons butter or margarine
¹/₂ teaspoon salt
1 teaspoon tarragon
²/₃ cup dry vermouth
2 thin lemon slices
chopped parsley for garnish

About 30 minutes before serving: Cut each chicken-breast half into 10 to 12 strips. In skillet over high heat, in butter or margarine, cook chicken, salt and tarragon 3 minutes, stirring occasionally. Add dry vermouth and lemon slices; cover and cook 5 minutes. Sprinkle with parsley. Makes 4 servings.

Diabetic diet: Prepare as directed but use margarine instead of butter. Carefully divide into 4 equal servings. Exchanges per serving = 3 meat and 1¹/₂ fat.
Egg-, gluten-, milk- and wheat-free diet: Prepare as directed but use milk-free margarine on milk-free diet.
Low-fat, low-cholesterol diet: Prepare as directed but use salad oil or margarine instead of butter. 10 grams fat per serving.
Low-sodium diet: Prepare as directed but use unsalted butter or margarine. 70 milligrams sodium per serving.

INDIAN CHICKEN KABOBS (240 calories per serving)

4 large whole chicken breasts
(about 3 pounds) split,
skinned and boned
¹/₂ teaspoon ginger
¹/₈ teaspoon crushed red pepper
¹/₈ teaspoon prepared mustard
¹/₈ teaspoon ground cardamom
¹/₈ teaspoon turmeric
1 teaspoon curry
2 teaspoons lemon juice
1¹/₂ teaspoons salt
1 tablespoon salad oil
1 small onion, quartered
paprika
1 20-ounce can cling-peach
halves, drained
1 lemon, cut into sixths
2 tablespoons chopped parsley
for garnish

About 1³/₄ hours before serving: Flatten halved chicken breasts with hand, then cut each crosswise into thirds. In medium bowl, combine ginger, pepper, mustard, cardamom, turmeric, curry, lemon juice, salt, salad oil and 1 tablespoon water; add chicken; mix well. Refrigerate 1 hour.

Preheat broiler 10 minutes if manufacturer directs. On six 8-inch skewers, alternate 2 pieces of chicken with piece or two of onion from one of quarters. Repeat until eack skewer is loosely filled, then sprinkle lightly with paprika. Place kabobs in jelly-roll pan; broil 15 minutes, turning once, or until chicken is cooked. Heat peaches under broiler for a minute or two. Serve garnished with lemon wedges and sprinkled with parsley. Makes 6 servings.

Diabetic diet: Prepare as directed but use water-packed peaches. Include 2 peach halves with each serving. Exchanges per serving = 4 meat and 1 fruit.
Egg-, gluten-, milk- and wheat-free diet: Prepare as directed.
Low-fat, low-cholesterol diet: 5 grams fat per serving.
Low-sodium diet: Prepare as directed but use dry mustard (not prepared); use curry which does not contain salt; omit salt. 95 milligrams sodium per serving.

CHICKEN ALGERIAN (260 calories per serving)

1 3-pound broiler-fryer, cut up
paprika
salt
1/4 teaspoon pepper
2 tablespoons butter or margarine
1/2 cup chicken broth
1 garlic clove
1 medium eggplant, pared,
cubed
1 medium onion, chopped
2 tomatoes, peeled, diced
1/4 teaspoon ground thyme
1 tablespoon chopped parsley

About 1 hour before serving: Sprinkle chicken with paprika, 1 tea-spoon salt and pepper. In large skillet over medium heat, in butter or margarine, brown chicken. Stir in broth, scraping brown parti-cles from bottom of skillet. Stick toothpick into garlic, then add to skillet with eggplant, 1 teaspoon salt and remaining ingredients. Simmer, covered, 30 minutes, or until chicken is tender. Remove garlic.

To serve: Turn into heated small soup tureen. Makes 6 servings.

Egg-, gluten-, milk- and wheat-free diet: Prepare as directed but use milk-free margarine on milk-free diet; water in place of broth on gluten- and wheat-free diets.

Low-fat, low-cholesterol diet: Use margarine or salad oil instead of but-ter; dieter should not eat skin of chicken. 10 grams of fat per serving.

Low-sodium diet: Prepare as directed but omit salt; use unsalted butter or margarine; substitute water for chicken broth. 100 milligrams sodium per serving.

CURRIED CHICKEN KABOBS (270 calories per serving)

2 whole chicken breasts (about
1 1/2 pounds) split, skinned
and boned
1 8-ounce container plain
yogurt
2 tablespoons minced onion
1 1/2 teaspoons curry
1/2 teaspoon salt
2 tablespoons lemon juice
2 tablespoons granulated sugar
32 cherry tomatoes or 8 large
tomatoes, quartered
3/4 pound fresh medium mushrooms

About 45 minutes before serving: Cut chicken into 32 pieces. Cover large cookie sheet with foil, turning up foil edges to prevent spilling. In medium bowl, let chicken stand in mixture of yogurt, onion, curry, salt, lemon juice and sugar for about 10 minutes.

Preheat broiler 10 minutes if manufacturer directs. Thread eight 8-inch skewers with chicken, alternating with tomatoes and mushrooms. Place kabobs on cookie sheet; coat with half of remaining yogurt mixture. Broil 7 minutes; turn; coat with rest of yogurt mixture, then broil 7 minutes more until chicken is tender and lightly browned. Makes 4 servings.

Diabetic diet: Prepare as directed but use low-fat yogurt; omit sugar and add liquid nonnutritive sweetener equivalent to 2 tablespoons sugar. Exchanges per serving = 4 meat, 1 vegetable and 1/2 milk.

Egg-, gluten- and wheat-free diet: Prepare as directed.

Low-fat, low-cholesterol diet: 5 grams fat per serving.

Low-sodium diet: Prepare as directed but use curry which does not con-tain salt; omit salt. 120 milligrams sodium per serving.

CHILI CHICKEN (220 calories per serving)

2 whole chicken breasts (about
1 1/2 pounds), split and
skinned
2 tablespoons flour
1 tablespoon salad oil
1 8-ounce can tomato sauce
with cheese
1 tablespoon granulated sugar
1 tablespoon parsley flakes
1 teaspoon salt
1/2 to 1 teaspoon chili powder

About 35 minutes before serving: Coat chicken lightly with flour; shake off excess. In medium skillet over medium heat, in oil, brown 5 minutes on each side. Add remaining ingredients. Cover and simmer 20 minutes, or until chicken is tender. Makes 4 serv-ings.

Diabetic diet: Prepare as directed but omit sugar. Exchanges per serv-ing = 3 meat and 1/2 vegetable.

Egg-, gluten-, milk- and wheat-free diet: Prepare as directed but substi-tute cornstarch for flour on gluten- and wheat-free diets; use plain tomato sauce in place of tomato sauce with cheese on milk-free diet.

Low-fat, low-cholesterol diet: Prepare as directed but use plain tomato sauce instead of tomato sauce with cheese. 5 grams fat per serving.

EASY CHICKEN SAUTÉ (225 calories per serving)

2 whole chicken breasts (about 1¹/₂ pounds), split and skinned
2 tablespoons salad oil
¹/₂ pound fresh mushrooms, thinly sliced
1 onion, thinly sliced
1 teaspoon salt

About 30 minutes before serving: In medium skillet over medium heat, in oil, brown chicken well. Add remaining ingredients; cover; cook over low heat, turning chicken occasionally, until tender. Makes 4 servings.

Bland diet: Prepare as directed but omit onion.
Diabetic diet: Exchanges per serving = 4 meat, 1 vegetable and 1 fat.
Low-fat, low-cholesterol diet: 10 grams fat per serving.
Low-residue diet: Prepare as directed but omit onion.
Low-sodium diet: Prepare as directed but omit salt. 80 milligrams sodium per serving.

SEAFARING CHICKEN POTPIE (350 calories per serving)

3 tablespoons butter or margarine
1 large stalk green celery, thinly sliced
1 medium onion, thinly sliced
¹/₄ cup flour
1 teaspoon salt
1 teaspoon poultry seasoning
1 8-ounce can sliced carrots, undrained
1 8-ounce can baby peas, undrained
2 7¹/₂-ounce can minced clams, undrained
2 cups coarsely chopped cooked chicken or turkey (about 8 ounces)
2 hard-cooked eggs, thinly sliced
pepper to taste
1 8-ounce package refrigerated crescent rolls

About 30 minutes before serving: Preheat oven to 350°F. In medium skillet over medium heat, in butter or margarine, sauté celery and onion until onion is golden. Stir in flour, salt and poultry seasoning. Cook, stirring constantly, about 1 minute. Add undrained carrots, peas, clams and chicken. Cook, stirring constantly, until liquid thickens slightly and boils. Turn mixture into 2-quart casserole; top with egg slices. Sprinkle with pepper to taste.

Cut crescent rolls (still rolled as they come from the package) crosswise into 12 rounds. Place on top of potpie. Bake 15 to 20 minutes, or until rolls are a dark golden-brown. (Place piece of foil under casserole to catch any drippings.) Makes 6 servings of about 1 cup each.

Diabetic diet: Prepare as directed but use margarine instead of butter. Carefully divide stew among 6 individual casseroles; top with 2 biscuit slices; bake as directed. Exchanges per serving = 3 meat, 2¹/₂ bread and 1¹/₂ fat.
High-iron diet: 5.5 milligrams iron per serving.

CURRIED CHICKEN SALAD (265 calories per serving)

³/₄ cup packaged precooked rice
¹/₄ cup thinly-sliced carrots
¹/₄ cup reduced-calorie creamy-style French dressing
2 tablespoons reduced-calorie mayonnaise
³/₄ teaspoon curry
³/₄ teaspoon salt
dash pepper
2 tablespoons milk
2 cups cooked chicken or turkey, cut into cubes (about 10 ounces)
¹/₄ cup thin green-pepper strips
romaine or lettuce
1 small red onion, thinly sliced

Early in day: Cook rice as label directs; toss rice with carrots and reduced-calorie French dressing; cover; refrigerate at least 2 hours.

Meanwhile, in medium bowl, combine reduced-calorie mayonnaise, curry, salt and pepper; slowly stir in milk; add chicken and green pepper; toss. Refrigerate, covered, at least 2 hours.

To serve: Combine rice and chicken mixtures. Arrange on romaine; garnish with onion. Makes 4 servings of a scant cup each.

Diabetic diet: Exchanges per serving = 3 meat and 1 bread.
Low-fat, low-cholesterol diet: Prepare as directed but use skimmed milk (not whole). 5 grams fat per serving.

CHICKEN CURRY—IN A HURRY (270 calories per serving)

1 cup uncooked long-grain rice
1 tablespoon salad oil
2 whole chicken breasts (about
    1½ pounds), split, skinned,
    boned and cut into bite-size
    pieces
½ pound fresh mushrooms,
    thinly sliced
⅓ cup chopped onion
3 tablespoons flour
1 chicken-bouillon cube
1 teaspoon salt
1½ teaspoons curry
1 apple, quartered, thinly sliced
¼ cup chopped parsley
¾ cup skimmed milk or re-
    liquefied nonfat dry milk

About 30 minutes before serving: Cook rice as label directs but omit butter. In large skillet over medium heat, in oil, brown chicken, mushrooms and onion until chicken is golden and completely cooked—about 10 minutes. Stir in flour, bouillon cube, salt and curry to form a smooth paste. Add apple and parsley, then stir in milk and 1 cup water. Cook, stirring constantly, until thickened; still stirring, simmer 3 minutes, or until apple is tender-crisp. Makes 6 servings.

Diabetic diet: Serve ½ cup curry sauce over ½ cup rice. Exchanges per serving = 3 meat, 1 bread, 1 vegetable and ½ fat.
Egg-, gluten- and wheat-free diet: Prepare as directed but use 1½ tablespoons cornstarch in place of flour; omit chicken-bouillon cube on gluten- and wheat-free diet.
Low-fat, low-cholesterol diet: 5 grams fat per serving.

WAISTLINE BARBECUED CHICKEN (245 calories per serving)

2 tablespoons salad oil
4 whole chicken breasts (about
    3 pounds), split
3 cups tomato juice
½ cup vinegar
1 tablespoon granulated sugar
4 medium onions, sliced
3 tablespoons Worcestershire
½ cup catchup
4 teaspoons prepared mustard
1 teaspoon pepper
1½ teaspoons salt

About 1 hour before serving: Preheat oven to 350°F. In skillet, in oil, brown chicken well on all sides. Remove to shallow baking pan. In saucepan, heat tomato juice and remaining ingredients; pour over chicken. Bake, uncovered, 40 minutes, or until tender, basting every 10 minutes with sauce. Makes 8 servings.

Low-fat, low-cholesterol diet: Prepare as directed; dieter should not eat skin of the chicken. 5 grams fat per serving.

CHICKEN TROPICALE (285 calories per serving)

¼ cup flour
salt
¼ teaspoon pepper
4 small whole chicken breasts
    (about 3 pounds), split,
    skinned and boned
1½ tablespoons salad oil
1 cup orange juice
2 tablespoons brown sugar
2 tablespoons vinegar
¼ teaspoon nutmeg
1 teaspoon basil
8 new potatoes, pared
1 16-ounce can freestone peach
    halves, drained
chopped parsley for garnish

About 1 hour and 10 minutes before serving: Mix flour, 1 teaspoon salt and pepper; dip chicken breasts in mixture; shake off excess. In large skillet or Dutch oven over medium heat, in oil, brown chicken breasts a few at a time on both sides. Return to skillet; add orange juice, brown sugar, vinegar, 1 teaspoon salt, nutmeg, basil and potatoes; cover; simmer 40 minutes, or until potatoes are tender. Add drained peach halves; heat to boiling. Sprinkle with parsley. Makes 8 servings.

Diabetic diet: Prepare as directed but omit sugar; use canned peaches packed in water or fruit juice. Exchanges per serving = 3 meat, 1 bread and 1 fruit.
Egg-, gluten-, milk- and wheat-free diet: Prepare as directed but sprinkle chicken with cornstarch instead of flour for gluten- and wheat-free diets.
Low-fat, low-cholesterol diet: 5 grams fat per serving.
Low-sodium diet: Prepare as directed but omit salt. 75 milligrams sodium per serving.

SPEEDY CHICKEN CREOLE (305 calories per serving)

3 large whole chicken breasts (about 2¹/₂ pounds), split, skinned and boned
2 tablespoons butter or margarine
1¹/₂ teaspoons salt
1 medium onion, minced
1 cup sliced celery
1 10-ounce package frozen whole okra, thawed, sliced
1 16-ounce can tomatoes
1 8-ounce can tomato sauce
1 teaspoon ground thyme
1 teaspoon parsley flakes
¹/₄ teaspoon Tabasco
6 slices toast

About 45 minutes before serving: Cut each chicken breast half into 10 or 12 strips. In large skillet over medium heat, in butter, brown chicken and salt, stirring constantly, 3 minutes. Add onion, celery and okra; cook 2 minutes, stirring. Add tomatoes, tomato sauce, thyme, parsley and Tabasco; stir; bring to boiling; cover; cook 5 minutes. Serve over toast slices. Makes 6 servings.

Diabetic diet: Prepare as directed but use margarine instead of butter. Carefully divide into 6 equal servings. Exchanges per serving = 4 meat, 2 vegetable, 1 bread and 1 fat.
Egg-, gluten-, milk- and wheat-free diet: Prepare as directed but use milk-free margarine on milk-free diets. Serve over cooked rice instead of toast for gluten- and wheat-free diets.
Low-fat, low-cholesterol diet: Prepare as directed but use salad oil or margarine instead of butter. 10 grams fat per serving.
High-iron diet: 3.5 milligrams iron per serving.

CHICKEN SALAD IN PINEAPPLE (305 calories per serving)

2 medium pineapples
3 cups cut-up cooked chicken
1 cup diced celery
¹/₂ to ³/₄ cup reduced-calorie Italian dressing
¹/₄ cup salted peanuts
2 tablespoons slivered crystallized ginger

Early in day: Halve each pineapple lengthwise through green crown. With long sharp knife, cut around each half pineapple, ¹/₂ inch from edge, to free meat; do not cut through rind. Cut pineapple meat crosswise into slices about ³/₄-inch thick; then run knife under meat down full length of center; lift out chunks; cut off core.

Toss together chicken, celery, reduced-calorie Italian dressing, half the peanuts and half the slivered ginger. Spoon a little into each pineapple shell; then arrange pineapple chunks, broad-side up, around sides of each. Place rest of chunks in center. Top with rest of chicken salad, peanuts and ginger. Refrigerate. Makes 4 servings.

Low-fat, low-cholesterol diet: 15 grams fat per serving.

PLYMOUTH CHICKEN SPECIAL (270 calories per serving)

2 cups uncooked egg noodles
1 tablespoon salad oil
¹/₂ pound fresh mushrooms, thinly sliced
2 tablespoons flour
¹/₂ teaspoon salt
¹/₂ teaspoon celery salt
1¹/₂ cups skimmed milk or reliquefied nonfat dry milk
2 cups cubed cooked chicken or turkey (about 10 ounces)
2 slices day-old bread, cubed

About 40 minutes before serving: Preheat oven to 375°F. Cook noodles as label directs; drain. Meanwhile, in large saucepan over medium heat, in oil, sauté mushrooms until golden. Stir in flour, salt and celery salt. Slowly add milk; cook, stirring constantly, until thickened and smooth. Stir in chicken; heat to boiling. In 2-quart casserole, mix noodles and mushroom-chicken mixture. Top with bread cubes. Bake 15 minutes, or until cubes are golden brown. Makes 6 servings of about 1 cup each.

Bland diet: Prepare as directed but omit celery salt if forbidden; ¹/₂ teaspoon ground thyme may be substituted.
Diabetic diet: Exchanges per serving = 3 meat, 2 bread and ¹/₂ fat.
Low-fat, low-cholesterol diet: 5 grams fat per serving.
Low-fat, bland (gall bladder) diet: Prepare as directed for bland diet.
Low-residue diet: Prepare as directed for bland diet.
Low-sodium diet: Prepare as directed but cook noodles and chicken without adding salt; omit salt; substitute celery seed for celery salt. 110 milligrams sodium per serving. If prepared with low-sodium bread, 75 milligrams sodium per serving.

DEVILED CHICKEN (295 calories per serving)

2 whole chicken breasts (about 1¹/₂ pounds), split and skinned
2 tablespoons salad oil
2 teaspoons Worcestershire
1 teaspoon dry mustard
1 tablespoon parsley flakes
1 teaspoon salt
¹/₄ teaspoon pepper
2 cups fresh bread crumbs

About 1 hour before serving: Preheat oven to 350°F. In medium baking dish, place chicken, skin side down. In medium bowl, mix remaining ingredients. Spread evenly over surface of chicken. Cover; bake 30 minutes; uncover and bake 15 minutes more, or until chicken is tender and bread crumbs are crisp. Makes 4 servings.

Diabetic diet: Exchanges per serving = 4 meat, 1 bread and 1 fat.
Low-fat, low-cholesterol diet: 5 grams fat per serving.

BAKED CHICKEN WITH PEACHES (260 calories per serving)

1 3-pound broiler-fryer, cut up
1 tablespoon flour
1 teaspoon salt
1 tablespoon butter or margarine
1 16-ounce can cling-peach halves
¹/₂ teaspoon cinnamon
¹/₂ teaspoon nutmeg
chopped parsley for garnish

About 1 hour before serving: Preheat oven to 400°F. Place chicken in shallow open roasting pan. Combine flour and salt; use to sprinkle chicken; dot chicken with butter. Bake, uncovered, 30 minutes. Place drained peach halves around chicken (reserve ¹/₂ cup peach syrup); sprinkle with combined cinnamon and nutmeg; spoon on reserved syrup. Bake 20 minutes longer, or until chicken is fork-tender. Arrange on platter; pour pan juices over all; sprinkle with parsley. Makes 6 servings.

Bland diet: Prepare as directed but omit nutmeg and parsley.
Egg-, gluten-, milk- and wheat-free diet: Prepare as directed but use cornstarch instead of flour on gluten- and wheat-free diets; use milk-free margarine on milk-free diet.
Diabetic diet: Prepare as directed but use margarine instead of butter; water-packed peaches. Include 2 peach halves with each serving. Exchanges per serving = 1 fruit plus 1 meat for each ounce of cooked chicken.
Low-fat, low-cholesterol diet: Prepare as directed but use salad oil or margarine instead of butter; dieter should not eat skin of chicken. 10 grams fat per serving.
Low-fat, bland (gall bladder) diet: Prepare as directed but omit nutmeg and parsley.
High-iron diet: 3 milligrams iron per serving.
Low-residue diet: Prepare as directed but omit nutmeg and parsley.
Low-sodium diet: Prepare as directed but omit salt and use unsalted butter or margarine. 90 milligrams sodium per serving.

CHICKEN-VEGETABLE MEDLEY (260 calories per serving)

2 tablespoons salad oil
¹/₂ cup thinly sliced onion
¹/₂ cup thinly sliced celery
1 4-ounce can sliced mushrooms, drained
1 5-ounce can water chestnuts, sliced
1¹/₂ cups cooked or canned chicken, in chunks
¹/₂ cup chicken broth
1 teaspoon cornstarch
soy sauce
1 16-ounce can bean sprouts, drained
3 cups hot fluffy rice
¹/₄ cup toasted almonds

About 30 minutes before serving: In large skillet over medium heat, in oil, sauté onion, celery, mushroom and water chestnut slices 5 minutes. Add chicken and broth; simmer, covered, 10 minutes.

Meanwhile, combine cornstarch with 1 teaspoon soy sauce and 2 tablespoons cold water; stir into chicken. Bring to boiling; add drained bean sprouts; then stir until thickened and bean sprouts are hot. Serve on rice, sprinkled with almonds. Pass soy sauce. Makes 6 servings.

Diabetic diet: Carefully divide chicken mixture into 6 equal servings, and serve each over ¹/₂ cup rice. Exchanges per serving = 3 meat, 1 bread, 1 vegetable and 1 fat.
Low-fat, low-cholesterol diet: 10 grams fat per serving.
High-iron diet: 3.5 milligrams iron per serving.

CHICKEN IN WINE (Coq au Vin) (310 calories per serving)

2 strips bacon, cut into ¹/₂-inch slices
2 small broiler-fryers (about 2 pounds each), quartered
1 tablespoon salad oil
1 pound mushrooms
1 pound small white onions
3 carrots, cut into 1-inch slices
2 garlic cloves, minced
2 medium onions, chopped
¹/₄ cup chopped parsley
salt
1¹/₂ teaspoons marjoram leaves
1 teaspoon thyme leaves
1 bay leaf
pepper
2 beef-bouillon cubes
1¹/₂ cups dry red wine (preferably Burgundy)
¹/₃ cup flour

Day before serving: In large Dutch oven, fry bacon until almost crisp, remove bacon. In bacon fat, brown a few chicken pieces at a time until golden. In same Dutch oven over medium heat, in oil, sauté mushrooms, white onions and carrots until onions brown lightly; remove all. Sauté garlic and chopped onions in remaining fat until golden.

Return chicken pieces to Dutch oven and cover with vegetables. Add parsley, 1 tablespoon salt, marjoram, thyme, bay leaf, ¹/₈ teaspoon pepper, bouillon cubes, wine and 1¹/₂ cups water. Cover; boil gently 20 minutes. Cool slightly; refrigerate, covered.

About 1 hour and 10 minutes before serving: Heat chicken mixture to boiling; then simmer, covered, 40 minutes, or until chicken is tender. Mix enough water with flour to form a smooth paste. Remove chicken to warm platter. Add flour paste to stock, stirring constantly; simmer until thickened. Add salt and pepper to taste. Remove vegetables from gravy and arrange around chicken. Spoon on some gravy; pass remaining gravy. Makes 8 servings.

Egg-, gluten-, milk- and wheat-free diet: Prepare as directed but omit bouillon cubes; thicken gravy with 2 tablespoons cornstarch (not flour) for gluten- and wheat-free diets.
Low-fat, low-cholesterol diet: Prepare as directed but omit bacon; add an extra 2 tablespoons salad oil. Dieter should not eat skin of chicken. 10 grams fat per serving.
High-iron diet: 4 milligrams iron per serving.

BEAN-AND-CHICKEN SALAD (210 calories per serving)

2 whole chicken breasts (about 1¹/₂ pounds), split, skinned and boned
2 16-ounce cans whole green beans, chilled and drained
¹/₂ teaspoon seasoned salt
¹/₄ teaspoon seasoned pepper
¹/₂ cup bottled reduced–calorie Italian dressing
chopped dill
1 apple, cut into thin wedges for garnish
lemon juice for garnish

Early in day: Cook chicken in salted boiling water until tender— about 20 minutes; drain; refrigerate.

About 1¹/₂ hours before serving: Cut chicken into thin strips. In large salad bowl, toss with green beans, seasoned salt, seasoned pepper, reduced–calorie dressing and 1 teaspoon dill. Toss apple wedges with lemon juice and use to garnish salad. Sprinkle with another teaspoon dill. Refrigerate until serving time. Makes 4 servings.

Diabetic diet: Carefully divide into 4 equal servings. Exchanges per serving = 3 meat and 1 bread.
Low-fat, low-cholesterol diet: 5 grams fat per serving.
High-iron diet: 4 milligrams iron per serving.

CHICKEN JAMBALAYA (310 calories per serving)

1 7¹/₂-ounce package Spanish-rice mix
¹/₂-pound slice boiled ham, trimmed of fat, cubed
1 tablespoon salad oil
1 cup chopped celery
1 cup coarsely chopped green pepper
¹/₄ cup chopped scallions
1 cup cubed cooked chicken
dash pepper
1 cup canned tomatoes, drained

About 1 hour before serving: In large skillet, cook Spanish-rice mix as label directs but omit butter. Stir in ham. In skillet over medium heat, in oil, sauté celery and green peppers until tender. Add scallions and sauté a few minutes longer. Add to rice mixture with chicken, pepper and tomatoes; heat to boiling. Makes 5 servings.

Diabetic diet: Carefully divide into 5 equal servings (about 1 cup each). Exchanges per serving = 3 meat, 1 vegetable, 2 bread and 1 fat.
Low-fat, low-cholesterol diet: 10 grams fat per serving.
High-iron diet: 3.5 milligrams iron per serving.

CHICKEN AND TOMATOES (255 calories per serving)

2 whole chicken breasts (about
1½ pounds), split, skinned
and boned
1 tablespoon sherry (optional)
2 tablespoons soy sauce
2 tablespoons cornstarch
2 tablespoons salad oil
1 medium onion, diced
1 teaspoon granulated sugar
¾ cup chicken broth
1 16-ounce can stewed tomatoes

About 30 minutes before serving: Cut chicken into 1-inch cubes. In medium bowl, blend sherry and 1 tablespoon soy sauce with 1 tablespoon cornstarch. Toss with chicken; let stand 15 minutes.

In medium skillet over medium heat, in oil, brown chicken, stirring occasionally; add onion and cook 2 minutes more. In bowl, mix remaining soy sauce and cornstarch, sugar and broth; pour over chicken and cook, stirring, until mixture thickens. Add tomatoes; simmer 2 minutes to heat through. Makes 4 servings.

Diabetic diet: Prepare as directed but omit sugar. Exchanges per serving = 3 meat, 1 vegetable and 1½ fat.
Low-fat, low-cholesterol diet: 10 grams fat per serving.

CHICKEN IN MUSTARD SAUCE (Pollo en Salsa de Mostaza) (205 calories per serving)

¼ cup flour
½ teaspoon salt
¼ teaspoon garlic salt
¼ teaspoon onion salt
2 whole chicken breasts (about
1½ pounds), split, skinned
and boned
2 tablespoons butter or margarine
1 chicken-bouillon cube
½ tablespoon lemon juice
¾ teaspoon dry mustard
1 teaspoon granulated sugar
1½ teaspoons cornstarch

About 45 minutes before serving: Mix flour, salt, garlic salt and onion salt. Use to coat chicken, shaking off excess. In large skillet over medium heat, in butter or margarine, brown chicken until golden—about 5 minutes to a side. Add bouillon cube and ¾ cup water; cover; simmer 20 minutes. Meanwhile, mix remaining ingredients with 1 tablespoon water to form a smooth paste. Remove chicken to warm platter; stir lemon-cornstarch mixture into chicken broth; stirring constantly, cook until thickened and smooth. Pour gravy over chicken. Makes 4 servings.

Diabetic diet: Prepare as directed but use margarine instead of butter; omit sugar; do not serve extra gravy with chicken. Exchanges per serving = 3 meat and 1½ fat.
Egg-, gluten-, milk- and wheat-free diet: Prepare as directed but coat chicken with cornstarch instead of flour and omit bouillon cube on gluten- and wheat-free diets; use milk-free margarine on milk-free diet.
Low-fat, low-cholesterol diet: Prepare as directed but use margarine or salad oil instead of butter. 10 grams fat per serving.
Low-sodium diet: Prepare as directed but omit salt; use garlic powder and onion powder (not the salts); use unsalted butter or margarine; omit bouillon cube. 70 milligrams sodium per serving.

CHICKEN WITH VEGETABLES (170 calories per serving)

4 large whole chicken breasts
(about 3 pounds), split,
skinned and boned
paprika
salt and pepper
2 tablespoons butter or margarine
3 medium yellow summer
squash or zucchini, sliced
diagonally ⅛-inch thick
5 scallions, tops and all, finely
sliced
½ teaspoon basil

About 30 minutes before serving: Sprinkle chicken with paprika, ¾ teaspoon salt and ⅛ teaspoon pepper. In large skillet over medium heat, in butter, brown chicken until golden on both sides; add ½ cup water and simmer, covered, 15 minutes. Now another ½ cup water, squash, scallions, ¾ teaspoon salt, ⅛ teaspoon pepper, and basil. Cover; cook 10 minutes, or until vegetables are tender. Makes 8 servings.

Diabetic diet: Prepare as directed but use margarine instead of butter. Exchanges per serving = 3 meat, 1 vegetable and 1 fat.
Egg-, gluten-, milk- and wheat-free diet: Prepare as directed but use milk-free margarine for milk-free diet.
Low-fat, low-cholesterol diet: Prepare as directed but use margarine or salad oil instead of butter. 5 grams fat per serving.
Low-sodium diet: Prepare as directed but omit salt and use unsalted butter or margarine. 70 milligrams sodium per serving.

CHICKEN IN ASPIC (195 calories per serving)

3 whole chicken breasts (about 2¹/₂ pounds) cut in half
¹/₂ teaspoon seasoned salt
¹/₄ teaspoon seasoned pepper
1¹/₂ teaspoons unflavored gelatin
1¹/₂ tablespoons water
2 10¹/₂-ounce cans condensed beef consommé
2 heads romaine
fresh dill sprigs
your favorite reduced–calorie salad dressing

Day before or early in day: Preheat broiler 10 minutes if manufacturer directs. Place chicken in jelly-roll pan, skin side down. Sprinkle with seasoned salt and seasoned pepper. Broil until golden-brown—about 18 minutes; then turn and broil until second side is golden-brown. Cool, then place, skin side down, in medium baking dish. In cup, mix gelatin with water; set in hot water and stir until dissolved. Stir into undiluted consommé, then pour over chicken. Refrigerate until consommé is partially set. Turn chicken over; spoon consommé over it; refrigerate until consommé sets a bit more, then continue spooning consommé over chicken; allow it to set until chicken is coated.

To serve: Arrange chicken breasts on platter, spoke fashion. Remove outer leaves of romaine; cut head into sixths; arrange between chicken breasts; top with dill. Pass salad dressing to spoon over romaine. Makes 6 servings.

Diabetic diet: Exchanges per serving = 4 meat.
Low-fat, low-cholesterol diet: Prepare as directed but remove skin from cooked chicken before glazing with aspic. 2 grams fat per serving.
High-iron diet: 3 milligrams iron per serving.

HERBED CHICKEN IN WINE (245 calories per serving)

1 3-pound broiler-fryer, cut up
¹/₄ cup flour
1 teaspoon salt
¹/₄ teaspoon pepper
2 tablespoons salad oil
1 cup dry white wine
1 cup sliced mushrooms (about ¹/₄ pound)
1 teaspoon tarragon
1 teaspoon thyme leaves
1 teaspoon chopped chives (optional)

About 45 minutes before serving: Skin and trim fat from chicken. In plastic or paper bag, combine flour, salt and pepper; shake a few pieces of chicken at a time in flour mixture until coated. In large skillet over medium heat, in hot oil, brown chicken on all sides—about 15 minutes. Reduce heat to low; add wine, mushrooms, tarragon, thyme and chives; cover and simmer 20 minutes, or until chicken is fork-tender. Makes 6 servings.

Egg-, gluten-, milk- and wheat-free diet: Prepare as directed but use cornstarch instead of flour on gluten- and wheat-free diets.
Low-fat, low-cholesterol diet: Prepare as directed. 10 grams fat per serving.
Low-sodium diet: Prepare as directed but omit salt. 105 milligrams sodium per serving.

CHICKEN LIVERS IN WINE (315 calories per serving on toast)

¹/₂ pound chicken livers (or frozen livers, thawed)
1 tablespoon salad oil
¹/₄ cup thinly sliced celery
¹/₂ teaspoon parsley flakes
¹/₂ teaspoon dried minced chives
2 whole cloves
³/₄ cup dry sherry
1 red-skinned cooking apple, chopped
1 teaspoon flour
salt
toast points prepared from 2 slices bread

About 20 minutes before serving: Remove connective tissue or fat from livers. In medium skillet over medium heat, in oil, sauté livers, celery, parsley and chives; remove from pan; add cloves, sherry and apples; simmer, covered, 5 minutes, or until apples are almost tender. Make paste of flour and a few drops of water; stir into apple mixture; simmer until thickened; return livers to pan; heat; add salt to taste. Serve on toast points. Makes 2 servings.

Diabetic diet: Exchanges per serving = 3 meat, ¹/₂ fruit and 1 bread.
Egg-, gluten-, milk- and wheat-free diet: Prepare as directed but use cornstarch in place of flour; serve livers over rice (not toast points) for gluten- and wheat-free diets.
High-iron diet: 9.5 milligrams iron per serving.
Low-sodium diet: Prepare as directed but omit salt. 195 milligrams sodium per serving. If served with low-sodium bread, 75 milligrams sodium per serving.

CHICKEN KABOBS ITALIANO (240 calories per serving)

2 whole chicken breasts (about 1¹/₂ pounds), split, skinned and boned
1 cup reduced–calorie Italian dressing
2 green peppers, cut into 1-inch slices
8 fresh medium mushrooms
8 small white onions, sliced
4 fresh medium tomatoes, quartered

About 4 hours before serving: Cut chicken into 1-inch pieces. Marinate in reduced–calorie Italian dressing, in refrigerator, at least 3¹/₂ hours.

About 30 minutes before serving: Preheat broiler 10 minutes if manufacturer directs. In water to cover, boil green peppers, mushrooms and onions 5 minutes. Line large baking or jelly-roll pan with foil; turn up edges to prevent spilling.

On eight 8-inch skewers, alternate chicken with tomatoes, green peppers, onions and mushrooms. Brush with remaining reduced–calorie Italian dressing. Place skewers, not touching, on lined baking pan. Place under broiler with skewers 3 to 5 inches from heat; broil 7 minutes; turn; brush again with dressing. Broil 7 minutes on other side, or until chicken is done but still tender. Makes 4 servings.

Diabetic diet: Exchanges per serving = 4 meat and 2 vegetable.
Low-fat, low-cholesterol diet: 5 grams fat per serving.
High-iron diet: 3 milligrams iron per serving.
Low-sodium diet: Prepare as directed but marinate chicken in home-made low-sodium dressing (such as ¹/₃ cup vinegar, ²/₃ cup salad oil, ¹/₈ teaspoon paprika, ¹/₄ teaspoon dry mustard, ¹/₈ teaspoon black pepper and 1 teaspoon minced onion). 90 milligrams sodium per serving.

CHICKEN LIVER SAUTÉ WITH ONION-CURRY SAUCE (235 calories per serving)

2 tablespoons butter or margarine
1 pound fresh chicken livers or frozen livers, thawed
1 medium onion, thinly sliced
¹/₃ cup nonfat dry-milk powder
1 tablespoon flour
¹/₄ teaspoon curry
¹/₂ teaspoon salt
dash pepper

About 25 minutes before serving: In skillet over low heat, in butter or margarine, cook livers about 5 minutes, turning often. Remove. In same skillet, cook onion slices with ¹/₂ cup boiling water, uncovered, 10 minutes, or until onions are tender. Stir together dry-milk powder, ¹/₂ cup water, and remaining ingredients. Gradually stir into onion mixture; cook, stirring constantly, until thickened. Serve over chicken livers. Makes 4 servings.

Diabetic diet: Prepare as directed but use margarine instead of butter. Exchanges per serving = 3 meat, 1 vegetable and 2 fat.
Low-fat diet: 10 grams fat per serving. Omit recipe from low-cholesterol diet.
High-iron diet: 9 milligrams iron per serving.
Low-sodium diet: Prepare as directed but use unsalted butter or margarine; use curry not containing salt; omit salt. 115 milligrams sodium per serving.

JULES' CHICKEN LIVERS (210 calories per serving)

1 pound fresh chicken livers (or 1 pound frozen chicken livers, thawed)
2 tablespoons salad oil
1 teaspoon flour
2 tablespoons to ¹/₃ cup wine vinegar
garlic and onion salt to taste

About 20 minutes before serving: Wash chicken livers and cut away any fat or filament; dry livers on paper toweling. In medium skillet over medium heat, in oil, brown about 2 minutes on each side, or until almost to desired degree of doneness. Stir in flour; add vinegar. Stirring constantly, simmer 2 minutes; then add garlic and onion salt to taste. Makes 4 servings.

Diabetic diet: Exchanges per serving = 3 meat and 2 fat.
Egg-, gluten-, milk- and wheat-free diet: Prepare as directed but use cornstarch in place of flour on gluten- and wheat-free diets.
High-iron diet: 9 milligrams iron per serving.
Low-sodium diet: Prepare as directed but use garlic and onion powder in place of the salts. 80 milligrams sodium per serving.

BAKED CHICKEN DINNER (220 calories per serving)

8 celery stalks
8 large carrots
3/4 pound small white onions
  (about 12)
4 chicken breasts, halved
  (about 3 pounds)
1/4 cup chopped parsley
2 10 1/2-ounce cans condensed
  cream of mushroom soup
paprika

About 1 hour and 45 minutes before serving: Preheat oven to 350°F. Cut celery and carrots into chunks. In covered medium saucepan over medium heat, in 1 cup boiling salted water, cook celery, carrots and onions 15 minutes; drain.

Remove skin from chicken breasts; place chicken in large baking dish; sprinkle with parsley. Arrange vegetables around chicken.

In small bowl, stir undiluted soup until smooth; pour evenly over chicken and vegetables. Sprinkle generously with paprika. Cover, and bake 1 hour or until chicken and vegetables are fork-tender. Makes 8 servings.

To do ahead: Early in day, prepare recipe as above but, instead of baking it, cover and refrigerate. About 1 hour and 15 minutes before serving, bake in preheated 350°F. oven until fork-tender.

Bland diet: Prepare as directed but omit celery and onions.
Low-fat diet: 10 grams fat per serving. Omit recipe from low-cholesterol diet.
Low-residue diet: Prepare as directed but omit celery and onions.

ORANGE BAKED CHICKEN (255 calories per serving)

5 whole chicken breasts (about
  4 pounds), skinned and split
1/4 cup minced onion
1/2 teaspoon paprika
1 teaspoon salt
1/4 teaspoon rosemary
1/8 teaspoon pepper
2 tablespoons flour
2 cups orange juice
1 8-ounce package noodles

About 1 hour and 15 minutes before serving: Preheat oven to 350°F. Spread chicken breasts in large shallow baking pan, not overlapping. Sprinkle with onion and seasonings. In medium bowl, blend flour with about 1/2 cup orange juice to form a smooth paste; stir in remaining juice; pour over chicken. Bake, uncovered, 1 hour or until tender, basting occasionally with juice in pan. Meanwhile, cook noodles as label directs; drain. Serve chicken and gravy over noodles. Makes 10 servings.

Bland diet: Prepare as directed but omit onion, rosemary and pepper.
Low-fat, low-cholesterol diet: 5 grams fat per serving.
Low-fat, bland (gall bladder) diet: Prepare as directed for bland diet.
Low-residue diet: Prepare as directed for bland diet.

TURKEY ORIENTALE (255 calories per serving)

1 tablespoon butter or marga-
  rine
1 medium onion, sliced
1 green pepper, sliced
2 stalks celery, sliced
1 3-ounce can sliced mush-
  rooms
1 16-ounce can bean sprouts
1 5 1/4-ounce can bamboo
  shoots, drained
1 1/2 cups leftover roast turkey,
  cut into strips
5 teaspoons soy sauce
2 tablespoons cornstarch

About 25 minutes before serving: In large skillet, in butter or margarine, sauté onion, green pepper and celery until tender. Add mushrooms and bean sprouts with their liquids, bamboo shoots and turkey. Cook, covered, over low heat, 15 minutes. Gradually stir 1/3 cup water and soy sauce into cornstarch. Stir into turkey-vegetable mixture; cook, stirring, until thickened. Makes 3 servings.

Low-fat, low-cholesterol diet: Prepare as directed but use margarine or salad oil instead of butter. 10 grams fat per serving.

HAM-AND-CHICKEN CROWN (220 calories per serving)

1 envelope unflavored gelatin
1 10¹/₂-ounce can condensed
  cream of celery soup
1 tablespoon lemon juice
dash pepper
1 cup diced cooked or canned
  chicken or turkey
2 tablespoons chopped onion
3 slices (3 ounces) boiled ham
8 stuffed olives, sliced
lettuce

Early in day: In double boiler, sprinkle gelatin onto ¹/₂ cup cold water; let stand 5 minutes; cook over hot water until gelatin is dissolved. Combine soup, ¹/₄ cup water, lemon juice and pepper; add to gelatin; stir in chicken and onion. Trim fat from ham; use to line sides of three 12-ounce custard cups; cover bottoms with sliced olives. Fill with chicken mixture. Refrigerate until firm.

To serve: Unmold on crisp lettuce. Makes 3 servings.

Diabetic diet: Exchanges per serving = 3 meat, 1 vegetable and 1 fat.
Low-fat diet: 10 grams fat per serving. Omit recipe from low-cholesterol diet.

SAVORY CHICKEN BAKE (255 calories per serving)

1 10-ounce package frozen
  broccoli spears
¹/₄ cup skimmed milk or reliquefied nonfat dry milk
2 cups cubed cooked or canned
  chicken
1 10³/₄-ounce can condensed
  cream-of-chicken soup
¹/₈ teaspoon savory
¹/₄ cup grated Cheddar cheese

About 45 minutes before serving: Preheat oven to 350°F. Cook broccoli as label directs; drain. Combine milk, chicken, soup and savory. In each of four 2-cup casseroles, place layer of broccoli; cover with chicken mixture; top with remaining broccoli; sprinkle with cheese. Bake, covered, 20 minutes, or until bubbling. Makes 4 servings.

Diabetic diet: Exchanges per serving = 4 meat, 1 vegetable and ¹/₂ skim milk.
Low-fat diet: 10 grams fat per serving. Omit recipe from low-cholesterol diet.

CHOPPED CHICKEN LIVERS (130 calories per serving)

¹/₂ pound fresh chicken livers
  (or frozen livers, thawed)
1 medium onion, finely chopped
1 tablespoon rendered chicken
  or bacon fat
1 hard-cooked egg
¹/₄ cup chopped parsley
¹/₂ teaspoon salt
¹/₂ teaspoon lemon juice

At least 3 hours before serving: Wash and remove any fat from livers. In medium skillet, in rendered chicken or bacon fat, sauté onion until well browned. (Take care not to burn fat.) Add chicken livers and brown 3 to 5 minutes.

In electric-blender container, at low speed, blend livers with fat, cooked onion and remaining ingredients until smooth. (Add small amount of water if needed.) Transfer to small container; cover; refrigerate until serving time. Makes filling for four sandwiches or serve on lettuce as appetizer.

Diabetic diet: Exchanges per serving = 2 meat and 2 fat.
Gluten-, milk- and wheat-free diet: Prepare as directed; serve as appetizer.
High-iron diet: 5 milligrams iron per serving.
Low-sodium diet: Prepare as directed but cook livers in chicken fat and omit salt. 60 milligrams sodium per serving.

FRUITED TURKEY SALAD (245 calories per serving)

2 cups cubed cooked turkey or
  chicken
¹/₂ cup chopped celery
¹/₂ cup drained canned
  mandarin-orange sections
¹/₂ cup halved seedless grapes
¹/₂ teaspoon salt
¹/₄ cup reduced–calorie mayonnaise
3 lettuce cups

At least 2 hours before serving: Toss together all ingredients but lettuce. Refrigerate to allow flavors to blend. Serve in lettuce cups. Makes 3 servings.

Low-fat, low-cholesterol diet: 5 grams fat per serving.

ROAST TURKEY-ROLL PLATTER (70 calories for each thin slice turkey; 170 calories per Stuffing Ball; 20 calories per ¼ cup gravy)

1 4-pound frozen turkey roll
1 teaspoon seasoned salt
6 strips bacon
½ cup chopped onion
1 cup chopped celery
1 cup chopped fresh mush-
 rooms
1 8-ounce package herb-
 seasoned stuffing mix
1 cup canned chicken broth,
 heated
2 tablespoons flour
parsley for garnish

2 days before serving: Thaw turkey roll by storing in refrigerator for 1½ to 2 days.

About 3 hours before serving: Remove wrapping from thawed turkey roll. Preheat oven to 375°F. Place turkey roll on rack in shallow roasting pan; sprinkle with seasoned salt; cover with foil; then insert roast-meat thermometer into center. Roast 1½ hours. Open foil and pour off drippings, reserving 6 tablespoons. Arrange bacon strips on roll; cover again with foil; roast 30 minutes longer. Uncover; roast until meat thermometer reads 175°F.—about 35 minutes per pound.

Meanwhile, prepare Stuffing Balls. In medium skillet over medium heat, in ¼ cup turkey drippings, sauté onion, celery and mushrooms till tender. In medium bowl, mix stuffing mix with chicken broth and onion mixture until moist. Form into 8 balls; arrange on greased cookie sheet.

About 15 minutes before turkey is done, spoon 1 teaspoon drippings over each stuffing ball. Bake balls, with turkey, for 15 minutes; then remove turkey to hot platter and bake balls 10 minutes longer.

Meanwhile, prepare gravy as follows: In roasting pan, mix 1 tablespoon drippings and flour, scraping up brown bits from bottom of pan. Slowly stir in 2 cups water and cook, stirring constantly, until thickened.

To serve: Carve turkey into thin slices; surround with stuffing balls; garnish with parsley. Pass gravy in gravy boat. Makes 8 servings.

Diabetic diet: Exchanges per stuffing ball = 1 vegetable, 1 bread and 1 fat. Count turkey as 1 meat exchange for each ounce. Up to ¼ cup gravy = 1 "free" exchange.

BRAISED CHICKEN LIVERS (265 calories per serving)

1 pound fresh chicken livers (or
 frozen livers, thawed)
¼ cup flour
½ teaspoon salt
1 tablespoon salad oil
⅔ to 1 cup canned tomato juice
4 slices toast, quartered

About 30 minutes before serving: Remove any fat from livers. Toss livers with flour, mixed with salt, just to coat; shake off excess. In medium skillet over medium heat, in oil, brown livers well on both sides. Add tomato juice; cover; boil gently 10 minutes, or until livers are done and tomato sauce has thickened slightly.

To serve: Top toast points with livers and sauce. Makes 4 servings.

Bland diet: Prepare as directed.
Diabetic diet: Exchanges per serving = 3 meat, 1 bread and 2 fat.
Egg-, gluten-, milk- and wheat-free diet: Prepare as directed but dust livers with cornstarch (not flour); serve over rice (not toast) for gluten- and wheat-free diets.
Low-fat, bland (gall bladder) diet: Prepare as directed.
High-iron diet: 10 milligrams iron per serving.
Low-residue diet: Prepare as directed.
Low-sodium diet: Prepare as directed but omit salt and use water instead of tomato juice. 195 milligrams sodium per serving. If served on low-sodium bread, 80 milligrams sodium per serving.

EASYGOING DINNER PLATTER (325 calories per serving)

1 10-ounce package frozen peas
1 tablespoon granulated sugar
butter or margarine
6 carrots, sliced
1 teaspoon seasoned salt
seasoned pepper
1 9-ounce package frozen whole
  green beans
dash nutmeg
2 summer squash, thinly sliced
3 small tomatoes
1/2 cup reduced-calorie mayonnaise
1 teaspoon prepared mustard
18 slices cold roast turkey or
  sliced turkey roll (about 1 1/4
  pounds)
parsley sprigs for garnish

About 35 minutes before dinner: Cook peas as label directs, adding sugar; drain, then add 1 teaspoon butter or margarine; keep warm. Cook sliced carrots in 1 inch boiling water, covered, until fork-tender; drain; add seasoned salt, a dash of seasoned pepper and 1 teaspoon butter or margarine; keep warm.

Cook whole green beans as label directs; drain; add nutmeg with 1 teaspoon butter or margarine; keep warm. Cook sliced summer squash in 1 inch boiling salted water, covered, until fork-tender; drain, then add dash of seasoned pepper and 1 teaspoon butter or margarine; keep warm.

Cut slice from top of each tomato; hollow out; fill with reduced-calorie mayonnaise mixed with mustard (to spoon onto sliced turkey later). Arrange tomatoes in center of round platter. Then arrange turkey slices in 4 overlapping rows with hot vegetables in between the slices. Tuck parsley sprigs around tomatoes. Makes 6 servings.

Low-fat, low-cholesterol diet: Prepare as directed but use margarine instead of butter. 10 grams fat per serving.
High-iron diet: 3.5 milligrams iron per serving.

QUICK CHICKEN LIVERS (265 calories per serving)

1 tablespoon butter or margarine
2 large onions, thinly sliced
2 large stalks green celery,
  thinly sliced
1 pound fresh chicken livers (or
  frozen livers, thawed)
salt, pepper and garlic salt to
  taste

About 15 minutes before serving: In large skillet over medium heat, in butter or margarine, sauté onion and celery slices until onion is just wilted. Push onions to one side; turn up heat to high. Add chicken livers; top with onions; cook, turning livers once or twice, until done as you like them—3 to 5 minutes. Season to taste with salt, pepper and garlic salt. Makes 3 servings.

Diabetic diet: Prepare as directed but use margarine instead of butter. Exchanges per serving = 4 meat, 1 vegetable and 3 fat.
Egg-, gluten-, milk- and wheat-free diet: Prepare as directed but use milk-free margarine for milk-free diet.
Low-fat diet: 10 grams fat per serving. Omit recipe from low-cholesterol diet.
High-iron diet: 12.5 milligrams iron per serving.
Low-sodium diet: Prepare as directed but use unsalted butter or margarine; omit salt; use garlic powder (not garlic salt). 135 milligrams sodium per serving.

BURGER POT-AU-FEU (305 calories per serving)

6 carrots, halved lengthwise
2 quarts (8 cups) hot water
6 chicken-bouillon cubes
2 medium leeks, halved lengthwise
1 pound lean ground beef
1/2 cup seasoned dried bread
crumbs
1 teaspoon cornstarch
1/2 cup skimmed milk or reliquefied nonfat dry milk
1 egg
1 tablespoon salad oil
1 15 1/2-ounce can small white
onions, drained
1 16-ounce can potatoes,
drained
2 small tomatoes, cut into
thirds crosswise
chopped parsley for garnish

About 45 minutes before serving: In covered Dutch oven, cook carrots in water with bouillon cubes for 10 minutes. Then add leeks; cover; cook 10 minutes, or until carrots are almost tender.

Meanwhile blend together meat, bread crumbs, cornstarch, milk and egg. Form mixture into 18 meatballs. In large skillet over medium heat, in oil, brown on all sides. Turn off heat; cover; keep warm. To carrots in broth add onions, potatoes and tomatoes; heat. Add meatballs; sprinkle with parsley. Makes 6 servings.

Diabetic diet: One serving = 2 carrot halves, 2 potatoes, 2 onions and 3 meatballs plus broth. Exchanges per serving = 2 meat, 1 vegetable and 1 bread.
Low-fat, low-cholesterol diet: Prepare as directed but use only white of egg. 10 grams fat per serving.
High-iron diet: 4 milligrams iron per serving.

LEMON-BARBECUED MEAT LOAVES (325 calories per serving)

1 1/2 pounds lean ground beef
3 slices day-old bread, diced
1/4 cup lemon juice
1/4 cup minced onion
1 egg, slightly beaten
2 teaspoons seasoned salt
1/2 cup catchup
1/4 cup brown sugar
1 teaspoon dry mustard
1/4 teaspoon allspice
1/4 teaspoon ground cloves
6 thin lemon slices

About 50 minutes before serving: Preheat oven to 350°F. In large bowl, combine meat, bread, lemon juice, onion, egg and salt. Mix well and shape into 6 individual loaves; place in greased medium (about 13″ by 9″) baking pan. Bake 15 minutes.

In small bowl, combine remaining ingredients except lemon slices. Use to cover loaves; top each with lemon slice; bake 30 minutes longer, basting occasionally with sauce from pan. Serve sauce over loaves. Makes 6 servings.

Low-fat, low-cholesterol diet: Prepare as directed but use only white of egg. 15 grams fat per serving.
High-iron diet: 4 milligrams iron per serving.

FAMILY HAMBURGER (245 calories per serving)

1 1/2 pounds lean ground beef
1 1/2 teaspoons salt
1/2 teaspoon pepper
1/4 teaspoon garlic powder
1 teaspoon Worcestershire
2 teaspoons butter or margarine
1 onion, cut into rings

About 30 minutes before serving: Preheat broiler if manufacturer directs. In bowl, mix meat, salt, pepper, garlic powder and Worcestershire. Shape into one large patty, about 1 1/2-inches thick. Broil about 7 minutes on each side for medium-rare, or until done as desired.

Meanwhile, in small skillet over medium heat, in butter, sauté onion rings until golden; arrange over patty on heated platter. Cut into 12 slices. Makes 6 servings.

Diabetic diet: Prepare as directed but use margarine instead of butter. Carefully divide into 6 equal servings. Exchanges per serving = 3 meat.
Egg-, gluten-, milk- and wheat-free diet: Prepare as directed but use milk-free margarine for milk-free diet.
Low-fat, low-cholesterol diet: Prepare as directed but use margarine instead of butter. 15 grams fat per serving.
High-iron diet: 3.5 milligrams iron per serving.
Low-sodium diet: Prepare as directed but omit salt and Worcestershire; use unsalted butter or margarine. 75 milligrams sodium per serving.

SWEET-AND-SOUR MEAT LOAF (230 calories per serving)

1 pound lean ground beef
1 medium onion, minced
12 individual saltine crackers, crushed
dash pepper
1/2 teaspoon salt
1 8-ounce can tomato sauce
2 egg whites
2 tablespoons vinegar
1/4 teaspoon dry mustard
2 tablespoons brown sugar

About 1 hour and 10 minutes before serving: Preheat oven to 350°F. In 9-inch pie plate or baking dish, mix meat, onion, crackers, pepper, salt, 1/2 cup tomato sauce, and egg whites; form round loaf. Mix remaining tomato sauce, vinegar, mustard and brown sugar; pour over meat loaf; pour 2/3 cup water around edge of loaf. Bake 1 hour, or to desired doneness.

To serve: Let cool 5 minutes, then cut into serving pieces. Makes 6 servings.

Diabetic diet: Prepare as directed but omit sugar, and use non-nutritive sweetner equivalent to 1 tablespoon sugar. Exchanges per serving = 2 meat and 1 bread.
Low-fat, low-cholesterol diet: 10 grams fat per serving.
High-iron diet: Prepare as directed but use enriched saltines. 3 milligrams iron per serving.

SURPRISE HAMBURGERS (225 calories per serving)

1 1/4 pounds lean ground beef
1 teaspoon salt
1 teaspoon Worcestershire
1/2 teaspoon dry mustard
1/4 teaspoon nutmeg
3 hard-cooked eggs

About 30 minutes before serving: Preheat broiler 10 minutes if manufacturer directs. Combine meat, salt, Worcestershire, mustard and nutmeg; shape into 12 patties.

Cut eggs in half lengthwise. Place one half, cut side down, on a patty; top with another patty; press firmly together. Repeat with remaining patties. Place on broiler rack. Broil 4 minutes; turn and broil 4 minutes longer, or to desired doneness. Makes 6 servings.

Diabetic diet: Exchanges per serving = 3 meat.
Gluten-, milk- and wheat-free diet: Prepare as directed.
High-iron diet: 4 milligrams iron per serving.

HAMBURGER CHOP SUEY (300 calories per serving)

1 pound lean ground beef
1 onion, sliced
1 cup chopped celery
1 16-ounce can bean sprouts, drained
1 10 1/2-ounce can condensed beef broth
1 3- or 4-ounce can mushrooms
2 tablespoons cornstarch
1/4 cup soy sauce
3 cups hot cooked rice

About 25 minutes before serving: In skillet, stirring constantly, cook meat with onion and celery until meat loses its red color. Add bean sprouts, beef broth and mushrooms (including liquid); cover; simmer 10 minutes. Mix cornstarch with soy sauce and stir into meat mixture; simmer 5 minutes. Serve over rice. Makes 6 servings of 3/4 cup meat sauce and 1/2 cup rice each.

Diabetic diet: Exchanges per serving = 2 meat, 1 1/2 vegetable and 2 bread.
Low-fat, low-cholesterol diet: 10 grams fat per serving.
High-iron diet: 3.5 milligrams iron per serving.

HAMBURGER, SPANISH STYLE (310 calories per serving)

1 pound lean ground beef
1 small onion, chopped
1 8-ounce can tomato sauce
dash Tabasco
1/2 teaspoon prepared mustard
dash pepper
1 8-ounce can French-style green beans, drained
4 slices toast

About 25 minutes before serving: In skillet over medium heat, cook meat and onion until meat loses red color. Stir in 1/4 cup water, tomato sauce, Tabasco, mustard and pepper; cook, covered, 10 minutes. Add green beans and simmer 5 minutes. Serve on toast. Makes 4 servings.

Diabetic diet: Exchanges per serving = 3 meat, 1 vegetable and 1 bread.
Low-fat, low-cholesterol diet: 15 grams fat per serving.
High-iron diet: 4.5 milligrams iron per serving.

GREEK PARSLEY MEATBALLS (235 calories per serving)

1/3 cup packaged dried bread
   crumbs
1/4 cup skimmed milk or reliquefied nonfat dry milk
1 medium onion, chopped
1 pound lean ground beef
chopped parsley
1 egg
1 garlic clove, minced
1/4 teaspoon oregano leaves
1 teaspoon salt
1/8 teaspoon pepper
2 tablespoons salad oil
2 tablespoons lemon juice or
   red wine vinegar

About 1 hour before serving: Let bread crumbs soak in milk until soft. In small saucepan, combine onion and 1/4 cup water; cook, covered, until water has almost boiled away and onions are transparent. In medium bowl, mix meat, 1/2 cup parsley, egg, garlic, oregano, salt, pepper, soaked bread crumbs and cooked onion. Form into 12 meatballs.

About 30 minutes before serving: In large skillet, in oil, brown meatballs on all sides. Transfer to heated serving dish or platter. Pour lemon juice into hot skillet; scrape up and blend drippings with juice; pour over meatballs. Sprinkle with a little parsley. Makes 6 servings.

Diabetic diet: Exchanges per serving = 2 meat, 1/2 bread and 1 fat.
Low-fat, low-cholesterol diet: Prepare as directed but use only white of egg. 15 grams fat per serving.

POLENTA MEAT PIE (330 calories per serving)

1 tablespoon salad oil
1/4 cup finely chopped onion
1 garlic clove, finely minced
1 pound lean ground beef
1 cup fresh bread crumbs
1 egg
buttermilk
1/4 cup catchup
salt
1/8 teaspoon pepper
1/2 cup yellow cornmeal
1 teaspoon granulated sugar
1/2 teaspoon baking soda
2 eggs, separated
1/4 cup grated sharp Cheddar
   cheese

About 1 hour before serving: Preheat oven to 350°F. In medium skillet over medium heat, in oil, sauté onion and garlic until golden; remove from heat. Stir in meat, bread crumbs, egg, 1/4 cup buttermilk, catchup, 1 1/2 teaspoons salt, and pepper; mix thoroughly. Use to line bottom and sides of 10-inch pie plate. Bake 15 minutes; pour off liquid.

Meanwhile, in medium saucepan, mix 2 cups buttermilk, cornmeal, sugar, 1 teaspoon salt, and baking soda. Cook, stirring constantly, until thickened. Remove from heat; stir in egg yolks. In small bowl, beat egg whites until stiff peaks form; fold into cornmeal mixture. Use to fill meat-pie shell; top with grated cheese. Bake 30 minutes, or until cheese is lightly browned. Let cool 5 minutes before cutting. Makes 6 servings.

Diabetic diet: Prepare as directed but omit sugar. Exchanges per serving = 3 meat, 1 bread and 1/2 milk.
High-iron diet: 3.5 milligrams iron per serving.

HAMBURGER SHELL PIE (230 calories per serving)

1 pound lean ground beef
1/3 cup packaged dried bread
   crumbs
1/4 teaspoon garlic salt
1/4 teaspoon celery salt
dash pepper
1 small onion, chopped
1/3 cup canned tomato juice
dash of Tabasco
2 17-ounce cans Italian tomatoes, well drained
seasoned salt
oregano leaves
1/4 cup grated Parmesan cheese

About 50 minutes before serving: Preheat oven to 375°F. In 9-inch (preferably glass) pie plate, thoroughly mix meat, bread crumbs, garlic and celery salts, pepper, onion, tomato juice and Tabasco. Press mixture into plate, building up sides to about 1/2-inch thickness. Bake 15 minutes, placing piece of foil on oven rack to catch drippings. At end of 15 minutes, remove meat shell from oven; drain off drippings.

Now arrange drained tomatoes in shell, making overlapping rows and sprinkling each tomato with seasoned salt. Sprinkle with oregano to taste; top with ring of grated cheese. Return to 375°F. oven for 15 to 20 minutes. Cool one minute; drain well again. Cut into 6 wedges. Makes 6 servings.

Diabetic diet: Exchanges per serving = 2 meat, 1 vegetable and 1/2 bread.
Low-fat, low-cholesterol diet: Prepare as directed but omit Parmesan. 10 grams fat per serving.
High-iron diet: 3 milligrams iron per serving.

CHILEAN BEEF AND CORN (Pastel de Choclo) (330 calories per serving)

1 tablespoon salad oil
1 large onion, chopped
1 12-ounce can whole-kernel
   corn
1 cup canned tomatoes
salt
3/4 pound lean ground beef
1 teaspoon granulated sugar
1/4 cup raisins
4 green olives, sliced

About 25 minutes before serving: In large skillet, in oil, sauté onion until golden; add corn, canned tomatoes and 1 teaspoon salt; cook, over low heat, about 8 to 10 minutes. Meanwhile, in medium skillet, cook meat with sugar and 1/2 teaspoon salt, stirring occasionally, until meat loses its red color; add raisins and olives; cook 2 minutes longer. In 8-inch round or square dish, alternate wide rows of meat and corn mixtures, 4 in all. Makes 4 servings.

Egg-, gluten-, milk- and wheat-free diet: Prepare as directed.
Low-fat, low-cholesterol diet: Prepare as directed but omit olives. 15 grams fat per serving.
High-iron diet: 4 milligrams iron per serving.

TAMALE CASSEROLE (330 calories per serving)

3/4 cup uncooked instant whole-
   wheat cereal
2 teaspoons salt
2 teaspoons chili powder
1 tablespoon butter or margarine
1 medium onion, sliced
3/4 pound lean ground beef
1 1/2 cups well-drained canned
   tomatoes

About 1 hour before serving: Preheat oven to 350°F. Into 2 cups boiling water in saucepan, stir cereal, 1 teaspoon salt and 1 teaspoon chili powder; boil 1 to 2 minutes. Remove from heat; cool.
    Meanwhile, in skillet, in butter, sauté onion until soft; add meat and continue cooking until meat loses its red color; drain well. Add tomatoes and remaining 1 teaspoon salt and 1 teaspoon chili powder; blend well. Line bottom of 1 1/2-quart casserole with half of cereal; cover with meat mixture; top with remaining cereal. Bake, uncovered, 45 minutes. Makes 4 servings.

Diabetic diet: Prepare as directed but use margarine instead of butter. Exchanges per serving = 2 meat, 1 vegetable, 2 bread and 1 fat.
Low-fat, low-cholesterol diet: Prepare as directed but use margarine instead of butter. 15 grams fat per serving.
High-iron diet: 3.5 milligrams iron per serving.

STROGANOFF SKILLET DINNER (320 calories per serving)

1 pound lean ground beef
1 small onion, chopped
1 1/2 cups uncooked noodles
1 1/2 cups tomato juice
1 teaspoon Worcestershire
1 teaspoon celery salt
1/2 teaspoon salt
dash pepper
1/3 cup sour cream
chopped parsley for garnish

About 45 minutes before serving: In skillet, cook meat with onion until meat loses its red color. Add noodles and remaining ingredients except sour cream and parsley; cover; simmer 25 minutes, stirring occasionally, or until noodles are tender. Stir in sour cream and sprinkle with parsley (do not boil again). Makes 5 servings.

Diabetic diet: Exchanges per serving = 3 meat, 1 vegetable, 1 bread and 1/2 fat.
High-iron diet: 3.5 milligrams iron per serving.

MARVELOUS MUENSTER BURGER (280 calories per serving)

1 pound lean ground beef
2 teaspoons prepared mustard
1/2 teaspoon salt
1/2 teaspoon Worcestershire
1/8 teaspoon pepper
2 ounces (or slices) Muenster
   cheese, chopped

About 20 minutes before serving: Combine meat with mustard, salt, Worcestershire and pepper; mix well and shape into 8 thin patties. Divide cheese among 4 patties; top each with another patty. Seal edges carefully. Panbroil 5 minutes on each side, or until done as desired. Makes 4 servings.

Bland diet: Prepare as directed but omit mustard, Worcestershire and pepper.
Diabetic diet: Exchanges per serving = 4 meat and 1/2 fat.
High-iron diet: 3.5 milligrams iron per serving.
Low-residue diet: Prepare as directed for bland diet.

CUCUMBER COOL BURGERS (290 calories per serving)

1 pound lean ground beef
1 teaspoon salt
¼ teaspoon pepper
2 tablespoons chopped parsley
⅓ cup chopped, pared cucumber
4 slices rye toast, quartered

About 25 minutes before serving: Combine all ingredients but bread. Shape into 4 patties, then broil or panfry to desired doneness. Serve on rye toast quarters. Makes 4 servings.

Diabetic diet: Exchanges per serving = 3 meat and 1 bread.
Egg-, gluten-, milk- and wheat-free diet: Prepare as directed but omit toast.
Low-fat, low-cholesterol diet: 15 grams fat per serving.
High-iron diet: 4 milligrams iron per serving.
Low-sodium diet: Prepare as directed but omit salt. 190 milligrams sodium per serving. If served on low-sodium bread, 75 milligrams sodium per serving.

MEAT-AND-POTATO PIE (300 calories per serving)

1 16-ounce can tomato wedges in tomato juice
1 pound lean ground beef
1 egg
⅓ cup packaged dried bread crumbs
1 teaspoon oregano leaves
1 teaspoon salt
¼ teaspoon pepper
instant mashed potatoes for 6 servings
skimmed milk or reliquefied nonfat dry milk
2 tablespoons butter or margarine
¼ teaspoon celery seeds

About 50 minutes before serving: Preheat oven to 350°F. Thoroughly drain tomato wedges, reserving ⅓ cup juice. In 9-inch pie plate, mix meat, egg, bread crumbs, ⅓ cup tomato juice, oregano, salt and pepper. Line bottom and sides of pie plate with mixture, mounding up sides about 1 inch above edge of plate. Bake 15 minutes; pour off liquid.

Meanwhile, prepare instant potatoes as label directs but use skimmed milk and only 2 tablespoons butter or margarine; stir in celery seed. Heap mixture into baked meat shell. Overlap tomato wedges around edge of potatoes. Bake 15 minutes more. Let stand 5 minutes, then slice. Makes 6 servings.

Bland diet: Prepare as directed but omit tomato wedges, oregano, pepper and celery seeds. Add ⅓ cup milk to meat mixture. Drain one 16-ounce can green beans; toss with 1 tablespoon butter or margarine; use, in place of tomatoes, to ring potatoes.
Diabetic diet: Prepare as directed but use margarine instead of butter. Exchanges per serving = 2 meat, 1 vegetable, 1 bread and 1 fat.
Low-fat, low-cholesterol diet: Prepare as directed but use 2 egg whites in place of whole egg; use margarine instead of butter. 15 grams fat per serving.
High-iron diet: 3.5 milligrams iron per serving.

CHILI-MEATBALL-AND-VEGETABLE SOUP (220 calories per serving)

1 pound lean ground beef
¼ cup packaged dried bread crumbs
¼ cup tomato juice
2 tablespoons minced onion
4 to 5 teaspoons chili powder
salt and pepper
1 tablespoon salad oil
2 10½-ounce cans condensed beef broth
1 16-ounce can tomatoes
1 10-ounce package frozen mixed vegetables
1 medium onion, sliced
½ cup packaged precooked rice

About 45 minutes before serving: In medium bowl, combine meat, crumbs, tomato juice, onion, chili powder, ½ teaspoon salt and ¼ teaspoon pepper. Shape into 1-inch balls. In large skillet, in oil, brown meatballs. Drain; set aside.

In large kettle, combine beef broth with 2 soup-cans water, 1 teaspoon salt and remaining ingredients. Cover and heat to boiling; reduce heat; add meatballs; let simmer 10 minutes. Makes 8 main-dish servings of about 1¼ cups each.

Diabetic diet: Exchanges per serving = 2 meat, 1 bread and 1 vegetable.
Low-fat, low-cholesterol diet: 10 grams fat per serving.
High-iron diet: 3 milligrams iron per serving.

MEXICAN CHILI (290 calories per serving)

³/₄ pound lean ground beef
¹/₂ cup thinly sliced onions
1 to 1¹/₂ tablespoons chili powder
1 cup canned tomatoes
¹/₂ teaspoon salt
1 teaspoon granulated sugar
1 garlic clove, minced
1 16-ounce can kidney beans

About 1 hour and 45 minutes before serving: In large skillet, cook meat with onion until meat loses its red color. Add 1 cup water and remaining ingredients except kidney beans; cover; simmer 1 hour. Uncover; add kidney beans; simmer 30 minutes more. Makes 4 servings of about 1 cup each.

Diabetic diet: Prepare as directed but omit sugar. Exchanges per serving = 3 meat, 1 vegetable and 1 bread.
Egg-, gluten-, milk- and wheat-free diet: Prepare as directed.
Low-fat, low-cholesterol diet: 10 grams fat per serving.
High-iron diet: 5 milligrams iron per serving.

CHILI CON CARNE (280 calories per serving)

1 tablespoon salad oil
1 garlic clove, thinly sliced
1 cup chopped onion
2 cups sliced celery
¹/₂ cup chopped green pepper
1 pound lean ground beef
1 16-ounce can kidney beans, thoroughly drained
2 16-ounce cans tomatoes
¹/₂ teaspoon salt
chili powder

About 1 hour and 15 minutes before serving: In large kettle over medium heat, in oil, sauté garlic, onion, celery and green pepper until onion is golden; add meat; cook until it is well browned. Stir in kidney beans, tomatoes, salt and 1¹/₂ teaspoons chili powder; simmer, uncovered, at least 45 minutes to blend flavors. Just before serving, stir in enough chili powder to give desired "hotness." Makes 6 servings of about 1¹/₂ cups each.

Diabetic diet: Exchanges per serving = 2 meat, 2 vegetable, 1 bread and ¹/₂ fat.
Egg-, gluten-, milk- and wheat-free diet: Prepare as directed.
Low-fat, low-cholesterol diet: 10 grams fat per serving.
High-iron diet: 4.5 milligrams iron per serving.
Low-sodium diet: Cook 1 cup dried kidney beans in 1 quart water for 1¹/₂ hours, or until almost tender; drain, reserving ¹/₂ cup liquid. Use liquid and beans in place of canned beans. Use low-sodium canned tomatoes; omit salt and celery; use chili powder not containing salt. 60 milligrams sodium per serving.

SAUCY CRANBERRY BURGERS (330 calories per serving)

1 pound lean ground beef
1 tablespoon parsley flakes
¹/₂ teaspoon celery salt
¹/₂ teaspoon salt
1¹/₂ teaspoons salad oil
1 8-ounce can jellied cranberry sauce
¹/₄ cup orange juice

About 20 minutes before serving: In medium bowl, mix meat, parsley flakes, celery salt and salt; form into 4 patties. In skillet over medium heat, in oil, brown 5 minutes on each side. Meanwhile, in small bowl, beat cranberry sauce and orange juice until smooth. Add to skillet; cover; simmer 5 minutes. Makes 4 servings.

Bland diet: Prepare as directed but omit celery salt if forbidden on diet.
Egg-, gluten-, milk- and wheat-free diet: Prepare as directed.
Low-fat, low-cholesterol diet: 20 grams fat per serving.
Low-fat, bland (gall bladder) diet: Prepare as directed for bland diet.
High-iron diet: 3.5 milligrams iron per serving.
Low-sodium diet: Prepare as directed but omit celery salt and salt. 75 milligrams sodium per serving.

20-MINUTE HASH (280 calories per serving)

1 pound lean ground beef
2 cups cubed cooked potatoes
¹/₂ cup minced onion
1 teaspoon salt
1 tablespoon Worcestershire

About 20 minutes before serving: In skillet, stirring constantly, cook meat with potatoes and onion until meat loses its red color. Add salt and Worcestershire; cook, over low heat, 15 minutes, stirring often. Makes 4 servings of about 1 cup each.

Diabetic diet: Exchanges per serving = 3 meat and 1 bread.
Low-fat, low-cholesterol diet: 15 grams fat per serving.
High-iron diet: 4 milligrams iron per serving.

CHILIBURGERS (270 calories per serving)

1 pound lean ground beef
1/2 cup chili sauce

About 20 minutes before serving: Mix meat with chili sauce. Form into 4 patties. In medium skillet, over medium heat, pan-broil on each side to desired doneness. Makes 4 servings.

Egg-, gluten-, milk- and wheat-free diet: Prepare as directed.
Low-fat, low-cholesterol diet: 15 grams fat per serving.
High-iron diet: 3.5 milligrams iron per serving.

HAMBURGER-VEGETABLE SOUP (210 calories per serving)

6 beef bouillon cubes
1 16-ounce can tomatoes
1 large onion, diced
3/4 cup diced celery
1 medium carrot, diced
1 garlic clove, crushed
1 bay leaf
1/8 teaspoon pepper
1 pound lean ground beef
1 10-ounce package frozen peas
3 tablespoons chopped parsley
  for garnish

About 1 hour before serving: In large saucepan over high heat, heat 5 cups water to boiling; add bouillon cubes, and stir until dissolved. Add next 8 ingredients; cover and simmer over low heat 20 minutes.

Meanwhile, in small skillet over medium-high heat, cook meat, stirring constantly, until it loses its bright red color. Add meat and peas to soup and cook 10 minutes, or until peas are fork-tender; discard bay leaf. Stir in parsley just before serving. Makes 6 servings.

Low-fat, low-cholesterol diet: 10 grams fat per serving.

TOMATO-BAKED MEAT LOAF (265 calories per serving)

3 cups soft bread crumbs
1 cup canned tomatoes
1/4 green pepper, chopped
1 medium onion, finely chopped
dash pepper
1/2 teaspoon prepared horserad-
  ish
1 1/2 teaspoons salt
2 eggs
1 pound lean ground beef
1/4 cup catchup

About 1 hour and 20 minutes before serving: Preheat oven to 375°F. In medium baking pan, mix all ingredients but catchup; form mixture into 9" by 5" loaf. Bake 50 to 60 minutes, or to desired doneness.

To serve: Let cool 10 minutes, then cut into 12 equal slices. Serve with catchup. Makes 6 servings of 2 slices each.

Diabetic diet: Prepare as directed but omit catchup. Exchanges per serving = 2 meat, 1/2 vegetable and 1 bread.
Low-fat, low-cholesterol diet: Prepare as directed but use only white of egg. 10 grams fat per serving.
High-iron diet: 3.5 milligrams iron per serving.

ITALIANA MEAT LOAF (290 calories per serving)

1 pound lean ground beef
1 cup fresh bread crumbs
1/4 cup grated Parmesan cheese
1/4 cup chopped parsley
2 tablespoons instant minced
  onion
basil
salt and pepper
3 eggs
1 1/2 cups well-drained creamed
  cottage cheese
1 teaspoon granulated sugar

About 1 hour and 15 minutes before serving: Preheat oven to 350°F. In large bowl, mix meat with crumbs, cheese, parsley, onion, 1 teaspoon basil, 1 teaspoon salt, 1/4 teaspoon pepper and 2 eggs.

In medium bowl, beat remaining egg with cottage cheese, 1/2 teaspoon salt, 1/4 teaspoon basil and sugar until well blended. In lightly greased 9" by 5" loaf pan, spread cheese mixture evenly over bottom. On waxed paper, shape meat mixture into oblong to fit into pan. Using 2 pancake turners, lift meat onto cheese mixture. Bake 1 hour. Drain off liquid. Makes 6 servings.

Diabetic diet: Prepare as directed but use low-fat cottage cheese; omit sugar. Exchanges per serving = 4 meat and 1/2 bread.
High-iron diet: 3 milligrams iron per serving.

BACON-STUFFED BURGERS (255 calories per serving)

2 strips bacon
1 pound lean ground beef
1 teaspoon salad oil
salt to taste

About 20 minutes before serving: Cook bacon until almost crisp; crumble. Form beef into 8 thin patties. Top each of 4 of the patties with one quarter of crumbled bacon. Cover with rest of patties; carefully seal edges together. In medium skillet over medium heat, in oil, cook burgers until well done. Sprinkle with salt to taste. Makes 4 servings.

Bland diet: Prepare as directed.
Diabetic diet: Exchanges per serving = 3 meat and 1 fat.
Egg-, gluten-, milk- and wheat-free diet: Prepare as directed.
High-iron diet: 4 milligrams iron per serving.
Low-residue diet: Prepare as directed.

QUICK CHILI LOAF (300 calories per serving)

1 pound lean ground beef
1/2 cup chili sauce
2 slices bread, finely cubed
1 egg
1/4 teaspoon garlic salt

About 45 minutes before serving: Preheat oven to 350°F. In medium baking pan, mix all ingredients. Shape into 4 loaves. Bake 30 minutes, or until meat is done as you like it. Makes 4 servings.

Low-fat, low-cholesterol diet: Prepare as directed but use 2 egg whites in place of whole egg. 15 grams fat per serving.
High-iron diet: 4 milligrams iron per serving.

PEPPERCORN STEAK (200 calories per serving)

1 2¹/₂-pound beef top round steak, boneless
instant meat tenderizer
1/3 cup Burgundy wine
1/4 cup minced onion
1 tablespoon salad oil
2 teaspoons peppercorns

About 50 minutes before serving: Trim excess fat from meat. Prepare steak with meat tenderizer as label directs. Place steak in large baking dish. In small measuring cup, combine wine, onion and salad oil. Pour over steak; refrigerate, loosely covered, 30 minutes turning occasionally.

Preheat broiler if manufacturer directs. Coarsely crush peppercorns in pepper mill or wrap peppercorns in cloth, then crush coarsely with rolling pin; press pepper well into both sides of steak. Place steak on broiling pan; pour remaining marinade over steak. Broil about 15 minutes or until of desired doneness, turning once. Serve steak cut in very thin slices. Makes 8 servings.

Diabetic diet: Exchanges = 1 meat for each ounce of meat.
Low-fat, low-cholesterol diet: 10 grams fat per serving.
High-iron diet: 4.5 milligrams iron per serving.
Low-sodium diet: Prepare as directed but omit meat tenderizer. 95 milligrams sodium per serving.

PINEAPPLE BEEF LOAF (290 calories per serving)

1/2 cup fresh bread crumbs
1/4 cup skimmed milk or reliquefied nonfat dry milk
1 pound lean ground beef
2 teaspoons Worcestershire
1 egg, slightly beaten
1 teaspoon salt
1/4 teaspoon pepper
1 4-ounce can mushroom slices, drained
1 8¹/₄-ounce can pineapple slices, drained and halved

About 1 hour before serving: Preheat oven to 375°F. In bowl, let bread crumbs and milk stand 5 minutes. With fork, mix in meat and all remaining ingredients but pineapple. Pack meat into 1¹/₂-quart loaf pan. Bake 50 minutes; remove from oven and let stand 5 minutes.

To serve: Pour off meat-loaf juices, then turn loaf onto heated platter. Lay overlapping pineapple slices on loaf. Makes 4 servings.

Low-fat, low-cholesterol diet: Prepare as directed but use only white of egg. 15 grams fat per serving.
High-iron diet: 4 milligrams iron per serving.

DELUXE PINEAPPLE MEAT LOAF (240 calories per serving)

1 pound lean ground beef
1 8-ounce can crushed pineap-
ple (do not drain off syrup)
bread cubes made from 2 slices
day-old bread
2 eggs
1/4 cup minced onion
1/8 teaspoon prepared horserad-
ish
1 teaspoon salt
catchup
1/4 cup orange or pineapple
juice

About 1 hour and 15 minutes before serving: Preheat oven to 350°F. In 9-inch baking pan, mix meat, pineapple, bread cubes, eggs, onion, horseradish, salt and 2 tablespoons catchup. Form into long narrow loaf. Bake 60 minutes. Meanwhile, prepare sauce by stirring together 2 tablespoons catchup with orange juice. Cut meat loaf into 12 slices; top with sauce. Makes 6 servings.

Diabetic diet: Prepare as directed but use crushed pineapple packed in pineapple juice. Exchanges per serving = 2 meat and 1 bread.
Low-fat, low-cholesterol diet: Prepare as directed but use only whites of eggs. 10 grams fat per serving.
High-iron diet: 3 milligrams iron per serving.

CHINESE BEEF AND PEPPERS (290 calories per serving)

1 1/2 pounds lean ground beef
2 tablespoons salad oil
1/2 teaspoon minced garlic
2 beef-bouillon cubes
1/4 teaspoon pepper
1/2 teaspoon ginger
6 to 8 whole green onions, cut
into 1/4-inch pieces
4 celery stalks, cut diagonally
into 1/4-inch pieces
3 medium green peppers, cut
into 1/2-inch strips
2 tablespoons cornstarch
1 tablespoon soy sauce

About 40 minutes before serving: Shape meat into 18 small patties. In large skillet over medium heat, in hot oil, brown patties and garlic; pour off fat. Add beef bouillon, pepper, ginger and 1 3/4 cups hot water. Simmer, uncovered, 15 minutes. Add vegetables; simmer 5 minutes, stirring occasionally. In cup, combine cornstarch, soy sauce and 1/4 cup water; stir into mixture in skillet. Cook, covered, 7 to 10 minutes until celery is tender-crisp. Makes 6 servings.

Diabetic diet: Exchanges per serving = 3 meat and 1 vegetable.
Egg-, gluten-, milk- and wheat-free diet: Prepare as directed but omit bouillon cubes and soy sauce for gluten- and wheat-free diets.
Low-fat, low-cholesterol diet: 10 grams fat per serving.
High-iron diet: 4 milligrams iron per serving.

FLANK STEAK ROLLED AND FILLED (Chilean Malaya) (250 calories per serving)

1 2-pound beef flank steak
1/2 teaspoon thyme leaves
1/8 teaspoon pepper
1 medium onion
3 tablespoons chopped parsley
3 tablespoons red wine vinegar
1/2 cup fresh bread crumbs
1/2 cup chopped cooked spin-
ach
1/2 cup cooked or canned peas
1/4 cup finely grated carrot
1 tablespoon grated Cheddar
cheese
1 hard-cooked egg, chopped
2 cooked bacon slices, crum-
bled
2 tablespoons salad oil
1 10 1/2-ounce can condensed
beef broth

Day before serving: With sharp knife score one side of flank steak in diamond pattern. Then sprinkle both sides with thyme and pepper. In large bowl, place flank steak with onion, parsley and vinegar; cover; refrigerate.

About 2 hours before serving: In large bowl, lightly combine bread crumbs, spinach, peas, carrot, cheese, chopped egg and bacon; spoon onto scored side of steak; pat until it extends nearly to edges. Then roll up, jelly-roll fashion, and tie securely with string at 1-inch intervals.

In Dutch oven, in oil, brown on all sides. Add onion-vinegar mixture in which meat was marinated, also broth. Simmer, covered, 1 1/2 hours, or until meat is fork-tender. Arrange on heated platter; remove strings; slice. Skim surface fat from gravy and pass. Makes 8 servings.

Low-fat, low-cholesterol diet: Prepare as directed but omit egg and bacon. 10 grams fat per serving.
High-iron diet: 4.5 milligrams iron per serving.

ROLLED FLANK STEAK (270 calories per serving)

1 10-ounce package frozen mixed vegetables
1/2 cup chopped onion
1/2 cup chopped celery
1 teaspoon salt
2 slices white bread
2 tablespoons chopped parsley
1 teaspoon seasoned salt
1/4 teaspoon seasoned pepper
1/4 teaspoon nutmeg
1 2 1/2-pound beef flank steak
1 tablespoon bottled sauce for gravy
2 tablespoons butter or margarine

About 1 hour and 40 minutes before dinner: Cook frozen mixed vegetables with onion, celery and salt as label directs; drain. Meanwhile, into large bowl, crumble bread slices; add parsley, seasoned salt and pepper and nutmeg; add drained vegetables; toss well.

Score flank steak crosswise in diamond pattern, on both sides. Spread with vegetable mixture, patting until mixture spreads nearly to edges of meat. Roll up, jelly-roll fashion; secure with string. Brush outside with bottled sauce for gravy. In Dutch oven over medium heat, in butter, brown steak on all sides. Add 3/4 cup water and simmer, covered, 1 hour, or until fork-tender. Place on heated platter. Remove string, then cut steak into 8 slices; pass any gravy left in Dutch oven. Makes 8 servings.

Low-fat, low-cholesterol diet: Prepare as directed but use salad oil or margarine instead of butter. 10 grams fat per serving.
High-iron diet: 5 milligrams iron per serving.

BERGENFIELD POTTED BEEF (310 calories per serving)

1 2-pound round rump roast beef
1/4 cup flour
1 tablespoon salad oil
1 envelope dried onion-soup mix
8 carrots, cut into 1-inch pieces
8 small white potatoes, pared
16 small white onions
1 16-ounce can tomatoes
1 teaspoon oregano leaves
2 tablespoons cornstarch

About 4 1/2 hours before serving: Trim fat from meat. Sprinkle meat with flour; shake off excess. In Dutch oven over medium heat, in oil, brown meat on all sides. Add onion-soup mix and 2 cups water; cover; boil gently 2 to 3 hours, or until meat is fork-tender.

About one hour before meat is done, add carrots, potatoes, onions, tomatoes, and oregano. Continue cooking until vegetables are tender. Mix enough water with cornstarch to form a smooth paste. Remove meat from Dutch oven; slice and arrange on serving platter; surround with vegetables. Stirring constantly, mix cornstarch with gravy in Dutch oven; cook until thickened and smooth.

To serve: Top meat and vegetables with a little hot gravy; pass rest of gravy. Makes 8 servings.

Diabetic diet: Carefully divide into 8 equal servings. Exchanges per serving = 3 meat, 1/2 vegetable and 2 bread.
Low-fat, low-cholesterol diet: 10 grams fat per serving.
High-iron diet: 5 milligrams iron per serving.

SKILLET BURGER LOAF (270 calories per serving)

3/4 pound lean ground beef
1 egg
1/2 teaspoon salt
2 tablespoons instant minced onion
1 12-ounce package pasteurized process American cheese slices
1/4 teaspoon pepper
chopped parsley for garnish

About 20 minutes before serving: Combine meat, egg, salt and instant minced onion. Grease 8-inch skillet; lightly pat one-half of meat over bottom; arrange cheese slices on top. Cover with rest of meat, patting smooth. Sprinkle with pepper; cut into 4 pie-shaped wedges. Cook, on top of range, over fairly high heat, until browned on bottom. Turn; brown other side; cook until done as desired. Garnish with parsley. Makes 4 servings.

Bland diet: Prepare as directed but omit onion, pepper and parsley.
Diabetic diet: Exchanges per serving = 4 meat and 2 fat.
High-iron diet: 3 milligrams iron per serving.
Low-residue diet: Prepare as directed for bland diet.

HERB-STUFFED FLANK STEAK (335 calories per serving)

butter or margarine
1 medium onion, chopped
1 4-ounce can mushroom stems
 and pieces, drained
¹/₄ cup chopped parsley
1¹/₂ cups fresh bread crumbs
1 teaspoon poultry seasoning
¹/₄ teaspoon salt
dash pepper
1 egg, slightly beaten
1 2-pound beef flank steak
1 10¹/₂-ounce can condensed
 beef broth

About 2 hours before serving: In skillet over medium heat, in 1 tablespoon butter, sauté onion and mushrooms until golden. In bowl, combine parsley, crumbs, poultry seasoning, salt, pepper and egg; then mix in onion and mushrooms. Remove fat from steak; score surface, in diamond pattern, on both sides. Place mushroom mixture lengthwise down center, then bring both ends together on top; fasten with string, tied at 1-inch intervals.

In skillet over medium heat, in 2 tablespoons butter, brown steak well on all sides; add broth; simmer, covered, 1¹/₂ hours, or until meat is fork-tender.

To serve: Remove meat to heated platter; remove strings; cut into 1-inch pieces. Thicken pan juices, if desired, and pass with meat. Makes 6 servings.

Low-fat, low-cholesterol diet: Prepare as directed but use only white of egg; use margarine instead of butter. 15 grams fat per serving.
High-iron diet: 5.5 milligrams iron per serving.

BOILED BEEF WITH DILL (Kikt Biff Med Dillsäs) (240 calories per serving)

2 pounds boneless beef loin sir-
 loin steak
1 tablespoon salad oil
1 10¹/₂-ounce can condensed
 beef broth
1 teaspoon salt
¹/₄ teaspoon pepper
1 bay leaf
1 teaspoon dried dill weed
1 tablespoon cornstarch
1 tablespoon vinegar
2 tablespoons granulated sugar
chopped parsley for garnish

About 2 hours before serving: Trim fat from meat; cut meat into 6 serving pieces. In large skillet over medium heat, in oil, brown on both sides. Add beef broth, 1 cup water, salt, pepper, bay leaf and dill; cover; simmer gently 1¹/₂ hours, or until meat is tender. Drain off broth; measure 1 cup into a small saucepan. Mix cornstarch, vinegar and sugar to form smooth paste. Stir into broth; cook, stirring constantly, until thickened and smooth. Serve meat topped with gravy; sprinkle with parsley. Makes 6 servings.

Diabetic diet: Prepare as directed but omit sugar. Exchanges per serving = 4 meat and ¹/₂ fat.
Low-fat, low-cholesterol diet: 10 grams fat per serving.
High-iron diet: 4.5 milligrams iron per serving.

STUFFED CUCUMBERS (325 calories per serving)

4 large cucumbers
1 pound lean ground beef
¹/₄ cup chopped celery
¹/₄ cup chopped onions
¹/₄ teaspoon salt
¹/₂ teaspoon ginger
3 tablespoons cornstarch
4 tablespoons soy sauce
1¹/₂ cups beef broth
3 cups cooked rice

About 1 hour before serving: Peel cucumbers and cut each in half crosswise, then lengthwise. With spoon, scoop out seeds. In medium bowl, mix meat, celery, onions, salt, ginger, 1 tablespoon cornstarch and 1 tablespoon soy sauce. Stuff cucumbers with mixture.

In large skillet over medium heat, in broth, arrange cucumbers, stuffed side up; simmer, covered, 35 minutes. Place on warm platter on bed of rice. Pour off pan liquid, reserving 1 cup; return it to skillet.

In cup, dissolve 2 tablespoons cornstarch in 3 tablespoons soy sauce. Gradually add to skillet and cook over medium heat, stirring constantly until thickened. Pour over cucumbers and rice. Makes 6 servings.

Low-fat, low-cholesterol diet: 10 grams fat per serving.

PEACHY MEAT LOAF (335 calories per serving)

2 pounds lean ground beef
1 cup packaged dried bread crumbs
1 2³/₄-ounce package onion soup mix
1 cup skimmed milk or re-liquefied nonfat dry milk
1 16-ounce can cling-peach halves, drained
chili sauce

About 1 hour before serving: Preheat oven to 425°F. Combine meat, crumbs, soup mix and milk; place in cake pan and shape into mound. With back of large spoon, make 3 indentations in meat; set peach, hollow side up, in each indentation; bake 50 minutes. Heat remaining peaches in oven with meat for last 10 minutes.

To serve: Remove loaf to heated platter; top peaches with chili sauce. Cut into 8 wedges. Makes 8 servings.

Low-fat, low-cholesterol diet: 15 grams fat per serving.
High-iron diet: 4 milligrams iron per serving.

FLANK STEAK WITH BLUE-CHEESE BUTTER (280 calories per serving)

1 2-pound beef flank steak
²/₃ cup bottled reduced-calorie Italian dressing
1/4 cup crumbled blue cheese
2 tablespoons butter or marga-rine
2 teaspoons chopped chives

About 4 hours before serving: Trim fat from steak, then score each side in diamond pattern, about 1/8-inch deep. Place in baking dish; pour on dressing; refrigerate, covered, turning once.

About 1/2 hour before serving: Preheat broiler if manufacturer directs. Meanwhile, mash blue cheese smooth with butter and chives; set aside. Lay flank steak on rack in broiler pan; broil about 5 minutes on each side for medium rare. Spread immediately with blue-cheese butter.

To serve: Cut on angle into thin slices. Makes 6 servings.

Diabetic diet: Prepare as directed but use margarine instead of butter. Each ounce meat = 1 meat exchange. One tablespoon blue-cheese topping = 2 fat exchanges.
High-iron diet: 5 milligrams iron per serving.

MEATBALLS PIEMONTE (315 calories per serving)

1 pound lean ground beef
1/4 teaspoon garlic salt
1 medium onion, finely chopped
salt
1/4 cup packaged dried bread crumbs
1 teaspoon dry mustard
1 egg
1 tablespoon salad oil
1 tablespoon instant coffee powder
1/2 teaspoon granulated sugar
1 tablespoon cornstarch

About 50 minutes before serving: In medium bowl, mix meat, garlic salt, chopped onion, 1/2 teaspoon salt, bread crumbs, mustard and egg. Form into 12 medium meatballs. In medium skillet over medium heat, in oil, brown on all sides. Add coffee powder, 1 cup water, 1/2 teaspoon salt, and sugar; cover; simmer 30 minutes. Meanwhile, stir 3/4 cup water into cornstarch until smooth. Add to meatballs; cook, stirring, until thickened. Makes 4 servings.

Diabetic diet: Prepare as directed but omit sugar. Exchanges per serving = 3 meat and 1 fat.
Low-fat, low-cholesterol diet: Prepare as directed but use only white of egg. 20 grams fat per serving.
High-iron diet: 4 milligrams iron per serving.

JOHNNY APPLESEED MEAT LOAF (320 calories per serving)

1 pound lean ground beef
1/2 cup packaged dried bread crumbs
3/4 cup applesauce
1/4 cup catchup
3/4 teaspoon salt
1/4 teaspoon cinnamon
1/8 teaspoon nutmeg

About 1 hour before serving: Preheat oven to 350°F. In 1-quart casserole, mix all ingredients and smooth top. Bake 50 minutes. Makes 4 servings.

Diabetic diet: Prepare as directed but use unsweetened applesauce. Carefully divide into 4 equal servings. Exchanges per serving = 3 meat, 1 fruit and 1/2 bread.
Low-fat, low-cholesterol diet: 15 grams fat per serving.
High-iron diet: 3.5 milligrams iron per serving.
Low-sodium diet: Prepare as directed but omit salt; use low-sodium catchup. 105 milligrams sodium per serving. Or make with bread crumbs from unsalted Melba toast. 75 milligrams sodium per serving.

STEAK-AND-POTATO CASSEROLE (325 calories per serving)

2 pounds beef bottom round
  steak, 1/2-inch thick
1/4 cup flour
1/2 teaspoon pepper
2 tablespoons salad oil
8 medium carrots, thickly sliced
8 medium potatoes, thickly
  sliced
1 1³/8-ounce envelope onion-
  soup mix
chopped parsley for garnish

About 2¹/2 hours before serving: Preheat oven to 350°F. Cut meat into 8 serving pieces, trimming fat and bone. On board or waxed paper, using meat mallet or edge of saucer, pound mixture of flour, and pepper into meat.

In large heavy skillet over medium heat, in oil, brown meat well on both sides. Arrange in 3-quart casserole; place carrots and potato slices on top. Sprinkle with onion-soup mix and cover with 3¹/2 cups water.

Bake, covered, 2 hours, or until meat is fork-tender. Skim off any fat. If desired, thicken gravy with 2 tablespoons flour mixed with 1/4 cup cold water; return casserole to oven for a few minutes. Sprinkle parsley on top. Makes 8 servings.

Low-fat, low-cholesterol diet: 10 grams fat per serving.
High-iron diet: 4.5 milligrams iron per serving.

MANDARIN SKILLET BEEF (350 calories per serving)

2 pounds beef loin sirloin steak,
  boneless, cut 1- to 1¹/2-inches
  thick
1 tablespoon salad oil
1/4 teaspoon ginger
1 teaspoon chili powder
1/4 teaspoon garlic powder
1 small onion, finely minced
3 beef-bouillon cubes
1 tablespoon plum jam
1 tablespoon vinegar
1 cup uncooked rice
1 tablespoon cornstarch

About 1 hour and 20 minutes before serving: Trim all fat from meat. Cut meat against grain, into very thin strips about 1/8-inch thick. Cut long strips in half. In large skillet over medium heat, in oil, brown meat, a few strips at a time. Add ginger, chili and garlic powders, onion, bouillon cubes, 2 cups water, plum jam and vinegar; cover; simmer 40 minutes or until meat is tender.

Meanwhile, cook rice as label directs but omit butter. Stir 1 tablespoon water into cornstarch; stir into meat mixture until slightly thickened.

To serve: Top rice with beef mixture. Makes 6 servings.

Diabetic diet: Prepare as directed but omit jam. One serving = one-sixth meat mixture served on 1/2 cup rice. Exchanges per serving = 4 meat, 1 bread and 1/2 fat.
Low-fat, low-cholesterol diet: 10 grams fat per serving.
High-iron diet: 4.5 milligrams iron per serving.
Low-sodium diet: Prepare as directed but omit bouillon cubes or use low-sodium bouillon cubes; omit salt when cooking rice; use chili powder not containing salt. 85 milligrams sodium per serving.

CHINESE PEPPER STEAK (290 calories per serving)

2 pounds beef bottom round
  steak, boneless, cut 1/2-inch
  thick
1/4 cup soy sauce
1 beef-bouillon cube
1/2 teaspoon ginger
1/2 teaspoon garlic powder
2 tablespoons salad oil
3 large green peppers, cut into
  thin strips
3 tablespoons cornstarch
4 cups cooked rice

Day before or early in day: Trim any fat from meat; cut meat into strips about 1/4-inch wide. In medium bowl, combine soy sauce, bouillon cube, ginger, garlic powder and 1 cup boiling water. Add meat strips; cover and refrigerate.

About 1 hour and 15 minutes before serving: Drain meat, reserving 1/2 cup marinade. In large skillet over high heat, in oil, cook meat until it loses its red color. Add reserved marinade and 1 cup water; reduce heat; simmer, covered, 1 hour. Add green pepper; cook 15 minutes, or until meat is tender.

To make gravy: In measuring cup, combine 1/4 cup cold water and cornstarch. Gradually stir into skillet liquid; cook, stirring, until mixture thickens slightly. Serve over rice. Makes 8 servings.

Diabetic diet: Carefully divide meat into 8 equal servings; serve over 1/2 cup rice. Exchanges per serving = 3 meat and 1 bread.
Low-fat, low-cholesterol diet: 10 grams fat per serving.
High-iron diet: 4 milligrams iron per serving.

SPICY BEEF (250 calories per serving)

2 pounds beef bottom round
   steak
1/4 cup flour
1 teaspoon salt
1/4 teaspoon pepper
2 tablespoons salad oil
2 medium onions, sliced
1 tablespoon Worcestershire
1 teaspoon curry
1 teaspoon molasses
dash ginger

About 3 hours before serving: Preheat oven to 350°F. Trim all fat from meat; cut into 1½-inch cubes. Mix flour, salt and pepper; coat meat with mixture. In Dutch oven over medium heat, in oil, brown meat well on all sides. Add remaining ingredients and 1 cup water.

Cover; bake 2½ hours, or until meat is fork-tender. Pass gravy. Makes 6 servings.

Diabetic diet: Prepare as directed but omit molasses; use non-nutritive sweetener equivalent to 1 teaspoon sugar. Exchanges for 1 slice (1 ounce) beef = 1 meat, and for up to ¼ cup gravy = 1 "free" exchange.
Egg-, gluten-, milk- and wheat-free diet: Prepare as directed but use cornstarch in place of flour on gluten- and wheat-free diets.
Low-fat, low-cholesterol diet: 10 grams fat per serving.
High-iron diet: 4.5 milligrams iron per serving.
Low-sodium diet: Prepare as directed but omit salt and Worcestershire; use curry not containing salt. 90 milligrams sodium per serving.

SPICY CHUCK ROAST (325 calories per serving)

1/2 cup bottled thick meat sauce
1 tablespoon salad oil
1 cup canned tomato puree
1 tablespoon prepared mustard
1/4 cup maple-flavored syrup
2 tablespoons vinegar
1 tablespoon Worcestershire
1/8 teaspoon garlic salt
1 3-pound beef top round roast

Day before serving: In large bowl, combine all ingredients but meat. Trim all fat from meat. Place meat in this marinade; refrigerate. Turn occasionally, until needed next day.

About 1¼ hours before serving: Preheat oven to 325°F. Place meat in foil-lined shallow open roasting pan; insert roast-meat thermometer in center of meatiest part. Spoon some marinade over meat, then roast 1 hour, or to 140°F. on meat thermometer, occasionally basting with marinade. When meat is done, remove to heated platter.

To serve: Slice thinly; pass hot marinade as gravy. Makes 8 servings.

Low-fat, low-cholesterol diet: 15 grams fat per serving.
High-iron diet: 5 milligrams iron per serving.

CUBED-STEAK SANDWICHES (265 calories per serving)

6 slices French bread, cut on
   diagonal, 3/4-inch thick
2 teaspoons prepared mustard
6 4-ounce beef cubed steaks
instant meat tenderizer
seasoned pepper
2 tablespoons butter or margarine
6 lettuce leaves
6 tomato slices
salt

About 15 minutes before serving: Preheat broiler 10 minutes if manufacturer directs. Broil bread slices until golden on one side; spread other side with mustard and broil until golden; keep warm. Sprinkle cubed steaks with meat tenderizer as label directs, then some seasoned pepper. In large skillet, in butter, brown steaks about 2 minutes on each side. Now, on mustard side of each bread slice, arrange lettuce leaf, cubed steak and tomato slice. Sprinkle with salt and seasoned pepper. Makes 6 servings.

Diabetic diet: Prepare as directed but use margarine instead of butter. Exchanges per serving = 3 meat, 1 bread and 3 fat.
Low-fat, low-cholesterol diet: Prepare as directed but use salad oil or margarine instead of butter. 10 grams fat per serving.
High-iron diet: 4 milligrams iron per serving.

BRAISED BEEF WITH GINGER (255 calories per serving)

**1 pound beef bottom round
   steak**
1 tablespoon salad oil
1 medium onion, thinly sliced
2 garlic cloves, minced
1/4 teaspoon ginger
1 tablespoon soy sauce
1/2 cup uncooked white rice
**2 stalks celery, cut into thin
   crosswise slices**
salt to taste

About 50 minutes before serving: Trim as much fat from meat as possible. Cut meat, against grain, into julienne strips. In large skillet over medium heat, in oil, sauté meat, onion and garlic until meat browns. Add ginger, soy sauce and 2/3 cup water; cover; simmer 25 minutes, or until meat is tender. Meanwhile, cook rice as label directs but omit butter. Add celery to meat mixture; cover; simmer 5 minutes more; salt to taste. Serve on hot fluffy rice. Makes 4 servings.

Diabetic diet: One serving = 1/4 meat mixture and 1/2 cup cooked rice. Exchanges per serving = 3 meat, 1/2 vegetable, 1 bread and 1/2 fat.
Low-fat, low-cholesterol diet: 10 grams fat per serving.
High-iron diet: Prepare as directed but be certain to use enriched rice. 3 milligrams iron per serving.
Low-sodium diet: Prepare as directed but omit soy sauce and salt. 105 milligrams sodium per serving.

BEEF BOURGUIGNON (310 calories per serving)

**1 pound beef bottom round
   steak**
flour
butter or margarine
3 tablespoons cognac
1 garlic clove, minced
2 carrots, thinly sliced
2 cups thinly sliced celery
1 cup chopped onions
1 tablespoon parsley flakes
1 bay leaf, crumbled
1/2 teaspoon thyme leaves
1 teaspoon salt
**1/2 teaspoon hickory-smoked
   salt**
1 pound small white onions
1 pound fresh mushrooms
1 teaspoon lemon juice

At least 3 hours before serving: Preheat oven to 350°F. Trim fat from meat; cut meat into 1-inch cubes. Toss in flour to coat. In Dutch oven in 1 tablespoon butter, brown on all sides. Add cognac; ignite. When flames have subsided, add garlic, carrots, celery, onions, parsley flakes, bay leaf, thyme, 2 cups water, salt and hickory salt. Stir; simmer 2 to 3 minutes; cover tightly; bake 2 hours, or until meat is tender.

One-half hour before meat is done, cook onions, in salted water to cover, until tender—about 20 minutes. Wash and stem mushrooms (halve larger ones). Sauté caps and stems in 1 tablespoon butter and lemon juice until golden—about 15 minutes. Make a smooth paste with 2 tablespoons flour and 1/4 cup water. Add with drained onions, mushrooms and 3/4 cup water to meat mixture. Stirring constantly, simmer until gravy thickens. Makes 4 servings.

Diabetic diet: Prepare as directed but use margarine instead of butter. Carefully divide into 4 equal servings. Exchanges per serving = 3 meat, 2 vegetable and 1 bread.
Low-fat, low-cholesterol diet: Prepare as directed but use margarine instead of butter. 10 grams fat per serving.
High-iron diet: 5.5 milligrams iron per serving.

HAMBURGER ROLLS (245 calories per serving)

1 pound lean ground beef
1 cup fresh bread crumbs
**1/2 cup skimmed milk or re-
   liquefied nonfat dry milk**
1 tablespoon lemon juice
**1/2 cup shredded Cheddar
   cheese**
1/4 cup chopped stuffed olives
1 teaspoon salt
3 bacon slices, halved

About 45 minutes before serving: Preheat oven to 400°F. Combine all ingredients but bacon. Divide mixture into sixths; form each portion into rolls about 4″ by 1 1/2″. Wrap each with bacon strip. Place in medium baking dish; bake 30 minutes. Broil an additional 2 to 3 minutes to crisp bacon. Makes 6 servings.

Diabetic diet: Exchanges per serving = 3 meat, 1/2 bread and 1 fat.

LEMON-BARBECUED POT ROAST (220 calories per serving)

1 3-pound beef rib roast, small
   end
seasoned instant meat tenderizer
1 tablespoon salad oil
1/2 cup lemon juice
2 garlic cloves, minced
1/4 cup minced onion
salt
1/2 teaspoon celery salt
1/2 teaspoon pepper
1/4 teaspoon ground thyme
1 1/2 teaspoons cornstarch
1/2 teaspoon bottled meat
   sauce for gravy
1 lemon, thinly sliced

Day before: Trim fat from meat. Sprinkle with meat tenderizer as label directs. In small Dutch oven over medium heat, in oil, brown meat on all sides. Add 2 cups water; cover; simmer 1 hour. Cool; then cover and refrigerate overnight.

In jar, combine lemon juice, garlic, onion, 1/2 teaspoon salt, celery salt, pepper and thyme; refrigerate, covered.

About 3 hours before serving: Strain lemon-garlic sauce and add to stock in Dutch oven. Simmer, covered, 2 1/2 hours, or until meat is tender. (Replenish water if necessary.) Remove meat from Dutch oven; carve, against the grain, into 16 slices. Arrange on heated platter; keep hot.

Add enough water to liquid in Dutch oven to make 1 cup. Slowly mix in cornstarch, then return to Dutch oven. Stir in bottled meat sauce for gravy. Cook, stirring, until thickened. Pass with meat. Makes 8 servings.

Diabetic diet: Count each ounce of meat as 1 meat and 1 fat exchange; use up to 1/4 cup gravy as 1 "free" exchange.
Low-fat, low-cholesterol diet: 10 grams fat per serving.
High-iron diet: 4.5 milligrams iron per serving.
Low-sodium diet: Prepare as directed but use low-sodium meat tenderizer; omit salt and bottled sauce for gravy; use celery seed in place of celery salt. 90 milligrams sodium per serving.

TRANSPARENT NOODLES WITH BEEF (Sun-Hie's Chopchae)
(280 calories per serving)

1 pound top round beef, thinly
   sliced
3 scallions, chopped
1/4 cup soy sauce
1 teaspoon granulated sugar
1/4 teaspoon pepper
1/4 teaspoon garlic powder
6 medium carrots, scraped
8 fresh medium mushrooms
1 6-ounce container dried mushrooms
1 10-ounce package frozen
   chopped spinach
sesame-seed oil*
4 ounces bean threads (transparent noodles)*
4 cups water

Day before or at least 3 hours before serving: Trim fat from meat, then slice meat into thin strips (about 1/4-inch wide); place in medium bowl.

In small bowl, combine scallions, soy sauce, sugar, pepper and garlic powder. Pour over meat; cover; refrigerate. Cut carrots into very thin strips, 2 inches long. Wash, then thinly slice fresh mushrooms; soak dried mushrooms as label directs; then cut into thin slices. Wrap and refrigerate carrots and mushrooms.

About 20 minutes before serving: Cook spinach as label directs. In large skillet over medium heat, in 4 teaspoons sesame-seed oil, sauté carrot strips until tender-crisp. Place in mixing bowl; sprinkle lightly with salt. In 1 tablespoon sesame-seed oil, in same skillet, sauté fresh and dried mushrooms until lightly browned. Add to carrots; sprinkle with salt. Again in same skillet, in another 4 teaspoons sesame-seed oil, quickly brown meat on both sides. Add to carrots.

Meanwhile, in medium saucepan, soak bean threads in water for 15 minutes. Bring water to boiling and cook bean threads until transparent; drain. Combine all ingredients and toss well. Makes 6 servings.

Low-fat, low-cholesterol diet: 10 grams fat per serving.

*Available in gourmet sections of many large department stores, or Chinese or Japanese groceries.

PIQUANT-SAUCED STEAK (310 calories per serving)

3 tablespoons packaged onion-
  soup mix
2 tablespoons granulated sugar
1/8 teaspoon pepper
1 tablespoon prepared mustard
1/2 cup catchup
1/4 cup cider vinegar
1 tablespoon lemon juice
1 2 1/2-pound boned beef chuck
  under blade steak about 1 1/2
  inches thick
instant meat tenderizer

About 30 minutes before serving: Preheat broiler if manufacturer directs. In small saucepan, combine onion-soup mix, sugar, pepper, mustard, catchup, vinegar, lemon juice and 3/4 cup cold water. Simmer, covered, 10 minutes.

Meanwhile, trim fat from meat. Apply meat tenderizer as label directs. Then broil meat, 4 inches from heat, about 10 minutes on each side, or to desired doneness. Arrange on board; cut diagonally across grain into thin slices. Pass sauce. Makes 6 servings.

Diabetic diet: Prepare as directed but omit sugar. Each ounce meat = 1 meat exchange. One-quarter cup gravy = 1/2 bread.
Low-fat, low-cholesterol diet: 10 grams fat per serving.
High-iron diet: 5 milligrams iron per serving.

MEAT-AND-FRUIT STEW (Carbonada Criolla) (300 calories per serving)

1 1/2 pounds boneless beef loin
  sirloin steak
1 tablespoon salad oil
1 cup chopped onion
1 tablespoon canned tomato
  paste
1 bay leaf
1/2 teaspoon salt
1/4 teaspoon pepper
1/4 teaspoon thyme leaves
1 10 1/2-ounce can condensed
  beef broth
2 medium potatoes, cut into
  large cubes
1/2 medium acorn squash, cut
  into large cubes
1 medium sweet potato, cut into
  large cubes
1 pear, pared, cubed
1 medium apple, pared, cubed
2 tablespoons raisins
1 tablespoon chopped parsley

About 2 hours before serving: Trim fat from meat; cut meat into 1-inch cubes. In large skillet over medium heat, in oil, brown on all sides. Add onion, tomato paste, bay leaf, salt, pepper, thyme, beef broth and 2 1/2 cups water; cover; simmer 1 hour and 15 minutes, or until meat is almost tender. Add potatoes, squash and sweet potato; cover; cook 20 minutes longer. Add pear, apple and raisins; cover; cook 10 minutes more. Serve in soup bowls; sprinkle with parsley. Makes 6 servings of about 1 1/2 cups each.

Diabetic diet: Exchanges per serving = 3 meat, 1 bread, 1 vegetable and 1 fruit.
Low-fat, low-cholesterol diet: 10 grams fat per serving.
High-iron diet: 4.5 milligrams iron per serving.

STUFFED BURGERS (250 calories per serving)

2 pounds lean ground beef
1/4 cup prepared mustard
8 large stuffed green olives,
  minced
salt and pepper to taste

About 20 minutes before serving: Preheat broiler if manufacturer directs. Shape meat into 16 thin patties. In small bowl, combine mustard and olives; place heaping spoonful in center of each of 8 patties. Top with rest of patties and pinch edges together to seal. Sprinkle with salt and pepper to taste. Broil patties about 5 minutes on each side, or until of desired doneness. Makes 8 servings.

Diabetic diet: Exchanges per serving = 3 meat.
High-iron diet: 3.5 milligrams iron per serving.

ROAST-BEEF DINNER WITH FRESH VEGETABLES (365 calories per serving)

1 4-pound beef eye round roast
12 small (about 2 pounds) new potatoes
butter or margarine
salt
1¹/₂ pounds fresh green beans
2 pounds carrots
1 teaspoon granulated sugar
¹/₂ teaspoon nutmeg
2 pounds zucchini
¹/₂ teaspoon basil
6 ears corn
seasoned salt

About 3 to 5 hours before serving: Trim fat from meat. Preheat oven to 325°F. Insert roast-meat thermometer into center of meat; place on rack in shallow open pan. Roast, uncovered, as follows:

	time at 325°F.	internal temperature
rare	2³/₄ to 3¹/₂ hours	140°F.
medium	3¹/₄ to 4¹/₄ hours	160°F.
well done	3¹/₂ to 4³/₄ hours	170°F.

Let stand 15 minutes before carving.

About 1¹/₂ hours before meat is done: Place potatoes in ovenproof dish; add ¹/₄ cup water, 1 teaspoon butter and 2 teaspoons salt. Cover; bake 1¹/₂ hours, or until fork-tender; drain.

Place green beans in ovenproof dish. Add ¹/₄ cup water, 1 teaspoon butter and 1 teaspoon salt. Cover and bake 1¹/₂ hours; drain.

Slice carrots into 3-inch chunks; place in ovenproof dish. Add ¹/₄ cup water, 1 teaspoon butter, sugar, 1 teaspoon salt and nutmeg. Cover and bake 1¹/₂ hours; drain.

Cut zucchini into 1-inch chunks; place in ovenproof dish. Add 1 teaspoon butter, 2 tablespoons water, 1 teaspoon salt and basil. Cover and bake 1 to 1¹/₂ hours, or until tender; drain.

Cut corn ears in half. Spread each lightly with butter; sprinkle with seasoned salt. Wrap in foil, 2 chunks at a time, twisting foil ends. Bake 1 hour. Makes 12 servings.

Bland diet: Prepare as directed but cook meat well done and serve only potatoes, green beans and carrots.
Diabetic diet: Prepare as directed but omit sugar from carrots; increase margarine in each vegetable to 1 tablespoon. Count one ounce meat as 1 meat exchange, and vegetables according to exchanges as follows: 1 potato and 1 piece corn = 1 bread and 1 fat; green beans, zucchini and ¹/₂ cup carrots = 1 vegetable and 1 fat.
Egg-, gluten-, milk- and wheat-free diet: Prepare as directed but use milk-free margarine on milk-free diet; substitute regular salt for seasoned salt on gluten-free diet.
Low-fat, low-cholesterol diet: Prepare as directed but use margarine or salad oil instead of butter. 10 grams fat per serving.
Low-fat, bland (gall bladder) diet: Prepare as directed for bland diet.
High-iron diet: 1.5 milligrams iron per serving of vegetables; 4 milligrams iron per serving of meat.
Low-residue diet: Prepare as directed for bland diet.
Low-sodium diet: Prepare as directed but omit salts, and use unsalted butter or margarine. 35 milligrams sodium per serving vegetables, or 5 milligrams per serving if carrots are omitted. Meat provides 75 milligrams sodium per 4-ounce serving.

ROAST BEEF PIQUANT (275 calories per serving)

2 pounds small potatoes, cooked, peeled and sliced
salt
seasoned pepper
1 tablespoon chopped fresh dill
1 cup reduced–calorie French dressing
1 9-ounce package frozen whole green beans
1 9-ounce package frozen cut wax beans
1 16-ounce can small whole carrots, drained
2 pounds cold sliced roast beef (about 20 slices)
3 small tomatoes, sliced
1/4 cup chopped parsley for garnish
1 small red onion, sliced for garnish

At least 6 hours before serving: In medium bowl, toss potatoes with 1/2 teaspoon salt, 1/4 teaspoon seasoned pepper, chopped dill and some reduced–calorie French dressing; refrigerate, covered.

Boil green and wax beans as labels direct; drain; cool; toss together with some dressing. Cut carrots into julienne strips; toss with some dressing. Refrigerate beans, carrots and leftover dressing.

About 1 hour before serving: Fold each roast-beef slice in quarters. Lay slices in one row down center of large rectangular tray. Then arrange bean, potato and carrot salads, as well as tomato slices, on opposite sides of roast beef. Garnish tray with parsley and onion rings. Refrigerate, covered, until served. Pass leftover dressing. Makes 10 servings.

Diabetic diet: Two slices meat = 2 meat exchanges. Select vegetables and count according to exchange system—potatoes = bread exchange, green beans, carrots and tomatoes = vegetables.
Low-fat, low-cholesterol diet: 5 grams fat per serving.
High-iron diet: 4.5 milligrams iron per serving.

BEEF-AND-CABBAGE CASSEROLE (310 calories per serving)

2 pounds beef round steak, cut into 1-inch cubes
2 tablespoons salad oil
1 tablespoon bottled sauce for gravy
4 medium onions, sliced
1 teaspoon salt
1/4 teaspoon pepper
1 bay leaf
1 1/2 teaspoons caraway seeds
10 gingersnaps, finely crushed
1/2 cup cider vinegar
2 tablespoons granulated sugar
1/2 head green cabbage
seasoned salt and pepper

About 2 hours before serving: Trim all fat from meat. In large oven-proof skillet over medium-high heat, in oil, brown meat cubes. Add bottled sauce for gravy, 3 cups water, 2 sliced onions, salt, pepper, bay leaf and caraway seeds. Simmer, covered, 1 hour, or until meat is fork-tender.

Stir in gingersnap crumbs, then cook, stirring, until dissolved; remove bay leaf. Preheat oven to 400°F. Stir in vinegar and sugar; cut cabbage into 6 thin wedges, then lay in row on top of meat; sprinkle with seasoned salt and seasoned pepper. Slice 2 onions into rings and scatter over top. Cover and bake 30 minutes, or until cabbage is tender-crisp.

To serve: Pour some of gravy over cabbage wedges. Makes 6 servings.

Low-fat, low-cholesterol diet: 10 grams fat per serving.
High-iron diet: 5 milligrams iron per serving.

POTTED BEEF (265 calories per serving)

1 tablespoon salad oil
2 pounds beef for stew, trimmed of all fat, cut into 2-inch cubes
1 medium onion, sliced
2 teaspoons salt
1/4 teaspoon pepper
6 large carrots, cut into chunks
6 stalks celery, cut into chunks
1 teaspoon dill weed
1 bay leaf

About 30 minutes before serving: In 4-quart pressure cooker, in hot oil, brown meat and onion. Add remaining ingredients and 3/4 cup water. (Use 1 cup if recommended in pressure-cooker manual.) Bring to 15 pounds pressure as manufacturer directs; cook 15 minutes. Remove from heat; reduce pressure quickly as manufacturer directs before uncovering. Makes 6 servings.

Egg-, gluten-, milk- and wheat-free diet: Prepare as directed.
Low-fat, low-cholesterol diet: 10 grams fat per serving.
High-iron diet: 5 milligrams iron per serving.

FLEMISH OVEN POT ROAST (245 calories per serving)

1 cup cider vinegar
salt
seasoned pepper
1 tablespoon whole allspice
1/4 teaspoon nutmeg
1 3-pound beef bottom round
　steak
3 bread slices
1 egg
1 tablespoon instant minced
　onion
1 1/2 teaspoons mixed dried
　herbs
1 6-ounce can tomato paste
1 tablespoon flour

About 3 1/2 hours before serving: Heat vinegar with 2 teaspoons salt, 3/4 teaspoon seasoned pepper, allspice and nutmeg 5 minutes. Trim fat from meat. Pour seasoning mixture over meat and let stand.

To prepare stuffing: With fork, pull bread into crumbs; mix with egg, onion, 1/2 teaspoon salt, 1/8 teaspoon seasoned pepper, mixed herbs and tomato paste. Preheat oven to 350°F. Remove meat from vinegar mixture; discard vinegar; gash meat deeply with sharp knife, then fill slit with stuffing; repeat on all sides until stuffing is used. In Dutch oven, brown meat on all sides—about 10 to 15 minutes; pour off fat; add 1/4 cup hot water; cover and bake 3 hours, or until tender.

When meat is tender, pour juices from Dutch oven into measuring cup; skim off fat. Return all but 1/4 cup juices to Dutch oven. Stir reserved juices into flour and 1/2 teaspoon salt; stir this mixture into Dutch-oven juices. Cook, stirring, until thickened.

To serve: Cut meat into thin slices; pass gravy. Makes 8 servings.

Low-fat, low-cholesterol diet: Prepare as directed but use only white of egg. 10 grams fat per serving.
High-iron diet: 5.5 milligrams iron per serving.
Low-sodium diet: Prepare as directed but omit salt; use tomato paste not containing added salt. 145 milligrams sodium per serving. If also prepared with low-sodium bread, 100 milligrams sodium per serving.

HEARTY BEEF-AND-VEGETABLE CASSEROLE (305 calories per serving)

1 1/2 pounds boneless beef bot-
　tom round of beef
unseasoned meat tenderizer
salad oil
1 pound onions, thinly sliced
5 fresh medium tomatoes
salt
pepper
1/2 pound green beans, cut up
2 carrots, sliced
1 1/2 cups diced green peppers
1 1/2 cups pared cubed eggplant
1/2 cup uncooked long-grain rice

Day before: Trim all fat from meat; sprinkle with meat tenderizer as label directs; cut into 1-inch cubes. In medium skillet over medium heat, in 2 tablespoons oil, sauté onions until tender; remove. In same skillet, brown meat; add 1/4 cup water, then simmer, covered, 1/2 hour. Refrigerate, covered.

About 2 1/2 hours before serving: Preheat oven to 375°F. Lightly oil medium baking dish; line bottom with half of onions and 3 tomatoes in 1/2-inch slices. Sprinkle with 1/2 teaspoon salt, 1/8 teaspoon pepper. Cover with half of each of following: beans, carrots, green peppers and eggplant. Top with rice, 1/2 teaspoon salt, dash pepper, meat and juices. Top meat with rest of vegetables, then 1/2 teaspoon salt. Pour 2/3 cup water over all. Arrange remaining sliced tomatoes down middle; sprinkle with 1/4 teaspoon salt. Cover with foil and bake 2 hours, or until tender. Makes 6 servings.

Egg-, gluten-, milk- and wheat-free diet: Prepare as directed.
Low-fat, low-cholesterol diet: 10 grams fat per serving.
High-iron diet: 4 milligrams iron per serving.
Low-sodium diet: Prepare as directed but use low-sodium meat tenderizer; omit salt. 105 milligrams sodium per serving.

NETHERLANDS BEEF BIRDS WITH ONIONS (230 calories per serving)

1¹/₂ pounds beef top round
  steak, cut ¹/₂-inch thick
salt and pepper
¹/₄ teaspoon marjoram leaves
6 small white onions, halved
flour
2 tablespoons salad oil
1 8-ounce can stewed tomatoes
  (1 cup)
2 tablespoons horseradish

About 1 hour and 45 minutes before serving: Trim fat from meat; cut into 6 serving pieces. With mallet, edge of plate or dull edge of French knife, pound meat until thin. Salt and pepper on both sides; sprinkle top with marjoram. Place 2 onion halves on each piece and roll up; secure with string or toothpicks. Roll in flour. In large skillet over medium heat, in hot oil, brown meat rolls; pour off any fat. Add tomatoes and horseradish; simmer covered, 1¹/₂ hours, or until meat is tender. Makes 6 servings.

Diabetic diet: Exchanges per serving = 3 meat and 1 vegetable.
Egg-, gluten-, milk- and wheat-free diet: Prepare as directed but dredge meat in cornstarch instead of flour for gluten- and wheat-free diets.
Low-fat, low-cholesterol diet: 10 grams fat per serving.
High-iron diet: 4 milligrams iron per serving.

MINUTE MEAT LOAVES (295 calories per serving)

1¹/₂ pounds lean ground beef
2 cups fresh bread crumbs
1 10¹/₂-ounce can condensed
  onion soup, undiluted
6 stuffed olives, halved

About 30 minutes before serving: Preheat oven to 400°F. Meanwhile, combine all ingredients but olive halves. Spoon meat mixture into 12 ungreased, 3-inch cupcake cups; lightly press to shape. Top each with olive half. Bake 15 minutes, or until well done. Makes 12 individual loaves or 6 servings.

Diabetic diet: Exchanges per serving = 3 meat and ¹/₂ bread.
Low-fat, low-cholesterol diet: Prepare as directed but omit olives. 15 grams fat per serving.
High-iron diet: 4 milligrams iron per serving.

SAUCY SWISS STEAK (230 calories per serving)

1 pound boneless beef top
  round steak, 1 inch thick
1¹/₂ tablespoons flour
salt and pepper
1 tablespoon salad oil
1 16-ounce can tomatoes
1 medium onion, sliced
1¹/₂ teaspoons basil
¹/₂ small green pepper, sliced

About 2 hours and 15 minutes before serving: Trim fat from meat; cut meat into serving pieces. Combine flour with 1 teaspoon salt and ¹/₈ teaspoon pepper. Place meat on chopping board; sprinkle with half flour mixture and pound with meat mallet, edge of plate or dull edge of French knife. Turn meat and repeat on other side. In medium skillet over medium heat, in oil, brown meat well on both sides. Add tomatoes, onion and basil. Simmer, covered, about 2 hours, or until meat is fork-tender, adding green pepper during last 30 minutes. Makes 4 servings.

Diabetic diet: Carefully divide into four equal portions. Exchanges per serving = 3 meat, 2 vegetable and ¹/₂ fat.
Egg-, gluten-, milk- and wheat-free diet: Prepare as directed but use cornstarch in place of flour on gluten- and wheat-free diet.
Low-fat, low-cholesterol diet: 10 grams fat per serving.
High-iron diet: 4.5 milligrams iron per serving.
Low-sodium diet: Prepare as directed but omit salt; use low-sodium canned tomatoes in place of regular. 80 milligrams sodium per serving.

HUNTER'S HARVEST STEW (275 calories per serving)

1¹/₂ pounds beef for stew
3 tablespoons flour
1 teaspoon salt
¹/₈ teaspoon pepper
2 tablespoons butter or margarine
1 16-ounce can tomatoes
2 teaspoons Worcestershire
6 medium carrots, scraped and cut into 1-inch slices
12 small white onions
¹/₂ pound fresh medium mushrooms

About 2 hours and 45 minutes before serving: Trim fat from meat; cube meat into 1-inch pieces. Coat with mixture of flour, salt and pepper.

In large skillet over medium heat, in butter, brown meat cubes. Add 1 cup water, tomatoes and Worcestershire; cover; simmer one hour. Add carrots and white onions; simmer 45 minutes more. Add quartered mushrooms; continue cooking 15 minutes. If stew is too thin, stir enough water into flour, left over from coating meat, to form a thin paste; use to thicken stew to desired consistency. Makes 5 servings.

Diabetic diet: Prepare as directed but use margarine instead of butter. Exchanges per serving = 3 meat, 2 vegetable and 1 bread.
Egg-, gluten-, milk- and wheat-free diet: Prepare as directed but substitute cornstarch for flour on gluten- and wheat-free diets; use milk-free margarine on milk-free diet.
Low-fat, low-cholesterol diet: Prepare as directed but use margarine or salad oil instead of butter. 15 grams fat per serving.
High-iron diet: 5 milligrams iron per serving.
Low-sodium diet: Prepare as directed but omit salt and Worcestershire; use unsalted butter or margarine and low-sodium tomatoes. 95 milligrams sodium per serving.

"PORCUPINE" LAMB BURGERS (225 calories per serving)

1 pound lean ground lamb
¹/₂ cup uncooked white rice
²/₃ cup minced onion
¹/₂ teaspoon salt
¹/₂ teaspoon pepper
1 teaspoon garlic salt
salad oil
1 10¹/₂-ounce can condensed beef or chicken broth
¹/₂ cup catchup
¹/₂ teaspoon basil or thyme leaves or savory or marjoram leaves

About 1¹/₄ hours before serving: Thoroughly combine meat, rice, onion, salt, pepper and garlic salt; form into eighteen 1-inch balls. Lightly rub bottom of skillet with oil; add balls and sauté until browned, shaking skillet to turn balls. Add remaining ingredients; cover; simmer 1 hour. Makes 6 servings.

Diabetic diet: Exchanges per serving (3 meatballs) = 2 meat and 1 bread.
Low-fat, low-cholesterol diet: 10 grams fat per serving.

GLORIFIED ROAST LAMB (220 calories per 4-ounce serving)

¹/₂ cup Dijon-style prepared mustard
2 tablespoons imported soy sauce
1 teaspoon garlic powder
1 teaspoon rosemary
¹/₄ teaspoon ginger
2 teaspoons salad oil
6 pound leg of lamb whole, trimmed of excess fat

Early in day: With electric-blender at low speed, blend mustard, soy sauce, garlic powder, rosemary and ginger, just until combined. On medium speed, blend in oil by droplets until smoothly mixed. Place meat in shallow pan and brush with sauce. Cover and refrigerate several hours.

About 3 hours before serving: Preheat oven to 325°F. Place meat on rack in shallow open pan and roast 2¹/₂ to 3 hours or until done as desired—175°F. internal temperature on roast-meat thermometer for medium-done, 180°F. for well-done. Makes 12 servings.

Diabetic diet: Exchanges = 1 meat for each ounce of meat in serving.
Egg- and milk-free diet: Prepare as directed.
Low-fat, low-cholesterol diet: 15 grams fat per serving.
Low-sodium diet: Prepare as directed but omit prepared mustard and soy sauce. For marinade, mix 1 cup dry mustard with ¹/₂ cup water and other seasonings. 140 milligrams sodium per serving.

INDIAN EGG-MEATBALLS (Nargis Kofta) (300 calories per serving)

4 eggs, hard-cooked
1 pound lean ground lamb
2 teaspoons dried mint flakes,
  crumbled
1 teaspoon salt
1/4 teaspoon pepper
1 tablespoon salad oil
1 large onion, sliced thin
1/2 fresh red pepper, cut into 1/2-
  inch strips (optional)
1/4 to 1/2 teaspoon chili powder
1 teaspoon turmeric
1 teaspoon ginger
1/4 teaspoon garlic salt
1/2 cup chicken broth

About 30 minutes before serving: Cut hard-cooked eggs in half crosswise. Mix meat with mint, 1 1/2 teaspoons salt and pepper. Divide into 8 parts; mold each into thin patty, then wrap patty around egg-half, covering it completely.

In large skillet, in oil, cook meatballs (kofta), onion and red pepper. Add chili powder, turmeric, ginger, garlic salt, 1/2 teaspoon salt and chicken broth; simmer 5 minutes. Makes 4 servings.

Diabetic diet: Exchanges per serving = 4 meat, 1/2 vegetable and 1 fat.
High-iron diet: 3 milligrams iron per serving.

LAMB-AND-PINEAPPLE BURGERS (280 calories per serving)

1 15 1/4-ounce can sliced pineapple packed in pineapple juice
3 slices white bread
1 1/2 pounds lean ground lamb
1 egg, beaten
1/2 cup chopped onion
1 1/2 teaspoons salt
1/2 teaspoon pepper
1/2 teaspoon rosemary
6 stuffed olives for garnish

About 30 minutes before serving: Drain can of sliced pineapple, reserving 2/3 cup juice. Preheat broiler if manufacturer directs. Soak bread slices in reserved pineapple juice; mix in remaining ingredients except olives. Shape mixture into 6 patties. Broil, 3 to 4 inches from heat, 6 to 8 minutes. Turn; top each patty with pineapple slice and broil 6 minutes. If desired, top center of each pineapple slice with stuffed olive. Makes 6 servings.

Diabetic diet: Prepare as directed. Exchanges per serving = 3 meat, 1 bread and 1/2 fruit.
Low-fat, low-cholesterol diet: Prepare as directed but use only white of egg. 10 grams fat per serving. Omit olive if forbidden on diet.
Low-sodium diet: Prepare as directed but omit salt and olives. 155 milligrams sodium per serving. If also prepared with low-sodium bread, 100 milligrams sodium per serving.

LAMB-AND-CARROT MEATBALLS (305 calories per serving)

1 pound lean ground lamb
1 cup finely grated carrots
1 medium onion, finely chopped
1/4 cup packaged dried bread
  crumbs
1 egg
1 teaspoon salt
1/4 teaspoon pepper
1/2 teaspoon basil
1/4 teaspoon thyme leaves
2 tablespoons butter or margarine
2 tablespoons flour

About 1 hour before serving: In large bowl, mix lamb, carrots, onion, bread crumbs, egg, salt, pepper, basil and thyme; form into 8 balls. In large skillet or Dutch oven over medium heat, in butter, cook lamb balls until well browned.

Meanwhile, in small bowl, slowly add 1 1/2 cups water to flour, stirring well. Stir mixture into skillet until smooth; cover, simmer 40 minutes. Arrange meatballs on small platter. Skim fat from gravy, then pour a little gravy over each meatball; pass rest. Makes 4 servings.

Diabetic diet: Prepare as directed but use margarine instead of butter. Exchanges per serving = 3 meat, 1 bread and 1 1/2 fat.
Low-fat, low-cholesterol diet: Prepare as directed but use only white of egg; use margarine instead of butter. 15 grams fat per serving.
Low-sodium diet: Prepare as directed but use ground unsalted Melba rounds instead of bread crumbs; omit salt; use unsalted butter or margarine. 115 milligrams sodium per serving.

MARINATED LAMB PATTIES (290 calories per serving)

¹/₂ cup soy sauce
1 garlic clove crushed
1 teaspoon curry
¹/₄ teaspoon ginger
1 pound lean ground lamb

At least 1¹/₂ hours before serving: In small bowl, combine soy sauce, garlic, curry and ginger. Shape meat into 4 patties and place in baking dish. Pour marinade over patties; refrigerate at least 1 hour, turning once, basting occasionally.

About 25 minutes before serving: Preheat broiler 10 minutes if manufacturer directs. Place patties on broiler pan; spoon half of marinade over them. Broil 5 minutes; turn; spoon on remaining marinade and broil 5 minutes more, or until done as desired. Makes 4 servings.

Diabetic diet: Exchanges per serving = 3 meat.

VEAL POLONAISE (295 calories per serving)

4 small veal loin chops (about 5 ounces each)
1 tablespoon salad oil
1 medium onion, minced
seasoned salt
flour
1 8-ounce can tomato sauce
1 beef-bouillon cube
¹/₂ cup buttermilk
2 tablespoons dry white wine
chopped parsley for garnish

About 45 minutes before serving: Trim fat from chops. In large skillet over medium heat, in oil, sauté onion. Meanwhile, sprinkle chops with seasoned salt; lightly dust with flour; brown on both sides in skillet with onion. Stir in tomato sauce, bouillon cube and ¹/₂ cup water. Bring to boiling; then simmer, covered, about 30 minutes, or until chops are fork-tender. Place chops on serving platter. Stir buttermilk and wine into liquid in skillet; do not boil; pour gravy over chops. Sprinkle with parsley. Makes 4 servings.

Diabetic diet: Prepare as directed but use margarine instead of butter. Exchanges per serving = 3 meat, 1 vegetable and ¹/₂ fat.
Low-fat, low-cholesterol diet: 15 grams fat per serving.
High-iron diet: 4.5 milligrams iron per serving.

DEVILED VEAL CUTLET (265 calories per serving)

1¹/₂ pounds veal cutlets, thinly sliced
2 tablespoons flour
1 teaspoon salt
1 teaspoon paprika
2 tablespoons butter or margarine
1 cup minced onions
1 beef-bouillon cube
1 teaspoon prepared mustard
2 teaspoons prepared horseradish
¹/₃ cup sour cream

About 45 minutes before serving: Cut meat into serving-size pieces; roll in flour mixed with salt and paprika. In skillet, in butter, sauté onions; remove; set aside. In same skillet, brown meat well. Dissolve bouillon cube in 1¹/₂ cups boiling water; pour over meat. Add sautéed onions, mustard, horseradish; simmer, covered, 25 minutes, or until meat is tender. Remove to serving dish. Gradually stir sour cream into gravy; spoon over meat. Makes 6 servings.

Diabetic diet: Prepare as directed but use margarine instead of butter. Carefully divide into 6 equal servings. Exchanges per serving = 3 meat, 1 vegetable and 1 fat.

VEAL TARRAGON (250 calories per serving)

1 pound veal cutlets, thinly
sliced
1 tablespoon flour
1 tablespoon butter or margarine
juice of 1/2 lemon
2 teaspoons tarragon
1/2 teaspoon salt
1/8 teaspoon pepper

About 20 minutes before serving: On board, pound cutlets with meat mallet or edge of saucer; cut into serving pieces. Dust with flour. In large skillet, brown quickly on both sides. Add 2 table-spoons water and remaining ingredients; cover; cook until tender—7 to 10 minutes. Makes 4 servings.

Diabetic diet: Prepare as directed but use margarine instead of butter. Exchanges per serving = 3 meat and 1/2 fat.
Egg-, gluten-, milk- and wheat-free diet: Prepare as directed but substitute cornstarch for flour on gluten- and wheat-free diets; use milk-free margarine on milk-free diet.
Low-fat, low-cholesterol diet: Prepare as directed but use margarine or salad oil instead of butter. 15 grams fat per serving.
Low-sodium diet: Prepare as directed but use unsalted butter or margarine; omit salt. 100 milligrams sodium per serving.

VEAL SCALOPPINI (260 calories per serving)

1 1/2 pounds veal leg sirloin
steak, cut 1/4-inch thick
2 tablespoons flour
2 teaspoons seasoned salt
1/4 teaspoon pepper
2 tablespoons salad oil
1 garlic clove
1 1 1/2-ounce package spaghetti-
sauce mix
1 20-ounce can tomatoes
2 tablespoons sherry

About 30 minutes before serving: Cut meat into 1 1/2-inch pieces; roll in flour combined with seasoned salt and pepper. In large skillet, in oil, heat garlic clove until light brown; remove. Then brown meat in oil; remove from skillet; set aside. Add spaghetti-sauce mix and tomatoes to skillet; stir thoroughly; simmer, covered, 15 minutes. Return meat to sauce; simmer, covered, 45 minutes longer. Add wine just before serving. Makes 6 servings.

Diabetic diet: Prepare as directed but use margarine instead of butter. Carefully divide into 6 equal servings. Exchanges per serving = 3 meat, 2 vegetable and 1 fat.
Low-fat, low-cholesterol diet: 15 grams fat per serving.

VEAL WITH MARSALA WINE (230 calories per serving)

1 pound veal leg round roast,
cut about 1/4-inch thick for
scaloppini
1/4 cup flour
1 teaspoon salt
generous dash pepper
1 1/2 tablespoons butter or margarine
1/4 cup dry Marsala wine
1/4 cup water

About 45 minutes before serving: If necessary, cut meat into pieces about 3-inches square. Cut away any white skin, connective tissue and fat. With mallet or bottom of bottle, pound meat into very thin slices—about 1/8-inch thick.

About 20 minutes before serving: Dip meat into mixture of flour, salt and pepper. In large skillet over medium heat, in butter, cook on both sides until lightly browned—about one minute on each side; remove pieces from pan as they are done. Return all meat to skillet; add Marsala and water; cook, gently scraping bottom of skillet to loosen browned particles until gravy thickens slightly—about 5 minutes. Makes 4 servings.

Egg-, gluten-, milk- and wheat-free diet: Prepare as directed but use cornstarch instead of flour for gluten- and wheat-free diets; use milk-free margarine on milk-free diet.
Low-fat, low-cholesterol diet: Prepare as directed but use margarine instead of butter. 15 grams fat per serving.
High-iron diet: 3.5 milligrams iron per serving.
Low-sodium diet: Prepare as directed but use unsalted butter or margarine; omit salt. 105 milligrams sodium per serving.

CURRIED VEAL CHOPS WITH APPLES (350 calories per serving)

4 veal loin chops, ³/₄-inch thick
(1¹/₂ pounds)
2 tablespoons flour
2 tablespoons salad oil
³/₄ cup chopped onions
2 to 3 teaspoons curry
1 teaspoon salt
¹/₄ teaspoon pepper
1 medium red apple
lemon juice

About 1 hour before serving: Trim all fat from chops; coat chops with flour. In large skillet over medium heat, in oil, brown on both sides. Spoon onions around chops, then sauté, stirring occasionally, until onions are browned. Sprinkle with curry, salt and pepper; add ¹/₄ cup water. Cover and cook, over medium heat, 45 minutes, or until chops are tender.

Meanwhile, core apple (do not remove skin); cut into 8 wedges; brush with lemon juice; place around chops. Cover and cook 10 minutes, or until apples are tender-crisp.

To serve: Remove chops and apples to heated platter; spoon pan juices over them. Makes 4 servings.

Diabetic diet: Exchanges per serving = 4 meat, 1 fruit and 1 fat.
Egg-, gluten-, milk- and wheat-free diet: Prepare as directed but use cornstarch in place of flour for gluten- and wheat-free diets.
Low-fat, low-cholesterol diet: 15 grams fat per serving.
High-iron diet: 4 milligrams iron per serving.

POTTED VEAL CHOPS (355 calories per serving)

4 ³/₄-inch veal loin chops (about
1¹/₂ pounds)
¹/₄ cup flour
1 teaspoon seasoned salt
¹/₄ teaspoon seasoned pepper
1 tablespoon salad oil
1 16-ounce can stewed tomatoes
3 tablespoons tomato paste
¹/₄ teaspoon basil
oregano leaves
4 ounces spaghetti

About 2 hours before serving: Trim fat from chops. Combine flour, seasoned salt and pepper; rub into chops. Set electric skillet at 300°F. In oil, brown chops on both sides—about 20 minutes. Stir in tomatoes, tomato paste, basil and ¹/₂ teaspoon oregano. Turn control to 215°F.; simmer, covered, 1 hour, or until chops are fork-tender.

About 15 minutes before chops are done, cook spaghetti as label directs; drain; keep hot.

To serve: Arrange hot spaghetti on heated platter; sprinkle with oregano. Top with chops and tomato sauce. Makes 4 servings.

Diabetic diet: Serve chops on ¹/₂ cup (1 bread) or 1 cup (2 bread) spaghetti. Exchanges per serving = 3 meat and 1 vegetable plus bread exchanges from spaghetti.
Low-fat, low-cholesterol diet: 15 grams fat per serving.
High-iron diet: 5 milligrams iron per serving.

VEAL STEAK WITH HAM AND MUSHROOMS (280 calories per serving)

1 veal leg sirloin steak, ³/₄-inch
thick (1¹/₂ pounds)
¹/₂ teaspoon salt
¹/₄ teaspoon seasoned pepper
1 tablespoon salad oil
1¹/₂ tablespoons bottled garlic
spread
15 ¹/₂-inch cubes lean ham
(about ¹/₂ pound)
2 fresh mushrooms, sliced
1 tablespoon lemon juice
1 teaspoon coarsely grated
lemon peel

About 1 hour before serving: Trim all fat from veal; sprinkle veal with salt and seasoned pepper. In skillet over medium heat, in oil, brown on both sides and smooth garlic spread over top. Add 2 tablespoons water to skillet; cover tightly, then simmer 45 minutes, or until veal is fork-tender.

Uncover, pour off, then measure drippings; add water to make ²/₃ cup, return to skillet and add ham cubes and mushroom slices; then cook 5 minutes, stirring occasionally. Remove veal to heated platter; add lemon juice to skillet and spoon sauce over veal. Sprinkle with lemon peel. Makes 6 servings.

Low-fat, low-cholesterol diet: 15 grams fat per serving.
High-iron diet: 4 milligrams iron per serving.

FRUITED RABBIT (245 calories per serving)

1 package frozen rabbit (about
  2¹/₂ pounds), thawed
salt
¹/₄ teaspoon pepper
1 cup orange juice
2 tablespoons brown sugar
2 tablespoons wine vinegar
1 teaspoon nutmeg
1 teaspoon basil
¹/₈ teaspoon garlic salt
¹/₄ cup flour
2 tablespoons salad oil
1 cup fresh orange sections
1 cup fresh grapefruit sections
2 tablespoons chopped parsley
  for garnish

About 1³/₄ hours before serving: Sprinkle rabbit with 1¹/₂ teaspoons salt and pepper; refrigerate 30 minutes. Meanwhile, in small bowl, combine orange juice, brown sugar, vinegar, nutmeg, basil, garlic salt and ³/₄ teaspoon salt. Combine flour and ¹/₂ teaspoon salt; use to coat rabbit evenly.

In large skillet over medium heat, in oil, brown rabbit on all sides until golden. Add orange-juice mixture; simmer, covered, 1 hour or until rabbit is fork-tender, stirring occasionally and turning once. Now lay orange and grapefruit sections over surface of rabbit; cook, covered, without stirring, until just heated through. Garnish with parsley. Makes 6 servings.

Egg-, gluten-, milk- and wheat-free diet: Prepare as directed but use cornstarch in place of flour on gluten- and wheat-free diets.
Low-fat, low-cholesterol diet: 10 grams fat per serving.
Low-sodium diet: Prepare as directed but omit salt and use garlic powder in place of garlic salt. 40 milligrams sodium per serving.

ITALIAN FRANKFURTERS (295 calories per serving)

1 tablespoon butter or margarine
1 pound frankfurters, sliced into
  1-inch lengths
1 10¹/₂-ounce can condensed
  beef broth
1 soup-can water
¹/₂ to 1 teaspoon oregano
  leaves
1 16-ounce can tomatoes
2 cups uncooked egg noodles
2 medium zucchini, sliced
  crosswise into ¹/₂-inch pieces
1 10-ounce package frozen Italian beans
2 tablespoons flour

About 30 minutes before serving: In large skillet over medium heat, in butter, brown franks. Add broth, water, oregano and tomatoes; bring to boiling, then stir in noodles. Bring to a simmer again, then top with zucchini; cover; simmer 5 minutes. Now add Italian beans (still frozen); cover; simmer 10 minutes more, or until zucchini is tender.

Meanwhile, stir a few tablespoons water into flour to form a smooth paste; stir into stew. Makes 8 servings of about 1 cup each.

Diabetic diet: Prepare as directed but use margarine instead of butter. Exchanges per serving = 2 meat, 1 vegetable, 1 bread and 2 fat.

SAY MORE FRANKS (155 calories per serving)

1 tablespoon butter or margarine
³/₄ medium onion, chopped
³/₄ cup water
3 tablespoons catchup
2 tablespoons vinegar
1 tablespoon brown sugar
1 tablespoon prepared mustard
2 teaspoons Worcestershire
³/₄ teaspoon salt
³/₄ teaspoon prepared horseradish
dash pepper
12 frankfurters

About 45 minutes before serving: In small saucepan in butter, sauté onion until tender. Stir in all remaining ingredients except frankfurters; simmer mixture 20 minutes, stirring occasionally. Preheat oven to 400°F. Place frankfurters in lightly oiled casserole; pour on sauce. Bake 20 minutes, basting occasionally.

To serve: Spoon sauce over frankfurters. Makes 6 servings.

Diabetic diet: Prepare as directed but use margarine instead of butter; omit brown sugar. Exchanges per serving (2 franks) = 2 meat, 1 vegetable and 2¹/₂ fat.

QUICK FRANK DINNER (350 calories per serving)

4 medium carrots, quartered
  lengthwise
1 cup chicken broth
1 small onion
1 bay leaf
1 small head cabbage (about 2
  pounds), quartered
salt
8 frankfurters

About 40 minutes before serving: In large skillet, place carrots, broth, onion and bay leaf; cover and cook over medium heat 5 minutes. Arrange cabbage wedges next to carrots; cover and continue cooking 5 minutes. Turn cabbage wedges. Sprinkle vegetables with salt. Add frankfurters and simmer 5 to 10 minutes longer, or until vegetables are tender. Makes 4 servings.

Diabetic diet: Exchanges per serving = 2 meat, 2 vegetable and 2 fat.

FRANKFURTER-AND-BEAN CASSEROLE (270 calories per serving)

1 16-ounce package frozen cut
  green beans
1 tablespoon butter or margarine
1 tablespoon flour
1 cup skimmed milk or reliquefied nonfat dry milk
1/4 teaspoon salt
dash pepper
dash paprika
4 frankfurters, cut into 1/2-inch
  slices
1 slice toast, cubed
1/2 cup shredded Cheddar
  cheese

About 50 minutes before serving: Preheat oven to 350°F. Cook green beans as label directs, but only for 3 minutes; drain. In same saucepan, over medium heat, blend butter and flour; slowly stir in milk, salt, pepper and paprika; cook until thickened. Add frankfurters and green beans; pour into 1 quart casserole; top with bread cubes and cheese. Bake 30 minutes. Makes 4 servings.

Diabetic diet: Prepare as directed but use margarine instead of butter. Exchanges per serving = 2 meat, 1 vegetable, 1 bread and 2 fat.

FRANKFURTER STEW (310 calories per serving)

1 16-ounce can tomatoes
2 beef-bouillon cubes
2 cups cubed pared potatoes
2 medium onions, cut into
  eighths
3 medium carrots, thinly sliced
3 stalks green celery, cut into
  1-inch pieces
1 tablespoon parsley flakes
1/2 pound frankfurters, cut into
  1-inch pieces
3 tablespoons flour
1/4 teaspoon thyme leaves
pepper to taste

About 40 minutes before serving: In large saucepan or Dutch oven, mix tomatoes, 3 cups water, bouillon cubes, potatoes, onions, carrots, celery and parsley; simmer 20 minutes, or until vegetables are almost tender. Add frankfurters, then simmer 10 minutes more, or until vegetables are tender.

Mix water with flour and thyme to make a smooth paste. Stir into stew, and heat until thickened. Add pepper to taste. Serve in soup bowls. Makes 5 servings of a scant 2 cups each.

Diabetic diet: Exchanges per serving = 2 meat, 2 vegetable, 1 bread and 2 fat.

LIVER AND ONIONS AU FROMAGE (250 calories per serving)

1 pound beef liver, sliced 1/2-inch thick
flour
salt
garlic salt
pepper
2 tablespoons butter or margarine
1/4 cup shredded Cheddar cheese
1 scallion, cut into thin rounds

About 20 minutes before serving: Remove skin and veins from liver; cut into serving pieces. Sprinkle lightly with flour (shake off excess); sprinkle to taste with salt, garlic salt and pepper. In medium skillet over medium heat, in butter, brown liver 2 to 3 minutes; turn and continue cooking until almost done as you like. Turn off heat, pour off most of butter and return skillet to burner. Sprinkle liver pieces with shredded cheese, then scallion. Cover; let stand 2 to 3 minutes, or until cheese is just melted. Makes 4 servings.

Bland diet: Prepare as directed but omit garlic salt, pepper and scallions; top with mild Cheddar cheese.
Diabetic diet: Prepare as directed but use margarine instead of butter; omit dredging liver in flour. Exchanges per serving = 3 meat and 2 fat.
Egg-, gluten- and wheat-free diet: Prepare as directed but omit dredging liver in flour for gluten- and wheat-free diets.
High-iron diet: 8 milligrams iron per serving.
Low-residue diet: Prepare as directed for bland diet.

ENGLISH LIVER BAKE (245 calories per serving)

1 pound beef liver
flour
1/2 teaspoon salt
1/4 teaspoon pepper
1 4-ounce package Canadian bacon (about 10 to 12 slices)
1 large onion, sliced

About 1 hour and 45 minutes before serving: Preheat oven to 350°F. Cut liver into 4 serving pieces. Dredge in 2 tablespoons flour mixed with salt and pepper. Trim fat from Canadian bacon.

In 2-quart casserole, place layers of liver, Canadian bacon and onion slices; add 1 1/2 cups water. Bake, uncovered, 1 1/2 hours. For a thicker gravy, make a smooth paste with 2 tablespoons flour and 2 tablespoons water; stir in about 10 minutes before end of cooking time. Makes 4 servings.

Bland diet: Prepare as directed but omit pepper and onion.
Diabetic diet: Exchanges per serving = 4 meat, 1 vegetable and 2 fat.
Egg-, gluten-, milk- and wheat-free diet: Prepare as directed but dredge liver in cornstarch instead of flour for gluten- and wheat-free diets.
Low-fat, bland (gall bladder) diet: Prepare as directed for bland diet.
High-iron diet: 8.5 milligrams iron per serving.
Low-residue diet: Prepare as directed for bland diet.

LEMONY LIVER (220 calories per serving)

1 1/2 tablespoons flour
1/2 teaspoon salt
1/4 teaspoon pepper
1 pound calves' liver, thinly sliced
2 tablespoons butter or margarine
1 tablespoon lemon juice
1 tablespoon chopped parsley for garnish

About 10 minutes before serving: Combine flour, salt and pepper; use to coat liver. In medium skillet over high heat, in butter, cook liver until tender—about 2 minutes on each side. Sprinkle with lemon juice and parsley. Makes 4 servings.

Diabetic diet: Prepare as directed but use margarine instead of butter. Exchanges per serving = 3 meat and 2 1/2 fat.
Egg-, gluten-, milk- and wheat-free-diet: Prepare as directed but use cornstarch in place of flour on gluten- and wheat-free diets; use milk-free margarine on milk-free diet.
High-iron diet: 10 milligrams iron per serving.
Low-sodium diet: Prepare as directed but omit salt; use unsalted butter or margarine. 85 milligrams sodium per serving.

LIVER CREOLE (230 calories per serving)

1 pound calves' liver, thinly
sliced
1 tablespoon flour
1 tablespoon butter or margarine
1 16-ounce can tomatoes
1 medium onion, sliced
1 green pepper, cut into thin
strips
1/2 cup diced celery
1/2 teaspoon salt
dash pepper
2 teaspoons cornstarch

About 30 minutes before serving: Cut liver into 1-inch strips; sprinkle lightly with flour. In medium skillet, in butter, quickly brown
liver; add remaining ingredients except cornstarch. Simmer, covered, 15 minutes. Mix cornstarch with a little water to form a
smooth paste. Stir into liver mixture; simmer, stirring, until sauce
thickens. Makes 4 servings.

Diabetic diet: Prepare as directed but use margarine instead of butter.
Exchanges per serving = 3 meat, 2 vegetable and 2 fat.
Egg-, gluten-, milk- and wheat-free diet: Prepare as directed but use
cornstarch in place of flour to dredge liver for gluten- and wheat-free
diets; use milk-free margarine on milk-free diet.
Low-fat diet: 10 grams fat per serving. Omit recipe from low-cholesterol
diet.
High-iron diet: 11 milligrams iron per serving.
Low-sodium diet: Prepare as directed but use unsalted butter or margarine; use low-sodium-packed canned tomatoes; omit salt. 95 milligrams sodium per serving.

LIVER JARDINIÈRE (275 calories per serving)

2 pounds beef liver, sliced
3 tablespoons flour
8 strips bacon
3 medium onions, thinly sliced
3 large green peppers, thinly
sliced
1 teaspoon salt
1/4 teaspoon pepper
1 16-ounce can whole tomatoes

About 1 hour and 15 minutes before serving: Lightly coat liver
slices with flour. In large skillet over medium heat, fry bacon until
crisp; drain on paper towels. Pour off bacon drippings and
reserve. Over medium heat, in 2 tablespoons bacon drippings, fry
liver, a few pieces at a time, until lightly browned on both sides.
Remove from pan.

Meanwhile, to skillet, add 1 tablespoon more bacon drippings,
onions, green peppers, salt and pepper; brown lightly. Add juice
from tomatoes (reserve tomatoes); place liver on top; cover and
cook over low heat 25 minutes, or until liver is tender. During last
minutes of cooking, add tomatoes and bacon slices to heat
through. Makes 8 servings.

Diabetic diet: Count one meat and 1/2 fat exchange for each ounce of
cooked liver, and 1 vegetable and 1 fat exchange for about 1/2 cup tomatoes and sauce.
Egg-, gluten-, milk- and wheat-free diet: Prepare as directed but use
cornstarch in place of flour to coat liver for gluten- and wheat-free
diets.
High-iron diet: 8 milligrams iron per serving.

YANKEE HAM (160 calories per serving)

1 11/2-pound smoked ham center slices, cut about 1/2-inch
thick
Worcestershire
chopped parsley for garnish

About 20 minutes before serving: Preheat broiler 10 minutes if
manufacturer directs. Trim fat from ham. Place ham on broiler
rack; brush with Worcestershire. Broil, 3 inches from heat, 4 minutes; turn; brush again; broil 4 minutes more. Sprinkle with
chopped parsley. Makes 6 servings.

Diabetic diet: Exchanges per serving = 1 meat for each ounce cooked
ham.
Low-fat, low-cholesterol diet: 10 grams fat per serving.

HAM STEAK WITH CURRANT GLAZE (225 calories per serving)

1 2-pound smoked ham center slices
1/4 cup currant jelly

About 40 minutes before serving: Preheat oven to 325°F. Trim fat from ham; place ham in shallow baking pan. Spoon jelly over it and bake 30 minutes, basting several times with jelly. Makes 6 servings.

Egg-, gluten-, milk- and wheat-free diet: Prepare as directed.
Low-fat, low-cholesterol diet: 10 grams fat per serving.
High-iron diet: 3 milligrams iron per serving.

BARBECUED HAM (300 calories per serving)

2 tablespoons salad oil
1 teaspoon salt
2 tablespoons prepared mustard
2 tablespoons white vinegar
2 tablespoons paprika
1 cup white corn syrup
1/4 cup catchup
1 48-ounce (3-pound) canned ham
heavy cord

About 1 1/4 hours before serving: In medium saucepan, combine oil, salt, mustard, vinegar, paprika, corn syrup and catchup. Heat slowly until time to use as glaze. Preheat oven to 350°F.

Open ham; scrape off "jelly," and trim extra fat; cut, crosswise, into 1/4-inch-thick slices. Reshape slices; tie together, lengthwise, with heavy cord; place on rack in foil-lined shallow roasting pan. Brush liberally with glaze. Roast about 1 hour; spoon on glaze 2 or three times. Transfer to platter; remove cord. Makes 10 servings.

Low-fat, low-cholesterol diet: 15 grams fat per serving.
High-iron diet: 4 milligrams iron per serving.

EGG-ON-HAM TOAST (210 calories per serving)

1 10-ounce package frozen chopped spinach
3 slices bread
1 teaspoon horseradish
1/2 teaspoon prepared mustard
3 eggs
3 slices boiled ham (about 3 ounces)
paprika

About 20 minutes before serving: Cook spinach as label directs; drain. Under broiler, toast bread on 1 side, then spread with blend of horseradish and mustard. Meanwhile, poach eggs until whites are firm.

Trim fat from ham; place ham on untoasted sides of bread; run under broiler until hot. Top each slice with poached egg; then sprinkle with paprika. Serve surrounded with spinach. Makes 3 servings.

Diabetic diet: Exchanges per serving = 2 meat, 1 vegetable, 1 bread and 1 fat.
Low-fat diet: 10 grams fat per serving. Omit recipe from low-cholesterol diet.
High-iron diet: 4.5 milligrams iron per serving.

OPEN-FACED HAM-AND-SWISS SANDWICHES (275 calories per serving)

4 large slices rye bread
reduced–calorie mayonnaise
4 1/2-inch thick slices canned or boiled ham (about 1/2 pound)
4 rectangular slices (about 4 ounces) Swiss cheese, halved crosswise
3/4 cup shredded cabbage
salt and pepper to taste

Just before serving: Spread each slice rye bread with 1 tablespoon reduced-calorie mayonnaise; top with slice canned or boiled ham. Roll cheese slices and place on top of ham—three slices for each sandwich. Toss cabbage with 2 tablespoons reduced-calorie mayonnaise and salt and pepper to taste. Arrange over cheese slices. Serve with knife and fork. Makes 4 servings.

Diabetic diet: Exchanges per serving = 3 meat, 1 bread and 1 1/2 fat.

HAM AND BANANAS (330 calories per serving)

1 2-pound smoked ham center
  slices
6 whole cloves
1/2 cup grapefruit juice
brown sugar
1/2 teaspoon dry mustard
4 medium bananas

About 1 hour and 15 minutes before serving: Preheat oven to 325°F. Trim fat from ham; place ham in shallow baking dish; stud with cloves. In cup, combine grapefruit juice, 2 tablespoons brown sugar and mustard; pour over ham. Bake 50 minutes, basting frequently with sugar mixture. Cut bananas lengthwise; arrange, cut sides down, on top of ham; brush with sugar mixture, then sprinkle with an additional 1/4 cup brown sugar. Bake 10 to 15 minutes more, or heat under broiler 5 to 10 minutes until brown sugar melts and forms glaze over bananas. Makes 8 servings.

Egg-, gluten-, milk- and wheat-free diet: Prepare as directed.
Low-fat, low-cholesterol diet: 10 grams fat per serving.

APRICOT-TOPPED HAM (210 calories per serving)

3/4 pound sliced smoked
  cooked ham (4 slices, each
  about 1/3-inch thick)
1 tablespoon salad oil
3 tablespoons apricot preserves

About 5 minutes before serving: Trim fat from ham. In large skillet, heat oil and preserves until bubbly. Add ham slices; cook, turning once, until heated through. Roll up ham; serve with sauce from pan. Makes 4 servings.

Egg-, gluten-, milk- and wheat-free diet: Prepare as directed.
Low-fat, low-cholesterol diet: 10 grams fat per serving.

SWEET-AND-TART TROPICAL HAM (290 calories per serving)

1 16-ounce canned ham
1 16-ounce can tropical fruit
  salad
1 tablespoon vinegar

About 20 minutes before serving: Drain ham, reserving gelatin; trim fat and slice ham into 4 serving pieces. Drain fruit, reserving 1/4 cup syrup. In medium skillet over high heat, bring reserved gelatin and syrup to boiling; cook 5 minutes, or until reduced to half of original volume. Add vinegar and ham; simmer 5 minutes more, turning ham once or twice. Add fruit to skillet; heat. Serve sauce over ham. Makes 4 servings.

Egg-, gluten-, milk- and wheat-free diet: Prepare as directed.
Low-fat, low-cholesterol diet: 10 grams fat per serving.

HAM-AND-POTATO CASSEROLE (310 calories per serving)

1 tablespoon butter or margarine
1 12-ounce can spiced luncheon
  meat, cut into 1/2-inch cubes
1 small onion, minced
2 tablespoons chopped green
  pepper
1 cup sliced celery
1/4 cup flour
2 cups skimmed milk or reliquefied nonfat dry milk
5 cups diced potatoes
1 teaspoon parsley flakes

About 1 hour and 10 minutes before serving: Preheat oven to 375°F. In large ovenproof skillet, in butter, cook meat cubes, onion, green pepper and celery until onion is lightly browned. Mix flour with bit of milk to form a smooth paste; add remaining milk. Stir flour-milk mixture into skillet; cook until thickened. Stir in potatoes and parsley flakes. Reheat to a simmer. Bake, uncovered, 40 to 50 minutes, or until potatoes are tender and lightly browned on surface. Makes 6 servings.

Diabetic diet: Prepare as directed but use margarine instead of butter. Carefully divide into 6 equal servings (about 1 cup each). Exchanges per serving = 1 meat, 1 bread, 1/2 milk and 1 fat.

PORK CHOPS IN MUSHROOM GRAVY (245 calories per serving)

2 tablespoons salad oil
8 thin pork loin rib chops (about
 two pounds), trimmed of all
 fat
1 medium onion, sliced
1 10¹/₂-ounce can mushroom
 gravy
1 tablespoon brown sugar
¹/₄ teaspoon salt
1 teaspoon lemon juice
¹/₂ teaspoon Worcestershire
dash Tabasco
2 8¹/₄-ounce cans pineapple
 slices, drained

About 1 hour before serving: In large skillet over medium heat, in oil, brown chops on both sides. Pour off fat; add remaining ingredients except pineapple. Simmer, covered, 40 minutes. Uncover; simmer until gravy thickens, stirring often. Add pineapple and heat through; transfer to heated platter. Makes 8 servings.

Diabetic diet: Prepare as directed but use margarine instead of butter; omit sugar and pineapple. One serving equals 1 chop and ¹/₄ cup gravy. Exchanges per serving = 2 meat and 1 fat.
High-iron diet: 3 milligrams iron per serving.

SMOKED PORK FLORENTINE (310 calories per serving)

1 2-pound pork shoulder roll
2 10-ounce packages frozen
 chopped spinach
1 10¹/₂-ounce can condensed
 cream-of-mushroom soup
¹/₄-cup grated Parmesan cheese
1 cup skimmed milk or reliquefied nonfat dry milk

About 2 hours before serving: In large kettle, place pork butt (remove any casing or stockinette covering first and trim away fat) and cover with hot water; cover and cook, over low heat, 2 hours, or until fork-tender; drain. Near end of cooking time, in medium saucepan, cook spinach as label directs but use no salt; drain.

In small saucepan over medium heat, combine undiluted soup and cheese; slowly stir in milk; heat through. Slice meat and place on platter; arrange spinach on top and pour on soup. Makes 8 servings.

Diabetic diet: Prepare as directed. Serve with ¹/₂ cup spinach and ¹/₃ cup soup-cheese mixture = 1 vegetable and ¹/₂ milk exchange. Count each ounce cooked pork as 1 meat exchange and ¹/₂ fat.
High-iron diet: 5 milligrams iron per serving.

PORK CHOPS JARDINIÈRE (275 calories per serving)

4 pork loin or loin rib chops, ³/₄-
 inch thick (about 1¹/₄ pounds)
1 tablespoon salad oil
1 13³/₄-ounce can chicken broth
¹/₄ teaspoon salt
¹/₈ teaspoon pepper
¹/₈ teaspoon granulated sugar
2 medium stalks celery
1 carrot
1 tablespoon flour

About 1 hour and 20 minutes before serving: Trim fat from chops. In medium skillet over medium heat, in oil, brown chops on both sides. Pour off fat. Add chicken broth, salt, pepper and sugar. Simmer, covered, 1 hour, or until chops are almost fork-tender.

Cut celery and carrot into thin strips. Push chops to one side of skillet; add celery and carrot. Simmer, covered, 5 minutes, or until vegetables are tender. Place chops on warm platter. Using slotted spoon, place vegetables on chops.

In measuring cup, blend flour and 2 tablespoons water until smooth; gradually stir in broth. Cook over medium heat, stirring often, until liquid is thickened; pour over vegetables. Makes 4 servings.

Diabetic diet: Prepare as directed but omit sugar and cook 4 carrots. One serving = 1 chop plus ¹/₂ cup carrots. Exchanges per serving = 3 meat and 1¹/₂ fat.
Low-fat, low-cholesterol diet: 15 grams fat per serving.
High-iron diet: 4.5 milligrams iron per serving.
Low-sodium diet: Prepare as directed but use unsalted chicken broth and omit salt. 110 milligrams sodium per serving.

EGGS AND CHEESE MAIN DISHES

DEVILED-EGG RAREBIT (315 calories per serving)

2/3 cup nonfat dry-milk powder
1/4 cup flour
1/2 teaspoon salt
2 hard-cooked eggs, sliced
1 41/2-ounce can deviled ham
2 tablespoons grated process Cheddar cheese
2 English muffins, split

About 20 minutes before serving: In double-boiler top, beat 2 cups water, dry-milk powder, flour and salt until smooth. Cook over hot, not boiling, water, stirring until thickened. Then stir in eggs, ham and cheese; continue cooking until cheese is melted. Serve 1/2 cup sauce on split toasted English muffin. Makes 4 servings.

Diabetic diet: Exchanges per serving = 1 meat, 1/2 bread, 1/2 milk and 1 fat.

SURPRISE EGGS (160 calories per serving)

2 10-ounce packages frozen broccoli spears
shredded Parmesan cheese
1 tablespoon butter or margarine
6 eggs
1/2 teaspoon salt

About 45 minutes before serving: Cook broccoli as label directs; drain. Cut into 1-inch pieces and arrange evenly over bottom of 10-inch pie plate. Preheat oven to 350°F. Sprinkle with 4 tablespoons Parmesan cheese and dot with butter. Separate eggs, leaving each yolk in one half of shell. Beat egg whites with salt until stiff. Spread half over broccoli; sprinkle with 4 tablespoons Parmesan; then top with rest of whites; shape 6 "nests" in whites with back of spoon. Bake 10 minutes. Carefully slide one egg yolk into each "nest." Cover all with foil; bake about 15 minutes, or until eggs reach desired doneness. Makes 6 servings.

Diabetic diet: Prepare as directed but use margarine instead of butter. Exchanges per serving = 2 meat, 1 vegetable and 1/2 fat.
High-iron diet: 3 milligrams iron per serving.
Low-purine diet: Prepare as directed.

TOMATO-MACARONI CHEESE (250 calories per serving)

2 cups uncooked macaroni
2 bacon slices
1 11-ounce can condensed Cheddar-cheese soup
1/4 teaspoon paprika
1/4 cup skimmed milk or reliquefied nonfat dry milk
3 tomatoes, thinly sliced
2 tablespoons shredded Parmesan cheese

About 1 hour before serving: Cook macaroni as label directs; drain. Fry bacon slices until crisp; crumble. Preheat oven to 350°F. Combine drained macaroni, cheese soup, paprika and milk. In 2-quart casserole, layer macaroni with crumbled bacon and tomato slices. Top with Parmesan cheese. Bake 30 minutes. Makes 5 servings of about 1 cup each.

Diabetic diet: Exchanges per serving = 1 meat, 1/2 vegetable, 2 bread and 1 fat.
Low-purine diet: Prepare as directed but omit bacon.

EGGS IN RICE NESTS (280 calories per serving)

1 10-ounce package frozen mixed vegetables
2 cups cooked rice
1/2 cup shredded process Cheddar cheese
1/4 teaspoon salt
1/8 teaspoon pepper
4 eggs

About 30 minutes before serving: Preheat oven to 400°F. Meanwhile, cook mixed vegetables as label directs; drain. In 1-quart casserole, combine cooked vegetables with remaining ingredients except eggs. With spoon, make 4 "nests" in rice mixture; break eggs into them. Bake, covered, 15 minutes, or until eggs are done as you like them. Makes 4 servings.

Diabetic diet: Exchanges per serving = 2 meat and 2 bread.
Low-fat diet: 10 grams fat per serving. Omit recipe from low-cholesterol diet.

MUSHROOM CHEESE SOUFFLÉ (260 calories per serving)

2 eggs, separated
2 tablespoons milk
3 tablespoons flour
1/2 teaspoon salt
dash pepper
1 8-ounce container (1 cup)
   creamed cottage cheese
2 tablespoons minced onion
1 3- or 4-ounce can sliced mushrooms, drained

About 1 hour and 10 minutes before serving: Preheat oven to 300°F. In medium bowl, beat egg yolks until light and foamy.

Stir milk gradually into flour, then add to egg yolks and beat well. Beat in salt, pepper and cottage cheese; stir in onion and mushrooms.

Beat egg whites until stiff peaks form; fold into yolk mixture. Turn into greased 1-quart casserole. Bake 50 minutes, or until golden brown. Makes 2 servings.

Bland diet: Prepare as directed but omit pepper and onions.
Diabetic diet: Prepare as directed but use low-fat cottage cheese. Exchanges per serving = 1 meat, 1/2 bread and 1 milk.
Low-purine diet: Prepare as directed but omit mushrooms.
Low-residue diet: Prepare as directed but omit pepper and onion.

CURRIED EGGS AND MUSHROOMS (320 calories per serving)

1 tablespoon butter or margarine
1/2 pound fresh mushrooms,
   thinly sliced
1 10 1/2-ounce can condensed
   cream-of-celery soup
1/2 cup skimmed milk or reliquefied nonfat dry milk
1 teaspoon curry
2 tablespoons slivered toasted
   almonds
4 hard-cooked eggs, sliced
2 English muffins, split and
   toasted
2 tablespoons chopped parsley
   for garnish

About 10 minutes before serving: In skillet over medium heat, in butter, sauté mushrooms until limp. Stir in soup, milk and curry; stir in almonds and egg slices and heat to boiling. Serve over English muffin halves. Garnish with parsley. Makes 4 servings.

Diabetic diet: Prepare as directed but use margarine instead of butter. Exchanges per serving (a scant cup sauce over muffin half) = 1 meat, 1 vegetable, 1 bread and 1 fat.
High-iron diet: 3.5 milligrams iron per serving.
Low-purine diet: Prepare as directed but omit mushrooms.

ZUCCHINI OMELET (140 calories per serving)

2 tablespoons butter or margarine
1 medium onion, sliced thinly
1 garlic clove, minced
2 pounds zucchini, coarsely
   grated
1 teaspoon salt
1/4 teaspoon pepper
2 eggs
1/2 cup skimmed milk or reliquefied nonfat dry milk
1/2 cup shredded Parmesan
   cheese
paprika

About 35 minutes before serving: Preheat oven to 350°F. In large skillet, in butter or margarine, sauté onion slices and garlic until golden. Remove garlic; add grated zucchini, salt and pepper; cook, covered, 5 to 7 minutes or until zucchini is fork-tender. Meanwhile, beat together eggs, milk and cheese. In 1 1/2-quart shallow casserole or ovenproof skillet, combine zucchini and egg mixture. Sprinkle with paprika. Bake about 20 minutes, or until firm. Serve at once. Makes 6 servings.

Diabetic diet: Prepare as directed but use margarine instead of butter. Exchanges per serving = 1 meat and 1 vegetable and 1 fat.
Low-purine diet: Prepare as directed.

PETAL CHEESE SALAD (145 calories per serving)

1 8-ounce container creamed
  cottage cheese
1 8-ounce container large-curd
  cottage cheese
1/2 cup coarsely grated carrot
2 tablespoons minced celery
1/2 teaspoon celery salt
2 teaspoons chopped watercress
1/2 teaspoon salt
1/4 teaspoon onion powder
dash pepper
11/2 carrots, thinly sliced crosswise
watercress sprigs
4 cherry tomatoes or 1 medium
  tomato, thinly sliced

About 30 minutes before serving: Mix cottage cheese with carrot, celery, celery salt, watercress, salt, onion powder and pepper. Divide among 4 salad bowls, or arrange on medium round plate; lay carrot slices around outside edge, just touching cottage cheese and overlapping slightly. Radiate watercress sprigs from center of cottage cheese; place tomato slices in center. Makes 4 servings.

Diabetic diet: Prepare as directed but use low-fat cottage cheese. Exchanges per serving = 2 meat and 1 vegetable.
Egg-, gluten- and wheat-free diet: Prepare as directed.
Low-fat, low-cholesterol diet: 5 grams fat per serving.
Low-purine diet: Prepare as directed.

GARDEN CHEESE SALAD (200 calories per serving)

1 16-ounce container creamed
  cottage cheese
1/2 teaspoon salt
1/8 teaspoon white pepper
chopped chives
1 cucumber
3 medium tomatoes

About 1 hour before serving: In medium bowl, combine cottage cheese with salt, pepper and 1/4 cup chives. Run tines of fork lengthwise along unpared cucumber, all around; cut into thin slices. Slice tomatoes thin, then cut slices in half. Arrange cottage cheese on 3 salad plates, reserving a bit for garnish. Around edge of each plate, alternate tomato and cucumber slices; in center of each cheese mound, arrange 4 cucumber and 2 tomato slices. Dot center tomato slices with reserved cheese mixture; sprinkle with more chives. Makes 3 servings.

Diabetic diet: Prepare as directed but use margarine instead of butter. Exchanges per serving = 2 meat, 1 vegetable.
Egg-, gluten- and wheat-free diet: Prepare as directed.
Low-fat, low-cholesterol diet: 5 grams fat per serving.
Low-purine diet: Prepare as directed.

COTTAGE-CHEESE PANCAKES (300 calories per serving)

1 cup sifted all-purpose flour
1/2 teaspoon salt
11/2 teaspoons double-acting
  baking powder
1 egg, slightly beaten
11/2 cups skimmed milk or reliquefied nonfat dry milk
1 tablespoon melted butter or
  margarine
2 8-ounce containers creamed
  cottage cheese

About 30 minutes before serving: Preheat griddle until drop of water "dances" on it. Sift together flour, salt and baking powder. In bowl, combine egg and milk; gradually beat milk mixture into dry ingredients. Stir in butter (batter will be quite thin). Bake pancakes, using a scant 1/4 cup batter for each, until bubbles break in top; turn; bake other side. Spread each pancake with cottage cheese; roll up. Makes 4 servings of 3 pancakes each.

Bland diet: Prepare as directed.
Diabetic diet: Prepare as directed but use margarine instead of butter and substitute low-fat cottage cheese. Exchanges per serving = 2 meat, 1 bread and 1 milk and 1 fat.
Low-fat, low-cholesterol diet: Prepare as directed but use only white of egg, use salad oil or margarine instead of butter. 10 grams fat per serving.
Low-fat, bland (gall bladder) diet: Prepare as directed.
Low-purine diet: Prepare as directed.
Low-residue diet: Prepare as directed.

DIETER'S LINGUINE ALFREDO (300 calories per serving)

4 ounces linguine
1 cup creamed cottage cheese
1/2 cup shredded Parmesan cheese
dash salt
2 tablespoons butter or margarine

About 15 minutes before serving: Cook linguine as label directs; drain. In small bowl, cream cottage cheese with Parmesan and salt. In small saucepan, melt butter; toss cooked linguine with melted butter, then with cheese mixture. Makes 3 servings.

Bland diet: Prepare as directed.
Diabetic diet: Prepare as directed but use margarine instead of butter; use low-fat cottage cheese. Carefully divide into 3 equal servings. Exchanges per serving = 3 meat and 2 bread.
Egg-, gluten- and wheat-free diet: Prepare as directed but for gluten- and wheat-free diets use bean threads or transparent noodles in place of linguine.
Low-purine diet: Prepare as directed.
Low-residue diet: Prepare as directed.

MUSHROOM-AND-CARROT OMELET BAKE (220 calories per serving)

6 eggs
1 cup skimmed milk
1 green onion, minced
1/8 teaspoon pepper
salad oil
salt
2 medium carrots, thinly sliced
1 pound mushrooms, sliced
1/2 teaspoon basil leaves
1 small tomato, sliced
watercress sprigs for garnish

Preheat oven to 375°F. Grease 10½-inch round au gratin pan or 9″ by 9″ baking pan. In medium bowl with wire whisk or hand beater, beat eggs, milk, green onion, pepper, 1 tablespoon salad oil, and 1/2 teaspoon salt until blended; pour mixture into baking pan. Bake 20 minutes or until set. Meanwhile, in 12-inch skillet over medium heat, in 1 tablespoon hot salad oil, cook carrots, stirring frequently, 5 minutes. Reduce heat to low; add mushrooms, basil and 1/2 teaspoon salt and cook 5 minutes longer or until vegetables are tender-crisp.

To serve, with slotted spoon, spoon vegetable mixture over baked omelet. Cut omelet and arrange on serving plates; garnish with tomato slices and watercress sprigs. Makes 4 servings.

Low-fat, low-cholesterol diet: Prepare as directed but use cholesterol- and fat–reduced liquid egg substitute equivalent to 6 eggs; reduce oil to 1 teaspoon. 5 grams fat per serving.
Diabetic diet: Exchanges per serving = 1 vegetable, 1½ meat and 2 fat.

GRAVIES AND SAUCES

GREEN SAUCE (5 calories per tablespoon)

1 13³/₄-ounce can chicken broth
3 tablespoons flour
¹/₂ teaspoon salt
dash white pepper
2¹/₂ cups coarsely chopped
    watercress

About 15 minutes before serving: In medium saucepan, heat chicken broth to boiling. Combine flour with ¹/₄ cup water to form a smooth paste. Slowly stir into broth; cook, stirring, until thickened and smooth. Add remaining ingredients; simmer 2 minutes. Makes about 2 cups.

Diabetic diet: Up to 3 tablespoons sauce = 1 "free" exchange.
Low-fat, low-cholesterol diet: Negligible fat per serving.

CRANBERRY SAUCE (20 calories per tablespoon)

2 tablespoons cornstarch
1 teaspoon lemon juice
1 teaspoon finely grated lemon
    peel
¹/₂ teaspoon ground cloves
¹/₈ teaspoon salt
1 16-ounce can whole cranberry
    sauce

About 10 minutes before serving: In medium saucepan, combine all ingredients and heat to boiling. Makes about 2¹/₂ cups.

Egg-, gluten-, milk- and wheat-free diet: Prepare as directed.
Low-fat, low-cholesterol diet: Negligible fat per serving.
Low-purine diet: Prepare as directed.
Low-sodium diet: Prepare as directed but omit salt. Negligible sodium per serving.

CREAMY-HAM SAUCE (15 calories per tablespoon)

2 tablespoons butter or marga-
    rine
¹/₄ cup flour
1 cup chicken broth
1 cup skimmed milk or reliq-
    uefied nonfat dry milk
1 cup finely chopped boiled
    ham
¹/₄ cup sliced pitted ripe olives
¹/₈ teaspoon pepper
salt to taste

About 10 minutes before serving: In medium saucepan over medium heat; melt butter; stir in flour. Stirring constantly, slowly blend in milk and cook until thickened and smooth. Add ham, olives and pepper. Cook, stirring, about 5 minutes; add salt to taste. Makes about 2¹/₂ cups.

Low-fat, low-cholesterol diet: Prepare as directed but use margarine or salad oil instead of butter; omit olives. 1 gram fat per tablespoon sauce.

CURRY SAUCE (15 calories per tablespoon)

2 tablespoons butter or marga-
    rine
¹/₄ cup flour
1 teaspoon curry
³/₄ teaspoon salt
2 cups skimmed milk or reliq-
    uefied nonfat dry milk

About 5 minutes before serving: In medium saucepan, melt butter or margarine; stir in flour, curry and salt. Slowly stir in milk and cook, stirring, until thickened and smooth. Makes about 2 cups.

Egg-, gluten- and wheat-free diet: Prepare as directed but use 2 tablespoons cornstarch in place of flour for gluten- and wheat-free diets.
Low-fat, low-cholesterol diet: Prepare as directed but use margarine or salad oil instead of butter. 1 gram fat per tablespoon.

CHILI-PINEAPPLE SAUCE (15 calories per tablespoon)

1 14-ounce bottle catchup
1 cup pineapple juice
³/₄ cup chopped scallions
¹/₂ teaspoon chili powder

About 10 minutes before grilling meat: In medium bowl, combine all ingredients. Use to baste meat, fish or poultry during grilling. Serve additional sauce with meat. Makes about 2¹/₂ cups.

Low-fat, low-cholesterol diet: Negligible fat per serving.

FRUIT SAUCE (10 calories per tablespoon)

1¹/₂ tablespoons cornstarch
¹/₄ teaspoon cinnamon
1 tablespoon finely grated
   orange peel
³/₄ teaspoon salt
1¹/₂ cups orange juice
1 16-ounce can fruit cocktail,
   drained

About 10 minutes before serving: In medium saucepan, combine cornstarch, cinnamon, orange peel, salt and orange juice; cook, stirring constantly, until thickened and smooth. Stir in drained fruit cocktail and heat to boiling. Makes about 2¹/₂ cups.

Diabetic diet: Prepare as directed but use dietetic-packed fruit cocktail packed in fruit juice. Exchanges per serving = 1 fruit for ¹/₂ cup sauce.
Egg-, gluten-, milk- and wheat-free diet: Prepare as directed.
Low-fat, low-cholesterol diet: Negligible fat per serving.
Low-purine diet: Prepare as directed.
Low-sodium diet: Prepare as directed but omit salt. Negligible sodium per serving.

SOY-SESAME MARINADE (35 calories per tablespoon)

¹/₄ cup chopped onion
¹/₄ cup soy sauce
1 tablespoon light brown sugar
1 tablespoon sesame seed
1 tablespoon salad oil
1 teaspoon lemon juice
¹/₄ teaspoon pepper
¹/₄ teaspoon ginger

Just before marinating meat: Combine all ingredients in small bowl. Brush on beef or lamb before marinating in refrigerator or immediately before grilling. Makes ¹/₂ cup.

Diabetic diet: Prepare as directed but omit sugar; use non–nutritive sweetener equivalent to 2 teaspoons sugar. 2 tablespoons sauce = 1 fat exchange.
Low-fat, low-cholesterol diet: 5 grams fat per 2 tablespoons marinade.

BUTTERY LEMON SAUCE (35 calories per tablespoon)

¹/₂ cup melted butter or margarine
1 cup lemon juice
¹/₄ cup chopped parsley
1 tablespoon grated lemon peel
2 teaspoons salt
1 teaspoon granulated sugar
¹/₄ teaspoon pepper

About 10 minutes before grilling: In medium bowl, combine all ingredients. Use to baste fish during grilling. Makes 1¹/₂ cups.

Diabetic diet: Prepare as directed but use margarine instead of butter and omit sugar. Exchanges per tablespoon = 1 fat.
Egg-, gluten-, milk- and wheat-free diet: Prepare as directed but use milk-free margarine on milk-free diet.
Low-fat, low-cholesterol diet: Prepare as directed but use margarine or salad oil instead of butter. 5 grams fat per tablespoon.
Low-sodium diet: Prepare as directed but use unsalted butter or margarine; omit salt. Negligible sodium per serving.

HORSERADISH SAUCE (10 calories per tablespoon)

¹/₃ cup reduced–calorie mayonnaise
¹/₄ cup minced dill pickle
2 tablespoons horseradish
1 tablespoon milk
dash pepper

At least 2 hours before serving: In small container, combine all ingredients. Cover; refrigerate. Makes ³/₄ cup sauce.

Low-fat, low-cholesterol diet: Prepare as directed but use skimmed milk. 1 gram fat per serving.

PIQUANT SAUCE (35 calories per tablespoon)

1¹/₂ cups catchup
3 tablespoons vinegar
2 tablespoons dark corn syrup
2 teaspoons salt
1 teaspoon paprika
³/₄ teaspoon chili powder
¹/₄ teaspoon pepper

Just before grilling meat: In medium bowl, combine all ingredients. Use to baste lean beef or lamb patties during grilling. Makes 1³/₄ cups.

Egg-, gluten-, milk- and wheat-free diet: Prepare as directed but be certain catchup does not contain forbidden ingredients.
Low-fat, low-cholesterol diet: Negligible fat per serving.

HOMEMADE TARTAR SAUCE (15 calories per tablespoon)

½ cup reduced-calorie mayonnaise
2 tablespoons minced parsley
2 tablespoons minced sweet
gherkins
1½ tablespoons lemon juice
1 tablespoon minced onion

At least 2 hours before serving: In small container, stir together all ingredients. Cover; refrigerate. Makes about ¾ cup sauce.

Low-fat, low-cholesterol diet: 1 gram fat per tablespoon.

GIBLET GRAVY (10 calories per tablespoon)

giblets and neck from turkey
2 small onions, thinly sliced
2 large stalks celery, thinly
sliced
1 teaspoon salt
¼ teaspoon pepper
¼ cup fat from roast turkey
½ cup flour
drained pan drippings
salt and pepper to taste

Early in day: Trim extra fat from gizzard and heart. In medium saucepan, simmer giblets (except liver) and neck, 3 cups water, onions, celery, salt and pepper, covered, 1 to 2 hours, or until tender. In the last 15 minutes, add liver; simmer until just done. Cool enough to handle, then trim gristle from gizzard; cut meat from giblets and neck into small pieces. Refrigerate, covered, in cooking liquid.

When ready to make gravy: Drain as much fat as possible from drippings in pan used to roast turkey; measure ¼ cup. Pour into saucepan; add flour and cook 1 minute. Measure pan drippings, giblets, cooking liquid and vegetables; add enough water to make 6 to 7 cups. Slowly stir into flour mixture. Cook, stirring constantly, until thickened and smooth. Season to taste with salt and pepper. Makes about 1½ quarts.

Diabetic diet: Use up to ¼ cup as "free" exchange. Count ½ cup gravy as ½ meat and ½ bread exchanges.
Egg-, gluten-, milk- and wheat-free diet: Prepare as directed but substitute 2 tablespoons cornstarch for flour on gluten- and wheat-free diets.
Low-fat, low-cholesterol diet: Prepare as directed but cook only neck with vegetables; omit giblets. Substitute margarine for turkey fat. Carefully drain all fat from pan drippings and discard. If desired, add a drop or two of brown sauce for gravy. 3 grams fat per ¼-cup serving.
Low-sodium diet: Prepare as directed but omit salt in cooking turkey, giblets and in making gravy. 15 milligrams sodium per ¼-cup serving.

MEXICALI MARINADE (25 calories per tablespoon)

2 tablespoons olive oil
2 garlic cloves, crushed
¼ cup vinegar
¼ cup apple juice
1 teaspoon chili powder
1 teaspoon granulated sugar
½ teaspoon salt
¼ teaspoon pepper

At least 24 hours before grilling meat: In medium saucepan over medium heat, in oil, cook garlic until golden. Stir in remaining ingredients and heat to boiling. Use to marinate lean beef, pork, lamb or veal and to baste also during cooking. Makes ¾ cup.

Diabetic diet: Prepare as directed but omit sugar. Exchanges per tablespoon = ½ fat.
Egg-, gluten-, milk- and wheat-free diet: Prepare as directed.
Low-fat, low-cholesterol diet: Prepare as directed but use salad oil instead of olive oil. 5 grams fat per tablespoon.
Low-sodium diet: Prepare as directed but use chili powder not containing salt; omit salt. Negligible sodium per tablespoon.

GRAVY JARDINIÈRE (20 calories per ¼-cup serving)

1 medium onion, thinly sliced
2 stalks celery, diced
1 10½-ounce can beef consommé
2 tablespoons cornstarch
¼ teaspoon bottled sauce for gravy

About 20 minutes before serving: In medium saucepan, combine onion, celery, consommé and 1 soup-can water; cover; boil gently, over low heat, until onion is transparent. Strain consommé, reserving vegetables; return consommé to saucepan. Mix cornstarch with a little water and bottled sauce for gravy to form a smooth paste; slowly stir into consommé; heat to boiling. Serve over beef or other meat, garnishing with cooked onions and celery. Makes 2 cups.

Diabetic diet: Exchanges per ¼ cup serving = 1 "free."
Low-fat, low-cholesterol diet: Negligible fat per serving.

HONOLULU SAUCE (10 calories per tablespoon)

2 tablespoons butter or margarine
½ cup catchup
½ cup orange juice
⅓ cup honey
¼ cup lemon juice
2 tablespoons soy sauce
½ teaspoon ginger

About 10 minutes before grilling poultry: In medium saucepan, heat all ingredients until blended. Use to baste poultry, pork or ham during grilling. Makes about 2 cups.

Low-fat, low-cholesterol diet: Prepare as directed but use margarine or salad oil instead of butter. 1 gram fat per tablespoon.

VEGETABLES

STEWED TOMATOES (70 calories per serving)

1 tablespoon butter or
  margarine
1 stalk green celery, cut into
  1/2-inch slices
1 small onion, sliced into rings
1/4 pound mushrooms, thinly
  sliced
1 20-ounce can tomatoes,
  undrained
1 tablespoon flour
1 tablespoon granulated sugar
1 slice slightly stale bread,
  cubed
1/2 to 1 teaspoon prepared
  horseradish
1 teaspoon salt
dash pepper

About 25 minutes before serving: In medium saucepan, in butter, sauté celery, onion and mushrooms until onion is golden. Add tomatoes; simmer mixture about 5 minutes. Meanwhile, mix flour with sugar; stirring constantly, add enough water to form a smooth paste; stir paste into tomato mixture. Return to boiling; add bread cubes, horseradish, salt and pepper; boil 5 minutes more. Makes 6 servings.

Diabetic diet: Prepare as directed but increase margarine to 2 tablespoons; omit sugar; add non-nutritive sweetener equivalent to 1 tablespoon sugar. Exchanges per serving = 2 vegetable and 1 fat.
Low-fat, low-cholesterol diet: Prepare as directed but use salad oil or margarine instead of butter. 2 grams fat per serving.

SCALLOPED TOMATOES (115 calories per serving)

2 tablespoons butter or
  margarine
2 stalks green celery, thinly
  sliced
1 medium onion, thinly sliced
1 29-ounce can tomatoes
1 tablespoon brown sugar
1 beef-bouillon cube
3 slices toast, cubed

About 20 minutes before serving: In medium saucepan, in butter, sauté celery and onion until onion is golden. Add tomatoes, sugar and bouillon cube; simmer 5 minutes. Add toast cubes; simmer 5 minutes more. Makes six 3/4-cup servings.

Diabetic diet: Prepare as directed but use margarine instead of butter and omit sugar; use non-nutritive sweetener equivalent to 2 teaspoons sugar. Exchanges per serving = 1 vegetable, 1/2 bread and 1 fat.
Low-fat, low-cholesterol diet: Prepare as directed but use only 1 tablespoon margarine or salad oil instead of butter. 3 grams fat per serving.
High-iron diet: 1 milligram iron per serving.
Low-purine diet: Prepare as directed but omit bouillon cube.

OVEN-BAKED SCALLOPED TOMATOES (100 calories per serving)

1 29 ounce can tomatoes
1 medium cucumber, pared and
  thinly sliced
1 medium onion, thinly sliced
1 1/2 cups cubed bread, toasted
salt
pepper
1/2 cup grated Cheddar cheese

About 1 hour before serving: Preheat oven to 375°F. Drain off 1 1/2 cups of juice from tomatoes (use later for stew or drinking). In 2-quart casserole, place half of tomatoes; add a layer of half of the cucumber slices, onion and bread cubes. Sprinkle generously with salt and lightly with pepper. Repeat layering with remaining tomatoes, cucumber, onion and bread cubes. Sprinkle with salt and pepper, then with cheese. Bake 40 to 45 minutes, or until mixture is bubbly and cheese begins to brown. Makes 6 servings.

Diabetic diet: Prepare as directed but omit cheese. Exchanges per serving = 1 bread and 1 vegetable.
Low-fat, low-cholesterol diet: Prepare as directed but omit cheese. Negligible fat per serving.
High-iron diet: 1.5 milligrams iron per serving.
Low-purine diet: Prepare as directed.

GARLICKY CHERRY TOMATOES (50 calories per serving)

1 tablespoon butter or margarine
1 small garlic clove, minced
1 pint cherry tomatoes, stemmed

About 10 minutes before serving: In large skillet over low heat, in butter, sauté garlic 2 to 3 minutes. Add tomatoes and cook 6 or 7 minutes, shaking skillet frequently. Makes 4 servings.

Diabetic diet: Prepare as directed but use margarine instead of butter. Divide into 3 servings. Exchanges per serving = 1 vegetable and 1 fat.
Egg-, gluten-, milk- and wheat-free diet: Prepare as directed but use milk-free margarine on milk-free diet.
Low-fat, low-cholesterol diet: Prepare as directed but use margarine or salad oil instead of butter. 3 grams fat per serving.
Low-sodium diet: Prepare as directed but use unsalted butter or margarine. 5 grams sodium per serving.

ITALIAN-STYLE TOMATOES (40 calories per serving)

2 16-ounce cans Italian plum tomatoes
1 small onion, minced
2 tablespoons granulated sugar
1 tablespoon basil
1 teaspoon salt
1/8 teaspoon pepper
1 teaspoon Worcestershire

About 20 minutes before serving: In saucepan, combine all ingredients; simmer 5 minutes. Makes 8 servings of 1/2-cup each.

Diabetic diet: Omit sugar; add non–nutritive sweetener equivalent to 2 tablespoons sugar; prepare as directed. Exchanges per serving = 1 vegetable.
Egg-, gluten-, milk- and wheat-free diet: Prepare as directed.
Low-fat, low-cholesterol diet: Negligible fat per serving.

SEASONED ASPARAGUS SPEARS (20 calories per serving)

2 pounds fresh asparagus
nutmeg

About 20 minutes before serving: In large covered skillet over high heat, in 1-inch boiling salted water, cook asparagus 12 to 15 minutes, or until tender; drain. Sprinkle lightly with nutmeg. Makes 6 servings.

Diabetic diet: Exchanges per serving = 1 vegetable.
Low-fat, low-cholesterol diet: Negligible fat per serving.
Low-sodium diet: Prepare as directed but cook in unsalted water. Negligible sodium per serving.

CHINESE-STYLE ASPARAGUS (50 calories per serving)

1 1/2 pounds fresh asparagus
1 tablespoon butter or margarine
1/2 teaspoon salt
dash pepper

Up to 45 minutes before serving: Cut off tough white part of asparagus stalks and discard; wash spears and remove scales. Lay 2 or 3 spears together on board; with sharp knife, cutting diagonally, make bias slices about 1/4-inch thick and 1 1/2 inches long.

About 10 minutes before serving: In large skillet; place butter and 1/4 cup water; cover; heat to boiling. Add asparagus, salt and pepper. Cook, covered, over high heat for 5 minutes, shaking skillet occasionally and checking water once. Cook until just tender-crisp. Makes 4 servings.

Bland diet: Prepare as directed but omit pepper.
Diabetic diet: Prepare as directed but use margarine instead of butter. Exchanges per serving = 1 vegetable and 1 fat.
Egg-, gluten-, milk- and wheat-free diet: Prepare as directed but use milk-free margarine on milk-free diet.
Low-fat, low-cholesterol diet: Prepare as directed but use margarine or salad oil instead of butter. 3 grams fat per serving.
Low-sodium diet: Prepare as directed but omit salt; use unsalted butter or margarine. 2 milligrams sodium per serving.

ASPARAGUS AUX HERBES (40 calories per serving)

1 10-ounce package frozen
  asparagus spears
1¹/₂ teaspoons butter or
  margarine
¹/₄ cup water
¹/₂ teaspoon salt
2 tablespoons chopped chives

About 20 minutes before serving: Run water over asparagus just enough to separate spears. Meanwhile, in medium skillet, bring butter, water, salt and chives to boiling. Immediately add asparagus; cover; simmer 15 minutes, or until tender-crisp. Makes 3 servings.

Bland diet: Prepare as directed but omit chives.
Diabetic diet: Prepare as directed but increase margarine to 1 tablespoon. Exchanges per serving = 1 vegetable and 1 fat.
Egg-, gluten-, milk- and wheat-free diet: Prepare as directed but use milk-free margarine on milk-free diet.
Low-fat, low-cholesterol diet: Prepare as directed but use margarine instead of butter. 2 grams fat per serving. (Or omit margarine for negligible fat per serving.)
Low-fat, bland (gall bladder) diet: Prepare as directed; omit chives.
High-iron diet: 1 milligram iron per serving.
Low-residue diet: Prepare as directed but omit chives.
Low-sodium diet: Prepare as directed but use unsalted butter or margarine; omit salt. 2 milligrams sodium per serving.

CELERY WITH CARAWAY SEEDS (25 calories per serving)

3 cups diagonally sliced celery
1 teaspoon salt
1 tablespoon butter or
  margarine
¹/₂ teaspoon caraway seeds
dash pepper

About 30 minutes before serving: In medium saucepan, combine celery, salt and enough water to cover. Simmer, covered, 15 to 20 minutes; drain. Add remaining ingredients; toss until well mixed. Makes 6 servings.

Diabetic diet: Prepare as directed but increase margarine to 2 tablespoons. Exchanges per serving = 1 vegetable and 1 fat.
Egg-, gluten-, milk- and wheat-free diet: Prepare as directed but use milk-free margarine on milk-free diet.
Low-fat, low-cholesterol diet: Prepare as directed but use margarine or salad oil instead of butter. 2 grams fat per serving.
Low-purine diet: Prepare as directed.

PEAS AND CELERY (105 calories per serving)

¹/₃ cup coarsely chopped celery
1 10-ounce package frozen peas
¹/₂ teaspoon thyme leaves
¹/₄ teaspoon salt
1 tablespoon butter or
  margarine

About 20 minutes before serving: In medium saucepan over medium heat, cook celery, covered, in ¹/₂ cup water, 5 minutes, or until tender-crisp. Add peas; cover and cook 8 to 10 minutes; drain. Sprinkle with thyme and salt; toss with butter. Makes 3 servings of about ¹/₂ cup each.

Diabetic diet: Prepare as directed but use margarine instead of butter. Exchanges per serving = 1 vegetable and 1 fat.
Low-fat, low-cholesterol diet: Prepare as directed but omit butter or margarine. Negligible fat per serving.
High-iron diet: 2 milligrams iron per serving.

CREAMED CELERY (45 calories per serving)

1 tablespoon butter or
  margarine
2 cups chopped green celery
2 tablespoons finely minced
  onion
¹/₂ teaspoon salt
1 teaspoon cornstarch
¹/₄ cup skimmed milk or
  reliquefied nonfat dry milk
generous dash pepper

About 25 minutes before serving: In skillet over low heat, in butter, sauté celery and onion until onion is golden. Add ¹/₄ cup water and salt; cover; simmer gently 10 minutes, or until celery is tender but still quite crisp.

Meanwhile, stir together cornstarch, milk and pepper. Stirring constantly, add to cooked celery; heat until thickened and smooth. Makes four ¹/₂-cup servings.

Diabetic diet: Prepare as directed but use margarine instead of butter. Exchanges per serving = 1 vegetable and 1 fat.
Egg-, gluten- and wheat-free diet: Prepare as directed.
Low-fat, low-cholesterol diet: Prepare as directed but use margarine instead of butter. 3 grams fat per serving.
Low-purine diet: Prepare as directed.

BRAISED CELERY AMANDINE (60 calories per serving)

4 small bunches green celery
1 10¹/₂-ounce can condensed chicken broth
2 tablespoons melted butter or margarine
paprika
1 tablespoon blanched slivered almonds

About 30 minutes before serving: From each celery bunch pull off outer stalks; then cut off tops, leaving about 5 inches on each; split each lower section in half, lengthwise. (Refrigerate outer celery stalks and tops for use another day.)

Place split celery stalks in skillet; pour on undiluted chicken broth; simmer, covered, 25 minutes, or until tender. Arrange in serving dish; pour melted butter over them, then sprinkle lightly with paprika and slivered almonds. Makes 8 servings.

Diabetic diet: Prepare as directed but use margarine instead of butter. Exchanges per serving = 1 vegetable and 1 fat.
Low-fat, low-cholesterol diet: Prepare as directed but use margarine instead of butter. 3 grams fat per serving.

SPINACH GOURMET STYLE (70 calories per serving)

1 tablespoon butter or margarine
¹/₂ pound fresh mushrooms, thinly sliced
1 garlic clove, minced
1 small onion, chopped
1 10-ounce package frozen chopped spinach
¹/₈ teaspoon pepper
¹/₃ cup sour cream
salt to taste

About 25 minutes before serving: In medium skillet over medium heat, in butter, sauté mushrooms, garlic and onion until golden. Place frozen spinach and pepper on top of mushroom mixture; cover. Stirring occasionally, cook 7 minutes, or until spinach is just heated through. Stir in sour cream; add salt to taste; serve immediately. Makes 6 servings.

Diabetic diet: Prepare as directed but use margarine instead of butter. Exchange per serving = 1 vegetable and 1 fat.
Egg-, gluten-, and wheat-free diet: Prepare as directed.
Low-fat, low-cholesterol diet: Prepare as directed but use salad oil instead of butter; omit sour cream. 2 grams fat per serving.
High-iron diet: 1 milligram iron per serving.

SOUTHERN SPINACH (40 calories per serving)

1 10-ounce package frozen chopped spinach
1 8-ounce can grapefruit sections
¹/₂ teaspoon salt
1 teaspoon lemon juice
cinnamon
pepper

About 20 minutes before serving: Cook spinach according to package directions, but substitute juice drained from grapefruit for water. During last minutes of cooking time, add grapefruit sections to heat through. Drain and toss with lemon juice. Serve in warm bowl; sprinkle lightly with cinnamon and pepper. Makes 6 servings.

Egg-, gluten-, milk- and wheat-free diet: Prepare as directed.
Low-fat, low-cholesterol diet: Negligible fat per serving.
High-iron diet: 1 milligram iron per serving.

CURRIED SPINACH (55 calories per serving)

2 10-ounce packages frozen chopped spinach
2 tablespoons butter or margarine
¹/₈ teaspoon pepper
¹/₈ teaspoon nutmeg
¹/₄ teaspoon curry

About 15 minutes before serving: Cook spinach as label directs. Meanwhile, in small saucepan, melt butter; remove from heat; stir in pepper, nutmeg and curry. Drain spinach well through fine strainer. Return to original pan and toss with butter mixture. Makes 6 servings.

Diabetic diet: Prepare as directed but use margarine instead of butter. Exchanges per serving = 1 vegetable and 1 fat.
Egg-, gluten-, milk- and wheat-free diet: Prepare as directed but use milk-free margarine on milk-free diet.
Low-fat, low-cholesterol diet: Prepare as directed but use margarine or salad oil instead of butter. 5 grams fat per serving.
High-iron diet: 2 milligrams iron per serving.

CRUNCHY PEAS (55 calories per serving)

1 10-ounce package frozen peas
1 cup chopped lettuce

About 10 minutes before serving: Cook peas as label directs. Add lettuce; simmer until wilted and transparent. Makes 4 servings.

Diabetic diet: Exchanges per serving (about 1/2 cup) = 1 1/2 bread (If desired, stir in 4 teaspoons butter or margarine and add 1 fat exchange.)
Egg-, gluten-, milk- and wheat-free diet: Prepare as directed.
High-iron diet: Make only 3 servings. 2 milligrams iron per serving.

ZUCCHINI PARMIGIANA (90 calories per serving)

2 medium zucchini, cut into
  1/2-inch slices
1/2 teaspoon oregano leaves
2 medium tomatoes, cut into
  eighths
salt
1/2 cup grated Parmesan cheese

About 20 minutes before serving: In salted water to cover, simmer zucchini slices and oregano 10 minutes, or until tender. Preheat broiler 10 minutes if manufacturer directs. In shallow baking pan, arrange drained zucchini and tomatoes; sprinkle with salt, then cheese. Broil 3 to 5 minutes, or until cheese browns lightly. Makes 4 servings.

Diabetic diet: Exchanges per serving = 1 vegetable and 1/2 meat.
Egg-, gluten-, milk- and wheat-free diet: Prepare as directed.
Low-purine diet: Prepare as directed.

ITALIAN MEDLEY (75 calories per serving)

1 12-ounce can whole-kernel
  corn, undrained
1 16-ounce can tomatoes
2 medium zucchini, thinly sliced
1 1/2 teaspoons salt
1/2 teaspoon whole cumin seeds
1/8 teaspoon pepper

About 20 minutes before serving: In medium saucepan, mix all ingredients. Bring to boiling; cover; simmer 10 minutes; drain. Makes six 3/4-cup servings.

Diabetic diet: Exchanges per serving = 1 vegetable and 1/2 bread.
Egg-, gluten-, milk- and wheat-free diet: Prepare as directed.
Low-fat, low-cholesterol diet: Negligible fat per serving.
High-iron diet: 1 milligram iron per serving.
Low-purine diet: Prepare as directed.

SPICY EGGPLANT (40 calories per serving)

1/2 medium eggplant (about 3/4
  pound)
1 medium onion, thinly sliced
1 8-ounce can meatless
  spaghetti sauce
1/4 teaspoon garlic salt

About 30 minutes before serving: Slice, peel, then cut eggplant into 1-inch cubes. In medium skillet over medium heat, cover and cook eggplant and onion slices in 1/2 cup water until onion is tender—about 10 minutes. Stir in spaghetti sauce and garlic salt; cook, stirring constantly, 5 minutes. Makes 6 servings.

Diabetic diet: Exchanges per serving = 1 vegetable.
Low-fat, low-cholesterol diet: 1 gram fat per serving.
Low-purine diet: Prepare as directed.

EGGPLANT AND POTATO ALEXANDRIA (85 calories per serving)

2 teaspoons salad oil
1/4 cup finely chopped onion
2 cups peeled diced eggplant
1 medium potato, finely diced
  (about 1 cup)
1 teaspoon salt
1/4 teaspoon dry mustard
1/4 teaspoon turmeric
dash ginger
dash cayenne

About 25 minutes before serving: In saucepan, in oil, sauté onion until golden. Stir in 1/2 cup water and remaining ingredients; cover; simmer 15 to 20 minutes, or until potatoes are tender. Makes three 3/4-cup servings.

Diabetic diet: Prepared as directed but use 1 tablespoon salad oil. Exchanges per serving = 1 vegetable, 1/2 bread and 1 fat.
Egg-, gluten-, milk- and wheat-free diet: Prepare as directed.
Low-fat, low-cholesterol diet: 3 grams fat per serving.
Low-sodium diet: Prepare as directed but omit salt. 5 milligrams sodium per serving.

SPICY ITALIAN CASSEROLE (120 calories per serving)

1 medium eggplant, peeled if desired (³/4 pound)
1 small zucchini, thinly sliced
3 small onions, thinly sliced
1 cup spaghettini, broken into 3-inch pieces
3 cups canned vegetable-juice cocktail
1 tablespoon Worcestershire
¹/2 teaspoon salt
1 teaspoon garlic salt
¹/4 teaspoon oregano leaves

About 1¹/2 hours before serving: Preheat oven to 325°F. Slice eggplant ¹/4-inch thick. In 1¹/2-quart casserole, place succeeding layers of eggplant, zucchini, onion and spaghettini. Repeat layering until casserole is full.

Combine vegetable-juice cocktail, Worcestershire, salt, garlic salt and oregano. Pour over eggplant and zucchini; cover. Bake 1¹/4 hours, or until vegetables are tender, placing foil, edges turned up, on lower rack to catch juices.

To serve: Spoon some of juice in casserole over top of zucchini and eggplant. Makes 6 servings.

Diabetic diet: Exchanges per serving (about 1 cup) = 1 bread and 1 vegetable.
Low-fat, low-cholesterol diet: Negligible fat per serving.
High-iron diet: 1.5 milligrams iron per serving. (Be sure to use enriched spaghettini.)
Low-purine diet: Prepare as directed.

CARAWAY RED CABBAGE (55 calories per serving)

2 tablespoons butter or margarine
1 cup chopped onion
4 teaspoons granulated sugar
2 teaspoons salt
1¹/2 teaspoons caraway seeds
4 teaspoons white vinegar
1 large red cabbage (about 3 pounds), shredded

About 1 hour before serving: In large saucepan, in hot butter, sauté onions until golden; stir in sugar. Add 1 cup water and remaining ingredients. Simmer, covered, stirring occasionally, about 35 minutes, or until cabbage is tender. Makes 12 servings.

Diabetic diet: Prepare as directed but omit sugar; at end of cooking time, add non-nutritive sweetener equivalent to 4 teaspoons sugar; increase margarine to 3 tablespoons. Exchanges per serving = 1 vegetable and 1 fat.
Egg-, gluten-, milk- and wheat-free diet: Prepare as directed but use milk-free margarine on milk-free diet.
Low-fat, low-cholesterol diet: Prepare as directed but use margarine or salad oil instead of butter. 2 grams fat per serving.

SKILLET CHINESE CABBAGE (35 calories per serving)

1 small head Chinese cabbage
1 tablespoon salad oil
¹/2 teaspoon salt

About 15 minutes before serving: Wash and cut Chinese cabbage into 1-inch cross-wise slices. In large skillet, heat oil, ¹/2 cup water and salt to boiling; add cabbage; cover; simmer 10 minutes, or until tender-crisp. Makes 6 servings.

Diabetic diet: Prepare as directed but increase oil to 2 tablespoons. Exchanges per serving = 1¹/2 fat.
Egg-, gluten-, milk- and wheat-free diet: Prepare as directed.
Low-fat, low-cholesterol diet: Prepare as directed but omit oil. Negligible fat per serving.
Low-purine diet: Prepare as directed.
Low-sodium diet: Prepare as directed but omit salt. 15 milligrams sodium per serving.

BROCCOLI WITH MUSTARD SAUCE (60 calories per serving)

2 10-ounce packages frozen broccoli spears
1 tablespoon butter or margarine
1 tablespoon flour
1 tablespoon prepared mustard
1 cup skimmed milk or reliquefied nonfat dry milk
1¹/2 teaspoons lemon juice

About 15 minutes before serving: Cook broccoli as label directs; drain. Meanwhile, in small saucepan over medium heat, melt butter; stir in flour and mustard. Slowly add milk; cook, stirring, until smooth and thickened. Remove from heat; stir in lemon juice. Serve on broccoli. Makes 6 servings.

Low-fat, low-cholesterol diet: Prepare as directed but use margarine instead of butter. 2 grams fat per serving.
High-iron diet: 1.5 milligrams iron per serving.

HARVEST VEGETABLES (95 calories per serving)

3 medium zucchini
salt
butter or margarine
2 cups peeled small white
    onions
1 16-ounce can small whole
    carrots
2 tablespoons orange juice
seasoned pepper

About 30 minutes before serving: Diagonally slice unpared zucchini about 1/4-inch thick. Place in skillet with about 1 cup hot water; sprinkle with 1 teaspoon salt. Cover; cook 15 minutes, or until tender. Drain; add 1 tablespoon butter, then toss. Meanwhile, cook peeled small white onions in 1/2 inch hot water, with 1/2 teaspoon salt, covered, about 15 minutes, or until tender. Drain; add 1 tablespoon butter or margarine and toss lightly. Drain carrots; in uncovered saucepan, heat with 1 teaspoon butter or margarine and orange juice. Arrange hot vegetables in large round serving dish, with onions in center, carrots around them, and zucchini in ring around outside. Sprinkle all generously with seasoned pepper. Makes 6 servings.

Diabetic diet: Prepare as directed but use margarine instead of butter. Exchanges per 1 cup serving = 2 vegetable and 1 fat.
Egg-, gluten-, milk- and wheat-free diet: Prepare as directed but use milk-free margarine on milk-free diet.
Low-fat, low-cholesterol diet: Prepare as directed but use margarine instead of butter. 5 grams fat per serving.
High-iron diet: 1 milligram iron per serving.
Low-purine diet: Prepare as directed.

CAULIFLOWER PARMESAN (65 calories per serving)

1 medium fresh cauliflower
1/2 teaspoon salt
4 teaspoons olive oil
1 garlic clove, minced
1 tablespoon chopped parsley
1/4 cup grated Parmesan cheese

About 30 minutes before serving: Wash cauliflower; divide into flowerets; boil, in salted water to cover, 15 to 20 minutes, or until almost tender; drain. In medium skillet, in oil, sauté garlic and parsley 2 minutes; add cauliflower and sauté 2 minutes more. Remove from heat; sprinkle with cheese. Makes 6 servings of about 1/2 cup each.

ONIONS WITH A ZEST (60 calories per serving)

16 small white onions, peeled or
    1 15 1/2-ounce can white
    onions, drained
1 tablespoon brown sugar
1/2 teaspoon Worcestershire
2 teaspoons butter or margarine
1 chicken-bouillon cube

About 20 minutes before serving: In saucepan, mix all ingredients with 1 cup water. Cook, covered, stirring occasionally, 20 minutes, or until onions are tender. Makes 4 servings.

Diabetic diet: Prepare as directed but omit sugar; add non-nutritive sweetener equivalent to 1 tablespoon sugar; use 1 tablespoon margarine. Exchanges per serving = 1 vegetable and 1 fat.
Low-fat, low-cholesterol diet: Prepare as directed but omit butter. Negligible fat per serving.

GINGER-GLAZED CARROTS (70 calories per serving)

8 medium carrots, pared
1/2 teaspoon salt
1 stick cinnamon
1 tablespoon butter or
    margarine, melted
1/4 teaspoon ginger
2 teaspoons granulated sugar
1 teaspoon chopped parsley

About 30 minutes before serving: In medium saucepan over low heat, cook carrots with salt, cinnamon, and enough water to cover, 20 minutes, or until tender-crisp. In small bowl, combine butter, ginger, sugar and parsley; toss lightly with drained carrots. Makes 4 servings.

Low-fat, low-cholesterol diet: Prepare as directed but omit butter or margarine. Negligible fat per serving.

CARROTS MEDLEY (80 calories per serving)

1 pound carrots, pared, cut into
1/4 inch slices
1 medium onion, thinly sliced
3 large stalks celery, cut into
1-inch slices
1 tablespoon butter or
margarine

About 25 minutes before serving: In medium saucepan, in salted water, cook carrots, onion and celery until tender—about 15 minutes; drain; stir in butter. Makes 4 servings.

Diabetic diet: Exchanges per serving (about 3/4 cup) = 1 bread and 1 fat.
Egg-, gluten-, milk- and wheat-free diet: Prepare as directed but use milk-free margarine on milk-free diet.
Low-fat, low-cholesterol diet: Prepare as directed but omit butter or margarine. Negligible fat per serving.
High-iron diet: 1 milligram iron per serving.
Low-purine diet: Prepare as directed.

BRUSSELS SPROUTS WITH BABY CARROTS (75 calories per serving)

1 10-ounce package frozen
Brussels sprouts
1/2 cup chicken broth
1 tablespoon butter or
margarine
1 8-ounce can tiny whole
carrots, drained
dash ginger
1/8 teaspoon seasoned salt

About 15 minutes before serving: Cook Brussels sprouts as label directs but use chicken broth as cooking "water." Meanwhile, in large skillet, in butter, sauté carrots with ginger about 5 minutes; add cooked Brussels sprouts and sauté a few minutes longer. Sprinkle with seasoned salt. Makes 4 servings.

Diabetic diet: Prepare as directed but use margarine instead of butter. Exchanges per serving = 1 vegetable and 1 fat.
Low-fat, low-cholesterol diet: Prepare as directed but use margarine or salad oil instead of butter. 3 grams fat per serving.
High-iron diet: 1 milligram iron per serving.

CURRIED CARROTS AND PINEAPPLE (70 calories per serving)

1 15 1/2-ounce can pineapple
chunks packed in pineapple
juice
8 medium carrots, cut into
strips
1/2 teaspoon curry
1/2 teaspoon salt
dash pepper

About 20 minutes before serving: Into measuring cup, drain pineapple juice, reserving pineapple chunks. Add enough water to make 1 cup liquid; pour into medium skillet. Add carrot strips, curry, salt and pepper. Cook, covered, over medium heat about 20 minutes, or until fork-tender. Stir in reserved pineapple chunks and cook, covered, a few minutes longer to heat through. Makes 6 servings.

Low-fat, low-cholesterol diet: Negligible fat per serving.
Low-purine diet: Prepare as directed.

CARROTS À L'ORANGE (125 calories per serving)

salt
6 medium carrots, thinly sliced
diagonally
2 tablespoons granulated sugar
1 teaspoon butter or margarine
4 small oranges, sectioned

About 20 minutes before serving: In covered medium saucepan, in salted water to just cover, boil carrots until tender—about 15 minutes; drain. Add 1 teaspoon salt, sugar, butter, orange sections; heat gently. Makes four 3/4-cup servings.

Bland diet: Prepare as directed.
Diabetic diet: Prepare as directed but omit sugar; add non-nutritive sweetener equivalent to 1 tablespoon sugar; use 1 tablespoon margarine. Exchanges per serving = 1 vegetable, 1 fruit and 1 fat.
Egg-, gluten-, milk- and wheat-free diet: Prepare as directed but use milk-free margarine on milk-free diet.
Low-fat, low-cholesterol diet: Prepare as directed but omit butter or margarine. Negligible fat per serving.
Low-fat, bland (gall bladder) diet: Prepare as directed.
High-iron diet: 1 milligram iron per serving.
Low-purine diet: Prepare as directed.
Low-residue diet: Prepare as directed but substitute 1/2-cup strained orange juice for orange sections.

CARROTS AND CELERY PLUS A SURPRISE (45 calories per serving)

1 pound carrots, cut diagonally into ¹/₂-inch slices
6 stalks celery, cut into ¹/₂-inch slices
1 to 2 teaspoons prepared horseradish
¹/₂ teaspoon salt
¹/₂ tablespoon butter or margarine

About 30 minutes before serving: In water to just cover, simmer carrots, celery, horseradish and salt 15 to 20 minutes, or until carrots are just tender-crisp. Drain; toss with butter. Makes 6 servings.

Diabetic diet: Prepare as directed but increase butter or margarine to 2 tablespoons. Exchanges per serving (about ³/₄ cup) = 2 vegetables.
Egg-, gluten-, milk- and wheat-free diet: Prepare as directed but use milk-free margarine on milk-free diet.
Low-fat, low-cholesterol diet: Prepare as directed but omit butter or margarine. Negligible fat per serving.
Low-purine diet: Prepare as directed.

CHEESE-TOPPED CARROTS (80 calories per serving)

1 16-ounce jar or can sliced carrots
¹/₄ cup grated sharp Cheddar cheese
salt and pepper
chopped parsley for garnish

About 10 minutes before serving: In saucepan, simmer carrots 5 minutes; turn off heat; thoroughly drain, then return carrots to saucepan. Sprinkle with cheese; cover; let stand until cheese is melted.

To serve: Sprinkle with salt and pepper to taste; stir to mix cheese; top with parsley. Makes three ¹/₂-cup servings.

Bland diet: Prepare as directed but use mild cheese; omit pepper and parsley.
Diabetic diet: Exchanges per serving = 1 vegetable.
Egg-, gluten-, milk- and wheat-free diet: Prepare as directed.
High-iron diet: 1 milligram iron per serving.
Low-purine diet: Prepare as directed.
Low-residue diet: Prepare as directed for bland diet.

JULIAN'S CARROTS (60 calories per serving)

10 medium carrots, thickly sliced
1 15¹/₄-ounce can pineapple chunks packed in pineapple juice
1 cup orange juice
1 tablespoon cornstarch
1 teaspoon salt
¹/₂ teaspoon cinnamon

About 20 minutes before serving: In medium saucepan, cook carrots in 1 inch of boiling water until tender—about 15 minutes; drain.

Into small saucepan, drain juice from pineapple and add orange juice. In small bowl, mix cornstarch, salt and cinnamon; stir in a few tablespoons juice; mix to smooth paste.

Heat juices, then stir in cornstarch mixture. Simmer, stirring constantly, until thickened. Add pineapple chunks and carrots; cook over low heat, stirring constantly, until hot and bubbly. Makes 10 servings.

Diabetic diet: Exchanges per serving (³/₄ cup carrots plus sauce) = 1 vegetable and 1 fruit.
Egg-, gluten-, milk- and wheat-free diet: Prepare as directed.
Low-fat, low-cholesterol diet: Negligible fat per serving.
Low-purine diet: Prepare as directed.

CARROTS CAROLINA (90 calories per serving)

2 16-ounce cans whole baby carrots
¹/₃ cup brown sugar
2 tablespoons orange juice
dash salt

About 30 minutes before serving: Preheat oven to 375°F. Thoroughly drain carrots. In ovenproof saucepan, mix brown sugar, orange juice and salt. Cook, stirring constantly, until sugar is dissolved. Add carrots; stir to coat with sugar mixture. Bake, stirring occasionally, 20 minutes. Serve with syrup. Makes six ¹/₂-cup servings.

Egg-, gluten-, milk- and wheat-free diet: Prepare as directed.
Low-fat, low-cholesterol diet: Negligible fat per serving.
High-iron diet: 1.5 milligrams iron per serving.
Low-purine diet: Prepare as directed.

VEGETABLES "CUNARD" (95 calories per serving)

1 pound carrots
1 pound white turnips
2 tablespoons granulated sugar
salt
1/2 teaspoon basil
1/8 teaspoon pepper
2 tablespoons bacon fat

About 45 minutes before serving: Wash, pare, finely dice carrots; prepare turnips in same way. Place vegetables in saucepan with 2 cups boiling water, sugar, 2 teaspoons salt, basil and pepper. Cover; cook until fork-tender—about 15 minutes.

When vegetables are fork-tender, drain well. Return to saucepan; toss with 1/2 teaspoon salt and bacon fat. Makes 6 servings.

Diabetic diet: Prepare as directed but omit sugar. Exchanges per serving = 1 vegetable and 1 fat.
Egg-, gluten-, milk- and wheat-free diet: Prepare as directed.
Low-fat, low-cholesterol diet: Prepare as directed but substitute margarine for bacon fat. 5 grams fat per serving.

FLORENTINE MUSHROOMS (Funghi Trifolati) (80 calories per serving)

1 1/2 tablespoons butter or
margarine
1 pound fresh mushrooms,
thinly sliced
1 garlic clove, minced
4 anchovy fillets, finely
chopped
2 tablespoons chopped parsley
1/2 tablespoon lemon juice
pepper

About 20 minutes before serving: In large skillet over medium heat, in butter, sauté mushrooms and garlic until lightly browned and liquid from mushrooms has evaporated.

Reduce heat to very low; cover; cook 5 minutes more, shaking skillet occasionally. Stir in chopped anchovies, parsley and lemon juice; add pepper to taste. Makes 4 servings.

Diabetic diet: Exchanges per serving = 1 vegetable and 1 fat.
Egg-, gluten-, milk- and wheat-free diet: Prepare as directed but use milk-free margarine on milk-free diet.
Low-sodium diet: Prepare as directed but use unsalted butter or margarine; omit anchovies. 15 milligrams sodium per serving.

FUN TWISTS (110 calories per serving)

1/4 pound uncooked spaghetti
twists
1 tablespoon salad oil
1/2 pound fresh mushrooms,
thinly sliced
1 medium onion, thinly sliced
1/2 teaspoon salt
dash pepper

About 20 minutes before serving: Cook spaghetti as label directs; drain. Meanwhile, in medium skillet, in oil, sauté mushrooms and onion until golden; season with salt and pepper. In warm serving bowl, mix spaghetti and mushrooms. Makes six 1/2-cup servings.

Diabetic diet: Prepare as directed but sauté onion in 2 tablespoons oil. Exchanges per serving = 1 bread and 1 fat.
Low-fat, low-cholesterol diet: 3 grams fat per serving.
High-iron diet: Use enriched spaghetti. 1 milligram iron per serving.
Low-sodium diet: Prepare as directed but cook spaghetti without added salt; omit salt. 10 milligrams sodium per serving.

HARVARD-STYLE BEETS (65 calories per serving)

1 16-ounce can sliced beets
2 tablespoons granulated sugar
1/2 teaspoon salt
1/2 teaspoon paprika
1 1/2 teaspoons cornstarch
2 tablespoons lemon juice

About 10 minutes before serving: Drain beets, reserving 1/3 cup liquid. In medium saucepan, mix remaining ingredients with reserved beet juice. Heat, stirring constantly, until thickened and smooth. Add beets and bring to boiling. Makes 4 servings.

Bland diet: Prepare as directed.
Egg-, gluten-, milk- and wheat-free diet: Prepare as directed.
Low-fat, low-cholesterol diet: Negligible fat per serving.
Low-fat, bland (gall bladder) diet: Prepare as directed.
Low-purine diet: Prepare as directed.
Low-residue diet: Prepare as directed.

APPLE-JUICE ACORN SQUASH (60 calories per serving)

2 cups apple juice
1 teaspoon salt
1/8 teaspoon cinnamon
1/8 teaspoon mace
1/8 teaspoon pepper
3 small acorn squash

About 1 hour and 15 minutes before serving: Preheat oven to 350°F. In large (about 15″ by 10″) roasting pan, combine all ingredients but squash. Cut squash in half; remove seeds.

Place, cut side down, in apple juice; bake 45 minutes. Turn, cut side up, and spoon a few tablespoons apple juice into cavity of each squash. Bake 10 minutes more, or until tender. Makes 6 servings.

Diabetic diet: Exchanges per serving = 1 bread and 1 fruit.
Egg-, gluten-, milk- and wheat-free diet: Prepare as directed.
Low-fat, low-cholesterol diet: Negligible fat per serving.
High-iron diet: 1 milligram iron per serving.
Low-sodium diet: Prepare as directed but omit salt. 5 milligrams sodium per serving.

DILLED BARLEY (145 calories per serving)

1 10-1/2-ounce can condensed chicken broth
1 cup dry barley
1 tablespoon chopped fresh dill or 2 teaspoons dried dill weed
1 tablespoon butter or margarine
1/4 teaspoon salt

About 1 hour before serving: In large saucepan, heat chicken broth and 1 1/2 soup-cans water to boiling; add barley and dill; simmer until barley is tender and broth absorbed—45 minutes to 1 hour. Stir in butter, and salt if needed. Makes six 1/2-cup servings.

Diabetic diet: Prepare as directed but stir 2 tablespoons margarine into cooked barley. Exchanges per serving = 1 vegetable, 1 bread and 1 fat.
Low-fat, low-cholesterol diet: Prepare as directed but use margarine or salad oil instead of butter. 2 grams fat per serving. If desired, omit fat for negligible fat per serving.
High-iron diet: 1 milligram iron per serving.
Low-sodium diet: Prepare as directed but cook barley in unsalted homemade chicken broth; use unsalted butter or margarine; omit salt. Negligible sodium per serving.

DUCHESS POTATO CROWNS (120 calories per serving)

3 small tomatoes
salt
instant mashed potatoes to make 4 servings
1/2 cup skimmed milk or reliquefied nonfat dry milk
1/2 teaspoon celery salt
1/2 cup grated mild Cheddar cheese

About 45 minutes before serving: Preheat oven to 400°F. Halve tomatoes; scoop out seeds; salt inside and out. Place, cut side up, in shallow baking pan.

Prepare instant potatoes as label directs but use skimmed milk and celery salt; omit butter; stir in cheese. Top tomatoes with potatoes.

Fill bottom of pan with 1/4 inch water; bake 25 to 30 minutes, or until tops of potatoes have brown peaks. Makes 6 servings.

Diabetic diet: Exchanges per serving = 1 vegetable, 1 bread and 1 fat.
Low-fat, low-cholesterol diet: Prepare as directed but omit cheese; stir 2 tablespoons margarine into potato mixture. 5 grams fat per serving.
High-iron diet: 1 milligram iron per serving.
Low-purine diet: Prepare as directed.

LEMON-PARSLEY POTATOES (125 calories per serving)

12 medium potatoes (about 4 pounds), pared
1/4 cup butter or margarine
2 tablespoons chopped parsley
1 tablespoon lemon juice
lemon slices for garnish

About 50 minutes before serving: In large pan, in about 1 inch boiling salted water, cook potatoes until fork-tender; drain. In small saucepan, melt butter with parsley and lemon juice; pour over potatoes. Garnish with lemon slices, if desired. Makes 12 servings.

Bland diet: Prepare as directed but omit parsley.
Diabetic diet: Prepare as directed but use margarine instead of butter and small potato for dieter. Exchanges per serving = 1 bread and 1 fat.
Egg-, gluten-, milk- and wheat-free diet: Prepare as directed but use milk-free margarine on milk-free diet.
Low-fat, low-cholesterol diet: Prepare as directed but use margarine instead of butter. 4 grams fat per serving.
Low-fat, bland (gall bladder) diet: Prepare as directed but omit parsley.
Low-purine diet: Prepare as directed.
Low-residue diet: Prepare as directed but omit parsley.
Low-sodium diet: Prepare as directed but cook potatoes in unsalted water; use unsalted butter or margarine. 5 milligrams sodium per serving.

PAPRIKA POTATO BALLS (100 calories per serving)

2 16-ounce cans tiny whole potatoes, drained
2 tablespoons butter or margarine
1 teaspoon paprika
1 teaspoon salt

About 25 minutes before serving: Preheat oven to 425°F. Meanwhile, dry potatoes on paper towels. Place butter in large baking dish; set in oven to melt. Arrange potatoes in melted butter; sprinkle with paprika and salt; toss until evenly coated. Bake 10 minutes. Makes 6 servings.

Bland diet: Prepare as directed.
Diabetic diet: Prepare as directed but use margarine instead of butter. Exchanges per serving = 1 bread and 1 fat.
Egg-, gluten-, milk- and wheat-free diet: Prepare as directed but use milk-free margarine on milk-free diet.
Low-fat, low-cholesterol diet: Prepare as directed but use margarine instead of butter. 5 grams fat per serving.
Low-fat, bland (gall bladder) diet: Prepare as directed.
Low-purine diet: Prepare as directed.
Low-sodium diet: Prepare as directed but use canned potatoes not containing added salt; use unsalted butter or margarine; omit salt. 2 milligrams sodium per serving.

BOHEMIAN MASHED POTATOES (120 calories per serving)

1/2 teaspoon salt
1 tablespoon butter or margarine
1/2 cup creamed cottage cheese
1/4 cup skimmed milk or reliquefied nonfat dry milk
mashed potatoes to make 4 servings
1/2 teaspoon poppy seeds

About 15 minutes before serving: In medium saucepan, bring 1 1/2 cups water, salt and butter to boiling. Meanwhile, in electric-blender container, at low speed, blend cottage cheese and milk until smooth. Add to boiling water; gradually stir in instant mashed potatoes. Beat until smooth; mix in poppy seeds. Makes 5 servings.

Bland diet: Prepare as directed but omit poppy seed.
Diabetic diet: Prepare as directed but use margarine instead of butter; use low-fat cottage cheese; make only 4 servings. Exchanges per serving = 1 bread and 1/2 milk.
Low-fat, low-cholesterol diet: Prepare as directed but use margarine instead of butter. 3 grams fat per serving.
Low-fat, bland (gall bladder) diet: Prepare as directed but omit poppy seed.
Low-purine diet: Prepare as directed.
Low-residue diet: Prepare as directed for bland diet.

SALTED BAKED POTATOES (105 calories per serving)

4 small baking potatoes
salad oil
butter or margarine
salt

About 30 minutes before serving: Preheat oven to 425°F. Wash and dry potatoes, then brush with salad oil. Place in oven and bake 25 minutes, or until soft. Let cool slightly, then rub with a little butter and sprinkle with salt. Makes 4 servings.

Bland diet: Prepare as directed. Dieter should not eat skin of potato.
Diabetic diet: Exchanges per serving = 1 bread and 1 fat.
Egg-, gluten-, milk- and wheat-free diet: Prepare as directed but use milk-free margarine on milk-free diet.
Low-fat, low-cholesterol diet: Prepare as directed but use margarine instead of butter. 5 grams fat per serving.
Low-fat, bland (gall bladder) diet: Prepare as directed. Dieter should not eat skin of potato.
Low-purine diet: Prepare as directed.
Low-residue diet: Prepare as directed for bland diet.

REBAKED POTATOES (150 calories per serving)

1 garlic clove, minced
1/2 teaspoon salt
2 tablespoons butter or margarine
2 tablespoons shredded Parmesan cheese
4 unpeeled cold baked small potatoes

About 30 minutes before serving: Preheat oven to 350°F. Blend together all ingredients but potatoes. Cut potatoes into 1/2-inch slices, almost all the way through. Spread garlic mixture between slices. Bake 20 minutes, or until hot. Makes 4 servings.

Bland Diet: Prepare as directed but omit garlic.
Diabetic diet: Exchanges per serving = 1 bread and 2 fat.
Egg-, gluten-, milk- and wheat-free diet: Prepare as directed.
Low-fat, low-cholesterol diet: Prepare as directed but use margarine instead of butter; substitute dried bread crumbs for Parmesan cheese. 5 grams fat per serving.
Low-fat, bland (gall bladder) diet: Prepare as directed but omit garlic; substitute dried bread crumbs for cheese.
High-iron diet: Prepare as directed but use a large baking potato. 1 milligram iron per serving.
Low-purine diet: Prepare as directed.
Low-residue diet: Prepare as directed but omit garlic.

TACY'S CREAMED POTATOES (125 calories per serving)

2 1/2 pounds potatoes (8 medium), pared and cubed
1 medium onion, thinly sliced
1 cup thinly sliced celery
2 teaspoons salt
1/8 teaspoon pepper
2 1/2 cups skimmed milk or reliquefied nonfat dry milk
1 tablespoon cornstarch

About 40 minutes before serving: In large saucepan, heat all ingredients but cornstarch to boiling; cover; simmer 20 minutes, or until potatoes are tender. Mix enough water with cornstarch to form a thin paste. Stir into potato-milk mixture; cook until thickened and smooth. Makes eight 3/4-cup servings.

Diabetic diet: Exchanges per serving = 1 bread and 1/2 milk.
Egg-, gluten-, milk- and wheat-free diet: Prepare as directed.
Low-fat, low-cholesterol diet: Negligible fat per serving.
Low-purine diet: Prepare as directed.

HELPFUL BAKED BEANS (115 calories per serving)

1/2 cup chopped onion
1/2 cup chopped green pepper
1/2 cup catchup
1 16-ounce can vegetarian baked beans

About 20 minutes before serving: In medium saucepan, gently boil onion, pepper and 3/4 cup water, covered, for 15 minutes. Add catchup and baked beans; bring to boiling. Makes 6 servings.

Low-fat, low-cholesterol diet: Negligible fat per serving.
High-iron diet: Make only 4 servings. 2 milligrams iron per serving.

LEMON MINT BEANS (25 calories per serving)

1 9-ounce package frozen cut
   green beans
1 9-ounce package frozen cut
   wax beans
2 tablespoons lemon juice
1 teaspoon dried mint leaves
1/2 teaspoon grated lemon peel
1/2 teaspoon salt

About 15 minutes before serving: In medium saucepan, cook green beans and wax beans together as labels direct, but use 1 cup water; drain. Add remaining ingredients and toss well. Makes 6 servings.

Diabetic diet: Exchange per serving = 1 vegetable.
Low-fat, low-cholesterol diet: Negligible fat per serving.
Low-purine diet: Prepare as directed.

GREEN BEANS WITH MARJORAM (30 calories per serving)

1 9-ounce package frozen green
   beans
2 chicken-bouillon cubes
1/2 teaspoon marjoram leaves

About 15 minutes before serving: Cook green beans as label directs but omit salt, add bouillon cubes and marjoram to cooking water. Drain before serving. Makes 3 servings.

Diabetic diet: Exchanges per serving = 1 vegetable.
Low-fat, low-cholesterol diet: Negligible fat per serving.

GREEN BEANS AND CELERY (25 calories per serving)

1 pound fresh green beans,
   trimmed
1 teaspoon salt
3 stalks celery, thinly sliced
pepper
2 tablespoons chopped parsley
   for garnish

About 20 minutes before serving: In saucepan, in 1 inch boiling water, simmer beans and salt, covered, 10 minutes. Add celery; sprinkle lightly with pepper. Simmer, covered, another 10 minutes; drain; sprinkle with parsley and serve. Makes 6 servings.

Diabetic diet: Exchanges per serving = 1 vegetable.
Egg-, gluten-, milk- and wheat-free diet: Prepare as directed.
Low-fat, low-cholesterol diet: Negligible fat per serving.
Low-purine diet: Prepare as directed.
Low-sodium diet: Prepare as directed but omit salt. 30 milligrams sodium per serving.

GREEN BEANS WITH MINT (45 calories per serving)

2 16-ounce cans green beans
1/4 cup dried mint flakes
1 tablespoon butter or
   margarine
salt and pepper

About 15 minutes before serving: In medium saucepan, heat green beans and mint flakes to boiling. Drain; toss with butter, then salt and pepper to taste. Makes 6 servings.

Diabetic diet: Prepare as directed but use 2 tablespoons margarine. Exchanges per serving = 1 vegetable and 1 fat.
Egg-, gluten-, milk- and wheat-free diet: Prepare as directed but use milk-free margarine on milk-free diet.
Low-fat, low-cholesterol diet: Prepare as directed but use margarine or salad oil instead of butter. 2 grams fat per serving.
Low-purine diet: Prepare as directed.
Low-sodium diet: Prepare as directed but select brand of canned beans not containing added salt; use unsalted butter or margarine; omit salt. 3 milligrams sodium per serving.

PLANTATION GREEN BEANS (60 calories per serving)

2 9-ounce packages frozen
   French-style green beans,
   thawed
2 slices bacon, diced
1/2 cup green onions, chopped
1/4 teaspoon pepper

About 20 minutes before serving: Prepare beans as label directs, but cook only 5 minutes. In medium skillet over medium-high heat, fry bacon until crisp; remove and drain well on paper towels. Cook green onions in 1 tablespoon of bacon drippings until just tender. Add pepper and green beans; cook over medium heat, stirring occasionally, until tender. Stir in bacon. Makes 6 servings.

Diabetic diet: Exchanges per serving = 1 vegetable and 1 fat.
Egg-, gluten-, milk- and wheat-free diet: Prepare as directed.

WAX BEANS LYONNAISE (60 calories per serving)

1 tablespoon butter or margarine
2 medium onions, thinly sliced
2 15½-ounce cans whole wax beans, drained
⅛ teaspoon pepper

About 15 minutes before serving: In saucepan over medium heat, in butter, sauté onions until golden. Add drained wax beans and pepper; cover; heat, shaking saucepan, until hot. Makes 6 servings.

Diabetic diet: Prepare as directed but use 2 tablespoons butter or margarine. Exchanges per serving = 1 vegetable and 1 fat.
Egg-, gluten-, milk- and wheat-free diet: Prepare as directed but use milk-free margarine on milk-free diet.
Low-fat, low-cholesterol diet: Prepare as directed but use margarine instead of butter. 2 grams fat per serving.
High-iron diet: 2 milligrams iron per serving.

ITALIAN GREEN BEANS WITH GRAPES (45 calories per serving)

1 9-ounce package frozen Italian green beans
1 cup seedless grapes
salt and pepper to taste

About 15 minutes before serving: Cook Italian green beans as label directs, but omit butter or margarine; add grapes during last 3 minutes of cooking. Drain; add salt and pepper to taste. Makes 4 servings.

Bland diet: Prepare as directed but omit pepper.
Diabetic diet: Exchanges per serving = 1 vegetable.
Egg-, gluten-, milk- and wheat-free diet: Prepare as directed.
Low-fat, low-cholesterol diet: Negligible fat per serving.
Low-fat, bland (gall bladder) diet: Prepare as directed but omit pepper.
Low-purine diet: Prepare as directed.
Low-residue diet: Prepare as directed but omit pepper.
Low-sodium diet: Prepare as directed but omit salt. 5 milligrams sodium per serving.

SAUTÉED GREEN BEANS (50 calories per serving)

1 9-ounce package frozen French-style green beans
2 teaspoons salad oil
½ teaspoon salt
2 teaspoons wine vinegar
⅛ teaspoon pepper

About 25 minutes before serving: Cook green beans as label directs until just tender-crisp; drain. In medium skillet over medium heat, in oil, sauté beans until they begin to brown. Season with salt, vinegar and pepper. Makes 3 servings.

Bland diet: Prepare as directed but omit vinegar and pepper.
Diabetic diet: Exchanges per serving = 1 vegetable and 1 fat.
Egg-, gluten-, milk- and wheat-free diet: Prepare as directed.
Low-fat, low-cholesterol diet: 5 grams fat per serving.
Low-purine diet: Prepare as directed.
Low-sodium diet: Prepare as directed but cook green beans without adding salt; omit salt. Negligible sodium per serving.

ONIONY GREEN BEANS (40 calories per serving)

1 tablespoon butter or margarine
1½ teaspoons instant minced onion
2 9-ounce packages frozen cut green beans
1 teaspoon salt

About 20 minutes before serving: In medium saucepan over medium heat, in butter, cook instant onion until browned. Add green beans, salt and ½ cup water; cook, covered, until tender—about 15 minutes. Makes 6 servings.

Diabetic diet: Prepare as directed but increase butter to 2 tablespoons. Exchanges per serving = 1 vegetable and 1 fat.
Egg-, gluten-, milk- and wheat-free diet: Prepare as directed but use milk-free margarine on milk-free diet.
Low-fat, low-cholesterol diet: Prepare as directed but use margarine instead of butter. 2 grams fat per serving.
Low-purine diet: Prepare as directed.

GREEN BEANS ITALIAN (70 calories per serving)

1 9-ounce package frozen
Italian green beans
1 16-ounce can white onions,
drained
1/2 teaspoon oregano leaves
1 tablespoon butter or
margarine
salt and pepper to taste

About 15 minutes before serving: Cook Italian beans as label directs, but add drained white onions and oregano. Drain; toss with butter; add salt, pepper. Makes 4 servings.

Diabetic diet: Exchanges per serving (about 3/4 cup) = 1 1/2 vegetable and 1 fat.
Egg-, gluten-, milk- and wheat-free diet: Prepare as directed but use milk-free margarine on milk-free diet.
Low-fat, low-cholesterol diet: Prepare as directed but omit butter or margarine. Negligible fat per serving.
High-iron diet: 1.5 milligrams iron per serving.
Low-purine diet: Prepare as directed.
Low-sodium diet: Prepare as directed but select canned onions not containing added salt; use unsalted butter or margarine; omit salt. 15 milligrams sodium per serving.

GREEN BEANS IN HERB SAUNCE (65 calories per serving)

1 tablespoon butter or
margarine
1 large onion, thinly sliced
1 large stalk green celery, thinly
sliced
1 tablespoon parsley flakes
1/4 teaspoon garlic salt
(optional)
3/4 teaspoon salt
dash pepper
1 tablespoon cornstarch
1 9-ounce package frozen cut
green beans

About 25 minutes before serving: In saucepan over medium heat, in butter, sauté onion, celery and parsley flakes until onion is golden. Meanwhile, mix garlic salt, salt, pepper and cornstarch; slowly stir in 1 cup water to form a smooth paste. Add this mixture and green beans to onion; cover; boil gently 10 minutes or until beans are tender-crisp and sauce has thickened slightly. Makes four 3/4-cup servings.

Diabetic diet: Exchanges per serving = 1 vegetable and 1 fat.
Egg-, gluten-, milk- and wheat-free diet: Prepare as directed but use milk-free margarine on milk-free diet.
Low-fat, low-cholesterol diet: Prepare as directed but use margarine instead of butter. 3 grams fat per serving.
Low-purine diet: Prepare as directed.
Low-sodium diet: Prepare as directed but use unsalted butter or margarine; substitute garlic powder for garlic salt; omit salt. 15 milligrams sodium per serving.

NOODLES WITH SESAME SEED (135 calories per serving)

1/2 8-ounce package egg
noodles
1/2 tablespoon butter or
margarine
1 1/2 tablespoons sesame seeds

About 15 minutes before serving: Cook noodles as label directs; drain. Meanwhile, in small skillet, in butter, brown sesame seeds; toss with noodles. Makes 4 servings.

Diabetic diet: Exchanges per serving (1/2 cup noodles) = 1 bread and 1 fat.
Low-fat, low-cholesterol diet: Prepare as directed but use margarine or salad oil instead of butter. 5 grams fat per serving.
Low-sodium diet: Prepare as directed but cook noodles without added salt; use unsalted butter or margarine. 2 milligrams sodium per serving.

VIENNESE RICE (135 calories per serving)

1 cup uncooked long-grain rice
1/4 teaspoon lemon juice
1 10-ounce package frozen peas
1 tablespoon salad oil
1 medium onion, diced
chopped parsley for garnish

About 30 minutes before serving: Cook rice as package directs, omitting butter but adding lemon juice. Meanwhile, cook peas as label directs. In medium skillet, in oil, sauté onion until golden. Toss rice with peas and onion; garnish with parsley. Makes 8 servings.

Diabetic diet: Prepare as directed but use 2 tablespoons salad oil. Exchanges per serving (2/3 cup) = 1 1/2 bread, 1 fat.
Egg-, gluten-, milk- and wheat-free diet: Prepare as directed.
High-iron diet: Use enriched rice. 1 milligram iron per serving.

BACON-TOMATO RICE (140 calories per serving)

2 bacon slices
1 cup chopped onions
2 8-ounce cans tomato sauce
1 teaspoon seasoned salt
1/8 teaspoon seasoned pepper
1 teaspoon granulated sugar
**1 cup uncooked regular white
rice**

About 1 hour before serving: In medium skillet, sauté bacon slices until crisp; pour off and reserve bacon fat; drain, then crumble bacon. Preheat oven to 375°F.

In skillet, in 1 tablespoon bacon fat, sauté onions until tender; stir in tomato sauce, seasoned salt, seasoned pepper, sugar and 1 1/2 cups water; simmer 10 minutes, then stir in rice. Pour rice mixture into 1 1/2-quart casserole; bake, covered, 30 minutes; fluff up rice with fork; stir in bacon bits; then bake, uncovered, 5 minutes longer. Makes 6 servings.

Diabetic diet: Prepare as directed but omit sugar. Exchanges per serving (about 3/4 cup) = 1 vegetable, 1 bread and 1/2 fat.
Egg-, gluten-, milk- and wheat-free diet: Prepare as directed but use regular (not seasoned) salt and pepper on gluten-free diet.
Low-fat, low-cholesterol diet: Prepare as directed but omit bacon; sauté onion in 1 tablespoon salad oil. 2 grams fat per serving.
High-iron diet: Use enriched rice. 1.5 milligrams iron per serving.

RICE WITH MUSROOMS (120 calories per serving)

1 beef-bouillon cube
**1 tablespoon butter or
margarine**
1/2 cup uncooked long-grain rice
1/2 cup coarsely chopped onion
**1/4 pound fresh mushrooms,
sliced**
1/2 teaspoon salt
1/4 teaspoon pepper
1/8 teaspoon thyme leaves
1/2 cup coarsely chopped celery

About 1 hour before serving: Preheat oven to 350°F. In 1- or 1 1/2-quart casserole, dissolve bouillon cube in 1 1/4 cups boiling water. In medium skillet over medium heat, in butter, sauté rice 5 minutes or until golden-brown, stirring constantly.

To broth in casserole, add rice, onion, mushrooms, salt, pepper and thyme. Bake covered, stirring occasionally, 40 minutes; then stir in celery and bake, uncovered, 5 minutes longer. Makes four 1/2-cup servings.

Diabetic diet: Prepare as directed but use margarine instead of butter. Exchanges per serving = 1 bread and 1 fat.
Egg-, gluten-, milk- and wheat-free diet: Prepare as directed but omit bouillon cube from gluten- and wheat-free diet; use milk-free margarine on milk-free diet.
Low-fat, low-cholesterol diet: Prepare as directed but use margarine or salad oil instead of butter. 3 grams fat per serving.
Low-sodium diet: Prepare as directed but omit bouillon cube and salt; use unsalted butter or margarine. 15 milligrams sodium per serving.

SAVORY LEMON RICE (130 calories per serving)

**1 tablespoon butter or
margarine**
**1 1/2 cups packaged precooked
rice**
1 1/2 cups chicken broth
1/2 teaspoon salt
2 tablespoons chopped parsley
1 tablespoon lemon juice
1 tablespoon grated lemon peel

About 15 minutes before serving: In saucepan, heat butter, rice, broth and salt to boiling; remove from heat; cover; let stand five minutes. Toss in parsley, lemon juice and peel. Makes six 1/2-cup servings.

Diabetic diet: Prepare as directed but cook rice with 2 tablespoons margarine. Exchanges per serving = 1 bread and 1 fat.
Egg-, gluten-, milk- and wheat-free diet: Prepare as directed but use milk-free margarine on milk-free diet, use home-made chicken broth on gluten- and wheat-free diets.
Low-fat, low-cholesterol diet: Prepare as directed but omit butter or margarine. Negligible fat per serving.

PINTO RICE (105 calories per serving)

4 cups hot fluffy cooked rice
3 tablespoons chopped green
  pepper
3 tablespoons chopped green
  onions
2 tablespoons chopped
  pimento
1/4 teaspoon celery salt
1/8 teaspoon pepper
dash cayenne

About 10 minutes before serving: Toss hot rice with remaining ingredients. Makes eight 1/2-cup servings.

Diabetic diet: Exchanges per serving = 1 bread.
Egg-, gluten-, milk- and wheat-free diet: Cook rice without adding butter. Prepare as directed.
Low-fat, low-cholesterol diet: Negligible fat per serving.

SALADS AND SALAD DRESSINGS

NOVELTY SALAD (45 calories per serving)

1 medium greem pepper, diced
1 medium tomato, cut into
  wedges (or 1 16-ounce can
  tomato wedges, drained)
1 medium apple, thinly sliced
2 stalks celery, thinly sliced
2 tablespoons chopped parsley
  (optional)
2 tablespoons reduced-calorie
  mayonnaise
$1/2$ tablespoon lemon juice

About 10 minutes before serving: In medium bowl, toss all ingredients until coated with mayonnaise. Makes four 1-cup servings.

Diabetic diet: Exchanges per serving = $1/2$ vegetable.
Low-fat, low-cholesterol diet: 1 gram fat per serving.
Low-purine diet: Prepare as directed.

SAVORY CARROT-AND-RAISIN SALAD (65 calories per serving)

2 cups grated carrots (4 to 6
  carrots)
$1/3$ cup raisins
1 $8^3/_4$-ounce can crushed
  pineapple, thoroughly drained
$1/8$ teaspoon salt
$1/3$ cup reduced-calorie creamy
  French dressing
pepper to taste
6 small lettuce cups

At least 1 hour before serving: In medium bowl, toss together all ingredients but lettuce; refrigerate at least 1 hour to "marry" flavors.

To serve: Divide salad among lettuce cups. Makes 6 servings.

Diabetic diet: Prepare as directed but substitute pineapple packed in pineapple juice for regular. Exchanges per serving = 1 vegetable and 1 bread.
Low-fat, low-cholesterol diet: 1 gram fat per serving.
Low-purine diet: Prepare as directed.

ASPARAGUS VINAIGRETTE SALAD (25 calories per serving)

3 10-ounce packages frozen
  jumbo asparagus spears
1 8-ounce bottle reduced-calorie
  Italian dressing

At least 4 hours before serving: Cook asparagus as label directs; drain. Place in shallow dish and pour on low-calorie dressing. Cover; refrigerate, turning spears occasionally.

To serve: Arrange asparagus on serving platter, discarding dressing. Makes 12 servings.

Diabetic diet: Exchanges per serving = 1 vegetable.
Low-fat, low-cholesterol diet: Negligible fat per serving.

MEXICAN POTATO SALAD (135 calories per serving)

4 pounds potatoes
1 medium onion, chopped
$1/2$ medium green pepper,
  chopped
4 medium carrots, thinly sliced
$1/3$ cup chopped canned
  pimentos
1 medium head lettuce,
  shredded
1 cup reduced-calorie
  mayonnaise
1 teaspoon salt
1 tablespoon lemon juice
chili powder

Early in day: Boil potatoes, in jackets, until fork-tender; cool; peel; cut into bite-size pieces. In large serving bowl, toss with onion, pepper, carrots, pimentos and lettuce. In small bowl, blend low-calorie mayonnaise with salt, lemon juice and 1 teaspoon chili powder; gently stir into potato mixture; refrigerate until serving time.

To serve: Sprinkle salad lightly with more chili powder. Makes about 12 servings.

Diabetic diet: Carefully divide into 12 servings (about $3/4$ cup each). Exchanges per serving = 1 bread.
Low-fat, low-cholesterol diet: 2 grams fat per serving.
High-iron diet: 1 milligram iron per serving.
Low-purine diet: Prepare as directed.

DILLED MACARONI SALAD (150 calories per serving)

1 8-ounce package macaroni
1 cup reduced-calorie
   mayonnaise
2 tablespoons vinegar
1 teaspoon salt
1/2 teaspoon dried dill weed
1/8 teaspoon pepper
1 cup coarsely chopped green
   pepper
2 tablespoons chopped onion
2 tablespoons chopped
   pimento
lettuce leaves

Several hours before serving: Cook macaroni as label directs; drain. In large bowl, combine mayonnaise, vinegar, salt, dill and pepper. Add macaroni, celery, green pepper, onion and pimento; toss well. Cover and refrigerate.

To serve: Arrange salad on lettuce leaves. Makes eight 1/2-cup servings.

Diabetic diet: Exchanges per serving = 1 vegetable, 1 bread and 1 fat.
Low-fat, low-cholesterol diet: 5 grams fat per serving.
High-iron diet: 1 milligram iron per serving.
Low-purine diet: Prepare as directed.

APPLE SLAW (65 calories per serving)

4 cups finely shredded green
   cabbage
1/4 cup reduced-calorie Italian
   dressing
1/4 cup juice drained from sweet
   pickles
1 apple, cubed
1/4 teaspoon salt

About 10 minutes before serving: In large bowl, toss together all ingredients. Makes 4 servings.

Low-fat, low-cholesterol diet: Negligible fat per serving.
Low-purine diet: Prepare as directed.

TOMATO HERB SALAD (40 calories per serving)

6 ripe medium tomatoes, peeled
4 tablespoons wine vinegar
11/2 teaspoons oregano leaves
11/2teaspoons salt
6 small lettuce cups

About 30 minutes before serving: Finely chop 11/2 tomatoes. In small bowl, combine chopped tomatoes, vinegar, oregano and salt. Thinly slice remaining tomatoes; divide among lettuce cups. Top with tomato-vinegar mixture. Refrigerate until serving time. Makes 6 servings.

Diabetic diet: Exchanges per serving = 1 vegetable.
Egg-, bluten-, milk- and wheat-free diet: Prepare as directed.
Low-fat, low-cholesterol diet: Negligible fat per serving.
High-iron diet: 1 milligram iron per serving.
Low-purine diet: Prepare as directed.
Low-sodium diet: Prepare as directed but omit salt. 5 milligrams sodium per serving.

SAVORY TOMATO ASPIC (30 calories per serving)

2 envelopes unflavored gelatin
1 quart (4 cups) tomato juice
2 tablespoons lemon juice
1/4 teaspoon granulated sugar
1/4 teaspoon Tabasco
6 to 8 springs parsley
1/4 medium green pepper
1/2 cup celery leaves and stalks,
   finely chopped

Day before or early in day: Stir gelatin into 1/2 cup tomato juice to soften. In medium saucepan over medium heat, cook remaining tomato juice, lemon juice, sugar, Tabasco, parsley and green pepper 6 to 8 minutes, or until parsley loses its bright green color. Discard parsley and green pepper. Stir in gelatin until dissolved. Pour into 11/2-quart mold and refrigerate until mixture reaches consistency of egg whites; stir in celery. Refrigerate 4 hours, or until firm. Makes 8 servings.

Diabetic diet: Prepare as directed but omit sugar. Exchanges per serving = 1 vegetable.
Low-fat, low-cholesterol diet: Negligible fat per serving.
Low-purine diet: Prepare as directed.

PEPPY CHIVE DRESSING (10 calories per tablespoon)

1 8-ounce container plain
    yogurt
2 teaspoons lemon juice
1 teaspoons seasoned salt
2 tablespoons chopped chives

At least 2 hours before serving: In small bowl, combine all ingredients. Refrigerate to blend flavors. Makes about 1 cup.

Low-fat, low-cholesterol diet: Negligible fat per serving.
Low-purine diet: Prepare as directed.

RELISH SALAD (100 calories per serving)

3 cups diced tomatoes
3 cups peeled, diced
    cucumbers
1 cup sliced radishes
1/3 cup sliced pitted ripe olives
1 carrot, grated
1/4 cup chopped parsley
2 teaspoons salt
1/4 teaspoon pepper
3 tablespoons olive oil
2 hard-cooked eggs

About 2 hours before serving: In large bowl, combine tomatoes, cucumbers, radishes, olives, carrot and parsley. Sprinkle with salt and pepper; toss with olive oil. Cover; refrigerate until serving time.

    To serve: Toss salad again, then arrange in salad bowl; sprinkle center with one chopped egg. Cut other egg into wedges; use as garnish. Makes 8 servings.

Diabetic diet: Prepare as directed but omit eggs. Exchanges per serving = 2 vegetables and 1 fat.
Egg-, gluten-, milk- and wheat-free diet: Prepare as directed but omit eggs.
Low-fat, low-cholesterol diet: Prepare as directed but omit eggs. 5 grams fat per serving. If olive oil is forbidden on diet, omit recipe.
High-iron diet: 2 milligrams iron per serving.
Low-purine diet: Prepare as directed.

MARINATED SLICED TOMATOES (60 calories per serving)

4 tomatoes
1 green onion
1/2 teaspoon salt
1/4 teaspoon basil
1/4 cup low-calorie French
    dressing

About 1 hour before serving: Thinly slice tomatoes and place in shallow dish. Thinly slice green onion (including top) and sprinkle on tomatoes with salt and basil. Top with French dressing; refrigerate.

    To serve: Drain excess dressing from tomatoes and serve. Makes 4 servings.

Diabetic diet: Exchanges per serving = 1 vegetable.
Low-fat, low-cholesterol diet: 1 gram fat per serving.
High-iron diet: 1 milligram iron per serving.
Low-purine diet: Prepare as directed.
Low-sodium diet: Prepare as directed but omit salt and use low-sodium French dressing. 5 milligrams sodium per serving.

WATERMELON COMPOTE SALAD (65 calories per serving)

1/2 small watermelon
escarole leaves
1 cucumber, cut into fingers
1/2 pear, thinly sliced, tossed
    with lemon juice
bottled reduced-calorie
    dressing (optional)

Up to 1 hour before serving: With melon-baller, scoop meat from watermelon, seeding as you go, if desired. (For a prettier compote, separate more perfect balls, for use where they show.)

    In compote or on platter, arrange bed of escarole leaves with cucumber fingers, spoke-fashion, around edge. Next, heap mound of watermelon balls in center, on top of cucumbers, with pear slices here and there. Pass dressing. Makes 6 servings

Diabetic diet: Exchanges per serving = 1 fruit.
Egg-, gluten-, milk- and wheat-free diet: Prepare as directed but omit salad dressing.
Low-fat, low-cholesterol diet: 1 gram fat per serving.
High-iron diet: 1.5 milligrams iron per serving.
Low-purine diet: Prepare as directed.
Low-sodium diet: Prepare as directed but omit salad dressing. 5 milligrams sodium per serving.

ICY SPICY PEACH SALAD (90 calories per serving)

1 30-ounce can cling-peach
halves
2 sticks cinnamon
1 teaspoon whole cloves
1 tablespoon vinegar
4 lettuce cups

At least 3 hours before serving: In medium saucepan, mix peach halves, cinnamon, cloves and vinegar. Over low heat, simmer 5 minutes; refrigerate.

To serve: Drain thoroughly; stud peach halves with whole cloves. Serve in lettuce cups. Makes 4 servings of 2 peach halves each.

Diabetic diet: Prepare as directed but substitute canned peaches packed in water for regular. Exchanges per serving = 1 fruit.
Egg-, gluten-, milk- and wheat-free diet: Prepare as directed.
Low-fat, low-cholesterol diet: Negligible fat per serving.
Low-purine diet: Prepare as directed.
Low-sodium diet: 3 milligrams sodium per serving.

DILLED COTTAGE-CHEESE DRESSING (15 calories per tablespoon)

1 cup creamed cottage cheese
1/2 teaspoon salt
scant 1/8 teaspoon cayenne
1/4 cup sour cream
1/4 cup fresh dill, finely chopped

At least 2 hours before serving: In electric-blender container, at low speed, blend cottage cheese, salt, cayenne, sour cream and 2 tablespoons water until smooth. Transfer to glass jar; stir in dill; cover; refrigerate at least 2 hours to "marry" the flavors. Use as a dressing for lettuce. Makes about 1 1/2 cups.

Diabetic diet: Exchanges per 1/4-cup dressing = 1 meat and 1 fat.
Egg-, gluten-, milk- and wheat-free diet: Prepare as directed.
Low-purine diet: Prepare as directed.

SUNSHINE SALAD (65 calories per serving)

2 envelopes unflavored gelatin
1/4 cup lemon juice
2 15 1/4-ounce cans pineapple
chunks packed in pineapple
juice
2 tablespoons vinegar
1/2 teaspoon salt
2 cups grated carrots
lettuce, green pepper, parsley
and maraschino cherry for
garnish

At least 4 hours before serving: In large bowl, mix gelatin, lemon juice and a bit of juice from canned pineapple; let stand 5 minutes to soften. Remove 3 pineapple chunks from can; wrap; refrigerate. Stir in 1 cup boiling water, then vinegar, salt, carrots, pineapple chunks and rest of pineapple juice. Pour into rinsed 9" by 5" by 3" loaf pan. Refrigerate until firm—at least 3 hours.

About 15 minutes before serving: Arrange nest of lettuce on oval platter. Unmold salad onto lettuce. Decorate with flower made from thin strips of green pepper for stem, parsley for leaf and reserved pineapple chunks, cut in half, for bud. Use maraschino cherry for center of flower.

To serve: Cut into slices with very sharp knife. Makes 10 servings.

Diabetic diet: Exchanges per serving = 1 fruit.
Egg-, gluten-, milk- and wheat-free diet: Prepare as directed.
Low-fat, low-cholesterol diet: Neglible fat per serving.
Low-sodium diet: Prepare as directed but omit salt. 5 milligrams sodium per serving.

CALORIE WATCERS' DRESSING (10 calories per tablespoon)

1 10 3/4-ounce can condensed
tomato soup, undiluted
1/4 teaspoon garlic powder
1/4 teaspoon onion salt
1/8 teaspoon pepper
1 tablespoon India relish
2 to 3 tablespoons wine vinegar

At least 8 hours before serving: In wide-mouth pint jar, stir all ingredients. Cover; refrigerate. Use as a dressing for salad greens. Makes 1 1/2 cups dressing.

Diabetic diet: Exchanges per tablespoons = "free."
Low-fat, low-cholesterol diet: Negligible fat per serving.

SUMMER FRUIT SLAW (55 calories per serving)

1 large head cabbage
³/₄ cup reduced-calorie mayonnaise
2 tablespoons vinegar
1¹/₂ teaspoons salt
1 teaspoon granulated sugar
1 13¹/₄-ounce can pineapple tidbits, drained
1 peach, cut into thin wedges for garnish
2 purple plums, cut into thin wedges for garnish

About 20 minutes before serving: Spread apart several outer leaves of cabbage. Carefully cut out center of cabbage, leaving outer leaves as "bowl"; also leave core intact for about an inch. Finely shred cut-out cabbage.

Combine reduced-calorie mayonnaise, vinegar, salt and sugar; toss with pineapple tidbits and shredded cabbage. Pile into prepared "bowl." For pretty garnish, arrange peach and plum wedges around slaw. Makes 12 servings.

Low-fat, low-cholesterol diet: 2 grams fat per serving.

PEACH SALAD (125 calories per serving)

2 teaspoons unflavored gelatin
¹/₈ teaspoon salt
2 tablespoons lemon juice
1 16-ounce can freestone-peach halves, drained (reserve syrup)
1 8-ounce container creamed cottage cheese
lettuce cups

At least 4 hours before serving: In small saucepan, sprinkle gelatin on ¹/₃ cup water to soften; add salt and lemon juice, then heat to dissolve gelatin. Refrigerate until consistency of unbeaten egg whites. Meanwhile, place 5 whole peach halves, smooth side down, in bottom of five ³/₄-cup custard cups.

When gelatin mixture has thickened, stir in cottage cheese and ²/₃ cup peach syrup. Divide mixture among custard cups. Refrigerate until firm.

To serve: Turn out into lettuce cups. Makes 5 servings.

Bland diet: Prepare as directed but dieter should not eat lettuce unless allowed on diet.
Diabetic diet: Prepare as directed but substitute canned peach halves packed in water for regular. Use low-fat cheese. Exchanges per serving = 1 meat and 1 fruit.
Egg-, gluten-, and wheat-free diet: Prepare as directed.
Low-fat, low-cholesterol diet: 2 grams fat per serving.
Low-fat, bland (gall bladder) diet: Prepare as directed for bland diet.
Low-purine diet: Prepare as directed.
Low-residue diet: Prepare as directed for bland diet.

MARINATED VEGETABLE SALAD (40 calories per serving)

1 9-ounce package frozen whole green beans
1 9-ounce package frozen cut wax beans
1 9-ounce package frozen artichoke hearts
1 pound zucchini, thickly sliced
1 small head cauliflower, cut into bite-size pieces
salt
1 8-ounce bottle reduced-calorie Italian salad dressing
¹/₂ pint cherry tomatoes

Day before: Cook green and wax beans and artichoke hearts as labels direct; drain well. In medium saucepan, cook zucchini and cauliflower in 1-inch boiling salted water until tender-crisp; drain.

Place cooked vegetables in individual containers. Pour Italian dressing over each vegetable. Cover and marinate in refrigerator overnight; stir once our twice.

To serve: Drain and discard marinade, then place vegetables in large serving jar and top with cherry tomatoes. Makes 12 servings.

Diabetic diet: Exchanges per serving = 1 vegetable.
Low-fat, low-cholesterol diet: 1 gram fat per serving.
High-iron diet: 1 milligram iron per serving.
Low-purine diet: Prepare as directed but omit cauliflower. Makes 9 servings.

ORANGES OREGANO (95 calories per serving)

1 tablespoon olive oil
1 teaspoon oregano leaves
¹/₂ teaspoon salt
4 black pitted olives, sliced
2 large oranges, sliced
lettuce leaves

About 10 minutes before serving: In small bowl, combine olive oil, 1 tablespoon hot water, oregano and salt; mix well. Add olives and orange slices and toss until well coated. Serve on lettuce leaves. Makes 4 servings.

Diabetic diet: Exchanges per serving = 1 vegetable, 1 fruit and 1 fat.
Egg-, gluten-, milk- and wheat-free diet: Prepare as directed.
Low-fat, low-cholesterol diet: Prepare as directed but use salad oil instead of olive oil; omit olives. 4 grams fat per serving.
Low-purine diet: Prepare as directed.
Low-sodium diet: Prepare as directed but omit salt and olives. Negligible sodium per serving.

FRESH MINTED PEAR SALAD (100 calories per serving)

1 tablespoon chopped fresh mint
1 tablespoon chopped parsley
¹/₂ teaspoon granulated sugar
2 tablespoons salad oil
1 tablespoon wine vinegar
3 large pears, sliced
lettuce leaves

About 10 minutes before serving: In small bowl, stir mint, parsley and sugar; crush lightly with back of spoon. Stir in oil, vinegar and 1 teaspoon water. Toss pears in dressing, a few slices at a time, until well coated. Serve on lettuce leaves. Makes 6 servings.

Diabetic diet: Prepare as directed but omit sugar. Exchanges per serving = 1 fruit and 1 fat.
Egg-, gluten-, milk- and wheat-free diet: Prepare as directed.
Low-fat, low-cholesterol diet: 5 grams fat per serving.
Low-purine diet: Prepare as directed.
Low-sodium diet: Negligible sodium per serving.

A & B SALAD (85 calories per serving)

2 tablespoons lemon juice
2 tablespoons honey
1 egg white
dash salt
about 2 cups shredded lettuce
1 large apple, thinly sliced
1 cup diced canned beets, drained

About 15 minutes before serving: In small bowl, combine lemon juice and honey; add egg white and salt; beat until blended. Cover bottom of serving platter with lettuce; arrange apple slices in pinwheel fashion and spoon beets in center. Then spoon honey dressing over salad. Makes 4 servings.

Diabetic diet: Prepare as directed but omit honey; add 2 tablespoons water and non-nutritive sweetener equivalent to 2 tablespoons sugar. Carefully divide into 4 equal individual servings. Exchanges per serving = ¹/₂ fruit.
Low-fat, low-cholesterol diet: Negligible fat per serving.
Gluten-, milk- and wheat-free diet: Prepare as directed.
Low-purine diet: Prepare as directed.
Low-sodium diet: Prepare as directed but omit salt and beets. 10 milligrams sodium per serving.

BLUSHING GREEN SALAD (150 calories per serving)

¹/₂ cup Yogurt Dressing (page 206)
2 cups seedless grapes
4 stalks celery, coarsely chopped
1 tablespoon lemon juice
2 fresh pears, diced
4 small lettuce cups

Up to 1 hour before serving: Make dressing. Toss grapes, celery and lemon juice with pears. Fill lettuce cups with salad mixture; refrigerate.

To serve: Top each salad with dollop of dressing; pass the rest. Makes 4 servings.

Diabetic diet: Exchanges per serving = ¹/₂ vegetable, 1 fruit and 1 fat.
Egg-, gluten-, and wheat-free diet: Prepare as directed.
Low-fat, low-cholesterol diet: 5 grams fat per serving.
High-iron diet: 1 milligram iron per serving.
Low-purine diet: Prepare as directed.

NEW YORK COLESLAW (85 calories per serving)

¹/₂ cup raisins
2 tablespoons flour
¹/₂ teaspoon salt
¹/₄ teaspoon dry mustard
3 tablespoons vinegar
1 egg
3 cups shredded cabbage
2 carrots, grated
1 small onion, minced
3 stalks celery, thinly sliced

Day before or early in the day: In small saucepan, heat raisins and 1 cup water to boiling; simmer 2 to 3 minutes; drain raisins thoroughly, reserving syrup. Cool, then refrigerate.

In medium saucepan, stir together flour, salt and mustard. Slowly stir in ³/₄ cup raisin syrup (if necessary, add enough water to syrup to make ³/₄ cup) and vinegar to form a smooth paste. Add egg; then beat until smooth. Cook over low heat, stirring constantly, until thickened.

Up to 1 hour before serving: In large bowl, toss cabbage with carrots, onion, celery and raisins; toss with chilled dressing. Makes 6 servings.

Diabetic diet: Exchanges per serving = 1 vegetable.
Gluten-, milk- and wheat-free diet: Prepare as directed but substitute 1 tablespoon cornstarch for flour.
High-iron diet: 1 milligram iron per serving.
Low-purine diet: Prepare as directed.

SIMPLE CAESAR SALAD (20 calories per serving)

1 tablespoon grated Parmesan cheese
2 tablespoons wine vinegar
1 tablespoon lemon juice
dash pepper
dash salt
dash Worcestershire
1 large head romaine, chopped

About 10 minutes before serving: In salad bowl, mix all ingredients but romaine. Toss romaine with this dressing. Makes 6 servings.

Diabetic diet: Exchanges per serving = 1 "free."
Low-fat diet: 1 gram fat per serving. Omit recipe from low-cholesterol diet.

FARMLAND PEPPER HASH (15 calories per serving)

1 quart (4 cups) very finely chopped fresh cabbage
¹/₂ cup finely chopped green pepper (for more color, use green peppers that are turning red)
¹/₂ cup cider vinegar
¹/₂ cup granulated sugar
¹/₂ cup water
2 teaspoons salt

At least 1 hour before serving: In large bowl, mix all ingredients. Let stand at least 1 hour to "marry" flavors. This salad may be kept, covered and refrigerated, for several weeks. Drain well before serving. Makes 16 servings.

Diabetic diet: Prepare as directed but omit sugar; substitute non-nutritive sweetener equivalent to ¹/₄ cup sugar. Exchanges per serving = 1 vegetable.
Egg-, gluten-, milk- and wheat-free diet: Prepare as directed.
Low-fat, low-cholesterol diet: Negligible fat per serving.
Low-purine diet: Prepare as directed.

COLORFUL VEGETABLE SLAW (80 calories per serving)

3 tablespoons vinegar
1 tablespoon salad oil
1 tablespoon chopped parsley
¹/₂ teaspoon dry mustard
¹/₄ teaspoon salt
dash pepper
¹/₄ medium cabbage, shredded
1 8-ounce can cut green beans, drained
1 medium green pepper, diced
¹/₄ cup minced onion

About 20 minutes before serving: In medium bowl, stir vinegar, oil, parsley, mustard, salt and pepper. Add vegetables and toss lightly. Makes 4 generous 1-cup servings.

Diabetic diet: Exchanges per serving = 2 vegetables and 1 fat.
Egg-, gluten-, milk- and wheat-free diet: Prepare as directed.
Low-fat, low-cholesterol diet: 5 grams fat per serving.
High-iron diet: 1.5 milligrams iron per serving.
Low-purine diet: Prepare as directed. Omit pepper if forbidden on diet.

NIPPY COLESLAW (50 calories per serving)

1 medium cabbage
3 tablespoons white vinegar
1 tablespoon granulated sugar
1 teaspoon salt
1 egg, slightly beaten

About 1 hour before serving: Shred cabbage. In small saucepan, combine ¼ cup water, vinegar, sugar and salt; add egg; cook over very low heat, stirring constantly, until slightly thickened. Pour over cabbage and toss lightly. Chill. Makes 6 servings.

Diabetic diet: Prepare as directed but omit sugar; substitute non-nutritive sweetener equivalent to 1 tablespoon sugar. Exchanges per serving = 1 vegetable.
Low-fat diet: 1 gram fat per serving. Omit recipe from low-cholesterol diet.
Gluten-, milk- and wheat-free diet: Prepare as directed.
Low-purine diet: Prepare as directed.

CUCUMBER-CHIVE SALAD (55 calories per serving)

2 cucumbers
1 teaspoon salt
¼ cup white vinegar
2 tablespoons salad oil
2 teaspoons chopped chives
1 teaspoon granulated sugar

About 1 hour before serving: Peel, then cut cucumbers into thin slices; sprinkle with salt. Refrigerate, covered, one hour. Combine vinegar with ¼ cup water, oil, chives and sugar for dressing. Drain off any liquid from cucumbers, then toss with dressing. Makes 6 servings.

Diabetic diet: Prepare as directed but omit sugar; use non-nutritive sweetener equivalent to 1 teaspoon sugar. Exchanges per serving = 1 vegetable and 1 fat.
Egg-, gluten-, milk- and wheat-free diet: Prepare as directed.
Low-fat, low cholesterol diet: 5 grams fat per serving.
High-iron diet: 1 milligram iron per serving.
Low-purine diet: Prepare as directed.
Low-sodium diet: Prepare as directed but omit salt. 5 milligrams sodium per serving.

PINEAPPLE-CARROT SLAW (60 calories per serving)

1 15¼-ounce can pineapple chunks packed in pineapple juice
¼ cup reduced-calorie Italian dressing
4 cups finely shredded green cabbage
1 small carrot, thinly sliced
¼ teaspoon tarragon
½ teaspoon salt

A few minutes before serving: Drain pineapple, reserving ¼ cup juice. Mix juice with reduced-calorie dressing; toss with pineapple chunks and remaining ingredients. Makes 6 servings.

Low-fat, low-cholesterol diet: Negligible fat per serving.
Low-purine diet: Prepare as directed.

PIMENTO COLESLAW (60 calories per serving)

1 medium onion, minced
⅓ cup reduced-calorie mayonnaise
2 tablespoons prepared mustard
1 teaspoon salt
¼ teaspoon pepper
⅓ cup juice from sweet pickles
4 cups finely shredded cabbage
1 4-ounce can pimentos, chopped

About 10 minutes before serving: Combine onion, reduced-calorie mayonnaise, mustard, salt, pepper and pickle juice. Toss with shredded cabbage, then sprinkle with chopped pimentos. Makes 6 servings.

Low-fat, low-cholesterol diet: 2 grams fat per serving.
Low-purine diet: Prepare as directed.

SWEDISH CABBAGE SALAD (70 calories per serving)

3 cups finely chopped cabbage
1 cup canned whole cranberry
    sauce
1/4 cup thawed frozen or fresh
    whole cranberries (optional)

About 1 hour before serving: In medium bowl, toss all but 1/4 cup chopped cabbage with cranberry sauce. Then heap in salad bowl; sprinkle with rest of cabbage and whole cranberries, if desired. Refrigerate until serving time. Makes 6 servings.

Egg-, gluten-, milk- and wheat-free diet: Prepare as directed.
Low-fat, low-cholesterol diet: Negligible fat per serving.
Low-purine diet: Prepare as directed.

AUTUMN VEGETABLE SALAD (55 calories per serving)

1 medium rutabaga, diced
1 cup bottled reduced-calorie
    Italian or French dressing
1 10-ounce package frozen
    Brussels sprouts
1 16-ounce can julienne beets

Day before serving: In medium saucepan, cook rutabaga in 1 inch boiling salted water until tender-crisp; drain. Place in small bowl and pour on 1/3 cup of dressing. Meanwhile, cook Brussels sprouts as label directs; drain and cut sprouts into halves. Place in small bowl and pour on 1/3 cup dressing. Drain beets well; place in small bowl; pour on 1/3 cup dressing. Refrigerate all vegetables, covered; toss them occasionally.

To serve: Drain vegetables and arrange in rows on platter. Makes 6 servings.

Diabetic diet: Exchanges per serving = 1 vegetable and 1 bread.
Low-fat, low-cholesterol diet: 2 grams fat per serving.
High-iron diet: 1 milligram iron per serving.

PALISADES PICKLED BEETS (115 calories per serving)

2 16-ounce cans sliced beets
3 tablespoons granulated sugar
1 teaspoon salt
1/4 teaspoon pepper
1 tablespoon pickling spice
1/2 cup vinegar
3 hard-cooked eggs, shelled

Day before serving: Drain beets, reserving 1/2 cup beet juice. In medium saucepan, mix juice, sugar, salt, pepper and pickling spice; simmer 5 minutes; strain. Stir in vinegar.

Place whole hard-cooked eggs and beet slices in flat baking dish; pour beet-juice marinade over them. Refrigerate over-night, turning eggs and beets occasionally.

To serve: Slice eggs with egg slicer. Top each serving of beet slices with bit of marinade, then egg slices. Makes 6 servings.

Diabetic diet: Prepare as directed but omit sugar; substitute saccharin equivalent to 2 tablespoons sugar; increase eggs to six. Exchanges per servings = 1/2 meat and 1 vegetable.
Gluten-, milk- and wheat-free diet: Prepare as directed.
High-iron diet: 1.5 milligrams iron per serving.
Low-purine diet: Prepare as directed.

ZUCCHINI SALAD (30 calories per serving)

1/2 cup pickle relish
2 tablespoons white vinegar
1 teaspoon granulated sugar
1/2 teaspoon salt
1 pound zucchini, sliced
    (about 3)
romaine or lettuce
1 tomato, cut in thin wedges

About 45 minutes before serving: In medium bowl, combine pickle relish, vinegar, sugar and salt. Add zucchini; toss gently. Refrigerate about 30 minutes.

To serve: Line salad bowl with romaine; add tomato wedges and toss with zucchini. Makes 6 servings.

Egg-, gluten-, milk- and wheat-free diet: Prepare as directed.
Low-fat, low-cholesterol diet: Negligible fat per serving.

HOT GERMAN COLESLAW (40 calories per serving)

4 slices bacon
1/4 cup vinegar
3/4 teaspoon salt
1/4 teaspoon pepper
1 small cinnamon stick
1 small cabbage, shredded

About 30 minutes before serving: In large saucepan over high heat, heat 1 1/2 quarts water, bacon, vinegar, salt, pepper and cinnamon to boiling. Add cabbage, and cook until cabbage is tender-crisp; drain. Remove bacon and cinnamon stick. Makes 6 servings.

RED-CABBAGE-GRAPE SLAW (45 calories per serving)

4 cups shredded red cabbage
few ice cubes
1/2 cup apple juice
6 tablespoons cider vinegar
1/2 teaspoon seasoned salt
1/4 teaspoon seasoned pepper
1/2 teaspoon basil
2 cups seedless grapes

About 3 hours before serving: In large bowl, place shredded cabbage; top with few ice cubes; refrigerate. Make dressing by combining apple juice, vinegar, seasoned salt and pepper and basil; refrigerate.

To serve: Drain cabbage well; toss with grapes and dressing. Makes 8 servings.

Low-fat, low-cholesterol diet: Negligible fat per serving.
Low-purine diet: Prepare as directed.

SUSAN'S CALICO COLESLAW (85 calories per serving)

5 cups shredded cabbage
2 tablespoons granulated sugar
1 teaspoon salt
1/2 teaspoon dry mustard
1/4 teaspoon pepper
1/4 cup minced green pepper
1/4 cup shredded raw carrots
1/4 cup coarsely diced pimentos
1/2 teaspoon grated onion
2 tablespoons salad oil
1/3 cup vinegar

Just before serving: Toss cabbage with sugar, salt, mustard, pepper, green pepper, carrots, pimentos and onion. In small bowl, combine salad oil and vinegar; pour over cabbage mixture; toss well. Makes 6 servings.

Diabetic diet: Prepare as directed but omit sugar; add liquid saccharin equivalent to 2 tablespoons sugar with oil and vinegar. Exchanges per serving = 1 vegetable and 1 fat.
Egg-, gluten-, milk- and wheat-free diet: Prepare as directed.
Low-fat, low-cholesterol diet: 5 grams fat per serving.
Low-purine diet: Prepare as directed.

CAJIK (tsayik) (65 calories per serving)

2 cucumbers
salt
1/4 teaspoon garlic salt
1 tablespoon vinegar
1 tablespoon chopped fresh dill
2 8-ounce containers (2 cups)
  plain yogurt
1 tablespoon olive oil
fresh mint leaves for garnish

About 30 minutes before serving: Pare cucumbers; quarter lengthwise, then slice crosswise into 1/4-inch slices. Place in bowl; sprinkle with salt; refrigerate.

In another bowl, stir garlic salt, vinegar, dill and yogurt together until consistency of thick soup. Pour yogurt mixture over cucumbers; toss; sprinkle with olive oil; toss, then garnish with mint.

To serve: Spoon into bowl and serve as a refreshing cold soup or serve on lettuce leaves as an unusual salad. Makes 6 servings.

Diabetic diet: Prepare as directed but use low-fat yogurt. Make into 4 generous servings. Exchanges per serving = 1 vegetable and 1/2 milk.
Egg-, gluten-, and wheat-free diet: Prepare as directed.
Low-fat, low-cholesterol diet: Prepare as directed but use salad oil (not olive oil). 4 grams fat per serving.
High-iron diet: 1 milligram iron per serving.
Low-purine diet: Prepare as directed.

MARINATED WHOLE MUSHROOMS (25 calories per serving)

²/₃ cup tarragon vinegar
1 tablespoon salad oil
1 small garlic clove, crushed
1 bay leaf
¹/₄ teaspoon thyme leaves
3 6-ounce cans whole
    mushrooms, drained

At least 1 hour and 15 minutes before serving: In large bowl, toss together all ingredients plus ¹/₃ cup water. Cover and refrigerate at least 1 hour. Drain marinade and discard bay leaf. Serve as salad. Makes 5 servings.

For fresh mushrooms: Prepare as directed above but substitute ³/₄ pound fresh mushrooms, thinly sliced, for canned mushrooms; season with salt, if desired.

Diabetic diet: Exchanges per serving = 1 vegetable.
Egg-, gluten-, milk- and wheat-free diet: Prepare as directed.
Low-fat, low-cholesterol diet: Negligible fat per serving.
Low-sodium diet: Prepare as directed for fresh mushrooms; omit salt. 5 milligrams sodium per serving.

DILLY CUKES (30 calories per serving)

3 cups peeled and chopped
    cucumber (2 small)
¹/₄ teaspoon salt
1 8-ounce container plain
    yogurt
2 tablespoons chopped fresh
    dill
dash pepper

About 30 minutes before serving: In medium bowl, mix cucumbers and salt; set aside.

To serve: Drain cucumber and discard liquid: toss with yogurt, dill and pepper. Makes 6 servings.

Egg-, gluten-, and wheat-free diet: Prepare as directed.
Low-fat, low-cholesterol diet: 1 gram fat per serving.
Low-purine diet: Prepare as directed. Omit pepper if forbidden on diet.

CHILLED BEAN SPROUTS AND CUCUMBERS (100 calories per serving)

3 medium cucumbers, pared
1 16-ounce can bean sprouts
¹/₄ cup soy sauce
2 tablespoons vinegar
1 tablespoon salad oil
2 tablespoons sesame oil*
1 teaspoon granulated sugar
2 tablespoons chopped green
    onions
1 tablespoon pimento strips for
    garnish

About 30 minutes before serving: Cut both tip ends from each cucumber. Then cut each cucumber into quarters lengthwise; scoop out all seeds; cut into julienne strips. Rinse sprouts under cold water; drain.

In small bowl, combine soy sauce, vinegar, oil, sesame oil and sugar; stir to mix well.

In serving bowl, combine cucumber strips, bean sprouts, soy-sauce mixture and chopped green onions; toss well. Garnish with pimento strips. Makes 6 servings.

Diabetic diet: Exchanges per serving = 1 vegetable and 1 fat.
Low-fat, low-cholesterol diet: 5 grams fat per serving.
High-iron diet: 1.5 milligrams iron per serving.
Low-purine diet: Prepare as directed.

* Available in specialty foodshops and Japanese and Chinese groceries.

POTATO SALAD WITH CREAMY SAUERKRAUT DRESSING
(110 calories per serving)

5 cups sliced cold cooked
    potatoes
1¹/₂ tablespoons chopped onion
¹/₄ cup chopped pimento
¹/₃ cup chopped parsley
¹/₃ cup canned sauerkraut juice
1 teaspoon salt
¹/₃ cup skimmed milk or
    reliquefied nonfat dry milk
¹/₃ cup reduced-calorie
    mayonnaise

About 15 minutes before serving: Combine potatoes, onion, pimento and parsley. In small bowl, blend sauerkraut juice, salt, milk and reduced-calorie mayonnaise. Toss with potato mixture. Makes 6 servings.

Low-fat, low-cholesterol diet: 2 grams fat per serving.
Low-purine diet: Prepare as directed.

PIQUANT SALAD DRESSING (10 calories per tablespoon)

1 cup tomato juice
1 tablespoon cornstarch
2 tablespoons salad oil
1/4 vinegar
1/2 teaspoon salt
1/4 teaspoon prepared
 horseradish
1/4 teaspoon paprika
1/4 teaspoon onion salt
1/2 teaspoon Worcestershire
1/4 teaspoon celery salt
scant 1/8 teaspoon dry mustard
2 dashes garlic salt

At least 2 hours before serving: In small saucepan, heat 1/2 cup water, tomato juice and conrnstarch, stirring constantly, until thickened. Cool to lukewarm; add remaining ingredients and beat until blended. Refrigerate. Shake well before serving. Makes 1³/4 cups.

Diabetic diet: Exchanges per tablespoon = 1 "free."
Egg-, gluten-, milk- and wheat-free diet: Prepare as directed.
Low-fat, low-cholesterol diet: 1 gram fat per tablespoon.

TANGY CHEESE DRESSING (15 calories per tablespoon)

1 8-ounce container creamed
 cottage cheese*
1/3 cup evaporated skimmed
 milk
2 tablespoons water
1 teaspoon vinegar
1/2 teaspoon garlic salt
1/2 teaspoon onion salt
1/4 teaspoon salt
dash Tabasco

About 1 hour before serving: In electric-blender container, at low speed, blend all ingredients until smooth—2 to 3 minutes. Chill until serving time. Delicious over salad greens. Makes 1¹/4 cups.

Egg-, gluten-, and wheat-free diet: Prepare as directed.
Low-fat, low-cholesterol diet: 1 gram fat for 2 tablespoons dressing.
Low-purine diet: Prepare as directed.

* For smoothest dressing, use a soft-curd cottage cheese.

HORSERADISH-HERB DRESSING (10 calories per tablespoon)

1 8-ounce container plain
 yogurt
1/2 to 1 tablespoon white
 prepared horseradish
1 tablespoon tarragon or garlic
 vinegar
1 tablespoon chopped chives
1 tablespoon fresh chopped dill
1 tablespoon granulated sugar
3/4 teaspoon salt
1/4 teaspoon paprika

At least 4 hours before serving: In medium bowl, stir together all ingredients. Cover; refrigerate until serving time. Dressing may be kept about 3 days. Makes about 1 cup.

Egg-, gluten-, and wheat-free diet: Prepare as directed.
Low-fat, low-cholesterol diet: Negligible fat per serving.
Low-purine diet: Prepare as directed.

WATERCRESS-ROQUEFORT DRESSING (15 calories per tablespoon)

2 tablespoons soft Roquefort
 cheese
1/3 cup reduced-calorie
 mayonnaise
1/4 cup skimmed milk or
 reliquefied nonfat dry milk
2 tablespoons chopped
 watercress

At least 2 hours before serving: In small bowl, mash Roquefort, and blend with remaining ingredients until creamy. Refrigerate. Makes 2/3 cup. Nice served with tossed salad.

Low-fat diet: 1 gram fat per tablespoon. Omit recipe from low cholesterol diet.

OLD-FASHIONED FRENCH DRESSING (10 calories per tablespoon)

²/₃ cup creamed cottage cheese
¹/₂ cup canned tomato juice
1 envelope (.6 ounces) French
   salad-dressing mix

At least 1 hour before serving: In electric-blender container, blend all ingredients; refrigerate until serving time. Makes 1 cup.

Low-fat, low-cholesterol diet: Less than 1 gram fat per tablespoon.
Low-purine diet: Prepare as directed.

YOGURT DRESSING (20 calories per tablespoon)

1 8-ounce container plain
   yogurt
2 tablespoons salad oil
1 tablespoon lemon juice
1 teaspoon paprika
1 teaspoon salt
¹/₄ teaspoon garlic powder
dash Tabasco

At least 1 hour before serving: In jar, combine all ingredients; stir well; refrigerate. Makes 1 cup.

Egg-, gluten-, and wheat-free diet: Prepare as directed.
Low-fat, low-cholesterol diet: 1 gram fat per tablespoon.
Low-purine diet: Prepare as directed.

TORINO DRESSING (3 calories per tablespoon)

¹/₃ cup tomato juice
¹/₄ cup vinegar
2 tablespoons water
1 envelope (.6 ounces) Italian
   salad-dressing mix

At least 1 hour before serving: Combine all ingredients in small bowl; refrigerate until serving time. Makes ²/₃ cup.

Diabetic diet: Exchanges per tablespoon = 1 "free."
Low-fat, low-cholesterol diet: Negligible fat per serving.
Low-purine diet: Prepare as directed.

DELICATE SALAD DRESSING (5 calories per tablespoon)

1 tablespoon granulated sugar
1¹/₂ teaspoons cornstarch
¹/₂ teaspoon salt
¹/₂ teaspoon dry mustard
¹/₃ cup vinegar
¹/₃ cup water
¹/₃ cup tomato juice
1 tablespoon minced onion

At least 1 hour before serving: In medium saucepan, mix sugar, cornstarch, salt and mustard; stir in rest of ingredients. Heat mixture just to boiling. Pour into jar; cover; refrigerate. Seasonings may be adjusted to taste, if desired. Makes 1 cup.

Diabetic diet: Prepare as directed but omit sugar; substitute saccharin equivalent to 1 tablespoon sugar. Exchanges per tablespoon = 1 "free."
Egg-, gluten-, milk- and wheat-free diet: Prepare as directed.
Low-fat, low-cholesterol diet: Negligible fat per serving.
Low-purine diet: Prepare as directed.
Low-sodium diet: Prepare as directed but omit salt; use low-sodium tomato juice. Negligible sodium per serving.

ISLAND FRUIT DRESSING (20 calories per tablespoon)

1 cup drained canned crushed
   pineapple
1 tablespoon butter or
   margarine
1¹/₂ teaspoons curry
dash salt
1 teaspoon cornstarch

At least 3 hours before serving: In small saucepan, heat pineapple, butter or margarine, curry and salt to boiling. Blend cornstarch with ¹/₃ cup water; stir into pineapple mixture and cook, stirring, until thickened. Refrigerate; serve as dressing for crab or tuna salad. Makes 1 cup.

Low-fat, low-cholesterol diet: Prepare as directed but use margarine instead of butter. 1 gram fat per tablespoon.
Low-sodium diet: Prepare as directed but use unsalted butter or margarine; use curry mixture not containing salt; omit salt. Negligible sodium per tablespoon.

HOT BREADS

BUTTERMILK CARAWAY BISCUITS (85 calories per biscuit)

2 cups all-purpose flour
2 teaspoons double-acting
  baking powder
1/4 teaspoon baking soda
1 teaspoon salt
2 teaspoons caraway seeds
2/3 cup buttermilk
1/3 cup salad oil

About 30 minutes before serving: Preheat oven to 475°F. Measure and pour dry ingredients into a bowl. Add caraway seeds and buttermilk to oil (don't stir together). Pour, all at once, over flour mixture; mix with fork to make soft dough that rounds up into a ball.

Wipe work surface with damp cloth, then spread with sheet of waxed paper; turn dough onto paper. Knead lightly, without additional flour, 10 times, or until smooth. Flatten slightly, then top with second sheet of waxed paper; pat or roll dough 1/4-inch thick. Remove top paper. Cut out with unfloured 3-inch biscuit cutter. Bake on ungreased cookie sheet 9 to 12 minutes, or until golden brown. Makes about 18.

Diabetic diet: Exchanges per serving = 1 bread and 1 fat.
Low-fat, low-cholesterol diet: 5 grams fat per biscuit.
Low-purine diet: Prepare as directed.

CRISP CRUSTS (45 calories each)

1 12-ounce loaf French bread
2 tablespoons butter or
  margarine
poppy, caraway or celery seeds

About 30 minutes before serving: Preheat oven to 375°F. With sharp knife, cut off oval-shaped pieces of crust, about 2-inches long and 1-inch wide, from entire surface of loaf of bread. Use center of bread for bread crumbs. Lightly spread each piece first with butter, then with poppy, caraway or celery seeds. Place on cookie sheet, cut side up, and bake 5 to 10 minutes, or until butter is bubbly. Makes about 14.

Bland diet. Prepare as directed but substitute Parmesan cheese for poppy, caraway or celery seeds.
Diabetic diet: Exchanges per serving (2 pieces) = 1bread and 1 fat.
Low-fat, low-cholesterol diet: Prepare as directed but use margarine instead of butter. 2 grams fat per piece.
Low-purine diet: Prepare as directed.

BUTTERMILK-PANCAKE COINS (150 calories per serving)

1/2 cup packaged
  buttermilk-pancake mix
1/3 cup skimmed milk or
  reliquefied nonfat dry milk
1/4 cup cold water
1/4 cup applesauce
cinnamon

About 30 minutes before serving: Preheat griddle until drop of water "dances" on it; grease lightly. In small bowl, stir together pancake mix, milk and water until almost smooth but still slightly lumpy.

Pour batter, by level measuring tablespoons, onto hot griddle. Cook until pancakes are covered with bubbles and edges are cooked; turn; cook other side until golden-brown.

To serve: Top each serving of 4 pancakes with 2 tablespoons applesauce. If desired, sprinkle lightly with cinnamon. Makes 2 servings.

Bland diet: Prepare as directed.
Diabetic diet: Prepare as directed but substitute unsweetened applesauce for regular. Exchanges per serving = 2 bread.
Low-fat, low-cholesterol diet: 1 gram fat per serving.
Low-fat, bland (gall bladder) diet: Prepare as directed.
High-iron diet: 1 milligram iron per serving.
Low-purine diet: Prepare as directed.
Low-residue diet: Prepare as directed.

WAFFLES (110 calories per waffle)

1¹/₂ cups all-purpose flour
3 teaspoons double-acting
  baking powder
2 tablespoons granulated sugar
¹/₂ teaspoon salt
1 cup skimmed milk or
  reliquefied nonfat dry milk
2 eggs
3 tablespoons salad oil

About 30 minutes before serving: Preheat waffle iron as manufacturer directs. In medium bowl, sift together flour, baking powder, sugar and salt. In small bowl beat milk, eggs and salad oil together. Add to flour mixture; beat until all flour is wet and batter is almost smooth. Bake waffles until dark golden brown. Makes about twelve 4-inch waffles.

Bland diet: Prepare as directed.
Diabetic diet: Prepare as directed but omit sugar; substitute non-nutritive sweetener equivalent to 2 tablespoons sugar; increase salad oil to ¹/₄ cup. Exchanges per serving = 1 bread and 1 fat.
Low-fat, low-cholesterol diet: Prepare as directed but substitute 3 egg whites for 2 whole eggs. 4 grams fat per serving.
Low-purine diet: Prepare as directed.
Low-sodium diet: Prepare as directed but substitute low-sodium baking powder for regular; omit salt; increase salad oil to ¹/₄ cup. 25 milligrams sodium per serving.

JAM ROLLS (65 calories per serving)

1 8-ounce can refrigerated
  crescent rolls
4 tablespoons apricot jam or
  preserves

About 25 minutes before serving: Preheat oven to 375° F. Unroll rolls; separate into 4 rectangles. Gently press seam together, across each rectangle. Spread each with 1 tablespoon jam; reroll to original shape; cut, crosswise, into 4 sections. Place on ungreased cookie sheet; bake 12 to 15 minutes, or until rich golden-brown. Makes 16.

Bland diet: Prepare as directed but substitute jelly for jam.
Diabetic diet: Prepare as directed but substitute sugar-free jam for regular. Exchanges per serving (2 rolls) = 1 bread and 1 fat.
Low-purine dit: Prepare as directed.
Low-residue diet: Prepare as directed for bland diet.

FLOWER BUNS (80 calories per bun)

1 7¹/₂-ounce can refrigerated
  buttermilk biscuits
milk
poppy seeds

About 20 minutes before serving: Preheat oven to 450°F. Grease large cookie sheet. Separate biscuits, then press each until twice its original size. With kitchen scissors, make 5 to 6 snips, from outer edge almost to center. Place on cookie sheet and shape "petals" to form "flower." Repeat with remaining dough. Brush each "flower" with milk; sprinkle with poppy seeds. Bake 6 to 8 minutes, or until golden-brown. Makes 8.

Bland diet: Prepare as directed but substitute Parmesan cheese for poppy seeds.
Diabetic diet: Exchanges per bun = 1 bread.
Low-purine diet: Prepare as directed.
Low-residue diet: Prepare as directed for bland diet.

"BREADBOARD" BISCUITS (80 calories per biscuit)

1 10-ounce package
  refrigerated artificial
  butter-flavored biscuits
sesame seeds or garlic salt or
  shredded Parmesan cheese

About 15 minutes before serving: Preheat oven to 450°F. On greased cookie sheet, roll each biscuit into oval about 4" by 6". Sprinkle with one of seasonings. Bake 8 minutes, or until golden brown. Makes 10.

Diabetic diet: Exchanges per biscuit = 1bread.
Low-purine diet: Prepare as directed.

PASTRY FINGERS (35 calories per finger)

1 8-ounce package refrigerated crescent rolls

About 15 minutes before serving: Preheat oven to 375°F. Unroll the 2 strips of perforated dough, but do **not** separate into triangles. Instead, cut crosswise, into strips 1-inch wide. Place on ungreased cookie sheet. Bake 5 to 7 minutes, or until golden-brown. Serve hot. Makes 24 fingers.

Bland diet: Prepare as directed.
Diabetic diet: Exchanges per serving (4 fingers) = 1 bread and 1 fat.
Low-purine diet: Prepare as directed.

SEEDED BREADSTICKS (95 calories each)

4 slices day-old bread
4 teaspoons butter or margarine
One of the following: poppy seeds, sesame seeds, celery seeds or grated Parmesan cheese

About 25 minutes before serving: Preheat oven to 375°F. Trim crust from bread. Spread each slice with 1 teaspoon butter, then sprinkle with poppy, sesame or celery seeds, or with Parmesan cheese. Roll, diagonally to form "stick" and fix with toothpick. Place on cookie sheet, and bake until crisp and lightly toasted—10 to 15 minutes. Makes 4 sticks.

Bland diet: Prepare as directed but sprinkle only with Parmesan cheese.
Diabetic diet: Exchanges per serving = 1 bread and 1 fat.
Low-fat, low-cholesterol diet: Prepare as directed but use margarine instead of butter; omit Parmesan-cheese topping. 5 grams fat per serving.

MUSHROOM PIZZETTES (75 calories per serving)

1 15³/₈-ounce package cheese-pizza mix
1 4-ounce can sliced mushrooms, thoroughly drained

About 30 minutes before serving: Preheat oven to 425°F. Prepare flour mixture as label directs, but separate dough into 12 balls. Thoroughly grease cookie sheets and hands. On cookie sheets, with hands, spread each ball into paper thin circle about 5 inches in diameter. (Circles may be close together, but not touching.) Spread each circle with heaping tablespoon tomato sauce from can. Divide mushroom slices among pizzettes; sprinkle each with a little Parmesan cheese. Bake 15 minutes, or until edges are brown. Makes 12 servings.

Diabetic diet: Exchanges per serving = 1 bread.
Low-fat diet: 1 gram fat per serving. Omit recipe from low-cholesterol diet.
Low-purine diet: Prepare as directed but omit mushrooms.

BRUNCH DELIGHT (245 calories per serving)

1 8-ounce container cottage cheese
2 tablespoons skimmed milk or reliquefied nonfat dry milk
4 teaspoons granulated sugar
¼ teaspoon vanilla extract
1 5-ounce package frozen waffles
1 cup frozen unsweetened strawberries, thawed

About 15 minutes before serving: In blender container, at low speed, blend cottage cheese, milk, sugar and vanilla. Toast waffles as label directs. Spoon cheese mixture over waffles, then top with strawberries. Makes 3 servings.

Diabetic diet: Prepare as directed but omit sugar; substitute non-nutritive sweetener equivalent to 1 tablespoon sugar; use low-fat cottage cheese. Exchanges per serving = 1 bread, 1 milk, 1 fruit and 1 fat.
Low-fat, low-cholesterol diet: 5 grams fat per serving.
High-iron diet: 1.5 milligrams iron per serving.
Low-purine diet: Prepare as directed.

MELON FESTIVE PARFAIT (50 calories per serving)

cantaloupe
watermelon
honeydew
1¹/₂ cups pineapple juice
mint sprigs for garnish

About 30 minutes before serving: From each melon, make 1¹/₂ cups balls. In 6 parfait glasses, alternate layers of three types. Pour pineapple juice over them; garnish with mint sprigs. Makes 6 servings.

Diabetic diet: Exchanges per serving = 2 fruit.
Egg-, gluten-, milk- and wheat-free diet: Prepare as directed.
Low-fat, low-cholesterol diet: Negligible fat per serving.
Low-sodium diet: 5 milligrams sodium per serving.

COMPOTE WAIKIKI (125 calories per serving)

¹/₄ cup granulated sugar
1 tablespoon lemon juice
1 stick cinnamon
20 whole cloves
³/₄ teaspoon vanilla extract
1 15¹/₄-ounce can pineapple
  chunks packed in pineapple
  juice, drained
1 30-ounce can freestone peach
  halves, drained

Early in day: In medium saucepan, stir together sugar, ¹/₂ cup water, lemon juice, cinnamon and cloves. Simmer 5 minutes; remove spices; stir in vanilla extract. Add pineapple chunks and peach halves; chill thoroughly before serving. Makes 6 servings.

Egg-, gluten-, milk- and wheat-free diet: Prepare as directed.
Low-fat, low-cholesterol diet: Negligible fat per serving.
Low-sodium diet: 2 milligrams sodium per serving.

OUR FAVORITE FRUIT COMPOTE (80 calories per serving)

1 pint lime or orange sherbet
1 pint fresh strawberries, chilled
1 medium cantaloupe, chilled

Day before serving or early in day: Line cookie sheet with waxed paper; store in freezer at least 10 minutes. Dipping melon baller into warm water between each ball, scoop sherbet into balls. Place on chilled cookie sheet. Cover with second sheet of waxed paper; freeze.

About 15 minutes before serving: Wash and stem strawberries; scoop balls from cantaloupe. Divide cantaloupe balls, strawberries and sherbet balls among 8 dessert dishes. Makes 8 servings.

Egg-, gluten-, wheat-free diet: Prepare as directed but use gluten-free sherbet on gluten-free diet.
Low-fat, low-cholesterol diet: Negligible fat per serving.
Low-purine diet: Prepare as directed.
Low-sodium diet: 10 milligrams sodium per serving.

MAPLE BAKED PEARS (120 calories per serving)

2 fresh ripe Bartlett pears
4 walnut halves
maple syrup

About 40 minutes before serving: Pare, then halve and core pears. (Scoop out seeds with a half-teaspoon measuring spoon.) Preheat oven to 350°F.

In medium baking dish, place pears, cut side up; top each with walnut half. Pour 1 tablespoon maple syrup over each. Cover; bake 20 to 25 minutes, or until pears are just tender. Serve warm, spooning syrup over pears. Makes 4 servings.

Egg-, gluten-, milk- and wheat-free diet: Prepare as directed.
Low-fat, low-cholesterol diet: 1 gram fat per serving.
Low-purine diet: Prepare as directed.
Low-sodium diet: 2 milligrams sodium per serving.

SPANISH CREAM WITH RASPBERRY SAUCE (150 calories per serving)

1¹/₂ teaspoons unflavored
  gelatin
granulated sugar
¹/₈ teaspoon salt
2 eggs, separated
1¹/₂ cups skimmed milk or
  reliquefied nonfat dry milk
¹/₂ teaspoon vanilla extract
1 10-ounce package frozen
  raspberries, thawed
1 tablespoon cornstarch

Early in day: In top of double boiler, mix gelatin, 2 tablespoons sugar, salt and egg yolks. In small saucepan, scald milk. Stirring constantly, slowly stir scalded milk into gelatin-sugar mixture. Place over boiling water; stirring constantly, cook until custard just begins to coat spoon—do not overcook or custard will separate. Remove from heat; stir in vanilla; refrigerate until consistency of soft gelatin dessert.

Meanwhile, drain raspberries, reserving syrup. In small saucepan, slowly stir raspberry syrup into cornstarch. Heat, stirring constantly, until slightly thickened; stir in raspberries; refrigerate, covered, until serving time.

In medium bowl, beat egg whites until soft peaks form; then, beating constantly, slowly add ¹/₄ cup sugar; beat until meringue forms stiff peaks. Beat custard until smooth, if necessary. Slowly pour custard over meringue; fold together until smooth. Divide among six ³/₄-cup custard cups. Refrigerate until set—at least 2 hours.

To serve: Warm cups slightly over hot water; turn custard out into dessert dishes; spoon on raspberry sauce. Makes 6 servings.

Low-fat diet: 2 grams fat per serving. Omit recipe from low-cholesterol diet.
Gluten- and wheat-free diet: Prepare as directed.
Low-purine diet: Prepare as directed.
Low-sodium diet: Prepare as directed but omit salt. 45 milligrams sodium per serving.

FRESH APPLE SNOW (130 calories per serving)

4 large apples, peeled
1 teaspoon ascorbic-acid
  mixture from fruit
granulated sugar
3 tablespoons lemon juice
¹/₄ teaspoon nutmeg
dash salt
2 egg whites
6 thin unpeeled apple slices for
  garnish

Early in day: In electric blender container or on grater, coarsely grate apples. In medium bowl, mix ascorbic-acid mixture with 1¹/₂ tablespoons water; add grated apples, 2 tablespoons sugar, lemon juice, nutmeg and salt; refrigerate; stir occasionally.

Just before serving: With electric mixer at high speed, beat egg whites with ¹/₄ cup sugar until soft peaks form. Drain apple mixture well; fold into egg whites; spoon into serving dishes; garnish with apple slices. Makes 6 servings.

Low-fat, low-cholesterol diet: Negligible fat per serving.
Gluten-, milk- and wheat-free diet: Prepare as directed.
Low-purine diet: Prepare as directed.

PEACHES AMANDINE GLACÉ (145 calories per serving)

¹/₃ cup skimmed milk or
  reliquefied nonfat dry mild
¹/₂ teaspoon almond extract
2 tablespoons granulated sugar
1 8-ounce container creamed
  cottage cheese
1 29-ounce can sliced peaches
2 tablespoons flaked coconut

About 2 to 3 hours before serving: In electric blender container, at low speed, blend milk, almond extract, sugar and cottage cheese into a smooth sauce.

Drain peaches; cover with sauce; refrigerate.

To serve: Divide among 5 dessert dishes; top with coconut. Makes 5 servings.

Bland diet: Prepare as directed but omit coconut.
Low-fat, low-cholesterol diet: Prepare as directed but omit coconut. 2 grams fat per serving.
Low-fat, bland (gall bladder) diet: Prepare as directed for bland diet.
Low-purine diet: Prepare as directed.
Low-residue diet: Prepare as directed for bland diet.

McINTOSH MERINGUE (90 calories per serving)

1 egg white
granulated sugar
dash ginger
2 8-ounce or 1 16-ounce jar
    unsweetened applesauce

Early in day or up to 1 hour before serving: Preheat oven to 425°F. In a small bowl, beat egg white until soft peaks form; beating constantly, gradually add 4 teaspoons sugar and ginger; beat until stiff glossy peaks form.

Stir 2 tablespoons sugar into applesauce; divide among four ³/₄-cup custard cups; top each with dollop of meringue. Bake 4 to 6 minutes, or until nicely browned. Serve warm or cold. Makes 4 servings.

Bland diet: Prepare as directed but omit ginger.
Low-fat, low-cholesterol diet: Negligible fat per serving.
Low-fat, bland (gall bladder) diet: Prepare as directed for bland diet.
Gluten-, milk- and wheat-free diet: Prepare as directed.
Low-purine diet: Prepare as directed.
Low-residue diet: Prepare as directed for bland diet.
Low-sodium diet: 15 milligrams sodium per serving.

BRIE WITH BUTTERY BAKED PEARS (125 calories per pear and about 100 for each cracker spread with cheese)

¹/₂ cup granulated sugar
2 tablespoons lemon juice
2 tablespoons butter or
    margarine
6 ripe pears, pared
1 round Brie cheese
sesame-seed crackers

Day before or early in day: Preheat oven to 350°F. Meanwhile, simmer sugar with lemon juice, 1 cup boiling water for 5 minutes. Arrange pears in 3-quart casserole; add syrup. Bake, covered, 55 to 60 minutes, or until tender; refrigerate.

About 3 hours before serving: Arrange cheese and crackers on wooden board; set aside at room temperature.

To serve: Arrange pears in dishes; pass tray of cheese and crackers. Makes 6 servings.

Diabetic diet: Instead of pears baked as directed, substitute 12 pear halves packed in water or fruit juice that have been brushed with margarine and lemon juice; refrigerate. Serve as above. One pear, a 1-inch cube of cheese and 3 crackers = 1 fruit, 1 meat, 1 bread and 1 fat exchange.
Low-purine diet: Prepare as directed.

SPANISH PEACHES (about 60 calories per serving)

1 29-ounce can cling-peach
    halves
3 tablespoons dark brown sugar
2 tablespoons lime juice
¹/₄ cup sherry (optional)
1 tablespoon grated lime peel

At least 2 hours before serving: Drain peaches, reserving ¹/₂ cup syrup. In small saucepan, combine peach syrup, brown sugar, lime juice and sherry; simmer 5 minutes.

Meanwhile, place peach halves, flat side down, side by side, in serving dish; pour syrup mixture over them. Sprinkle with grated lime peel. Refrigerate until serving time. Serve 1 peach half per serving. Makes 8 to 9 servings.

Bland diet: Prepare as directed but omit sherry and lime peel.
Egg-, gluten-, milk- and wheat-free diet: Prepare as directed.
Low-fat, low-cholesterol diet: Negligible fat per serving.
Low-fat, bland (gall bladder) diet: Prepare as directed for bland diet.
Low-purine diet: Prepare as directed but omit sherry.
Low-residue diet: Prepare as directed for bland diet.
Low-sodium diet: 2 milligrams sodium per serving.

PINEAPPLE CUSTARD (Quesilla de Piña) (160 calories per serving)

1 cup canned pineapple juice
¹/₂ cup granulated sugar
6 eggs
dash salt
¹/₂ teaspoon vanilla extract

Early in day: In small saucepan, simmer pineapple juice with sugar for 15 minutes. Cool; refrigerate.

About 2 hours before serving: Preheat oven to 350°F. In large bowl, with electric mixer at high speed, beat eggs and salt until light and fluffy—at least 5 minutes. With mixer at medium speed, slowly beat in cold pineapple-sugar mixture, then vanilla. Turn into 2-quart casserole. Place casserole in shallow pan of hot water.

Bake 45 minutes, or until custard sinks in center, turns a dark golden-brown around edges, and is set. Serve warm. Makes 6 servings.

Bland diet: Prepare as directed. Omit recipe if pineapple juice is forbidden on diet.
Gluten-, milk- and wheat-free diet: Prepare as directed.
Low-purine diet: Prepare as directed.
Low-residue diet: Prepare as directed. Omit recipe if pineapple juice is forbidden on diet.

PEACHES MERINGUE (135 calories per serving)

3 egg whites (at room
**   temperature)**
¹/₈ teaspoon salt
¹/₈ teaspoon cream of tartar
¹/₂ cup granulated sugar
1 29-ounce can peach halves
6 teaspoons red raspberry
**   preserves**

About 1 hour before serving: Preheat oven to 275°F. In small bowl, with electric mixer at high speed, beat egg whites with salt and cream of tartar until frothy; add sugar, a little at a time, beating well after each addition. Beat until stiff peaks form. Drain 6 peach halves on paper towels; place, cut side up, in shallow baking dish. Spoon teaspoon of preserves into each. Cover with meringue; bake 40 minutes. Serve warm. Makes 6 servings.

Bland diet: Prepare as directed but use strawberry jelly instead of raspberry preserves.
Low-fat, low-cholesterol diet: Negligible fat per serving.
Low-fat, bland (gall bladder) diet: Prepare as directed for bland diet.
Gluten-, milk- and wheat-free diet: Prepare as directed.
Low-purine diet: Prepare as directed.
Low-residue diet: Prepare as directed for bland diet.
Low-sodium diet: Prepare as directed but omit salt. 25 milligrams sodium per serving.

ALMOND TORTONI (60 calories per serving)

¹/₂ cup canned evaporated
**   skimmed milk**
8 fluted paper baking cups
1 egg white
¹/₄ cup packed light brown
**   sugar**
¹/₄ teaspoon almond extract
2 tablespoons flaked coconut
2 tablespoons blanched
**   almonds, ground**
4 maraschino cherries, each cut
**   in half**

In small bowl, freeze undiluted evaporated skimmed milk until ice crystals form throughout, about 1 hour. Place a paper baking cup in each of eight 2¹/₂-inch muffin-pan cups. In small bowl with mixer at high speed, beat egg white until soft peaks form. Beating at high speed, gradually sprinkle in light brown sugar, beating until sugar is completely dissolved. In chilled bowl with mixer at high speed, beat iced evaporated skimmed milk and almond extract until stiff and color turns white, scraping bowl frequently with rubber spatula. Fold whipped milk, 1 tablespoon coconut, and 1 tablespoon almonds into beaten egg white. Spoon mixture into paper cups. Sprinkle remaining coconut and almonds on top; arrange cherry half on each center. Freeze. Makes 8 servings.

Low-fat diet: 1 gram fat per serving.
Gluten- and wheat-free diet: Prepare as directed.
Low-sodium diet: Prepare as directed but omit maraschino cherries. 25 milligrams sodium per serving.

PEARS WITH BRANDIED CREAM (165 calories per serving)

3 ripe medium pears, peeled,
cored and cut into bite-size
pieces
1/4 cup water
1/4 teaspoon ground cinnamon
sugar
1/4 cup heavy or whipping cream
1 1/2 teaspoons brandy

In 2-quart saucepan over high heat, heat pears, water, cinnamon and 2 tablespoons sugar to boiling. Reduce heat to low; cover and simmer 10 to 15 minutes until pears are tender. Pour mixture into medium bowl; cover and refrigerate at least 6 hours to allow mixture to thicken. To serve, spoon pear mixture into four 6-ounce dessert dishes. In small bowl with mixer at medium speed, beat heavy or whipping cream, brandy and 1 1/2 teaspoons sugar until stiff peaks form. Spoon whipped cream mixture over pears. Makes 4 servings.

Low-fat, low-cholesterol diet: Prepare as directed but omit heavy or whipping cream and brandy. Negligible fat per serving.
Low-sodium diet: Prepare as directed. 15 milligrams sodium per serving.
Diabetic diet: Prepare as directed but omit sugar, heavy or whipping cream and brandy. Exchanges per serving = 1 fruit.
Egg- and wheat-free diet: Prepare as directed. For milk-free diet, prepare as directed but omit heavy or whipping cream and brandy.

CANTALOUPE CHIFFON (60 calories per serving)

1/2 cup canned evaporated
skimmed milk
1 small cantaloupe
1/4 cup lemon juice
1/2 cup skimmed milk
3 eggs, separated
1/2 teaspoon salt
sugar
2 envelopes unflavored gelatin
yellow food color
red food color

In small bowl, freeze undiluted evaporated skimmed milk until ice crystals form throughout, about 1 hour. Meanwhile, cut cantaloupe in half; discard seeds and rind. Cut cantaloupe into bite-size chunks. In blender at medium speed, blend cantaloupe and lemon juice to make about 2 cups puree. In heavy, 2-quart saucepan with wire whisk or fork, mix milk, egg yolks, salt, and 2 tablespoons sugar; sprinkle gelatin evenly over mixture. Cook over very low heat, until gelatin is completely dissolved and mixture is thickened and coats a spoon (do not boil, or mixture will curdle), about 15 minutes, stirring constantly. Stir in cantaloupe puree. Add enough yellow and red food color to tint to a deep orange color. (Color will become lighter when beaten egg whites and whipped evaporated skimmed milk are folded in.) Refrigerate until mixture mounds when dropped from spoon. In large bowl with mixer at high speed, beat egg whites until soft peaks form; gradually sprinkle in 2 tablespoons sugar, beating until sugar is completely dissolved. In chilled bowl with mixer at high speed, beat iced evaporated skimmed milk until stiff and color turns white. Fold whipped milk and cantaloupe mixture into 8" by 8" baking pan; refrigerate until set. Makes 8 servings.

Low-fat diet: Negligible fat per serving.
Diabetic diet: Substitute non-nutritive sweetener equivalent to 2 tablespoons sugar. Exchanges per serving = 1/2 meat and 1/2 fruit.
Low-residue diet: Prepare as directed.
Low-purine diet: Prepare as directed.

PINEAPPLE COMPOTE (120 calories per serving)

1 15 1/4-ounce can pineapple
chunks packed in pineapple
juice
1/3 cup plain yogurt
1 tablespoon granulated sugar
1 1/2 tablespoons chopped
walnuts

About 2 hours before serving: Drain pineapple chunks; toss with yogurt and sugar. Divide among 3 dessert dishes; top each with one-third of walnuts. Refrigerate until serving time to blend flavors. Makes 3 servings.

Bland diet: Toss yogurt with peach halves and sugar; omit walnuts.
Diabetic diet: Prepare as directed but omit sugar; use liquid non-nutritive sweetener equivalent to 2 teaspoons sugar. Exchanges per serving = 1 fruit. Makes 4 servings.
Egg-, gluten-, and wheat-free diet: Prepare as directed.
Low-fat, low-cholesterol diet: 1 gram fat per serving.
Low-fat, bland (gall bladder) diet: Prepare as directed for bland diet.
Low-purine diet: Prepare as directed.
Low-residue diet: Prepare as directed for bland diet.
Low-sodium diet: 15 milligrams sodium per serving.

AMBROSIA TROPICALE (145 calories per serving)

2 large seedless oranges
3 large bananas
3 tablespoons flaked coconut
1/2 pint orange sherbet

About 20 minutes before serving: Carefully peel and section oranges; press juice from remaining orange pieces; add to sections. Peel and slice bananas; add to orange; toss; divide among 6 dessert dishes. Sprinkle each serving with 1/2 tablespoon coconut; top with sherbet. Makes 6 servings.

Egg-, gluten-, and wheat-free diet: Prepare as directed but use sherbet not containing gluten on gluten-free diet.
Low-purine diet: Prepare as directed.
Low-sodium diet: Use coconut not containing salt or sodium compounds. 5 milligrams sodium per serving.

MEXICAN FRUIT BOWL (50 to 100 calories per serving, depending on fruit)

1 fresh pineapple
1 melon (honeydew, cantaloupe
  or cranshaw)
2 seedless oranges
seedless grapes

Early in day or at least 1 hour before serving: Prepare pineapple as follows: Grasp by crown; then, holding firmly, cut off rind all around, from top down, following curve of fruit; remove eyes if desired. Cut into 1/4-inch crosswise slices, then reassemble into pineapple shape. Pare skin from melon, just as if it were an apple; cut off top, 1 inch down; scrape out seeds. Cut melon into 1/4-inch crosswise slices; reassemble, using picks if necessary. With sharp knife cut peel from oranges in a continuous spiral, to one-third of way down from top. Refrigerate all.

To serve: In fruit bowl assemble fruits, with pineapple and melon, side by side, and grapes and oranges tucked here and there. Makes 8 servings.

Low-fat, low-cholesterol diet: Negligible fat per serving.
Low-purine diet: Prepare as directed.
Low-sodium diet: 5 milligrams sodium per serving.

BAKED APPLE SURPRISE (155 calories per serving)

2 medium bananas
1 tablespoon lemon juice
1/4 cup granulated sugar
dash salt
1/4 teaspoon nutmeg
6 medium baking apples
1 cup orange juice

At least 3 hours before serving: Preheat oven to 375°F. In medium bowl, mash bananas with fork and mix with lemon juice, sugar, salt and nutmeg. Wash and core apples; place in large baking dish. Fill with banana mixture; pour orange juice over them. Bake one hour, or until tender, basting occasionally with orange juice. Makes 6 servings.

Bland diet: Prepare as directed but substitute cinnamon for nutmeg.
Egg-, gluten-, milk- and wheat-free diet: Prepare as directed.
Low-fat, low-cholesterol diet: Negligible fat per serving.
Low-fat, bland (gall bladder) diet: Prepare as directed for bland diet.
Low-purine diet: Prepare as directed.
Low-residue diet: Prepare as directed for bland diet.
Low-sodium diet: Prepare as directed but omit salt. 5 milligrams sodium per serving.

BAKED BANANA AMBROSIA (90 calories per serving)

3 bananas, peeled
1 1/2 tablespoons melted butter
  or margarine
2 tablespoons lemon or lime
  juice
1/3 cup flaked coconut

About 30 minutes before serving: Preheat oven to 375°F. Grease medium baking dish. Halve bananas crosswise, then lengthwise; place in dish. Brush with butter, then with juice; sprinkle with coconut. Bake 15 to 20 minutes, or until easily pierced with fork. Serve warm. Makes 6 servings.

Egg-, gluten-, milk- and wheat-free diet: Prepare as directed but use milk-free margarine on milk-free diet.
Low-purine diet: Prepare as directed.
Low-sodium diet: Prepare as directed but use unsalted butter or margarine; use coconut not containing added salt or sodium-containing compounds. 2 milligrams sodium per serving.

GRAPEFRUIT BRÛLÉE (90 calories per serving)

2 medium grapefruit
4 teaspoons granulated sugar
1/8 teaspoon cinnamon

About 20 minutes before serving: Preheat broiler 10 minutes if manufacturer directs. Meanwhile, halve grapefruit; with knife, cut around each section. Mix sugar and cinnamon; sprinkle evenly over grapefruit halves. Broil 5 minutes, or until warm and bubbly. Makes 4 servings.

Diabetic diet: Prepare as directed but omit sugar; sprinkle grapefruit halves lightly with granulated non-nutritive sweetener to taste. Exchanges per serving = 1 fruit.
Egg-, gluten-, milk- and wheat-free diet: Prepare as directed.
Low-fat, low-cholesterol diet: Negligible fat per serving.
Low-purine diet: Prepare as directed.
Low-sodium diet: Prepare as directed. Negligible sodium per serving.

HOT-COLD SPICED FRUIT (70 calories per serving)

1 16-ounce can cling-peach slices, chilled
1 15¼-ounce can pineapple chunks, packed in pineapple juice, chilled
1/4 teaspoon cinnamon

About 10 minutes before serving: Drain syrup from peaches and pineapple; reserve pineapple syrup. In medium saucepan, heat pineapple syrup and cinnamon to boiling.

To serve: Place fruit in serving bowl; cover with hot pineapple syrup. Makes 6 servings.

Bland diet: Prepare as directed but substitute one 16-ounce can pear halves for pineapple chunks.
Egg-, gluten-, milk- and wheat-free diet: Prepare as directed.
Low-fat, low-cholesterol diet: Negligible fat per serving.
Low-fat, bland (gall bladder) diet: Prepare as directed for bland diet.
Low-purine diet: Prepare as directed.
Low-residue diet: Prepare as directed for bland diet.
Low-sodium diet: 1 milligram sodium per serving.

APRICOT SNOWBALLS (35 calories per snowball)

24 large dried apricots
1 cup flaked coconut
2 teaspoons orange juice confectioners' sugar

At least 1 hour before serving: Put apricots and coconut through food grinder. Blend in orange juice, confectioners' sugar. Shape into 3/4-inch balls. Makes 2 dozen.

Egg-, gluten-, milk- and wheat-free diet: Prepare as directed.
Low-purine diet: Prepare as directed.
Low-sodium diet: Prepare as directed but use coconut not containing added salt or sodium-containing compounds. 2 milligrams sodium per serving.

SNOW-PEAK RASPBERRY SAUCE (130 calories per serving)

1 egg white
2 tablespoons granulated sugar
dash salt
1 16-ounce can or jar raspberry applesauce, chilled

Up to 20 minutes before serving: Preheat oven to 375°F. In small bowl, beat egg white until soft peaks form. Slowly add sugar and salt, beating constantly, until stiff peaks form. Divide raspberry applesauce among four 6-ounce custard cups. Top with dabs of meringue. Bake 5 to 7 minutes, or until golden-brown on top. Serve warm or cold. Makes 4 servings.

Bland diet: Prepare as directed.
Low-fat, low-cholesterol diet: Negligible fat per serving.
Low-fat, bland (gall bladder) diet: Prepare as directed.
Gluten-, milk- and wheat-free diet: Prepare as directed.
Low-purine diet: Prepare as directed.
Low-residue diet: Prepare as directed.
Low-sodium diet: Omit salt. 15 milligrams sodium per serving.

APRICOT DELIGHT (70 calories per serving)

2 egg whites
1/8 teaspoon salt
1 tablespoon granulated sugar
1 16-ounce can peeled apricots, pitted and drained

About 15 minutes before serving: In medium bowl, with electric mixer at high speed, beat egg whites and salt until frothy. Gradually add sugar, beating constantly for 2 minutes, or until sugar is dissolved. Then gradually beat in apricots until shredded. Makes 4 servings.

Bland diet: Prepare as directed.
Low-fat, low-cholesterol diet: Negligible fat per serving.
Low-fat, bland (gall bladder) diet: Prepare as directed.
Gluten-, milk- and wheat-free diet: Prepare as directed.
Low-purine diet: Prepare as directed.
Low-residue diet: Prepare as directed.

FROSTED WATERMELON (90 calories per serving

1/2 watermelon
1 pint raspberry sherbet
1 pint fresh raspberries, washed and hulled

Several hours ahead: With serving spoon, scoop meat from watermelon half in spoonfuls, reserving shell. If desired, with tip of paring knife, remove surface seeds from each spoonful of watermelon; then return watermelon to shell, with rounded side up; refrigerate.

To serve: Top watermelon with spoonfuls of raspberry sherbet; scatter raspberries over sherbet. Makes 16 servings.

Low-fat, low-cholesterol diet: Negligible fat per serving.
Low-purine diet: Prepare as directed.
Low-sodium diet: 5 milligrams sodium per serving.

STRAWBERRIES IN ALMOND YOGURT (155 calories per serving)

2 pints fresh strawberries
1 8-ounce container plain yogurt
2 teaspoons vanilla extract
1 1/2 or 2 teaspoons almond extract
5 tablespoons granulated sugar

Early in day: Wash and hull strawberries; drain on paper towelling. Mix together yogurt, extracts and sugar; taste, adding more almond extract, if desired. Fold in strawberries. Spoon strawberries into 4 champagne or sherbet glasses; cover with yogurt sauce. Refrigerate. Make 4 servings.

Diabetic diet: Prepare as directed but use low-fat yogurt, omit sugar. Stir granulated or liquid non-nutritive sweetener equivalent to 3 tablespoons sugar into yogurt. Exchanges per serving = 1/4 milk and 1 fruit.
Egg-, gluten-, and wheat-free diet: Prepare as directed.
Low-fat, low-cholesterol diet: Prepare as directed. 1 gram fat per serving.
Low-purine diet: Prepare as directed.

BAKED CHERRY TAPIOCA (125 calories per serving)

1 16-ounce can pitted red sour cherries, undrained
1 tablespoon lemon juice
1/3 cup granulated sugar
1 teaspoon salt
dash nutmeg
1/3 cup quick-cooking tapioca
1/2 cup frozen whipped topping

At least 1 1/2 hours before serving: Preheat oven to 350°F. In 1 1/2-quart casserole, stir together 3/4 cup hot water, cherries and all remaining ingredients but whipped topping. Stirring occasionally, bake 35 to 45 minutes, or until tapioca granules are clear and pudding has thickened. Serve warm, dabbed with whipped topping. Makes 6 servings.

Egg-, gluten-, milk- and wheat-free diet: Prepare as directed but omit frozen whipped topping on milk-free diet.
Low-fat, low-cholesterol diet: Prepare as directed but omit frozen whipped topping. Negligible fat per serving.
Low-purine diet: Omit frozen whipped topping. Prepare as directed.
Low-sodium diet: Prepare as directed but omit salt and frozen whipped topping. 5 milligrams sodium per serving.

PEACH DUMPLINGS (150 calories per serving)

4 peach halves from 1 16-ounce
    can freestone peach halves
1 cup orange juice
3 tablespoons skimmed milk or
    reliquefied nonfat dry milk
1/4 teaspoon grated lemon peel
scant 1/8 teaspoon almond
    extract
1/2 cup packaged biscuit mix
1 teaspoon granulated sugar
pinch cinnamon

At least 1 hour before serving: Drain peach halves; reserve 1/2 cup syrup. In heavy skillet, heat 1/2 cup syrup and orange juice to boiling. Meanwhile, in medium bowl, slowly stir milk, lemon peel and almond extract into biscuit mix. Drop batter, in 4 tablespoonfuls, onto syrup. Simmer, covered, 10 minutes; then sprinkle with sugar, mixed with cinnamon; cover again; simmer 5 minutes more.

To serve: Top peach halves with dumplings and syrup from skillet. Makes 4 servings.

Bland diet: Prepare as directed. Omit recipe if orange juice is forbidden on diet.
Low-fat, low-cholesterol diet: Prepare as directed.
Low-fat, bland (gall bladder) diet: 3 grams fat per serving.
Low-purine diet: Prepare as directed.
Low-residue diet: Prepare as directed. Omit recipe if orange juice is forbidden on diet.

CUSTARD RICE PUDDING (150 calories per serving)

1 cup hot cooked rice †
2 eggs
1/3 cup granulated sugar
dash salt
1/2 teaspoon vanilla extract
1/4 cup raisins‡
1/4 teaspoon cinnamon
2 cups skimmed milk or
    reliquefied nonfat dry milk,
    scalded

At least 1 1/2 hours before serving: Preheat oven to 350°F. In 1-quart casserole, mix all ingredients but milk. Slowly stir in hot milk.

Place casserole in shallow baking dish; fill baking dish 1-inch deep with water. Bake 30 minutes; stir well to prevent rice from settling to bottom. Bake, stirring occasionally, 20 to 30 minutes more, or until consistency of soft custard sauce. Serve warm or cold. Makes six 1/2-cup servings.

Bland diet: Prepare as directed but omit raisins.
Diabetic diet: Prepare as directed but omit sugar; substitute non-nutritive sweetener equivalent to 1/3 cup sugar. Exchanges per serving = 1/2 skim milk and 1 fruit.
Gluten- and wheat-free diet: Prepare as directed.
Low-purine diet: Prepare as directed.
Low-residue diet: Prepare as directed for bland diet.

† Use regular long-grain, packaged precooked or converted rice. Consistency of pudding varies, from relatively thin and saucy to quite firm, with cooking time and type of rice used. Thin puddings are best served cold; thick ones warm.
‡ If raisins are omitted, count 130 calories per serving.

PINEAPPLE-TAPIOCA FLUFF (125 calories per serving)

1 egg, separated
2 cups skimmed milk or
    reliquefied nonfat dry milk
granulated sugar
1/8 teaspoon salt
2 tablespoons quick-cooking
    tapioca
1/4 teaspoon vanilla extract
1 8-ounce can pineapple tidbits,
    drained

At least 2 hours before serving: In saucepan, beat egg yolk with 1/2 cup milk. Add 1 1/2 cups milk, 1 tablespoon sugar, salt and tapioca. Cook mixture over medium heat, stirring constantly, until boiling—about 5 to 8 minutes. (Do not overcook; mixture thickens as it cools.) Remove from heat.

In medium bowl, beat egg white until foamy. Gradually add 2 teaspoons sugar, continuing to beat until mixture forms soft peaks. Add hot tapioca mixture, stirring constantly. Add vanilla; cool, stirring once after 15 to 20 minutes. Then stir in 1/3 cup pineapple tidbits. Refrigerate.

To serve: Top each serving with remaining pineapple. Makes 4 servings.

Bland diet: Prepare as directed but omit pineapple. Substitute 1/2 cup chopped, drained peach slices.
Low-purine diet: Prepare as directed.
Low-residue diet: Prepare as directed for bland diet.

GEORGIA DELIGHT (135 calories per serving)

1 cup boiling water
1 20-ounce can sliced freestone
   peaches
1/4 teaspoon salt
1/8 teaspoon cinnamon
2 tablespoons lemon juice
1/4 cup quick-cooking tapioca
1/3 cup heavy or whipping
   cream, whipped and
   sweetened

At least 1 1/2 hours before serving: Prepare as directed for Baked Cherry Tapioca (page 217). Makes 6 servings.

Bland diet: Prepare as directed.
Egg-, gluten-, milk- and wheat-free diet: Preapre as directed but omit whipped cream on milk-free diet.
Low-fat, low-cholesterol diet: Prepare as directed but omit whipped cream. Negligible fat per serving.
Low-fat, bland (gall bladder) diet: Prepare as directed but omit whipped cream.
Low-purine diet: Prepare as directed.
Low-sodium diet: Prepare as directed but omit salt. 5 milligrams sodium per serving.

BANANA & STRAWBERRY TAPIOCA (125 calories per serving)

3 ripe small bananas, cut up
1 tablespoon lemon juice
1 10-ounce package frozen
   strawberries in quick-thaw
   pouch, thawed
water
1/4 cup quick-cooking tapioca
1/8 teaspoon salt
1/2 cup heavy or whipping cream
2 tablespoons confectioners'
   sugar

Blend bananas and lemon juice until smooth. In 4-cup glass measure, combine banana mixture, strawberries with their syrup, and water to make 4 cups. In 2-quart saucepan, combine banana mixture, tapioca, and salt; let stand 5 minutes. Over medium heat, heat to boiling, stirring frequently. Remove from heat; let stand 20 minutes; then stir. Spoon mixture into eight dessert glasses; refrigerate until chilled, about 2 hours. In small bowl with mixer at medium speed, beat heavy or whipping cream and sugar until stiff peaks form. Spoon whipped-cream mixture over chilled tapioca. Makes 8 servings.

Low-fat diet: Prepare as directed but subsitute 1 tablespoon frozen whipped topping per serving for heavy cream. 1 gram fat per serving.
Low-sodium diet: Prepare as directed. 40 milligrams sodium per serving.
Low-purine diet: Prepare as directed but omit heavy cream.

TIP-TOP ORANGE PUDDING (155 calories per serving)

4 medium oranges
granulated sugar
2 cups skimmed milk or
   reliquefied nonfat dry milk
1 4-serving package vanilla
   pudding and pie filling mix
3 egg whites
dash salt
1/2 teaspoon vanilla extract

At least 1 hour before serving: Prepare 1/2 tablespoon finely grated orange peel. Peel oranges; section into 1 1/2-quart casserole. Press remaining juice from pulp into casserole. Sprinkle orange sections with 2 tablespoons sugar.

Preheat oven to 325°F. In medium saucepan, slowly stir milk and grated orange peel into pudding mix. Cook, stirring constantly, as label directs; pour over orange sections.

In medium bowl, beat egg whites until soft peaks form. Beating constantly, slowly add 6 tablespoons sugar, salt and vanilla until stiff peaks form. Spread over top of pudding, sealing all around edges of casserole. Bake 15 minutes, or until peaks are golden-brown. Cool about 30 minutes and serve warm. Makes 8 servings.

Low-fat, low-cholesterol diet: Negligible fat per serving.
Low-purine diet: Prepare as directed.

DANISH FRUIT PUDDING (Rogrod) (120 calories per serving)

2 10-ounce packages frozen
    raspberries, thawed
dash cinnamon
finely grated peel of 1/2 lemon
juice of 1/2 lemon
2 tablespoons cornstarch
1/2 teaspoon vanilla extract
dash salt
2 tablespoons slivered almonds

Early in day: Into medium saucepan, drain syrup from raspberries. Mix cinnamon, grated peel, lemon juice, cornstarch, vanilla and salt to form a smooth paste; stir into raspberry syrup. Cook, stirring constantly, until thickened. Stir in raspberries. Refrigerate.

To serve: Top with sprinkling of slivered almonds. Makes 6 servings.

Egg-, gluten-, milk- and wheat-free diet: Prepare as directed.
Low-fat, low-cholesterol diet: 2 grams fat per serving
Low-purine diet: Prepare as directed
Low-sodium diet: Prepare as directed but omit salt. 1 milligram sodium per serving.

APRICOT-AND-PUDDING PLEASER (150 calories per serving)

1 16-ounce can peeled whole
    apricots
1 4-serving package vanilla
    instant pudding and pie filling
    mix
2 cups skimmed milk

Early in day: Remove pits and thoroughly drain apricots. Meanwhile, prepare pudding as label directs, but use skimmed milk. Immediately stir in drained apricots. Divide among 5 dessert dishes. Refrigerate until serving time. Makes 5 servings.

Bland diet: Prepare as directed.
Low-fat, low-cholesterol diet: Negligible fat per serving.
Low-fat, bland (gall bladder) diet: Prepare as directed.
Low-purine diet: Prepare as directed.
Low-residue diet: Prepare as directed.

BLUEBERRY COTTAGE PUDDING (190 calories per serving)

1 3/4 cups sifted all-purpose
    flour
2 1/2 teaspoons double-acting
    baking powder
salt
1/4 cup butter or margarine,
    softened
granulated sugar
1 egg
2/3 cup skimmed milk or
    reliquefied nonfat dry milk
1/2 teaspoon lemon extract
1 1/2 tablespoons lemon juice
3/4 cup orange juice
1 1/2 10-ounce packages frozen
    blueberries, thawed and
    drained

Early in day: Preheat oven to 375°F. Grease, then lightly flour 9-inch square cake pan. Mix together flour, baking powder and 1/2 teaspoon salt. In medium bowl, with electric mixer at medium speed, cream butter with 1/2 cup sugar until almost cream-colored. Add egg, beating until smooth. Beat in one-third of flour mixture until smooth, then one-half milk and lemon extract until just smooth. Beat in remaining milk, then remaining one-third flour mixture. Beat for 30 seconds. Turn into prepared cake pan. Bake 30 to 35 minutes, or until a cake tester, inserted in center, comes out clean. Cool on rack 15 minutes; then turn cake out of pan onto rack.

About 1 hour before serving: In medium saucepan, mix cornstarch, 1/3 cup sugar and dash of salt; slowly stir in lemon juice, orange juice and blueberries. Cook, stirring, until sauce is thickened.

To serve: Cut cake into 12 servings. Place on dessert dishes; dribble scant 1/4 cup of warm sauce over each. Makes 12 servings.

Low-purine diet: Prepare as directed.
Low-sodium diet: Prepare as directed but omit salt, use unsalted butter or margarine and substitute 2 1/2 teaspoons low-sodium baking powder for double-acting. 10 milligrams sodium per serving.

BLUEBERRY RICE PUDDING (150 calories per serving)

1 quart skimmed milk or
   reliquefied nonfat dry milk
5 tablespoons uncooked rice
1/4 cup nonfat dry-milk powder
1/4 teaspoon cinnamon
1/4 teaspoon nutmeg
1/4 teaspoon salt
1/4 cup granulated sugar
1 cup fresh blueberries (or
   frozen unsweetened
   blueberries, thawed, drained)

Early in day: Preheat oven to 325°F. Lightly grease 1½-quart casserole. In casserole, mix all ingredients but blueberries. Bake, uncovered, 1½ to 2 hours, or until rice is tender. Stir in surface skin whenever it forms. Refrigerate. Immediately before serving, stir in blueberries. Makes 6 servings.

Diabetic diet: Prepare as directed but omit sugar. Substitute non-nutritive sweetener equivalent to 1/4 cup sugar. Exchanges per serving = 1 milk and 1/2 fruit.
Egg-, gluten-, and wheat-free diet: Prepare as directed.
Low-fat, low-cholesterol diet: Negligible fat per serving.
Low-purine diet: Prepare as directed.

LIGHT-AND-LEMON PUDDING (175 calories per serving)

granulated sugar
3 tablespoons cornstarch
1/4 cup cake flour
1/4 teaspoon salt
1 tablespoon grated lemon peel
1/2 cup lemon juice
3 eggs, separated

At least 1 hour before serving: In medium saucepan, stir together 1 cup sugar, cornstarch, cake flour and salt, until smooth. Stirring constantly, slowly add 3 cups boiling water; mix until smooth; add grated lemon peel. Stirring regularly, boil gently over medium heat for 10 minutes.

Preheat oven to 425°F. Beat lemon juice and egg yolks until smooth; stirring constantly, add to pudding. Still stirring, cook 2 minutes longer. Divide among eight 3/4-cup custard cups; place on cookie sheet.

In medium bowl, beat egg whites until soft peaks form; still beating, slowly add 6 tablespoons sugar; beat until glossy peaks form. Drop generous dollop of this meringue onto each pudding; bake 4 to 6 minutes, or until golden-brown. Serve warm or cold. Makes 8 servings.

Low-purine diet: Prepare as directed.
Low-sodium diet: Prepare as directed but omit salt. 25 milligrams sodium per serving.

BAKED LEMON PUDDING (140 calories per serving)

2 eggs, separated
1/4 teaspoon salt
granulated sugar
1 tablespoon grated lemon peel
1½ tablespoons lemon juice
1 tablespoon melted butter or
   magarine
2 tablespoons flour
1 cup skimmed milk or
   reliquefied nonfat dry milk

At least 2 hours before serving: Preheat oven to 350°F. Grease 1-quart casserole. Beat egg whites with salt until moist peaks form. Gradually add 1/4 cup sugar, beating until stiff. With same beater, beat yolks with lemon peel, lemon juice and melted butter until blended. Stir in 2 tablespoons sugar mixed with flour, then milk. Fold into beaten egg whites.

Pour batter into greased casserole. Set in pan containing 1/2 inch hot water. Bake, uncovered, 55 to 65 minutes, or until top of pudding is firm and brown (pudding will separate into cake and sauce layers). Serve warm or chilled. Makes 5 servings.

Bland diet: Prepare as directed but omit lemon peel.
Low-purine diet: Prepare as directed.
Low-residue diet: Prepare as directed but omit lemon peel.

RHUBARB PUDDING (170 calories per serving)

1¹/₂ pound fresh rhubarb
1 cup granulated sugar
4 teaspoons cornstarch
¹/₂ teaspoon vanilla extract
¹/₂ cup frozen whipped topping

Early in day: Clean, then cut rhubarb into ¹/₂-inch slices. Combine rhubarb with 1 cup water and 1 cup granulated sugar; simmer 5 minutes, or until tender. Blend cornstarch, ¹/₄ cup water; stir into rhubarb; cook, stirring, until thick and clear; stir in vanilla. Pour into serving dish; refrigerate, covered.

To serve: Top pudding with whipped topping. Makes 6 servings.

Egg-, gluten-, and wheat-free diet: Prepare as directed.
Low-fat, low-cholesterol diet: Prepare as directed but omit frozen whipped topping. Negligible fat per serving.
Low-purine diet: Prepare as directed but omit frozen whipped topping if fat is restricted on diet.
Low-sodium diet: Prepare as directed but use whipped cream instead of frozen whipped topping. 5 milligrams sodium per serving.

BAKED CUSTARD (120 calories per serving)

4 eggs
¹/₄ cup granulated sugar
¹/₄ teaspoon salt
2¹/₂ cups skimmed milk or
reliquefied nonfat dry milk
1 teaspoon vanilla extract

At least 2 hours before serving: Preheat oven to 300°F. In large bowl, beat eggs, sugar and salt until lemon-colored. Beat in milk and vanilla. Pour into greased custard cups. Set cups in shallow pan; place in oven and pour hot water to within ³/₄ inch of top of pan. Bake 1 hour, or until set; refrigerate. Makes 6 servings.

Bland diet: Prepare as directed.
Low-fat diet: 5 grams fat per serving. Omit recipe from low-cholesterol diet.
Low-purine diet: Prepare as directed.
Low-residue diet: Prepare as directed.

RHUBARB WHIP (130 calories per serving)

1 pound rhubarb, cut into
¹/₂-inch cubes
¹/₂ cup granulated sugar
1 cup evaporated skimmed milk
2 drops red food color

At least 2 hours before serving: In top of double boiler, mix rhubarb and sugar; cook, stirring occasionally, over rapidly boiling water until rhubarb is just tender—about 20 minutes. Refrigerate.

About 30 minutes before serving: In medium freezer-proof bowl, stir evaporated skimmed milk and food color; freeze until ice crystals form around edge of bowl.

To serve: With electric mixer at high speed, beat chilled milk until consistency of whipped cream. Fold in rhubarb (and its syrup). Serve immediately. Makes 4 servings.

Egg-, gluten-, and wheat-free diet: Prepare as directed.
Low-fat, low-cholesterol diet: Negligible fat per serving.
Low-purine diet: Prepare as directed.

LIME-GRAPE FRUIT SHIMMER (100 calories per serving)

1 3-ounce package lime-flavor
gelatin
1 tablespoon lime juice
²/₃ cup whole or halved
seedless grapes

Early in day: Prepare lime gelatin as label directs, then stir in lime juice. Layer gelatin and grapes as directed in paragraph 2 of Lemon-Orange Fruit Shimmer (see recipe opposite). Makes 4 servings.

Diabetic diet: Prepare as directed but substitute one 4-serving envelope low-calorie lemon flavor gelatin for regular lime gelatin. Exchanges per serving = ¹/₂ fruit.
Egg-, gluten-, milk- and wheat-free diet: Prepare as directed.
Low-fat, low-cholesterol diet: Negligible fat per serving.
Low-purine diet: Prepare as directed.

LEMON-ORANGE FRUIT SHIMMER (120 calories per serving)

1 11-ounce can mandarin
  orange sections
1 3-ounce package lemon-flavor
  gelatin

Early in day: Drain juice from mandarin-orange sections; add enough boiling water to make 2 cups liquid. Stir into lemon gelatin until dissolved.

Fill 4 parfait glasses or large goblets with one-third of gelatin; add one-third fruit; refrigerate parfait glasses until gelatin mixture is just set, but not quite firm. (Refrigerate remaining gelatin and fruit as well.) Add half of remaining gelatin and fruit. Chill until just set, but not firm. Add remaining gelatin, then fruit; refrigerate. Makes 4 servings.

Bland diet: Prepare as directed.
Egg-, gluten-, milk- and wheat-free diet: Prepare as directed.
Low-fat, low-cholesterol diet: Negligible fat per serving.
Low-fat, bland (gall bladder) diet: Prepare as directed.
Low-purine diet: Prepare as directed.
Low-residue diet: Prepare as directed.

FLUFFY LIME SOUFFLÉ (145 calories per serving)

1 envelope unflavored gelatin
1/2 teaspoon salt
sugar
4 eggs, separated, at room
  temperature
3/4 cup water
1/3 cup lime juice
1/8 teaspoon green food color
grated peel of 1 lime
1 8-ounce container frozen
  whipped topping, thawed

To prepare collar for 1-quart soufflé dish, tear off 20-inch strip of waxed paper and fold lengthwise into 20″ by 6″ strip. Wrap around outside of dish so collar stands 2 inches above rim; secure with tape. In heavy, 2-quart saucepan, mix gelatin, salt and 1/4 cup sugar. With fork, beat egg yolks, water and lime juice into gelatin mixture until mixed. Cook over low heat, stirring constantly, until gelatin is completely dissolved and mixture thickens and coats a spoon, about 10 minutes. Remove saucepan from heat; stir in food color and 1 teaspoon of the grated lime peel. (Wrap remaining peel in plastic wrap for garnishing the soufflé later.) Refrigerate until mixture mounds when dropped from a spoon, about 30 minutes. In large bowl with mixer at high speed, beat egg white until soft peaks form. Then, beating at high speed, gradually sprinkle in 1/4 cup sugar, beating until sugar is completely dissolved. With rubber spatula, gently fold whipped topping and lime mixture into beaten egg whites. Pour mixture into prepared soufflé dish; refrigerate until set, at least 3 hours. To serve, remove collar from dish. Garnish top of soufflé with reserved grated lime peel. Makes 10 servings.

Low-fat diet: Prepare as directed. 4 grams fat per serving.
Low-sodium diet: Prepare as directed but omit salt. 27 milligrams sodium per serving.
Diabetic diet: Exchanges per serving = 1 fat.
Low-purine diet: Prepare as directed.

CRANBERRY FROTH (85 calories per serving)

1 3-ounce package lemon-flavor
  gelatin
1 cup cranberry-juice cocktail
2 egg whites

Several hours before serving: Dissolve gelatin in 1 cup boiling water; stir in cranberry juice. Refrigerate until slightly thickened, stirring occasionally. Beat egg whites stiff, but not dry; gradually pour in thickened gelatin mixture, beating until frothy. Spoon into 8 parfait glasses (mixture will separate into 2 layers). Refrigerate several hours before serving. Makes 8 servings.

Bland diet: Prepare as directed.
Gluten-, milk- and wheat-free diet: Prepare as directed.
Low-fat, low-cholesterol diet: Negligible fat per serving.
Low-fat, bland (gall bladder) diet: Prepare as directed.
Low-purine diet: Prepare as directed.
Low-residue diet: Prepare as directed.

CHERRY-BANANA FESTIVE PARFAIT (110 calories per serving)

1 3-ounce package cherry-flavor
  gelatin
1 8-ounce can Bing cherries,
  drained
4 medium bananas, halved,
  then quartered
lemon juice
1/2 cup vanilla ice milk

At least 4 hours before serving: Prepare cherry gelatin as label directs, but stir in drained cherries; refrigerate until firm.

To serve: Dip banana quarters into lemon juice to prevent discoloration. Place 2 banana quarters along sides of each of 8 parfait glasses, then spoon in gelatin to top of glass. Top with small dollop of ice milk. Makes 8 servings.

Bland diet: Prepare as directed
Diabetic diet: Prepare as directed, but substitute one 4-serving envelope low-calorie strawberry-flavor gelatin for regular; omit cherries and ice milk. Exchanges per serving = 1 fruit.
Egg-, gluten-, and wheat-free diet: Prepare as directed but use gluten-free ice milk on gluten-free diet.
Low-fat, low-cholesterol diet: Negligible fat per serving.
Low-fat, bland (gall bladder) diet: Prepare as directed.
Low-purine diet: Prepare as directed.
Low-residue diet: Prepare as directed.

GOLDEN-GLOW PARFAIT (150 calories per serving)

2 3-ounce packages
  lemon-flavor gelatin
2 10-ounce containers frozen
  raspberries, thawed
1/3 cup heavy cream, whipped
  and sweetened to taste

Early in day: Prepare both packages gelatin, as label directs, but use only 1 1/2 cups boiling water and 2 1/2 cups cold water.

Drain 1 cup syrup from thawed raspberries. (Use this syrup later as a sauce for puddings or fruit.) Evenly divide one-half of raspberries and remaining syrup among 8 parfait glasses. Spoon 3 tablespoons gelatin into each glass; refrigerate until firm (tilt glass by catching base between bars of rack and leaning side against refrigerator wall, to make gelatin set at slant). Cover remaining gelatin and raspberries and reserve at room temperature.

Add 1/4 cup gelatin to firm gelatin in each parfait glass. Again refrigerate, with glass tipped at angle, until firm. Divide remaining gelatin, raspberries and syrup among glasses; refrigerate, not tipped this time, until firm.

To serve: Top each serving with a dab of whipped cream. Makes 8 servings.

Egg-, gluten-, milk- and wheat-free diet: Prepare as directed but omit whipped cream for milk-free diet.
Low-fat, low-cholesterol diet: Prepare as directed but omit whipped cream. Negligible fat per serving.
Low-purine diet: Prepare as directed.

PARFAIT ROYALE (125 calories per serving)

1 16-ounce can or jar raspberry
  applesauce
1 package
  vanilla-rennet-custard mix
2 cups skimmed milk

At least 4 hours before serving: Divide half of applesauce among six 3/4-cup parfait glasses or custard cups. Prepare rennet mix as label directs but use skimmed milk. Immediately divide among parfaits; let stand in warm spot until firm—about 10 minutes. Spoon remaining applesauce on top of each serving; refrigerate. Makes 6 servings.

Bland diet: Prepare as directed.
Egg-, gluten-, and wheat-free diet: Prepare as directed.
Low-fat, low-cholesterol diet: Negligible fat per serving.
Low-fat, bland (gall bladder) diet: Prepare as directed.
Low-purine diet: Prepare as directed.
Low-residue diet: Prepare as directed.
Low-sodium diet: 45 milligrams sodium per serving.

RASPBERRY PARFAIT (150 calories per serving)

2 10-ounce packages frozen
raspberries, thawed
1 package
vanilla-rennet-custard mix
2 cups skimmed milk

At least 4 hours before serving: Prepare as directed for Parfait Royale (see recipe opposite), substituting thawed raspberries for raspberry applesauce.

Egg-, gluten-, and wheat-free diet: Prepare as directed.
Low-fat, low-cholesterol diet: Negligible fat per serving.
Low-purine diet: Prepare as directed.
Low-sodium diet: 45 milligrams sodium per serving.

FESTIVE PINEAPPLE SNOW PARFAIT (75 calories per serving)

1 3-ounce package lime-flavor
gelatin
2 egg whites
1 15¼-ounce can pineapple
slices packed in pineapple
juice

At least 4 hours before serving: Prepare lime gelatin as label directs. Refrigerate until consistency of thin pudding. Beat egg whites until stiff peaks form. Still beating, slowly add gelatin and continue to beat until light and frothy. Refrigerate until firm.

Drain pineapple; cut 4 slices in half and the rest into tidbits. Divide half of tidbits among 8 parfait glasses; top with layer of gelatin mixture. Repeat layers with remaining tidbits and gelatin to top of glass. Decorate with half-pineapple slice. Makes 8 servings.

Bland diet: Prepare as directed but substitute canned peaches for pineapple.
Diabetic diet: Prepare as directed but substitute one 4-serving envelope low-calorie lemon-flavor gelatin for regular. Exchanges per serving = ½ fruit.
Low-fat, low-cholesterol diet: Negligible fat per serving.
Low-fat, bland (gall bladder) diet: Prepare as directed but substitute peaches for pineapple.
Gluten-, milk- and wheat-free diet: Prepare as directed.
Low-purine diet: Prepare as directed.
Low-residue diet: Prepare as directed for bland diet.

HEART OF CREAM (Coeur à la Crème) (160 calories per serving)

2 8-ounce containers creamed
cottage cheese
2 3-ounce packages Neufchâtel
cheese, softened slightly
½ teaspoon salt
¼ cup granulated sugar
3 cups fresh strawberries or
Bing cherries, halved and
pitted

Day before serving: In small bowl, thoroughly blend cottage cheese, Neufchâtel cheese, salt and sugar; refrigerate.

About 15 minutes before serving: On serving platter, form cheese mixture into heart shape; surround with berries. Makes 8 servings.

Bland diet: Prepare as directed but substitute two 16-ounce cans peeled apricots, peaches or pears for strawberries.
Low-purine diet: Prepare as directed.
Low-residue diet: Prepare as directed for bland diet.

COTTAGE-CHEESE DESSERT-SALAD (about 100 calories per serving)

1 30-ounce can freestone peach
halves
⅛ teaspoon cinnamon
1 8-ounce container creamed
cottage cheese

About 10 minutes before serving: Drain peaches, reserving syrup. Mix ¼ cup reserved syrup with cinnamon and cottage cheese. Use as topping for peaches. Makes 6 servings.

Bland diet: Prepare as directed.
Diabetic diet: Prepare as directed but use low-fat cottage cheese; substitute peach halves packed in water or fruit juice for regular. Exchanges per serving (2 peach halves and ¼ cup cottage-cheese sauce) = 1 fruit and 1 meat.
Egg-, gluten-, and wheat-free diet: Prepare as directed.
Low-fat, low-cholesterol diet: 2 grams fat per serving.
Low-fat, bland (gall bladder) diet: Prepare as directed.
Low-purine diet: Prepare as directed.
Low-residue diet: Prepare as directed.

APRICOT CLOUD (140 calories per serving)

24 dried apricot halves
³/₄ cup granulated sugar
2 envelopes unflavored gelatin
2 tablespoons lemon juice
6 egg whites

At least 4 hours before serving: In medium saucepan, mix apricot halves, 1¹/₂ cups water and sugar; cover; simmer 45 minutes, or until apricots are tender; cool; refrigerate.

Reserve 8 apricot halves and ¹/₄ cup syrup for garnish. In electric-blender container, at low speed, blend remaining apricots and syrup smooth. (Or press through food mill.)

In medium saucepan, mix gelatin into 1 cup water and let stand 5 minutes; heat just to boiling to dissolve; stir in lemon juice and apricot puree. Refrigerate, stirring occasionally, until mixture mounds when dropped from spoon.

In large bowl, beat egg whites until stiff peaks form. Add apricot puree, then continue beating until completely mixed. Divide among 8 dessert dishes; top each with reserved apricot half and bit of syrup. Refrigerate 3 hours, or until serving time. Makes 8 servings.

Bland diet: Prepare as directed.
Diabetic diet: Prepare as directed but omit sugar. Stir non-nutritive sweetener equivalent to ¹/₂ cup sugar into apricot puree before it is refrigerated. Exchanges per serving = 1 fruit.
Low-fat, low-cholesterol diet: Negligible fat per serving.
Low-fat, bland (gall bladder) diet: Prepare as directed.
Gluten-, milk- and wheat-free diet: Prepare as directed.
High-iron diet: 1 milligram iron per serving.
Low-purine diet: Prepare as directed.
Low-residue diet: Prepare as directed.
Low-sodium diet: 40 milligrams sodium per serving.

FLUFFY GELATIN TREAT (55 calories per serving)

1 3-ounce package
  cherry-flavored gelatin
  dessert
2 egg whites

About 3 to 4 hours before serving: In medium bowl, dissolve gelatin in 1 cup boiling water; stir in 1 cup cold water; refrigerate. When gelatin is consistency of unbeaten egg white, beat with egg beater or electric mixer until light and frothy. Then, in medium bowl, beat egg whites until soft peaks form. Fold beaten gelatin mixture into whites until smooth. Divide among 6 sherbet glasses; refrigerate until firm—2 to 3 hours. Makes 6 servings.

Bland diet: Prepare as directed.
Diabetic diet: Prepare as directed but use one 4-serving envelope low-calorie strawberry-flavor gelatin for regular. Exchanges per serving = 1 "free."
Low-fat, low-cholesterol diet: Negligible fat per serving.
Low-fat, bland (gall bladder) diet: Prepare as directed.
Gluten-, milk- and wheat-free diet: Prepare as directed.
Low-purine diet: Prepare as directed.

STRAWBERRY SPLIT (110 calories per serving)

5 ladyfingers, split
1 package
  strawberry-rennet-custard
  mix
2 cups skimmed milk

About 2 hours before serving: Use ladyfingers to line sides of 5 parfait glasses. Prepare rennet pudding as label directs but use skimmed milk. Pour into prepared glasses; let stand 10 minutes; refrigerate. Makes 5 servings.

Bland diet: Prepare as directed.
Low-fat, low-cholesterol diet: 1 gram fat per serving.
Low-fat, bland (gall bladder) diet: Prepare as directed.
Low-purine diet: Prepare as directed.
Low-residue diet: Prepare as directed.

MELON RINGS WITH STRAWBERRIES (35 calories per serving)

1 medium Spanish or honeydew melon
1 pint strawberries

About 30 minutes before serving: Cut melon crosswise into rings 1 inch thick; remove seeds.

Place slices on individual plates; with knife, carefully loosen meat by cutting around slice $1/4$ inch from rind; do not remove rind. Slice meat to make bite-size pieces, leaving rind intact.

Rinse strawberries under cold running water; do not hull. Arrange 5 or 6 berries in center of each melon slice. Makes 5 servings.

Diabetic diet: Exchanges per serving = 1 fruit.
Egg-, gluten-, milk- and wheat-free diet: Prepare as directed.
Low-fat, low-cholesterol diet: Negligible fat per serving.
Low-purine diet: Prepare as directed.
Low-sodium diet: 5 milligrams sodium per serving.

BUTTERSCOTCH TREAT (140 calories per serving)

$3/4$ cup graham-cracker crumbs
1 tablespoon butter or margarine, softened
1 4-serving package butterscotch pudding and pie filling mix
2 cups skimmed milk or reliquefied nonfat dry milk
$3/4$ cup frozen whipped topping, thawed

Early in day: Preheat oven to 350°F. In medium bowl, combine crumbs, 1 tablespoon water and butter or margarine. Line 9″ by 5″ by 3″ loaf pan with foil; press crumb mixture in thin layer in bottom of pan. Bake 7 minutes; chill. Meanwhile, prepare pudding as label directs but use skimmed milk. Pour into crust; refrigerate.

To serve: Slice and place on chilled plates. Top each with dab of whipped topping. Makes 8 servings.

Bland diet: Prepare as directed.
Low-fat, low-cholesterol diet: Prepare as directed but use margarine instead of butter; substitute marshmallow cream for whipped topping. 1 gram fat per serving.
Low-fat, bland (gall bladder) diet: Prepare as directed for low-fat, low-cholesterol diet.
Low-purine diet: Prepare as directed but omit frozen whipped topping.
Low-residue diet: Prepare as directed.

PERSIAN RICE DESSERT (145 calories per serving)

$2^{1}/4$ cups skimmed milk or reliquefied nonfat dry milk
$1/4$ cup uncooked long-grain rice
$1/4$ teaspoon salt
$1/4$ cup granulated sugar
2 tablespoons raisins
$1/4$ teaspoon cinnamon
generous dash nutmeg
$1^{1}/2$ teaspoons vanilla extract
$1/2$ cup creamed cottage cheese, sieved until smooth
$1/2$ teaspoon finely grated lemon peel

Early in day: In top of double boiler, mix milk, rice, salt and sugar; cover; cook over boiling water, stirring occasionally, 30 minutes.

Add raisins, cinnamon and nutmeg; cook, uncovered, 45 minutes longer, stirring every 10 minutes. Stir in vanilla. Refrigerate.

To serve: Mix sieved cottage cheese with lemon peel; fold into rice mixture until almost smooth. Makes five $1/2$-cup servings.

Bland diet: Prepare as directed but omit raisins, nutmeg and lemon peel.
Diabetic diet: Prepare as directed but omit sugar; use non-nutritive sweetener equivalent to $1/4$ cup sugar. Exchanges per serving = $1/2$ bread and $1/2$ skim milk.
Egg-, gluten-, and wheat-free diet: Prepare as directed.
Low-fat, low-cholesterol diet: Negligible fat per serving.
Low-fat, bland (gall bladder) diet: Prepare as directed for bland diet.
Low-purine diet: Prepare as directed.
Low-residue diet: Prepare as directed for bland diet.

COCONUT-CREAM BANANA DESSERT (110 calories per serving)

**3 under-ripe bananas
lemon juice
1 2-ounce envelope
   whipped-topping mix
1 tablespoon flaked coconut**

About 25 minutes before serving: Preheat oven to 325°F. Slice bananas diagonally into 1-inch pieces; sprinkle with lemon juice. Arrange in lightly greased, shallow baking dish; bake 12 minutes to heat through.

Prepare whipped topping as label directs but use skimmed milk. (Refrigerate 1 cup topping in airtight container for later use with fruit or gelatin.) Fold coconut into remaining 1 cup topping; serve over bananas. Makes 6 servings.

Bland diet: Prepare as directed but omit coconut.
Low-residue diet: Prepare as directed but omit coconut.

FROZEN DESSERTS CHURNED IN AN ICE-CREAM MAKER

General Instructions: The two recipes that follow were developed for the traditional crank-type ice-cream maker. Both hand-turned and electric makers come in 4- and 6-quart capacities. They are available in most large department stores and through mail-order houses. After freezing ice cream, place in freezer section in chilled bowl for a few hours, to allow ice cream to ripen. These recipes produce 1½ to 2 quarts of ice cream—fine for a 4-quart maker.

APRICOT ICE (120 calories per serving)

**2 30-ounce cans peeled whole
   apricots
2¼ cups orange juice
⅓ cup lemon juice
1 cup granulated sugar**

About 2 to 3 hours before churning ice cream: Drain apricots; remove seeds. In electric-blender container, at low speed, puree apricots. Stir together with remaining ingredients. Refrigerate at least 1 hour.

Churn and freeze in ice-cream maker as manufacturer directs. Makes 1½ quarts or twelve ½-cup servings.

Bland diet: Prepare as directed.
Egg-, gluten-, milk- and wheat-free diet: Prepare as directed.
Low-fat, low-cholesterol diet: Negligible fat per serving.
Low-fat, bland (gall bladder) diet: Prepare as directed.
Low-purine diet: Prepare as directed.
Low-residue diet: Prepare as directed.
Low-sodium diet: 1 milligram sodium per serving.

PINK MINT ICE CREAM* (90 calories per serving)

**6 ounces peppermint-stick
   candy
2 cups skimmed milk or
   reliquefied nonfat dry milk
2 cups evaporated skimmed
   milk**

About 3 hours before churning ice cream: Crush candy to a fine powder by placing between sheets of waxed paper or in plastic bag and pounding with rolling pin. In medium bowl, mix candy with milk; refrigerate and let soak 2 hours, stirring occasionally. Stir together candy mixture and evaporated skimmed milk. Chill thoroughly—about 1 hour.

Churn and freeze in ice-cream maker as manufacturer directs. Makes 1½ quarts or twelve ½-cup servings.

Egg-, gluten-, and wheat-free diet: Prepare as directed.
Low-fat, low-cholesterol diet: Negligible fat per serving.
Low-purine diet: Prepare as directed.

* This ice cream has a refreshing but sharp mint flavor. For a milder flavor, reduce candy to 4 ounces and add ⅓ cup granulated sugar; prepare as directed.

SHERBET BLUEBERRY FESTIVE PARFAIT (150 calories per serving)

**1 10-ounce package
unsweetened frozen
blueberries, thawed
1 pint raspberry sherbet**

To serve: In 4 parfait glasses, alternate layers of blueberries and sherbet. Makes 4 servings.

Egg-, gluten-, and wheat-free diet: Prepare as directed but use gluten-free sherbet on gluten-free diet.
Low-fat, low-cholesterol diet: Negligible fat per serving.
Low-purine diet: Prepare as directed.
Low-sodium diet: 5 milligrams sodium per serving.

RUBY ICE (130 calories per serving)

**2 10-ounce packages frozen
raspberries, thawed
2 egg whites
¼ cup granulated sugar**

At least 5 hours before serving: Press raspberries through sieve and discard seeds. In bowl to be used for freezing, beat egg whites until soft peaks form. Beating contantly, slowly beat in sugar until stiff peaks form. Fold in raspberry puree. Freeze, stirring occasionally, until consistency of soft sherbet. Makes 6 servings.

Low-fat, low-cholesterol diet: Negligible fat per serving.
Gluten-, milk- and wheat-free diet: Prepare as directed.
Low-purine diet: Prepare as directed.
Low-sodium diet: 15 milligrams sodium per serving.

ORANGE FLOATS (85 calories per serving)

**6 very large eating oranges
1½ cups orange sherbert
2 cups (from 2 12-ounce bottles)
orange carbonated beverage**

About 40 minutes before serving: Slice tops from oranges about one-fifth of the way down. Hollow out oranges sections (use fruit for salads later), leaving shells intact. Cut very thin slice from bottom of each orange so it stands upright. Place 1 small scoop sherbet in each orange shell; fill with orange soda. Serve with straws. Makes 6 servings.

Egg-, gluten- and wheat-free diet: Prepare as directed but use gluten-free sherbert on gluten-free diet.
Low-fat, low-cholesterol diet: Negligible fat per serving.
Low-sodim diet: 5 milligrams sodium per serving.

SHERBET LEMON CUPS (80 calories per serving)

**6 large lemons
1 pint lemon sherbet, slightly
softened**

About 45 minutes before serving: With sharp knife, slice tops from lemons, one-third of the way down. Slice a bit of peel from bottom of each so it stands upright. Then cut out all inside sections. Fill each shell with sherbet and mound up over rim. Freeze. Makes 6 servings.

Bland diet: Prepare as direced.
Egg-, gluten-, and wheat-free diet: Prepare as directed but use gluten-free sherbert on gluten-free diet.
Low-fat, low-cholesterol diet: Negligible fat per serving.
Low-fat, bland (gall bladder) diet: Prepare as directed.
Low-residue diet: Prepare as directed.
Low-sodium diet: 5 milligrams sodium per serving.

MIX-AND-FREEZE FROZEN DESSERTS

General Instructions: The 5 recipes that follow are for ice creams frozen in bowls. For the best results, have freezer as cold as possible and freeze mixture quickly. Freeze, uncovered, but cover before storing to prevent drying out. If you prefer to freeze this type of ice cream in ice-cube trays, keep special trays for this purpose. (Cubes will stick in trays which have been used previously for ice cream.)

MILLICENT'S LEMON CRÈME (90 calories per serving)

1 lemon
1 cup granulated sugar
1 envelope unflavored gelatin
1½ cups skimmed milk or
    reliquefied nonfat dry milk
2 teaspoons vanilla extract
dash salt
1 cup evaporated skimmed milk

About 4 to 6 hours before serving: Finely grate all peel from lemon. Slice lemon, remove seeds, then finely snip lemon slices with scissors, reserving all juice. In small saucepan, mix grated lemon peel and juice of lemon with ½ cup sugar; heat gently until sugar is dissolved.

In large bowl, soften gelatin in ¾ cup skimmed milk for 5 minutes. Meanwhile, scald ¾ cup skimmed milk with ½ cup sugar. Stir hot milk into gelatin mixture until gelatin is dissolved. Slowly stir in sugar-lemon mixture, then vanilla and salt.

Freeze, in same bowl, until firm about 2 inches in around edge. Meanwhile, in medium bowl, freeze evaporated skimmed milk until ice crystals form 1 inch in from edge of bowl. Whip until consistency of whipped cream. Then beat lemon mixture until smooth. Carefully fold whipped evaporated milk into lemon mixture. Freeze until firm. Makes 1 quart or eight ½-cup servings.

Egg-, gluten-, and wheat-free diet: Prepare as directed.
Low-fat, low-cholesterol diet: Negligible fat per serving.
Low-purine diet: Prepare as directed.

GRAPE ICE CREAM (120 calories per serving)

¼ cup cornstarch
1 cup granulated sugar
dash cinnamon
dash nutmeg
1½ cups bottled grape juice
1 teaspoon vanilla extract
2 or 3 tablespoons lemon juice
1 14½-ounce can evaporated
    skimmed milk

Day before or early in day: In medium saucepan, mix cornstarch, sugar, cinnamon and nutmeg. Stir in a little grape juice to form a smooth paste; then add remaining grape juice, vanilla, ½ cup water and lemon juice. Cook, stirring constantly, until mixture boils and thickens. Refrigerate, stirring occasionally.

While grape mixture is chilling, freeze evaporated skimmed milk in large mixing bowl until ice crystals form ½-inch to 1-inch from edge of bowl.

When grape and milk mixtures are ready, beat milk with electric mixer at highest speed, until consistency of whipped cream. Beating continuously, slowly add grape-juice mixture. Mix completely. Freeze until firm—at least 4 hours. Makes 2 quarts or twelve ¾-cup servings.

For 6 servings: Use ¾ cup of skimmed evaporated milk; halve all other ingredients.

Diabetic diet: Prepare as directed but omit sugar. Substitute non-nutritive sweetener equivalent to ¾ cup sugar. Exchanges per serving = 1 fruit.
Egg-, gluten-, and wheat-free diet: Prepare as directed.
Low-fat, low-cholesterol diet: Negligible fat per serving.
Low-purine diet: Prepare as directed.
Low-sodium diet: 40 milligrams sodium per serving.

WINTER SHERBET (120 calories per serving)

2 8¹/₂-ounce cans crushed
   pineapple
1 16-ounce can peaches
2 tablespoons lemon juice
¹/₄ teaspoon vanilla extract
dash salt

About 6 hour before serving: In electric-blender container, at low speed, blend crushed pineapple (and syrup) until smooth; pour into medium mixing bowl. Blend peaches (and syrup) until smooth; add to pineapple. Stir in remaining ingredients. Freeze, stirring occasionally, until mushy—about 2 hours. Again blend mixture, one-third at a time, until smooth. Freeze until consistency of sherbet. If softer texture is preferred, thaw at room temperature a few minutes before serving. Makes six ¹/₂-cup servings.

Egg-, gluten-, milk- and wheat-free diet: Prepare as directed.
Low-fat, low-cholesterol diet: Negligible fat per serving.
Low-purine diet: Prepare as directed.
Low-sodium diet: Prepare as directed but omit salt. 2 milligrams sodium per serving.

STRAWBERRY ICE (90 calories per serving)

1 pint strawberries
¹/₂ cup granulated sugar
2 tablespoons orange juice
2 egg whites
¹/₄ teaspoon salt

Early in day: With food grinder or fork, puree strawberries. In medium pan, combine strawberries and sugar. Cover and simmer, over low heat, 5 minutes. Add ¹/₂ cup water and orange juice; cool slightly. Pour into freezer-proof medium bowl, and freeze until a thick mush throughout.

At least 3 hours before serving: In medium bowl, with electric mixer at high speed, beat egg whites and salt until stiff peaks form. Then beat strawberry mixture until light and frothy. Fold in egg whites; return to freezer until firm. Makes 6 servings.

Low-fat, low-cholesterol diet: Negligible fat per serving.
Gluten-, milk- and wheat-free diet: Prepare as directed.
Low-purine diet: Prepare as directed.
Low-sodium diet: Prepare as directed but omit salt. 15 milligrams sodium per serving.

HOMEMADE PINEAPPLE SHERBET (105 calories per serving)

1 envelope unflavored gelatin
1 cup syrup drained from
   20-ounce can crushed
   pineapple
¹/₄ cup granulated sugar
1 teaspoon grated lemon peel
¹/₂ teaspoon vanilla extract
2 tablespoons lemon juice
dash salt
2 cups cold skimmed milk or
   reliquefied nonfat dry milk
drained pineapple from can of
   crushed pineapple

About 5 to 6 hours before serving: In small saucepan, sprinkle gelatin on pineapple syrup; let stand 5 minutes. Heat, stirring constantly, until gelatin is dissolved—do not boil. Stir in sugar, lemon peel, vanilla extract, lemon juice and salt. Place milk in medium bowl; slowly stir in gelatin mixture. (Mixture may appear curdled.) Freeze, stirring occasionally, until ice crystals form throughout most of mixture. Beat until smooth; fold in drained pineapple. Freeze until firm enough to spoon out. (If sherbet freezes too hard, let stand at room temperature to soften slightly.) Makes eight ¹/₂-cup servings.

Egg-, gluten-, and wheat-free diet: Prepare as directed.
Low-fat, low-cholesterol diet: Negligible fat per serving.
Low-purine diet: Prepare as directed.
Low-sodium diet: Prepare as directed but omit salt. 35 milligrams sodium per serving.

SHERBET ARRAY (120 calories per serving)

favorite sherbets
crushed ice
liquid food color
sprig of mint for garnish

Day before serving: Using ice-cream scoop, make large balls of orange, lime and raspberry sherbert. Place in freezer.

About 20 minutes before serving: Prepare about ¹/₂ cup crushed ice for each serving. Tint with liquid food color that matches sherbet, then place in bottom of seafood (or dessert) server. Now place ball of sherbet in cup of each seafood server; add sprig of mint and set cups in servers. Serve at once.

Bland diet: Prepare as directed.
Egg-, gluten-, and wheat-free diet: Prepare as directed but use a gluten-free sherbet on gluten-free diet.
Low-fat, low-cholesterol diet: Negligible fat per serving.
Low-fat, bland (gall bladder) diet: Prepare as directed.
Low-purine diet: Prepare as directed.
Low-residue diet: Prepare as directed.
Low-sodium diet: 10 milligrams sodium per serving.

SPECIAL STRAWBERRY FROST (65 calories per serving)

¹/₂ cup nonfat dry-milk powder
2 tablespoons lemon juice
¹/₄ cup granulated sugar
1 pint fresh strawberries, stemmed

About 4 to 6 hours before serving: In large bowl, stir together milk powder, ¹/₂ cup cold water, lemon juice and sugar. Beat, with electric mixer at high speed (about 15 to 20 minutes), until consistency of whipped cream. Meanwhile, in blender container, at low speed, blend strawberries; fold into milk mixture. (Or puree strawberries through food mill.)

Freeze, in same bowl, until mixture is solid about 3 inches in from sides of bowl. Then beat with electric mixer until smooth. Refreeze until firm. Makes 1 quart or eight ¹/₂-cup servings.

Diabetic diet: Prepare as directed but omit sugar; use non-nutritive sweetener equivalent to ¹/₄ cup sugar. Exchanges per serving = 1 fruit.
Egg-, gluten-, and wheat-free diet: Prepare as directed.
Low-fat, low-cholesterol diet: Negligible fat per serving.
Low-purine diet: Prepare as directed.
Low-sodium diet: Prepare as directed. 40 milligrams sodium per serving. If prepared with low-sodium nonfat dry-milk powder, 3 milligrams sodium per serving.

BLUEBERRY SHERBET (120 calories per serving)

2 teaspoons unflavored gelatin
¹/₄ cup granulated sugar
1 10-ounce package frozen unsweetened whole blueberries, thawed
3 tablespoons light corn syrup
3 tablespoon lemon juice

At least 6 hours before serving: Sprinkle gelatin on ¹/₃ cup water to soften. In saucepan, add sugar to ¹/₃ cup water; boil 5 minutes; add softened gelatin. In blender container at low speed, blend sugar-gelatin mixture and blueberries until smooth. Strain to remove pulp; stir in corn syrup and lemon juice. Pour into ice-cube tray and fit with divider; freeze 5 to 6 hours.

To serve: Place sherbet cubes and ¹/₃ cup water in blender; blend until smooth. Serve immediately in sherbet glasses. Makes 4 servings.

Egg-, gluten-, milk- and wheat-free diet: Prepare as directed.
Low-fat, low-cholesterol diet: Negligible fat per serving.
High-iron diet: 1 milligram iron per serving.
Low-purine diet: Prepare as directed.
Low-sodium diet: 10 milligrams sodium per serving.

FROZEN FRUIT MOUSSE (130 calories per serving)

¹/₃ **cup cinnamon drops**
1 envelope unflavored gelatin
2 16-ounce jars applesauce
1 teaspoon cinnamon
¹/₈ **teaspoon mace**
1 tablespoon lemon juice
1 2-ounce envelope
whipped-topping mix

Up to 4 hours before serving: In small saucepan, simmer and stir cinnamon drops with ¹/₄ cup water until drops dissolve completely. In measuring cup, stir gelatin into ¹/₄ cup cold water; set cup in boiling water, and stir until gelatin is dissolved.

In large bowl, combine applesauce, cinnamon, mace, lemon juice, cinnamon-drop mixture and gelatin. Make up whipped-topping mix as label directs but use skimmed milk; fold into applesauce mixture. Turn into ice-cube trays; freeze until solid 1 inch in from edge. Turn into chilled bowl and beat with hand beater, or electric mixer at low speed, until smooth but not melted. Return mixture to trays; freeze until just firm enough to spoon out. Makes 12 servings.

Low-purine diet: Prepare as directed.
Low sodium diet: Prepare as directed but use 2 cups whipped cream instead of whipped topping. 10 milligrams sodium per serving.

RAINBOW WHIP (145 calories per serving)

1 3-ounce package lemon-flavor
gelatin
1 3-ounce package lime-flavor
gelatin
1 3-ounce package
strawberry-punch-flavor
gelatin
1 cup frozen whipped topping

Early in day: In 3 separate bowls, make up each of the gelatin flavors as label directs. Refrigerate until each mounds when dropped from spoon.

Then, with electric mixer at high speed, beat lemon-flavored gelatin until fluffy; spoon into 8 sherbet glasses. Refrigerate until gelatin sets a little. Top each with layer of lime gelatin; again refrigerate until gelatin sets a little. Use strawberry-punch gelatin for top layer; refrigerate until firm. Top each serving with dab of whipped topping. Makes 8 servings.

Bland diet: Prepare as directed.
Egg-, gluten-, and wheat-free diet: Prepare as directed.
Low-fat, low-cholesterol diet: Prepare as directed but omit frozen whipped topping. Negligible fat per serving.
Low-fat, bland (gall bladder) diet: Prepare as directed but omit frozen whipped topping.
Low-purine diet: Prepare as directed but omit frozen whipped topping if fat is restricted on diet.
Low-residue diet: Prepare as directed.

BANANA POPS (90 calories per pop)

2 cups crushed bananas
(approximately 3 bananas)
1 cup orange juice
2 tablespoons granulated sugar
1 teaspoon lemon juice

About 4 to 6 hours before serving: In medium bowl, combine ¹/₄ cup water, bananas and remaining ingredients, mixing well. Divide among six 4-ounce paper cups. Freeze until firm. (If desired, add popsicle sticks or wooden spoons when semi-firm.)

To serve: Let stand at room temperature for 5 minutes; to eat, peel paper cup down from pop. Makes 6 servings.

Bland diet: Prepare as directed.
Egg-, gluten-, milk- and wheat-free diet: Prepare as directed.
Low-fat, low-cholesterol diet: Negligible fat per serving.
Low-fat, bland (gall bladder) diet: Prepare as directed.
Low-sodium diet: 1 milligram sodium per serving.

LADYFINGERS PROFITEROLE (60 calories each)

1 3³/₄-ounce package chocolate whipped-dessert mix
skimmed milk or reliquefied nonfat dry milk
2 tablespoons instant-coffee powder
3 3-ounce packages ladyfingers
1 cup granulated sugar
¹/₄ teaspoon cream of tartar

Day before serving or early in day: Prepare dessert mix as label directs, but use skimmed milk for regular milk and add coffee powder with water; refrigerate. Meanwhile, separate ladyfingers. Spread whipped dessert on bottom halves of ladyfingers; cover with tops.

In small skillet, mix sugar, ³/₄ cup water and cream of tartar; bring to boiling; lower heat to medium, then simmer until very light amber, stirring occasionally. Drizzle a bit of the caramel syrup over each ladyfinger; refrigerate.

To serve: Arrange ladyfingers on cake stand in pyramid. Makes 36.

Bland diet: Prepare as directed. (Substitute vanilla whipped-dessert mix for chocolate if chocolate is forbidden on diet.)
Low-purine diet: Prepare as directed but substitute vanilla whipped-dessert mix for chocolate if chocolate is forbidden on diet.
Low-residue diet: Prepare as directed. (See note for bland diet.)

CHOCOLATE-VANILLA-PEACH GEM (155 calories per serving)

1 29-ounce can cling peaches, chilled
2 3³/₄-ounce packages vanilla whipped-dessert mix
1 cup skimmed milk or reliquefied nonfat dry milk
2 teaspoons almond extract
1 9-inch round chocolate-cake layer

Early in day: Drain peaches, reserving syrup. Dry peaches on paper towels; cube; set aside. Prepare 1 package whipped dessert mix as label directs, but use ¹/₂ cup peach syrup and ¹/₂ cup skimmed milk as liquid; stir in 1 teaspoon almond extract. Refrigerate 10 minutes, then fold in half of cubed peaches.

Cut chocolate-cake layer into 6 even wedges. Arrange 3 of these, spoke-fashion, on cake plate. Fold 30-inch piece of foil in half lengthwise; grease lightly, then coil around outside of cake wedges, forming collar; tape in place. Now spoon whipped dessert evenly into empty spaces; refrigerate.

Meanwhile, prepare other package of whipped-dessert mix, using ¹/₂ cup peach syrup, ¹/₂ cup skimmed milk and 1 teaspoon almond extract, as above. Now make second layer on top of first one by laying remaining 3 cake wedges on top of whipped-dessert wedges in first layer; spoon newly prepared whipped dessert into empty spaces. Refrigerate 2 hours. Just before serving, peel foil collar off cake. Cut into 16 wedges.

MAX'S LOW-CALORIE CHEESECAKE (185 calories per serving)

Graham-Cracker Crust (see recipe page 239)
12 ounces creamed cottage cheese (1¹/₂ 8-ounce containers)
2 eggs
¹/₂ cup granulated sugar
¹/₂ teaspoon vanilla extract

Early in day: Prepare Graham-Cracker Crust as directed but make 8-inch pie shell, and do not bake. In electric-blender container, at low speed, blend cottage cheese, eggs, sugar and vanilla. (Or sieve cottage cheese, then mix with other ingredients.) Pour into prepared pie shell. Bake 35 minutes in preheated 350°F. oven, or until filling puffs slightly and seems dry on top. Refrigerate at least 2 hours to chill thoroughly. Makes 8 servings.

Bland diet: Prepare as directed.
Low-purine diet: Prepare as directed.
Low-residue diet: Prepare as directed.

LEAN MAN'S CAKE (130 calories per serving)

2 cups sifted cake flour
2¹/₂ teaspoons double-acting baking powder
³/₄ teaspoon salt
¹/₃ cup shortening
³/₄ granulated sugar
1 egg, unbeaten
1 cup less 2 tablespoons skimmed milk or reliquefied nonfat dry milk
1 teaspoon vanilla extract (or 1 tablespoon grated orange or lemon peel)

At least 3 hours before serving: Preheat oven to 350°F. Grease bottom of 8-inch square cake pan, then line with waxed paper. Sift flour with baking powder and salt. In large bowl, with electric mixer at medium speed, cream shortening with sugar, then with egg, until **very light and fluffy**—about 4 minutes altogether. Then, at low speed, beat in alternately, **just until smooth**, flour mixture in fourths and combined milk and vanilla in thirds. Turn into pan. Bake 45 minutes, or until cake tester, inserted in center, comes out clean. Cool on rack about 10 minutes. Remove from pan; peel off paper; cool on rack. Makes 16 servings.

Bland diet: Prepare as directed.
Low-purine diet: Prepare as directed.
Low-residue diet: Prepare as directed.

NUT-TOPPED LEAN MAN'S CAKE (160 calories per serving)

Lean Man's Cake batter (see recipe above)
¹/₄ cup packed brown sugar
2 teaspoons cinnamon
2 tablespoons flour
1¹/₂ tablespoons melted butter or margarine
3 tablespoons chopped walnuts

At least 3 hours before serving: Make Lean Man's Cake as directed. Meanwhile, with fork, thoroughly mix remaining ingredients.

When cake is done, before cooling, sprinkle with topping. Bake at 350°F. 5 minutes more; cool as directed. Makes 16 servings.

CHOCO-NUT CAKE (165 calories per serving)

1 cup flaked coconut
3 tablespoons water
¹/₄ cup melted chocolate morsels
Lean Man's Cake batter (recipe above)

At least 2 hours before serving: Preheat oven to 375°F. Grease bottom of 8-inch square cake pan, then line with waxed paper. Combine coconut, water and chocolate. Prepare cake batter. Pour half into pan; sprinkle with half of coconut-chocolate mixture; repeat. Bake 35 minutes. Cool in pan, on rack, about 10 minutes. Remove from pan; peel off paper; cool on rack. Makes 16 servings.

UPSIDE-DOWN SPICE CAKE (155 calories per serving)

2 16-ounce cans freestone peach halves, drained
6 maraschino cherries, halved
¹/₄ cup packed brown sugar
1 18¹/₂-ounce package spice-cake mix
water and 1 egg for cake mix

About 1¹/₂ hours before serving: Preheat oven to 350°F. In 12″ by 8″ by 2″ baking dish, arrange 12 peach halves, cut side down. Tuck cherry half under each peach. Sprinkle with brown sugar.

Prepare half of cake mix according to package directions for one layer. Pour batter evenly over peach halves. Bake 30 to 35 minutes, or until cake is a rich golden-brown and just beginning to come away from edges of pan. Cool on rack 10 minutes; loosen sides with spatula. Place large serving plate over baking dish; invert both; let stand 2 minutes; remove baking dish. Serve cake warm. Makes 12 servings.

Egg-free diet: Prepare as directed but for cake batter use milk in place of water and omit egg.
Low-purine diet: Prepare as directed.

ANGEL LOAF WITH ORANGE GLAZE (70 calories per serving)

3/4 cup egg whites, at room
temperature (about 6 egg
whites)
1 teaspoon cream of tartar
1/2 teaspoon orange extract
1/8 teaspoon salt
1/3 cup sugar
1/3 cup all-purpose flour
2 tablespoons orange
marmalade
2 tablespoons orange-flavored
liqueur

Line bottom of 8½" by 4½" loaf pan with waxed paper. Preheat oven to 350°F. In large bowl, with mixer at high speed, beat egg whites, cream of tartar, orange extract and salt until foamy. Gradually sprinkle in sugar, beating just until soft peaks form and sugar is dissolved. Gently fold flour into egg whites until blended. Spoon mixture into prepared loaf pan; bake 30 minutes or until top springs back when touched lightly. Invert cake in pan, resting edges of pan on two other inverted pans; cool completely. With metal spatula, loosen cake from sides of loaf pan.

To serve, invert cake from pan onto dessert dish; discard waxed paper. In small saucepan over low heat, stir marmalade and orange flavored liqueur until mixed. With pastry brush, brush mixture over top and sides of cake. Makes 10 servings.

Low-fat, low-cholesterol diet: Prepare as directed. Negligible fat per serving.
Milk-free diet: Prepare as directed.
Low-sodium diet: Prepare as directed. 50 milligrams sodium per serving.

ANGEL-BERRY SHORTCAKE (170 calories per serving)

1 16-ounce package angel-food
cake mix
confectioners' sugar
1 2-ounce envelope
whipped-topping mix
3 pints large strawberries,
halved
1/4 cup fresh blueberries

Early in day: Preheat oven to 375°F. Line bottom of 15" by 10" by 1" greased jelly-roll pan with waxed paper; grease well. Prepare angel-food cake mix as label directs. Spread batter evenly in jelly-roll pan; bake 20 minutes, or until done. Cover large rack with sheet of waxed paper, then lightly dust with confectioners' sugar. When cake is done, loosen from sides of pan; invert onto waxed paper. Lift off pan, and peel off paper. Let cake stand at room temperature until just cool; then return to clean jelly-roll pan; wrap; refrigerate.

About 30 minutes before serving: Prepare whipped-topping mix as label directs but use skimmed milk. Spread evenly on top of cake. Top with rows of strawberries; garnish with blueberries. Cut into 15 rectangles.

SPECTATOR'S SPONGE CAKE (130 calories per serving)

1 7.2-ounce package fluffy
white-frosting mix
1 13.5 ounce 6-inch square
packaged sponge cake
9 large perfect fresh
strawberries, washed and
stemmed

At least 20 minutes before serving: Into small bowl, measure 1/4 cup plus 1 tablespoon frosting mix; stir in 2 tablespoons boiling water, then beat with electric mixer at highest speed until stiff peaks form—about 5 minutes. (Carefully seal remaining frosting mix for later use. To prepare it, use 6 tablespoons boiling water and follow label instructions. Makes enough frosting for two 8-inch layers.)

Use frosting to frost top of sponge cake; then, with knife, mark frosting into 2" by 2" squares to indicate serving sizes. Place strawberry, cut side down, in center of each square. Refrigerate until serving time. Makes 9 servings.

Low-purine diet: Prepare as directed but omit whipped topping.

POUND-CAKE TIDBITS WITH ORANGE-WALNUT BUTTER (50 calories per serving)

1 10³/₄- to 12-ounce package
  frozen ready-to-serve pound
  cake, thawed
2 tablespoons finely chopped
  California walnuts
1 tablespoon butter or
  margarine, softened
¹/₄ teaspoon grated orange peel

Preheat oven to 375°F. Cut pound cake in foil pan, lengthwise, into thirds, then crosswise into eigths; set aside. In cup, combine walnuts, softened butter or margarine and orange peel; carefully spread walnut mixture over top of pound cake. Bake 15 minutes or until heated through.

To serve, remove cake from pan; arrange, top-side up, in bread basket or serving bowl. Makes 24 servings.

Low-purine diet: Prepare as directed.
Low-fat diet: Prepare as directed. 4 grams fat per serving.
Low-sodium diet: Prepare as directed but substitute unsalted butter or margarine. 68 milligrams sodium per serving.

DOUBLE APPLE UPSIDE-DOWN CAKE (170 calories per serving)

1 16-ounce jar raspberry
  applesauce
1 18¹/₂-ounce package
  applesauce-cake mix
2 eggs for cake mix

About 1¹/₂ hours before serving: In greased 13″ by 9″ by 2″ baking pan, spread applesauce. Prepare cake mix as label directs. Pour batter over applesauce, spreading it to edges. Bake 35 minutes, or until cake tester, inserted in center, comes out clean. Cool 10 minutes on rack. With spatula, loosen cake from sides of pan; place cake plate on top of pan; invert. Cool. Makes 16 servings.

Bland diet: Prepare as directed.
Egg-free diet: Prepare as directed but omit eggs; substitute milk for water in cake mix.
Low-fat diet: Prepare as directed but use only whites of eggs. 3 grams fat per serving. Omit recipe from fat-controlled diet.
Low-fat, bland (gall bladder) diet: Prepare as directed for low-fat diet.
Low-purine diet: Prepare as directed.
Low-residue diet: Prepare as directed.

RAINBOW ANGEL CAKE (160 calories per serving)

1 16-ounce package angel-food
  cake mix
2 tablespoons chocolate sauce
  (from a jar)
2 tablespoons skimmed milk
2 tablespoons caramel sauce
  (from a jar)
2 tablespoons cranberry-juice
  cocktail
red food color

Early in day: Make and bake angel-food cake in 10-inch tube pan as label directs. Cool; place, top side down, on wire rack. Into measuring cup, pour chocolage sauce and 1 tablespoon milk; set in a little boiling water in saucepan; heat to pouring consistency.

Mark top of cake into thirds. About ¹/₂ inch out from center of edge of cake, with wooden meat skewer, make deep hole; into it pour some chocolate sauce. Now, in same third of cake, make a number of holes of varying depths. Fill each hole with chocolate sauce.

Make and fill holes in second third of cake, using caramel sauce.

In cup, tint cranberry-juice cocktail with few drops red food color. Make and fill holes in last third of cake, using tinted juice.

To serve: Cut into wedges. Makes 16 servings.

Low-fat, low-cholesterol diet: Prepare as directed. About 1 gram fat per serving.
Low-purine diet: Prepare as directed.

RAINBOW CUPCAKES (100 calories per serving)

1/2 cup cake flour
1/2 teaspoon double-acting
   baking powder
1/8 teaspoon salt
1 egg
3 tablespoons granulated sugar
3/4 teaspoon lemon juice
2 tablespoons plus 1 1/2
   teaspoons hot skimmed milk
   or reliquefied nonfat dry milk

At least 2 hours before serving: Preheat oven to 350°F. Lightly grease 8 medium muffin cups. Sift flour with baking powder and salt 3 times. With electric mixer at high speed, beat egg **until very thick and light**—about 5 minutes. Gradually add sugar, beating constantly. Beat in lemon juice. Fold in flour mixture, a small amount at a time. Add hot milk; stir quickly until blended. Immediately turn batter into prepared muffin cups. Bake 15 minutes, or until done. Cool in pans 10 minutes. Makes 8 cupcakes.

Bland diet: Prepare as directed.
Low-purine diet: Prepare as directed.
Low-residue diet: Prepare as directed.

HOLIDAY CUPCAKES (80 calories per cupcake)

36 fluted paper baking cups
1 14 1/2- to 16-ounce package
   white angel food cake mix
1/4 cup chocolate sprinkles
1 6-ounce package
   semisweet-chocolate pieces
2 tablespoons butter or
   margarine
2 tablespoons light corn syrup
nonpareils for garnish

Place a paper baking cup in each of thirty-six 2 1/2-inch muffin-pan cups; set aside.

Prepare angel food cake mix as label directs, but add chocolate sprinkles with flour mixture. Spoon batter into paper cups; bake 10 minutes or until golden brown. Cool cupcakes on wire racks. When cupcakes are cooled, in double boiler over hot, **not boiling,** water, heat chocolate pieces, butter or margarine, and corn syrup until chocolate is melted and mixture is smooth, stirring frequently. With spatula, spread warm chocolate mixture on top of cupcakes. Sprinkle cupcakes with nonpareils, if you like. Makes 36 cupcakes.

Low-fat, low-cholesterol diet: Prepare as directed. 3 grams fat per serving.
Low-sodium diet: Prepare as directed. 50 milligrams sodium per serving.
Milk-free diet: Substitute 2 tablespoons salad oil for butter or margarine.

STRAWBERRY SHORTCAKES (190 calories per serving)

1 teaspoon cornstarch
1/4 cup orange juice
1 14- or 16-ounce package
   frozen unsweetened whole
   strawberries, partially thawed
1/3 cup granulated sugar
2 baker's 6-inch sponge-cake
   layers
1 cup whipped topping

Early in day: Mix cornstarch with orange juice until smooth. In sauce pan over medium heat, heat strawberries and sugar to boiling, then stir in orange-juice mixture. Cook, stirring, until slightly thickened; refrigerate.

About 30 minutes before serving: Place one cake layer on cake plate; spread with some of strawberry mixture; top with other cake layer, then with prepared whipped topping.

To serve: Cut shortcake into 8 wedges; serve each topped with some of remaining strawberry mixture. Makes 8 servings. (If whipped topping is omitted, 150 calories per serving.)

GRAHAM-CRACKER CRUST (575 calories per pie crust)

³/₄ cup graham-cracker crumbs
1 tablespoon granulated sugar
2 tablespoons butter or
   margarine
1 tablespoon water
dash salt

About 1 hour before serving: Preheat oven to 350°F. In 9-inch pie plate, mix all ingredients. Press on bottom and sides of plate. Bake 6 to 8 minutes, or until brown around edges. Cool before filling.

Bland diet: Prepare as directed.
Diabetic diet: Prepare as directed but use margarine instead of butter; use cornflake crumbs; omit sugar; substitute granulated non-nutritive sweetener equivalent to 1 tablespoon sugar. Exchanges per serving = ¹/₂ fat per ¹/₈ pie crust.
Low-fat, low-cholesterol diet: Prepare as directed but use margarine instead of butter. 3 grams fat per 1/10 crust.
Low-fat bland (gall bladder) diet: Prepare as directed.
Low-purine diet: Prepare as directed.
Low-residue diet: Prepare as directed.

LEMON PARFAIT PIE (160 calories per serving)

Graham Cracker Crust (see
   recipe above)
1 3-ounce package lemon-flavor
   gelatin
1 teaspoon grated lemon peel
3 tablespoons lemon juice
1 pint vanilla ice milk

At least 2 hours before serving: Make, bake and cool Graham-Cracker Crust as directed. In 2-quart saucepan, dissolve lemon-flavor gelatin in 1¹/₄ cups boiling water; add lemon peel and juice. Add vanilla ice milk by spoonfuls, stirring until melted. Refrigerate until mixture is thickened but not set—25 to 30 minutes. Turn into graham crust. Refrigerate until firm—at least 1 hour. Makes 8 servings.

Bland diet: Prepare as directed.
Low-fat, bland (gall bladder) diet: Prepare as directed.
Low-purine diet: Prepare as directed.
Low-residue diet: Prepare as directed.

LEMON CHIFFON PIE (155 calories per serving)

1 envelope unflavored gelatin
granulated sugar
2 egg yolks
1 tablespoon finely grated
   lemon peel
¹/₄ cup lemon juice
1 3¹/₂-ounce can flaked coconut
1 tablespoon butter or
   margarine, softened
4 egg whites
¹/₄ teaspoon salt

Early in day: In small saucepan, mix gelatin, ¹/₄ cup granulated sugar, egg yolks, lemon peel, lemon juice and ¹/₃ cup water. Cook over low heat, stirring constantly, until mixture just begins to boil around edges. Refrigerate, stirring occasionally, until mixture mounds slightly when dropped from spoon; beat smooth.

Meanwhile, preheat oven to 350°F. In 9-inch pie plate, mix coconut and butter. Then spread evenly over bottom and up the sides of pie plate. Bake 7 minutes, or until coconut is dark golden-brown around edges; cool.

When lemon mixture mounds slightly: In medium bowl, beat egg whites and salt until soft peaks form; slowly beat in ¹/₄ cup sugar until stiff peaks form. Fold in lemon mixture; heap into pie shell. Refrigerate until serving time—at least 3 hours. Makes 8 servings.

Low-purine diet: Prepare as directed.

MELON CHIFFON PIE (175 calories per serving)

Graham Cracker Crust (see recipe page 239)
2 tablespoons cornstarch
grated peel of 1/2 lemon
2 tablespoons lemon juice
1/2 cup granulated sugar
2 eggs
1 1/2 teaspoons unflavored gelatin
3 cups finely diced cantaloupe

Early in day: Prepare, bake and cool Graham-Cracker Crust as directed.

To make filling: In top of double boiler, mix cornstarch with 2 tablespoons water; stir in lemon peel and juice, sugar, egg yolks and gelatin. Beating with spoon, stir in 1 cup boiling water. Cook over boiling water, beating constantly with egg beater or electric mixer, until thickened. Refrigerate until consistency of soft pudding.

About 4 hours before serving: Beat egg whites until stiff peaks form. Into lemon mixture, fold in cantaloupe then egg whites. Turn into pie shell. Refrigerate until set. Makes 8 servings.

PEACHES WITH CINNAMON CREME (100 calories per serving)

1 16-ounce can sliced cling peaches in juice, drained
1 teaspoon lemon juice
dash salt
1/2 cup frozen whipped topping, thawed
1/4 teaspoon ground cinnamon
1/2 3-ounce package ladyfingers
1 tablespoon walnuts, chopped

In blender at medium speed, blend peaches, lemon juice, and salt until smooth; set aside. In small bowl, stir whipped topping and cinnamon until blended. Separate ladyfingers; arrange in bottom of four dessert dishes. Pour peach mixture over ladyfingers. Top with whipped topping mixture; sprinkle with walnuts. Makes 4 servings.

Low-fat: 3 grams fat per serving.
Low-residue diet: Prepare as directed.
Low-purine diet: Prepare as directed.
Milk-free diet: Prepare as directed.

APPLE DESSERT PANCAKES (155 calories per serving)

2 eggs
2/3 cup milk
1 tablespoon melted shortening
1/4 teaspoon salt
granulated sugar
2/3 cup sifted all-purpose flour
2 apples
butter or margarine

Early in day or at least 1 1/2 hours before serving: In electric blender container or electric mixer, beat eggs thoroughly. Add milk, shortening, salt and 1 teaspoon sugar, then beat once more. Add flour and beat until a smooth batter. Pare and core apples; slice very thin into 16 slices.

Heat 1 teaspoon butter in 7-inch skillet; add 2 apple slices; sauté until tender-crisp. Then, using 1/4-cup measuring cup as scoop, pour scant 1/4 cup batter over apple slices; tilt skillet to spread batter over bottom. Cook pancake until brown on bottom. With narrow spatula, loosen sides and underpart of apple slices; now invert pancake into another hot buttered skillet; sauté until underside is golden-brown, then slip onto square of waxed paper, on rack. In same way, continue making pancakes (8 in all), placing each on waxed-paper square and piling one on top of another.

Now remove each pancake from waxed paper; carefully fold in half, then lay, in overlapping row, down center of cookie sheet or stainless-steel platter. Set aside.

Just before serving: Sprinkle pancakes with 2 tablespoons sugar; broil till hot and bubbly. If pancakes were broiled on cookie sheet, transfer to heated platter for serving. Makes 8 servings.

Bland diet: Prepare as directed.
Low-fat diet: 5 grams fat per serving. Omit recipe from low-cholesterol diet.
Low-purine diet: Prepare as directed.
Low-residue diet: Prepare as directed.
Low-sodium diet: Prepare as directed but omit salt and use unsalted butter or margarine. 35 milligrams sodium per serving.

GERMAN DESSERT PANCAKE (140 calories per serving)

¹/₃ cup sifted all-purpose flour
¹/₄ teaspoon double-acting
baking powder
¹/₃ cup milk
2 eggs, slightly beaten
2 tablespoons butter or
margarine
1 tablespoon confectioners'
sugar
4 lemon wedges for garnish

About 25 minutes before serving: Preheat oven to 425°F. In small bowl, combine flour and baking powder. Beat in milk and eggs, leaving batter a bit lumpy. In 10-inch skillet with heat-proof handle, melt butter. When butter is very hot, pour in batter all at ounce. Bake in oven 15 to 18 minutes, or until pancake is golden. Sprinkle with sugar. Serve hot, with lemon wedges for squeezing over pancake. Makes 4 servings.

Bland diet: Prepare as directed.
Low-fat diet: 10 grams fat per serving. Omit recipe from low-cholesterol diet.
Low-purine diet: Prepare as directed.
Low-residue diet: Prepare as directed.

Special Diets

Physicians prescribe special diets to treat many disorders. If you are following one of these prescriptions, you'll find here the reasons "why," suggestions to simplify planning and delicious recipes. See the index for recipes in the main section that can be adapted, as indicated at the end of each, for use in particular special diets.

The seven therapeutic diets discussed in this chapter are used to treat some common ailments and disorders. They are: Allergy Diets (pages 242-252) for those who are allergic to egg, gluten, milk or wheat; Bland Diets (pages 253-265) for ulcer, gall bladder and colitis sufferers; Diabetic Diet (pages 266-277), with an explanation of the "exchange" system; High-Iron Diet (pages 278-285) for sufferers from anemia; Low-Fat, Low-Cholesterol Diet (pages 286-296) for those who are concerned about heart attacks; Low-Purine Diet (pages 297-305) for people with chronic gout; Low-Sodium Diets (pages 306-318) for those who have kidney trouble or hypertension.

Remember, these diets should be used only with your doctor's approval.

ALLERGY DIETS

In terms of meal planning, the most difficult allergies to cope with are those involving egg, gluten, milk and wheat. Each is a basic food ingredient (gluten is found in wheat and several other grains); eliminating these ingredients in recipes requires careful planning. See page 244 for some guidelines to aid in adapting recipes for allergy diets. The recipes in this section are for baked goods—the problem area in cooking for egg-, gluten-, milk- and wheat-free diets. How to make egg-free cakes from cake mixes is discussed on page 245.

The questions and answers that follow cover the more general problems allergy-sufferers must face, along with some specific suggestions for treatment.

Q. *What is an allergy?*
A. An allergy is an unusual physical reaction to some substance in the environment that is normally harmless. The allergic reaction or sensitivity may be to food or to such substances as pollen, dust, feathers or fur. When the offending substance comes in contact with the skin or the mucous membrane lining the eyes, nose, lungs or digestive system of an allergic person, antibodies are formed; the interaction of the foreign substance with these antibodies results in a reaction. The reaction can show up as skin rashes, asthma, red nose, headaches, digestive upsets, and many other things.

Q. *Are allergies inherited?*
A. Allergies aren't inherited in the way that blue eyes and red hair are, but a predisposition or tendency to allergies does run in families. If both parents have allergies, there is a greater chance that their children will also have them. Pediatricians consider this tendency when prescribing formulas and introducing new foods.

Q. *Are people born with allergies?*
A. In most cases, allergies develop after birth—a person first must become sensitive to a food or other substance before an allergic reaction can develop. Though children are the most likely ones to develop allergies as they change from formula to regular food, allergies can develop at any time.

Q. *How can I recognize a food allergy?*
A. While it's not fair to blame all adverse reactions to food on allergies, it's essential to take a child to the doctor if he repeatedly suffers from any of the symptoms mentioned above. If the doctor suspects a food allergy, he will review the child's eating habits with you, and try to correlate the onset of reactions with the eating of certain foods. This is not always as simple as it may sound. In some cases, the allergic reaction begins as soon as the food is eaten. But in most cases, the food must be digested first; symptoms won't occur until hours later. In trying to pinpoint the cause of the reaction, the

physicians will often suggest eliminating foods such as chocolate, nuts, milk or eggs from the diet for a week or two. If symptoms clear up, it's then relatively easy to pick out the offending food. The child is given the suspected food again; if symptoms return, the allergy is considered confirmed. For adults, too, recurring symptoms should be brought to a doctor's attention. He can help identify the allergens (the offending substances) if they are what is causing the reaction. But beware of jumping to conclusions about allergic reactions to foods. Food poisoning and overeating, among other things, cause similar symptoms.

Q. *Do children outgrow allergies?*
A. A true allergy is not outgrown. Often the reaction will be milder or "outgrown" if the offending food is omitted from the diet for several years. However, allergies can reappear later, indicating that they were dormant, not outgrown.

Q. *Are allergic reactions always equally severe?*
A. No. In the case of a mild allergy, it's possible to eat a small portion of a certain food with little reaction. Also, if the eating is paced (for instance, eggs twice a week, not every day), no reaction may occur.

Your emotional state can play a part in the degree of reaction, too. When you're tense or tired, reactions will often be more violent than usual.

Cooking some foods may change them enough to prevent a reaction to them. For instance, cooked vegetables and fruits are easier to tolerate than raw ones; some children who are allergic to fresh milk can tolerate evaporated milk.

Q. *Is there a common factor in food that causes allergic reactions?*
A. Although the most common offender is the protein portion of food, there is no one universal factor that causes allergies. In fact, it is often only one part of a particular food that causes a reaction. For example, in the case of a reaction to orange juice, it may be oil from the orange peel that causes a reaction—not the orange juice itself.

Q. If you are allergic to a certain food, what others should you suspect?

A. Foods can be divided into common botanical and animal families, and allergic reactions often run in families. If you are allergic to peanuts, a legume, you'll also tend to be allergic to peas, beans and lentils. If onions are a problem, also suspect leeks, garlic and asparagus. Your doctor can give you a list of commonly associated food allergies.

Q. How can you know what packaged foods contain?

A. Read the list of ingredients on the label to be found on virtually all packaged foods.

In some cases, however, the listing is not specific enough. For example, "starch" may be wheat starch, cornstarch, potato starch, or other types. For more information write to the manufacturer. All large companies have consumer services departments. Several have also prepared lists of their products which may be used on various allergy diets.

Some products do not list their ingredients on the label. These products have federal "standards of identity" that limit the type and proportion of ingredients that may be used. Two examples are mayonnaise and ice cream. For these it is then necessary to write the manufacturer for information.

Q. If you are allergic to gluten or wheat, what other grain products may be used?

A. Gluten-free diets are primarily for treatment of children's celiac disease and adults' nontropical sprue. Wheat must be eliminated mainly because of allergic reactions.

On wheat-free diets, cornmeal and corn-starch, oatmeal, tapioca, rice and rice cereals are readily available. In addition, rye, barley, potato starch, rice and soybean flours may be used. They are available in some super-markets and health-food stores.

Gluten is found in unrefined wheat, barley, rye and oats as well as in many of their common processed forms (bread, flour, cereal). If gluten must be avoided, you may still use arrowroot, cornstarch and wheat starch (the gluten has been removed, but in severe cases, wheat starch may not be tolerated). Corn flour and cornmeal, rice flour and rice in other forms, potato starch, tapioca, soybean flour may also be used. If you must avoid either gluten or wheat, you usually need special recipes, especially for baking.

ADAPTING RECIPES FOR ALLERGY DIETS

Many favorite recipes can be adapted with only slight modifications for allergy diets. Here are some general guide lines.

- Look for recipes that either lack the allergenic food, or include it only in small quantities, so that a substitution can be easily made.
- When experimenting with cookies, bake just a few at first until you see that the recipe is right. You may find you should add more flour, liquid, etc. Also, bake the first few cookies in a pan with a rim—a cake pan or pie plate—rather than on a cookie sheet. This will save an oven-cleaning job if the cookies spread too much.

- Since cakes are particularly delicate, when making layer cakes, first grease pans, then line with waxed paper and grease again; then flour.

FOR EGG-FREE DIETS:

- Recipes that call for no more than two eggs, plus relatively large amounts of baking powder (1½ to 2 teaspoons) or baking soda (1 to ½ teaspoons), can often be made without eggs. The extra baking powder or soda helps to increase the volume and compensates for the lack of eggs.
- Egg-free cakes have a moist, chewy texture and a more "bready" flavor.

Compensate for this by adding more flavoring—spices, raisins, etc.
- Increase beating time by one-half minute after each step; beat batter an additional two minutes before adding any fruit or nuts. This will get more air into the batter and make the product higher and lighter. Then spoon batter or dough onto baking pan or onto cookie sheet; handle as little as possible; bake immediately.

FOR MILK-FREE DIETS:

- Look for recipes which require only small amounts of milk; substitute water or fruit juices for milk.
- Use only milk-free margarine for butter or margarine. There are several milk-free brands—check lists of ingredients.
- If evaporated milk can be tolerated on the diet (check with your doctor), use one part evaporated milk to one part water as a substitute for milk in recipes.
- Special non-milk formulas, generally used for infants allergic to milk, usually may be substituted for milk in recipes. Most coffee lighteners and other milk substitutes contain caseinates—often the allergenic factor in milk—and should be used only with your doctor's approval.

FOR WHEAT-FREE DIETS:

- Try recipes using grain products that are readily available—cornstarch, cornmeal, oatmeal, etc.
- Look for recipes, such as corn bread, that use a small amount of wheat flour combined with another flour. This makes it easier to substitute another flour for the wheat flour.
- Use half the amount of wheat flour called for when substituting cornstarch, rice flour, potato flour or arrowroot starch in puddings, sauces and gravies.
- Use the table below as a rough estimate of the amount of other flours to substitute for 1 cup all-purpose flour:
    1 cup barley flour
    1 cup corn flour
    3/4 cup cornmeal
    7/8 cup rice flour
    1 1/4 cups rye flour
    1 1/3 cups oat flour
    3/8 cup potato-starch flour
    1 cup soybean flour, plus 1/4 cup potato-starch flour

MAKING EGG-FREE CAKES FROM MIXES

- *To choose a mix:* Read the list of ingredients; select one that doesn't contain eggs or egg products. Success can't be guaranteed with every brand and flavor of cake mix on the market, but most flavors of the four major brands in 16- to 19-ounce packages should give acceptable results.
- *To mix:* Prepare cake as label directs but omit eggs; substitute milk for water.
- *To select cake pans:* Do not use 8-inch layer-cake pans or cake will sink in center. Bake cakes in two 9-inch layer-cake pans, a 9-inch square pan or in 13" by 9" by 2" oblongs. Thoroughly grease and flour pans. Or use medium muffin cups and baking-cup liners; fill cups with only a heaping tablespoon of batter.
- *To bake:* Bake as label directs. Do not underbake. When cakes are done, they will come away from the edge of the pan.
- *To cool:* Cool and remove from pan as directed; cool on rack. Cakes made without eggs are very fragile, so handle with care.
- *To frost and store:* Cool completely before frosting. Spread frosting with a gentle touch. Keep cakes tightly covered. Freeze for long-term storage.
- *To freeze:* For unfrosted layers, cool completely, then wrap snugly with heavy-duty foil or saran, or put in plastic bags. For frosted layers, freeze cake, uncovered, one or two hours. Then wrap and replace in freezer. Freeze individual cake slices and cupcakes in the same way.

ALLERGY DIETS: 25 Recipes for Baked Goods

POTATO-FLOUR SPONGE CAKE (gluten-, milk- and wheat-free diet)

4 eggs, separated
granulated sugar
1/2 cup potato-starch flour
3/4 teaspoon double-acting
　baking powder
1/8 teaspoon salt
1/2 teaspoon finely grated
　lemon peel
1/2 teaspoon lemon juice

About 4 hours before serving: Preheat oven to 325°F. In medium bowl, with electric mixer at high speed, beat egg yolks until thick and fluffy—at least 5 minutes. Gradually beat in 1/2 cup sugar. Then **fold** potato starch into yolk mixture.

In large bowl, with electric mixer at high speed, beat egg whites until almost stiff. Gradually beat in 1/4 cup sugar mixed with baking powder and salt. Beat until stiff—but not dry—peaks form.

Fold yolk mixture, lemon peel and lemon juice into whites. Turn into ungreased 9-inch square cake pan. Bake 60 minutes, or until golden. Invert pan to cool. Cool thoroughly before removing from pan.

CHERRY UPSIDE-DOWN CAKE (gluten-, milk- and wheat-free diet)

1 16-ounce can pitted tart red
　cherries
3 tablespoons milk-free
　margarine
3/4 cup granulated sugar
1/4 teaspoon cinnamon
2 eggs, separated
2/3 cup uncooked cream-of-rice
　cereal
1/2 teaspoon salt

About 1 hour before serving: Preheat oven to 350°F. Drain cherries, reserving 1/4 cup liquid. In 9-inch round cakepan, in oven, melt milk-free margarine. In small bowl, combine cherries, 1/2 cup sugar and cinnamon; spread in cake pan. In small bowl, with electric mixer at high speed, beat egg whites until stiff peaks form; gradually add 1/4 cup sugar. In another small bowl, with electric mixer at high speed, beat egg yolks until thick and lemon-colored. Blend reserved juice, cereal and salt into egg yolks; fold into whites until well blended. Pour batter over cherries, spreading evenly; bake 40 minutes, or until cake pulls away from sides of pan. Immediately loosen from pan with knife; invert on platter. Serve warm. Makes 8 servings.

ORANGE-BLOSSOM CAKE (egg- and milk-free diet)

1/2 cup milk-free margarine
3/4 cup granulated sugar
1 3/4 teaspoons vanilla extract
1 tablespoon grated orange
　peel
3 cups sifted cake flour
1 1/4 teaspoons salt
4 teaspoons double-acting
　baking powder
1 1/4 teaspoons baking soda
1/2 cup orange juice
yellow food color (optional)
Creamy Apricot Frosting (page
　248)

About 4 hours before serving: Preheat oven to 350°F. Grease two 8-inch layer-cake pans; line with waxed paper; grease and flour the paper.

In medium bowl, with electric mixer at medium speed, cream margarine with sugar until cream-colored, light and fluffy. Beat in vanilla and orange peel. Sift together flour, salt, baking powder and baking soda.

With electric mixer at medium speed, beat one-third flour mixture into margarine mixture until smooth; beat orange juice into batter until smooth. Repeat with second third of flour; beat in 1/2 cup plus 2 tablespoons water; beat in remaining flour mixture. Add yellow food color; beat one minute. Batter will be consistency of soft cookie dough.

Divide between pans; push batter slightly up around edges. Bake 30 to 35 minutes, or until cake shrinks from sides of pan. Let cool on rack about 30 minutes before turning out of pans. Fill and frost with Creamy Apricot Frosting.

ORANGE CHIFFON CAKE (gluten-, milk- and wheat-free diet)

3/4 cup potato-starch flour
3/4 cup granulated sugar
2 teaspoons double-acting
  baking powder
1/2 teaspoon salt
1/4 cup salad oil
4 eggs, separated
1 tablespoon finely grated
  orange peel
1/3 cup orange juice
1/4 teaspoon cream of tartar

About 5 hours before serving: Preheat oven to 350°F. Into small bowl, sift potato-starch flour with sugar, baking powder and salt. Make well in center; pour in (in order) salad oil, egg yolks, orange peel and orange juice. Beat, with electric mixer at medium speed, 1 minute.

In large bowl, beat egg whites with cream of tartar until whites are very stiff and almost dry. Carefully fold in yolk mixture. Divide batter evenly between 2 ungreased 8-inch layer-cake pans.* Bake 30 to 35 minutes, or until a cake tester, inserted in center, comes out clean. To cool, invert pans and suspend by rim. Cool completely, then carefully remove cake from pans—it will be delicate.

* This cake may also be baked in an 8-inch square cake pan. Baking time will be 5 to 10 minutes longer.

GINGER CAKE (egg- and milk-free diet)

2 1/2 cups sifted all-purpose flour
1 1/2 teaspoons double-acting
  baking powder
1 teaspoon baking soda
1 teaspoon salt
2 teaspoons cinnamon
1 1/2 teaspoons ginger
1/2 teaspoon nutmeg
1/2 teaspoon ground cloves
1/2 cup raisins
1/2 cup chopped walnuts
  (optional)
1 cup packed brown sugar
2/3 cup molasses
2/3 cup shortening
confectioners' sugar

About 1 hour and 10 minutes before serving: Preheat oven to 350°F. Grease and flour 13" by 9" baking pan. On waxed paper, sift together flour, baking powder, baking soda, salt and spices. In small bowl, toss raisins and nuts with 1/4 cup flour mixture until well coated. In large mixing bowl, with electric mixer at medium speed, blend brown sugar and molasses. Add shortening, then dry ingredients, beating well after each addition. Gradually beat in 1 cup boiling water until smooth. Beat 2 minutes more. Stir in raisin mixture. Pour into pan; bake 45 to 50 minutes, or until cake shrinks from sides of pan. Sprinkle with confectioners' sugar; serve warm. Makes 8 to 10 servings.

APPLESAUCE SPICE CAKE (egg-, milk- and wheat-free diet)

1/2 cup shortening
1/2 cup granulated sugar
1/2 cup sifted rye flour
1 1/2 cups sifted barley flour
3 teaspoons double-acting
  baking powder
1 teaspoon baking soda
1 teaspoon salt
1/2 teaspoon cinnamon
1/4 teaspoon nutmeg
1 cup minus 2 tablespoons
  canned applesauce
sifted confectioners' sugar

About 4 hours before serving: Preheat oven to 350°F. Grease bottom of 9-inch square cake pan; line with waxed paper; grease and flour (with barley flour) the paper.

In medium bowl, with electric mixer at medium speed, cream shortening with sugar until light and fluffy. Sift together: rye and barley flour, baking powder, baking soda, salt, cinnamon and nutmeg.

With electric mixer at medium speed, beat one-third of flour mixture into sugar mixture until smooth; beat in half of applesauce until smooth. Repeat with flour and remaining applesauce. Then beat in remaining flour. Beat one minute.

Turn batter into cake pan; smooth surface. Bake 30 to 35 minutes, or until cake shrinks from sides of pan. (Center of this cake will not be as firm as that of regular cake.) Let cool on rack 30 minutes; turn out of pan. Serve sprinkled with confectioners' sugar.

FRUIT-AND-SPICE CAKE (egg- and milk-free diet)

2 cup raisins
1 cup packed dark brown sugar
1/2 cup shortening
1/2 teaspoon cinnamon
1/2 teaspoon allspice
1/2 teaspoon salt
1/8 teaspoon nutmeg
2 cups sifted cake flour
1 teaspoon double-acting
　baking powder
1 teaspoon baking soda
1 cup chopped pecans
　(optional)
confectioners' sugar

About 4 hours before serving: In medium saucepan, heat 1 cup water, raisins, brown sugar, shortening, cinnamon, all-spice, salt and nutmeg to boiling; simmer, uncovered, 3 minutes. Cool to room temperature.

Grease 9-inch square cake pan. Preheat oven to 375°F. Sift together flour, baking powder and baking soda. In medium bowl, stir together raisin-sugar mixture, flour mixture and pecans. Beat, with electric mixer at medium speed, until smooth—about 1 minute.

Pour into cake pan; bake 35 to 40 minutes, or until cake just comes away from edge of pan. Cool about 15 minutes; turn out of pan. Cool completely, then sprinkle with confectioners' sugar. Cut into 16 squares.

For gluten- and wheat-free diet: Prepare as directed but substitute 1 1/2 cups potato-starch or rice flour for cake flour.

CREAMY COFFEE FROSTING (egg-, gluten-, milk- and wheat-free diet)

2/3 cup milk-free margarine
about 6 cups sifted
　confectioners' sugar
　(approximately 1 1/2 16-ounce
　boxes)
6 tablespoons boiling water
1 tablespoon instant-coffee
　powder
2 teaspoons vanilla extract
1/4 teaspoon salt

About 20 minutes before frosting cake: In medium bowl, with electric mixer at low speed, blend milk-free margarine and 4 cups sugar. Beat in remaining ingredients until smooth. With electric mixer at low speed, beat in enough confectioners' sugar to make frosting with a good spreading consistency. At high speed, beat 1 minute. Use to frost 36 cupcakes or one 13" by 9" by 2" oblong cake, or to fill and frost an 8- or 9-inch layer cake.

CREAMY APRICOT FROSTING: Prepare as directed, but heat one 4 3/4-ounce jar strained apricots with tapioca to boiling; use hot apricots and 2 teaspoons lemon juice in place of water and instant coffee.

CREAMY CHOCOLATE FROSTING: Prepare as directed, but mix 6 tablespoons cocoa with margarine and sugar; omit instant coffee.

MOLASSES DROP COOKIES (egg and wheat-free diet)

2 cups sifted rye flour
2 teaspoons double-acting
　baking powder
1/2 teaspoon salt
1/4 teaspoon ginger
1/2 teaspoon nutmeg
1/2 cup shortening
1/2 cup granulated sugar
1/2 cup light molasses
1/2 cup evaporated milk
1/2 cup raisins or chopped nuts
　(optional)

At least 2 hours before serving: Preheat oven to 400°F. Lightly grease cookie sheets. Onto sheet of waxed paper, sift together rye flour, baking powder, salt, ginger and nutmeg. In medium bowl, with electric mixer at medium speed, cream together shortening and sugar until light and fluffy; beat in molasses until smooth.

Add one-third of rye-flour mixture to shortening; beat, at low speed, until smooth. Add one-half evaporated milk; beat until smooth. Repeat, then beat in remaining flour mixture until smooth. Beat in raisins or nuts, if desired.

Drop, by level tablespoonfuls, 2 inches apart, onto cookie sheets. Bake 7 minutes, or until browned around the edges and cookies feel "set." Makes 3 1/2 to 4 dozen.

For milk-free diet: Prepare as directed but substitute 1/2 cup canned applesauce for evaporated milk.

PEANUT-BUTTER COOKIES (gluten-, milk- and wheat-free diet)

**1/2 cup creamy- or chunky-style
  peanut butter**
1/2 cup shortening
1/2 cup granulated sugar
**1/2 cup packed dark brown
  sugar**
**1/2 teaspoon double-acting
  baking powder**
1 egg

About 4 hours before serving: Preheat oven to 350°F. In medium bowl, with electric mixer at medium speed, cream peanut butter, shortening and sugars until fluffy. Add baking powder and egg; beat until smooth.

Drop batter, by level tablespoonfuls, 2 inches apart, onto ungreased cookie sheets. Bake 15 minutes, or until edges of cookies brown. Allow to cool on sheets 2 to 3 minutes before removing. Makes 2 1/2 dozen.

BUTTERBALLS (egg- and milk-free diet)

1 1/2 cups sifted all-purpose flour
1/2 cup granulated sugar
1/4 teaspoon salt
**2 teaspoons instant-coffee
  powder**
**1 cup milk-free margarine,
  softened to room
  temperature***
**3/4 cup chopped walnuts
  (optional)**
granulated sugar

About 1 hour before serving: Preheat oven to 300°F. In medium bowl, sift together flour, sugar, salt and instant coffee. With pastry blender, cut in margarine until the size of peas. Press together dough to form large ball. Break off pieces size of small walnuts; roll in chopped walnuts. (Or omit nuts and bake plain, as directed.)

Place cookies, about 2 inches apart, on ungreased cookie sheet. Dip flat-bottomed glass in water, then sugar; use to flatten cookies. Bake 20 to 25 minutes, or until cookies feel "set." (They will brown only slightly.) Cool a minute; remove from cookie sheets. Makes 2 to 3 dozen.

* Do **not** use shortening.

FORGOTTEN COOKIES (gluten-, milk- and wheat-free diet)

2 egg whites
3/4 cup granulated sugar
**1 6-ounce package
  semisweet-chocolate pieces**

At least 6 hours before serving: Preheat oven to 375°F. Grease 2 cookie sheets. In deep medium bowl, with mixer at high speed, beat egg whites until soft peaks form; continuing to beat, slowly add sugar. Beat until stiff meringue forms. Fold in chocolate pieces.

Drop, by level tablespoonfuls, onto greased cookie sheets. Place in oven, then turn off heat. Let remain in oven until it cools to room temperature. Remove from cookie sheet. Store in an air-tight container. Makes 2 1/2 dozen.

If your wish, substitute 1 cup raisins or chopped nuts for the chocolate pieces; prepare as directed.

APRICOT CANDY COOKIES (egg-, gluten-, milk- and wheat-free diet)

24 large dried apricots
1 3 1/2-ounce can flaked coconut
2 teaspoons orange juice
confectioners' sugar

About 1 day before serving: With food grinder, grind together apricots, coconut and orange juice at least 2 times to mix thoroughly. Form mixture into about 24 small balls. Roll in confectioners' sugar to coat completely. Keep in airtight container until ready to serve. Makes about 24.

OVERNIGHT SURPRISES (milk- and wheat-free diet)

2 cups uncooked rolled oats
1 cup packed light brown sugar
1/2 cup salad oil
1 egg
1/2 teaspoon salt
1/2 teaspoon almond extract

Night before: In medium bowl, with electric mixer at low speed, mix rolled oats, sugar and salad oil about 3 minutes. Cover; refrigerate overnight.

When ready to bake cookies: Preheat oven to 350°F. Generously grease 2 cookie sheets. To oatmeal mixture, add egg, salt and almond extract. Beat, with mixer at lowest speed, until mixture just begins to form a ball and stick together. Drop batter by level tablespoonfuls, 2 inches apart, onto cookie sheets. Bake 10 minutes or until golden-brown around the edges; let cool 2 to 3 minutes before removing from sheets. Makes about 2 dozen.

APPLE-OATMEAL DESSERT (egg-, milk- and wheat-free diet)

2 1/2 cups uncooked rolled oats
2/3 cup packed light brown
   sugar
1/4 teaspoon salt
1 teaspoon cinnamon
1/2 cup milk-free margarine,
   melted
1 cup applesauce
cinnamon and nutmeg for
   garnish

At least 2 hours before serving: Preheat oven to 375°F. In electric-blender container, coarsely chop half the oats. (Or chop oatmeal in nut chopper.) In medium bowl, mix all oats together with brown sugar, salt and cinnamon. Add melted margarine; blend well. Pack firmly into bottom of well-greased 9-inch pie plate. Bake 12 to 15 minutes. Cool. Then slice; top each serving with applesauce; sprinkle with cinnamon and nutmeg, if desired. Makes 6 servings.

APPLE, SPICE AND EVERYTHING NICE (egg- and milk-free diet)

2 cups sifted all-purpose flour
1 teaspoon baking soda
1/2 teaspoon salt
1 teaspoon cinnamon
1 teaspoion ground cloves
1/2 teaspoon nutmeg
1/2 cup shortening
1 1/3 cups packed light brown
   sugar
1/3 cup apple juice or water
1 cup apple juice or water
1 cup chopped walnuts
   (optional)
1 cup finely chopped cooking
   apples
1 cup raisins

About 1 hour before serving; Preheat oven to 400°F. Grease two large cookie sheets. In medium-size bowl, mix flour with baking soda, salt, cinnamon, cloves and nutmeg. In medium bowl, with electric mixer at medium speed, cream shortening with sugar until light, fluffy and cream-colored; beat in apple juice until smooth. Stir in flour mixture until dampened, then mix, at medium speed, until smooth. (Mixture will be extremely thick.) Stir in walnuts, apples and raisins.

Drop dough, by level tablespoonfuls, about 2 inches apart, onto greased cookie sheets. Bake 8 to 10 minutes, or until golden-brown around edges and cookies feel "set." Cool slightly; remove from cookie sheet; cool completely, then store in an airtight container. Makes about 3 dozen.

AMAZING PANCAKES (gluten-, milk- and wheat-free diet)

2 eggs
2 medium bananas
2 teaspoons granulated sugar
maple syrup for topping

Just before serving: Preheat griddle until a drop of water "dances" on it; grease lightly. In electric-blender container, at low speed, blend eggs, bananas and sugar until smooth. (Or mash bananas; add eggs and sugar; mix until smooth.) Pour batter by 1/4-cup portions onto hot griddle. Cook until edges of pancakes are browned; turn; cook other side until golden-brown. Serve with maple syrup. Makes six 4-inch pancakes.

APPLESAUCE PANCAKES (gluten- and wheat-free diet)

1¹/₂ cups unsifted rice flour
2 tablespoons unsifted
  potato-starch flour
3 tablespoons cornstarch
1¹/₂ teaspoons double-acting
  baking powder
¹/₂ teaspoon salt
1 teaspoon lemon juice
1 cup applesauce
3 tablespoons butter or
  margarine, melted
1 cup milk
2 eggs, separated
bananas (optional)
maple syrup (optional)

About 45 minutes before serving: Preheat lightly greased griddle until a drop of water "dances" on it. In medium bowl, stir together dry ingredients. Add lemon juice, applesauce, melted butter or margarine, milk and egg yolks; mix only until dry ingredients are dampened.

In small bowl, beat egg whites until stiff peaks form; fold beaten egg whites into pancake batter. Drop batter, by ¹/₄-cupfuls, onto heated griddle; spread each pancake with back of spoon into circle about 4 inches in diameter. Cook until rim of each cake is full of broken bubbles and underside is brown. Turn and brown other side. Makes about 16. Serve with freshly sliced bananas and syrup, if desired.

CORNMEAL WAFFLES (gluten-, and wheat-free diet)

¹/₂ cup yellow cornmeal
¹/₂ cup potato-starch flour
2 tablespoons cornstarch
1¹/₂ teaspoons double-acting
  baking powder
¹/₄ teaspoon salt
1 tablespoon granulated sugar
1 egg
¹/₂ cup milk*
3 tablespoons melted butter or
  margarine*

About 30 minutes before serving: Preheat waffle iron if manufacturer directs. In medium bowl, stir together dry ingredients. Beat egg until light, then stir in milk and butter. Gradually beat into dry ingredients until smooth. Bake waffles as usual. Makes 2 to 3 waffles.

* For milk-free diet, substitute water for milk and milk-free margarine for regular.

CARAWAY SPONGE BREAD (gluten-, milk- and wheat-free diet)

6 eggs, separated
³/₄ cup potato-starch flour
¹/₂ cup rice flour
2 teaspoons double-acting
  baking powder
1¹/₄ teaspoons salt
¹/₈ teaspoon pepper
6 tablespoons granulated sugar
caraway seeds*

About 6 hours before serving: Separate eggs and let warm to room temperature. When ready to make bread, preheat oven to 350°F. Line bottom of 8″ by 4″ by 3″ loaf pan with waxed paper. Sift together, twice, potato-starch flour, rice flour, baking powder, salt and pepper. In large bowl, beat egg whites until soft mounds form; beat in sugar, a tablespoon at a time, then continue to beat until stiff peaks form. In medium bowl, beat egg yolks until light, creamy and fluffy—at least 5 minutes at high speed.

Sprinkle about one-third flour mixture over whites; fold together; repeat two times; fold in 1 tablespoon caraway seeds. Carefully fold beaten yolks into flour mixture.

Pour batter into pan. (Pan will be very full.) Lightly sprinkle top of bread with caraway seeds. Bake 45 to 50 minutes, or until top is golden-brown and crisp. Cool 1 hour before removing from pan. Center of bread may shrink slightly during cooling. Let bread stand about 3 hours before slicing.

* Poppy or sesame seeds may be substituted for caraway seeds.

100% RYE BREAD (egg-, milk- and wheat-free diet)

1 envelope active dry yeast
2 teaspoons salt
1 tablespoon dark brown sugar
unsifted rye flour*
salad oil

At least 6 hours before serving: Dissolve yeast in 1/4 cup lukewarm water. Combine salt, sugar and 1 cup water; stir in 4 cups rye flour; beat smooth. Turn out onto rye-floured board, then knead (at least 10 minutes), using additional flour as necessary to make a firm elastic dough. Place in greased bowl; brush top with oil; cover; let rise in warm (about 85° to 95°F.) place until double in bulk.

Knead as before. Place in bowl and let rise again 1 hour. Preheat oven to 450°F. Shape dough into loaf; place in greased 9" by 5" by 3" loaf pan. Cover with clean towel; let rise until double in bulk. Bake 15 minutes; reduce heat to 350°F. and bake 55 minutes longer. Cool slightly, then turn out of pan to complete cooling. Makes 1 loaf.

* Finely milled rye flour gives best results.

RYE BAKING-POWDER BISCUITS (egg-, milk- and wheat-free diet)

1 cup unsifted rye flour
1 1/2 teaspoons double-acting
    baking powder
1/4 teaspoon salt
3 tablespoons shortening

About 30 minutes before serving: Preheat oven to 450°F. Grease baking sheet. Sift together rye flour, baking powder and salt. Cut in shortening until mixture is like coarse cornmeal. Stir in 3 to 4 tablespoons water to form a thick pliable dough. Turn onto lightly rye-floured board; roll about 1/2-inch thick. Cut with 2-inch cutter; place on sheet; bake 12 to 16 minutes. Makes 6.

CORN MUFFINS (gluten- and wheat-free diet)

1 cup cornmeal
3/4 cup unsifted rice flour
4 teaspoons double-acting
    baking powder
1/2 teaspoon salt
1/4 cup granulated sugar
1 egg, separated
1/4 cup butter or margarine,
    melted
1 cup milk

About 45 minutes before serving: Preheat oven to 425°F. Grease 12 medium muffin-pan cups. In medium bowl, stir together cornmeal, rice flour, baking powder, salt and sugar. Beat egg white until stiff peaks form. Stir egg yolk, butter and milk into dry ingredients until smooth. Fold in beaten egg white.

Divide batter among muffin cups (a scant 1/4 cup of batter per cup). Bake 25 minutes, or until sides of muffins brown lightly and pull away from edges. Makes 12.

ONION-POTATO MUFFINS (gluten-, milk- and wheat-free diet)

1/2 cup potato-starch flour
2 tablespoons granulated sugar
1 teaspoon double-acting
    baking powder
1/2 teaspoon salt
2 teaspoons instant minced
    onion (optional)
4 eggs separated

About 40 minutes before serving: Preheat oven to 375°F. Sift together dry ingredients; add onion. In small bowl, beat egg whites until stiff. In cup, beat egg yolks lightly, then fold into whites. Fold in flour mixture slowly, not more than 2 tablespoons at a time, until blended. Sprinkle on 2 tablespoons ice water, then gently fold in. Spoon into greased 2-inch muffin cups—about 2/3 full; bake 20 minutes, or until golden brown. Turn out immediately. Makes about 10.

RYE-AND-RICE MUFFINS (egg-, milk- and wheat-free diet)

2/3 cup unsifted rye flour
1/3 cup rice flour
2 teaspoons double-acting
    baking powder
1/4 teaspoon salt
4 teaspoons granulated sugar
3 tablespoons melted
    shortening

About 50 minutes before serving: Preheat oven to 400°F. Grease 6 cups of medium muffin pans. In medium bowl, stir together dry ingredients. Stir 1/2 cup water and shortening into flour mixture until mixed but still lumpy. Divide batter among muffin cups. Bake 30 to 35 minutes, or until muffins pull away from edge of pan. Makes 6.

BLAND, LOW-RESIDUE AND GALL BLADDER DIETS

A trio of chronic conditions—hiatal hernias, ulcers or simply "touchy" stomachs; gall bladder upsets; and colitis are often treated with bland diets. Although the outline for all three is essentially the same, they vary in their application. For example, the ulcer patient must eat six to eight meals a day; the patient with colitis can eat the broths and gravies denied to the ulcer patient but may need his vegetables pureed; the gall bladder sufferer must severely limit fat intake. In each case, the restrictions will vary with the severity of the condition. At the acute stages the emphasis is on limiting foods to the mildest and least irritating. But as the patient improves, the diet can be liberalized.

Precise diet restrictions vary from hospital to hospital and doctor to doctor, but they are all similar in rationale.* The three outlines that follow are composites of the "maintenance" or "discharge" diets given in the diet manuals of several large teaching hospitals. Ask your doctor to check the outline for your problem; if he eliminates some foods, avoid the recipes that contain them. (See 24 main dish recipes beginning on page 259.) The "Outline of Allowed Foods" and the "Week of Menus" on the following pages are designed for all three diets; necessary adaptations for specific problems are indicated.

*Dietary management of patients with chronic ulcer disease is controversial. Experiments show no significant difference in the response of these patients to a bland or regular diet. The American Dietetic Association says the only known gastric irritants are black pepper, alcohol, caffeine, chili powder, cocoa, coffee, drugs and tea.

BUYING AND COOKING CUES

Main Dishes for Bland Diets:

- Season meat, fish or poultry main dishes with ground thyme, sage, parsley and paprika. For the more liberal bland diet, add celery salt, oregano and basil.
- Serve sandwiches on a variety of breads, filled with sliced hard-cooked eggs, roast beef, chicken or turkey, or tuna. Use butter on the bread. Add lettuce if allowed on diet.
- Pan-broil meats by placing meat in skillet before heating; heat quickly to cooking temperatures and cook, draining away fat as it accumulates.
- Use seafood regularly. Clams, oysters, lobster, shrimp and crab all have distinct flavors, yet are perfect for a bland diet. *To serve:* Make chowders, broil or pan-broil, or dip seafood in butter or margarine, then bake.

- Liver is another meat with a distinctive flavor that should be used often. Broil or pan-broil with bacon or mushrooms rather than onion.
- Use canned chicken in casseroles; keep frozen quick steaks on hand for quick meals; try unbreaded frozen shrimp and crab; use canned tuna or salmon (pick out the bones and skin).
- Make homemade-creamed soups in a blender with canned peas or asparagus and half-and-half or light cream.

Vegetables:

- Top potatoes, vegetables or fruit with sour cream. To save calories (or for gall bladder diets), substitute cottage cheese pureed smooth in a blender, or yogurt.
- To puree vegetables at home, place cooked (or canned) drained vegetables

in blender container with 2 tablespoons cooking liquid for each cup of vegetables. Blend until smooth.

- Mashed squash is available frozen.
- Canned boiled potatoes need only be heated for an "instant" vegetable.
- Use packaged precooked rice and instant mashed potatoes for quick-to-fix vegetables.

Milk:

- Buttermilk has more tang than plain milk.
- To save calories, drink skimmed milk. The modified skimmed milks have more "body" than the regular kind. Or make your own modified-skimmed milk by adding 1 or 2 tablespoons extra dry-milk powder for each glass reliquefied nonfat dry milk.

Breads:

- Use the full range of allowed breads— white or rye (without seeds), hard rolls, refrigerated biscuits and rolls, hamburger and frankfurter rolls, Melba toast or breadsticks (not salted).
- Toasting bread adds textural appeal. Make homemade Melba toast by thinly slicing French bread and toasting in 250°F. oven 15 minutes, or until crisp.

Desserts:

- Use cinnamon, allspice and mace to season desserts.
- Make fruit toppings from pureed canned peaches, pears, apricots, etc. for ice cream and ice milk. For gall bladder diet, use as topping for sherbets.
- To puree fruits, place drained cooked or canned fruit in blender container, and blend until smooth. There's no need to add extra liquid.
- Use the sponge-cake and chiffon-cake mixes as well as angel-food mix.

Miscellaneous:

- Grinding and pureeing of foods is only necessary when teeth are impaired.
- Try a wide variety of flavors in jellies. They make an excellent substitute for butter on a gall bladder diet.
- Use yogurt plain, or try vanilla or coffee as a tangy snack. Make your own flavored yogurts with jellies. Use yogurts made with partially skimmed milk on gall bladder diets.

OUTLINE OF ALLOWED FOODS

BLAND DIET (for peptic ulcers, hiatal hernias and gastric indigestion):
Foods are smooth and bland in consistency and texture; their flavor is bland and chemically non-irritating. Choose meals from the following. Follow your doctor's advice concerning the number and timing of meals.

SOUPS
Creamed soups using allowed vegetables
Avoid: All meat-stock-based soups

FISH, MEAT AND POULTRY
Fish: All boned fish fillets or steaks
  Seafood prepared with allowed ingredients
Meat: Very tender cuts of beef, lamb, mild fresh pork and veal—all cooked "well done"

Variety meats include heart, liver and sweetbreads
Poultry: All forms of poultry prepared with allowed ingredients
Avoid: Tough, stringy meat
  Highly seasoned, salted or smoked meats
  Excessively fatty meats
  Fried meat, fish or poultry

CHEESE AND EGGS
Cheese: Cottage cheese, cream cheese, mild-flavored hard cheese used in cooking
Eggs: Any style but fried. Do not over-cook the eggs
Avoid: Strong cheeses and those containing spices. Fried eggs.

VEGETABLES

Tender, well-cooked asparagus tips, beets, carrots, green beans, wax beans, green peas, mushrooms, potatoes (sweet and white), spinach (chopped), squash (acorn or yellow) and tomato juice

Lettuce or tomatoes with skin and seeds removed if approved by doctor

Avoid: Strong-flavored vegetables: Brussels sprouts, cabbage, cauliflower, cucumber, onion, peppers, radishes, turnips

All raw vegetables (note exceptions above) and those containing seeds, skins or tough fibers

BREADS AND CEREALS

Breads: plain rolls, rye (without seeds), enriched white, biscuits, muffins

Cereals: Cornflakes, puffed rice, rice flakes, farina, grits, strained oatmeal

Pastas: Macaroni, noodles, spaghetti, etc.

Specialty breads: Melba toast, rusk, saltines (unsalted), soda crackers, zwieback

Rice: White only

Avoid: Coarse or whole grain breads and cereals, pretzels, salty crackers, sweet rolls

FATS

Butter, cream, margarine, vegetable fats, oils

Avoid: Excessive fats, mineral oil, salad dressings, mayonnaise

FRUITS

Canned or cooked: Apricots, apples, peaches, pears, plums and Royal Anne cherries

Juices: Apple, apricot, grapefruit,* lemon* (in moderation), orange,* pineapple* and prune (in moderation)

Strained: All others

Raw: Avocado and banana

Avoid: All other raw fruit

Fruit containing seeds, skin or fibers

etc. All plain without seeds

*Not to be included on diet for those with hernia.

DESSERTS

Cakes and cookies: All plain and not excessively sweet or rich

Gelatin: Plain or with allowed fruits

Ice cream, ice milk or sherbet: Plain without seeds or nuts (in moderation)

Puddings: Blanc mange, custards, junkets,

Avoid: All excessively sweet desserts. All containing nuts, seeds, etc.

BEVERAGES

Coffee, decaffeinated coffee, or tea, only if doctor approves

Milk and milk drinks: Buttermilk, evaporated, skimmed, whole, yogurt, etc.

Avoid: Alcoholic beverages, carbonated beverages

MISCELLANEOUS

Candy: Gum drops, hard candy, marshmallows, etc. (all in moderation)

Jellies: No jams or preserves

Seasonings: Allspice, cinnamon, lemon, mace, paprika, parsley, sage, salt, thyme (all in moderation)

Sugar: Corn syrup, granulated sugar, honey, molasses, etc. (all in moderation)

Avoid: Condiments and highly seasoned foods

Gravies and all meat stocks

Nuts, salty foods—pickles, smoked fish, etc.

Seasonings: Particularly garlic, onion, red and black pepper, chili powder

LOW RESIDUE DIET (for colitis and similar conditions):

Foods are extremely smooth and bland in consistency and form a minimum of residue in the large intestine. To choose meals, follow bland diet (page 254), but make the following adjustments:

SOUPS

Meat-stock-based and strained cream soups are allowed

FISH, MEAT AND POULTRY

No changes

CHEESE AND EGGS

No changes unless milk products are limited on diet. Check with physician

VEGETABLES

Omit all raw vegetables. Vegetables should be cooked and strained

BREADS AND CEREALS

No changes

FATS

No changes

FRUITS

Ripe banana and avocado. Strain fruit juices. Canned or cooked fruit without seeds or tough skin. Citrus fruit without membrane.

DESSERTS

No changes unless milk products are limited on diet

BEVERAGES

No changes unless milk products are limited on diet

(Check specifically with your doctor; milk and milk products are occasionally restricted on a low-residue diet. Include them unless specifically forbidden.)

MISCELLANEOUS

Herbs and spices are allowed in moderation, with the following exceptions:

Any seeds or coarse leaves, garlic, mustard, onion and pepper

LOW-FAT, BLAND DIET (for gall bladder conditions):

Foods are bland in nature, and the total fat content of the diet is restricted. Choose meals from the following:

SOUPS

Mildly seasoned meat-stock-based soups

Creamed soups prepared with skimmed milk and allowed vegetables

Avoid: Soups containing fat and forbidden foods

FISH, MEAT AND POULTRY

Fish: Boned fish fillets or steaks from low-fat fish. Seafood prepared with allowed ingredients

Meat: Tender or well-cooked cuts of lean beef, lamb and veal

Variety meats low in fat, including heart, liver and sweetbreads

Poultry: Chicken, turkey and game birds prepared with allowed ingredients

Avoid: Fatty fish such as herring, mackerel, salmon, trout, etc.

Tough, stringy meat; fatty meats; highly seasoned, salted or smoked meats

Duck and goose

CHEESE AND EGGS

Cheese: Cottage cheese (uncreamed cottage cheese allowed at all times; fat in creamed cottage cheese must be calculated into diet)

Eggs: Prepared with no added fat. Avoid egg yolks if they cause distress

Avoid: Cream cheese, hard cheeses

Fried eggs and egg yolks if necessary

VEGETABLES

Tender, well-cooked asparagus, beets, carrots, green beans, wax beans, green peas, mushrooms, potatoes (sweet and white), spinach (chopped), pumpkin, squash (acorn and yellow) and tomato juice

Lettuce or tomatoes with skin and seeds removed if doctor approves

Avoid: Strong-flavored vegetables: Brussels sprouts, cabbage, cauliflower, cucumber, onion, peppers, radishes, turnips

All raw vegetables (note exceptions above) and those containing seeds, skins or fibers

BREADS AND CEREALS

Bread: Plain rolls, rye (without seeds), enriched white bread

Cereals: Cornflakes, puffed rice, rice flakes, farina, grits, strained oatmeal

Pastas: Macaroni, noodles, spaghetti, etc.

Specialty breads: Melba toast, rusk, saltines, soda crackers, zwieback

Avoid: Coarse-grained breads and cereals, hot breads, pretzels, salty crackers, sweet rolls

FATS

Butter, cream, margarine, vegetable fats and oils—a maximum of 3 teaspoons a day

Avoid: Excessive fats, mineral oil, salad dressings, mayonnaise

FRUITS

Canned or cooked: Apricot, apple, peach and pear

Juices: Apple, apricot, grapefruit, lemon (in moderation), orange, pineapple and prune (in moderation)

Raw: Bananas

Avoid: All other raw fruits, avocado, fruits containing seeds, skins or fiber

DESSERTS

Cakes: Angel-food cake only

Gelatin: Plain or with allowed fruits

Puddings: Plain puddings prepared with skimmed milk

Sherbet

Avoid: All desserts containing fats

All desserts containing nuts, seeds, etc.

All excessively sweet desserts

BEVERAGES

Coffee, decaffeinated coffee or tea as doctor approves; no cream

Milk and milk drinks: Buttermilk, skimmed milk, skimmed-milk yogurt

Avoid: Alcoholic and carbonated beverages
All beverages containing fat

MISCELLANEOUS

Candy: Gum drops, hard candy, marshmallows, etc. (in moderation)
Jellies: No jams or preserves
Seasonings: Cinnamon, lemon, nutmeg, oregano, paprika, poultry seasoning, sage, salt and thyme (all in moderation)

Sugar: Corn syrup, granulated sugar, honey, molasses, etc. (in moderation)

Avoid: Condiments and highly seasoned foods
Gravies and sauces rich in fat
Nuts, salty foods, pickles, smoked fish
Seasonings: Particulary garlic, onion and pepper

A WEEK OF MENUS

BREAKFAST

orange juice
baked eggs on toast
milk
coffee or tea*

orange-pineapple juice
oatmeal with brown sugar
toast with butter or jelly
milk

applesauce
cornflakes with bananas and sugar
milk

apricot nectar
scrambled eggs on toast with bacon
milk

canned whole apricots
soft-cooked eggs
English muffins with butter and jelly
milk

orange juice
cream of rice with light cream
toasted hard roll with butter
milk

sliced bananas in orange juice
shirred eggs
toasted French bread with butter
milk

LUNCH OR SUPPER

pan-broiled beef cubed steaks on open-faced sandwich
buttered green beans
tapioca pudding (topped with peach slices)
milk

*Use coffee or tea as recommended by physician.

cream-of-pea soup (made from pureed canned peas)
chicken sandwich on roll (with lettuce if allowed on diet)
purple plums
milk

scrambled egg-and-bacon sandwich on toast
canned apricots
milk

roast-beef sandwich on rye bread (with lettuce if allowed)
applesauce sprinkled with cinnamon
buttermilk

stew of hamburger, potatoes and peas
French bread and butter
raspberry applesauce
milk

cheese soufflé
chopped spinach
buttered refrigerated biscuits
Royal Anne cherries
milk

broiled hamburger on hard roll
buttered carrots
vanilla-rennet custard pudding
butterscotch cookies

DINNER

oven-fried chicken parts
buttered peas
cranberry sauce
rice pudding

broiled minute veal steaks (sprinkled with mild Cheddar cheese)
buttered green beans and mushrooms
buttered rice
angel-food cake

meat loaf
baked potatoes with butter or sour cream
buttered Italian green beans
breadsticks
vanilla ice cream and raspberry sherbet
(mixed)

baked swordfish steaks
buttered carrots
buttered green beans
buttered clover-leaf roll
baked apple

broiled chicken livers (on toast points)
pan-sautéed mushroom slices
buttered peas
peach-and-cottage-cheese salad-dessert

broiled hamburgers (stuffed with cottage
cheese)
buttered whipped squash
buttered asparagus or green beans
buttered toast fingers
hot canned apricots (with vanilla wafers)

leg of lamb (with pear halves filled with
jelly)
buttered beets
buttered parslied potatoes
fruited gelatin

LOW-RESIDUE DIET

Follow menus as given but:
   strain fruit juices
   use pureed vegetables if necessary
   add seasonings as allowed on diet

LOW-FAT, BLAND (GALL BLADDER) DIET

Follow menus as given but:
   use skimmed milk in place of whole
   omit eggs and bacon (substitute hot and cold
      cereals or cottage cheese)
   omit buttering of foods, or limit as diet pre-
      scribes
   prepare puddings with skimmed milk
   substitute bread or plain rolls for quick
      breads
   omit cheese (except cottage cheese) and
      sour cream
   substitute sherbet for ice cream

BLAND, LOW-RESIDUE AND GALL BLADDER DIETS:
24 Recipes for Main Dishes

STEAK ROLL-UPS (bland and low-residue diets)

4 slices white bread, cut into small cubes
1 egg
1/4 teaspoon ground sage
1/4 teaspoon ground thyme
salt
2 pounds beef top round steak, cut into 6 pieces, 1/4-inch thick
2 tablespoons butter or margarine
1 10 1/2-ounce can condensed cream-of-mushroom soup
1 4-ounce can mushrooms, drained (optional)
1/2 cup plain yogurt (optional)

About 1 hour and 30 minutes before serving: In medium bowl, combine bread cubes, egg, sage, thyme and 1/2 teaspoon salt. Place 1/3 cup bread mixture down center of each steak; roll; secure with toothpicks or skewers.

In medium skillet over medium heat, in heated butter, brown roll-ups; remove to plate. Pour soup and 1/2 cup water into skillet; heat to boiling, stirring occasionally. Return roll-ups to skillet; cook, covered, over low heat 1 hour, or until meat is tender.

Occasionally spoon sauce over meat. Place meat on warm platter; remove toothpicks. To sauce in skillet, add mushrooms and yogurt; heat. Spoon sauce over roll-ups. Makes 6 servings.

POLISH VEAL SCALLOPS (bland, low-residue and gall bladder* diets)

1 20-ounce can sliced apples
2 tablespoons butter or margarine
1 pound veal cutlets
1/4 cup packed brown sugar
1 tablespoon flour
1/2 teaspoon cinnamon
1/2 teaspoon allspice

About 30 minutes before serving: Drain apples, reserving syrup. In large skillet over medium heat, in butter, brown veal on both sides; place on warm platter. Add reserved syrup to skillet. Stir in sugar, flour, cinnamon and allspice; cook until slightly thickened. Return veal to skillet; add apple slices and simmer, covered, 5 minutes. Makes 4 servings.

*15 grams fat per serving.

RICE-A-ROUND LAMB STEW (bland, low-residue and gall bladder* diets)

2 pounds lean lamb stew meat
1 tablespoon salad oil
1/2 pound mushrooms, sliced
3 tablespoons parsley flakes
1 teaspoon ground sage
2 teaspoons salt
5 carrots, diced
4 cups hot cooked rice
1 10-ounce package frozen peas, cooked and drained (or 1 16-ounce can peas, drained)
flour or cornstarch to thicken gravy

About 1 hour and 45 minutes before serving: In large saucepan over medium heat, in oil, brown meat. Add 2 cups water, one-half mushrooms, parsley, sage and salt. Simmer, covered, 1 hour. Add carrots and remaining mushrooms; cook 15 minutes, or until meat and vegetables are fork-tender.

Grease 1 1/2-quart ring mold. Combine rice and peas; pack into mold; then unmold onto warm large platter. With slotted spoon, spoon stew into center and around rice ring. If desired, thicken liquid with flour or cornstarch. Serve as gravy. Makes 6 to 8 servings.

*15 grams fat per serving.

SAUCY SWEDISH MEATBALLS (bland and low-residue diets)

2 pounds lean ground beef
1/2 cup unseasoned dried
  bread crumbs
tomato juice
1 teaspoon salt
2 eggs
2 tablespoons salad oil
1 tablespoon cornstarch
1/4 to 1/2 cup sour cream
hot cooked noodles or rice

About 45 minutes before serving: In medium bowl, mix meat, bread crumbs, 1/2 cup tomato juice, salt and eggs. Form into 24 meatballs. In large skillet, in oil, brown well on all sides; remove from skillet; pour off remaining oil. Return meatballs to skillet; add 2 cups tomato juice; cover; boil gently 30 minutes, or until meat is done and tender.

Meanwhile, mix cornstarch with 1/4 cup water to form a smooth paste. Remove meatballs to warm platter. Stir cornstarch mixture into tomato juice until sauce is thickened and smooth.

Remove skillet from heat. Stir in sour cream until just smooth. Do not boil. Use as gravy for meatballs, served with noodles or rice. Makes 6 servings.

PEEKABOO BURGER (bland and low-residue diets)

1 1/2 pounds lean ground beef
5 eggs
salt
1/4 teaspoon ground sage
1/4 teaspoon ground thyme
1/2 cup unseasoned packaged
  dried bread crumbs
1/4 cup tomato juice
1 1/2 cups sifted all-purpose flour
1 1/2 teaspoons double-acting
  baking powder
1 1/2 cups milk
3 tablespoons melted butter
  or margarine

About 1 hour and 30 minutes before serving: Preheat oven to 350°F. Grease 13" by 9" baking pan. In medium bowl, combine ground beef, 1 egg, 1 teaspoon salt, sage, thyme, bread crumbs and tomato juice. Shape mixture into 24 small meatballs; place in 4 rows in baking pan. On waxed paper, sift together flour, baking powder and 1 teaspoon salt. In medium bowl, beat 4 eggs until foamy; beat in milk and butter. Beat in flour mixture until smooth. Pour over meatballs. Bake 50 to 60 minutes, or until lightly browned on top. Remove from oven and allow to stand 5 minutes before serving. Makes 8 servings.

HAMBURG DUMPLING STEW (bland and low-residue diets)

1 pound lean ground beef
salt
flour
1/2 teaspoon ground sage
1 tablespoon granulated sugar
1 24-ounce can tomato juice
2 teaspoons double-acting
  baking powder
2 tablespoons butter or margarine
1/2 cup milk

About 40 minutes before serving: In large skillet, brown beef with 1 teaspoon salt; stir in 1 tablespoon flour. Add sage, sugar and tomato juice; cover; simmer gently 10 minutes.

Meanwhile, in medium bowl, sift together 1 cup sifted flour, baking powder and 1/4 teaspoon salt. Cut in butter or margarine until like coarse corn meal; stir in milk to make a soft dough. Make 4 dumplings by dropping dollops of dough into hot hamburg mixture; cover; simmer 14 minutes. Serve in soup bowls with dumplings on top. Makes 4 servings.

OVEN-BAKED CRANBERRY POT ROAST (bland, low-residue and gall bladder* diets)

1 pound beef top-round roast,
  cut 1/2- to 3/4-inch thick
2 tablespoons salad oil
1 tablespoon flour
1 7-ounce can jellied cranberry sauce
1/2 teaspoon salt
1 tablespoon granulated sugar
3 medium potatoes, quartered

About 2 hours before serving: Preheat oven to 350°F. Trim fat from beef; cut into 3 serving portions. In ovenproof skillet, in oil, brown meat on both sides; mix 1 tablespoon flour with oil in pan. Mash cranberry sauce into small pieces; then add, with 1/2 cup water, salt and sugar, to meat. Bake, covered, 30 minutes; then add potatoes and turn meat. Bake 1 hour longer, or until potatoes and meat are tender. Makes 3 servings.

*15 grams fat per serving.

BRAISED CHICKEN LIVERS (bland, low-residue and gall bladder* diets)

1 pound fresh chicken livers
  (or frozen livers, thawed)
1/4 cup flour
1/2 teaspoon salt
1 tablespoon salad oil
2/3 to 1 cup tomato juice
4 slices toast, quartered

About 30 minutes before serving: Remove any fat from livers. Toss livers with flour, mixed with salt, to just coat; shake off excess. In medium skillet, in oil, brown livers well on both sides. Pour off any oil remaining in skillet. Add tomato juice; cover; boil gently 10 minutes, or until livers are done and tomato sauce has thickened slightly.

To serve: Cover toast points with livers and sauce. Makes 4 servings.

*10 grams fat per serving.

BROILED CHICKEN BREASTS (bland, low-residue and gall bladder* diets)

3 whole chicken breasts,
  halved (about 3 pounds)
salad oil
salt
paprika

About 60 minutes before serving: Preheat broiler 10 minutes if manufacturer directs. Remove rack from broiler pan, then line pan with foil. Arrange halved chicken breasts, skin side down, in pan. Brush with salad oil; sprinkle with salt and paprika. Place pan in broiler so surface of chicken is 7 to 9 inches from heat. If it is impossible to place broiler pan this low in your range, lower heat. (If broiler-oven is thermostatically controlled, turn temperature to about 350°F.) Broil chicken 30 minutes on one side; turn; brush with salad oil; sprinkle with salt and paprika; then broil 15 to 20 minutes, or until fork-tender, nicely browned and crisp. Makes 6 servings.

*5 grams fat per serving. Don't eat chicken skin.

CHICKEN AND SHRIMP ON RICE (bland, low-residue and gall bladder* diets)

1/2 cup flour
1 teaspoon ground thyme
1 teaspoon salt
4 whole chicken breasts
  (about 3 pounds), split,
  skinned and boned
3 tablespoons salad oil
2 cups uncooked long-grain
  rice
1 24-ounce can tomato juice
1/4 cup parsley flakes
1 pound package frozen
  shelled, deveined shrimp,
  thawed and drained

About 30 minutes before serving: On waxed paper, mix flour, thyme and salt. Dip chicken in mixture to coat. In large skillet, in oil, brown chicken on all sides. Pour off any excess oil.

Meanwhile, cook rice as label directs. Add tomato juice and parsley flakes to chicken in skillet; cover; simmer 10 minutes. Add shrimp; simmer 5 minutes more, or until shrimp curl and turn pink. Add salt to taste. Serve on rice. Makes 6 to 8 servings.

*10 grams fat per serving.

SPANISH CHICKEN AND EGGPLANT (bland and gall bladder* diets)

1 teaspoon salt
1/2 teaspoon ground thyme
1 small or 1/2 medium eggplant, peeled and thinly
  sliced
1 8-ounce can tomato sauce
1 9-ounce package frozen
  whole green beans, separated
2 chicken breasts, split and
  skinned

About 1 hour and 15 minutes before serving: Preheat oven to 350°F. Mix salt and thyme. In greased casserole, layer eggplant, half of tomato sauce, half of seasoning mixture, green beans and chicken; top with remaining tomato sauce and seasonings. Bake, covered, 1 hour. Makes 4 servings.

*10 grams fat per serving.

CHICKEN-AND-SWEET-POTATO SHORTCAKE (bland and low-residue diets)

2 cups sifted all-purpose flour
1 tablespoon granulated
   sugar
2¹/₂ teaspoons double-acting
   baking powder
1¹/₂ teaspoons salt
¹/₄ cup shortening
¹/₂ cup mashed sweet potatoes
1 cup milk
1 10¹/₂-ounce can condensed
   cream-of-chicken soup
1 cup cubed cooked chicken
paprika for garnish

About 40 minutes before serving: Preheat oven to 450°F. In medium bowl, sift together 1¹/₂ cups flour, sugar, baking powder and salt; with pastry blender or 2 knives used scissor fashion, cut in shortening until mixture resembles coarse crumbs.

In small bowl, combine sweet potatoes and ¹/₂ cup milk; stir into flour mixture just until dry ingredients are moistened. Place remaining flour on work surface and knead dough about 10 times. Roll dough ¹/₄-inch thick; fold in half. Cut 6 biscuits with 3-inch round cutter. Place, almost touching, on ungreased cookie sheet; bake 15 to 20 minutes, or until golden brown.

In medium saucepan over medium heat, stir ¹/₂ cup milk, undiluted soup and chicken until boiling. Split biscuits; top with chicken mixture. Sprinkle with paprika. Makes 6 servings.

BAKED CHICKEN CASSEROLE (bland and low-residue diets)

¹/₂ 8-ounce package elbow
   macaroni (about 1 cup)
2 tablespoons butter or margarine
2 tablespoons flour
1¹/₂ cups milk
¹/₂ teaspoon salt
¹/₂ teaspoon ground thyme
¹/₄ teaspoon paprika
1 cup grated mild Cheddar
   cheese
1 8-ounce can sliced carrots,
   drained
1 8-ounce can peas, drained
2 cups cubed cooked chicken

About 45 minutes before serving: Preheat oven to 350°F. Cook macaroni as label directs; drain. Meanwhile, in small saucepan, melt butter or margarine. Stir in flour, then slowly add milk, salt, thyme and paprika. Cook, stirring constantly, until thickened. Stir in ¹/₂ cup cheese until just melted.

In 2-quart casserole, toss together drained macaroni, cheese sauce, carrots, peas and chicken. Top with remaining cheese. Cover; bake 20 minutes. Makes 4 servings.

CHICKEN-MUSHROOM SOUFFLÉ (bland and low-residue diets)

3 tablespoons butter or margarine
¹/₄ cup flour
1 cup milk
¹/₂ cup chopped fresh mushrooms
1 cup finely diced cooked
   chicken
¹/₂ teaspoon celery salt
¹/₂ teaspoon salt
4 eggs, separated

About 1 hour before serving: Preheat oven to 350°F. Grease 1¹/₂-quart casserole. In medium saucepan, melt butter; stir in flour. Stirring constantly, add milk and cook until thickened and smooth. Stir in mushrooms, chicken, celery salt and salt until smooth; stir in egg yolks.

In large bowl, beat egg whites until stiff peaks form. Fold chicken mixture into egg whites. Turn into casserole; bake 45 to 55 minutes, or until soufflé is golden-brown. Serve immediately. Makes 4 servings.

LIVER-AND-RICE SKILLET DINNER (bland and low-residue diets)

1/4 **pound sliced bacon**
1 pound fresh chicken livers
  (or frozen livers, thawed)
1 cup uncooked long-grain
  rice
3 tablespoons chopped parsley

2 or 3 carrots, thinly sliced
1/4 **teaspoon salt**
1 teaspoon ground thyme

About 40 minutes before serving: In medium skillet, fry bacon until crisp; remove; drain and crumble. In bacon fat in same skillet, sauté livers until brown but still slightly pink in center; remove. Add rice, parsley, carrots, salt, thyme, crumbled bacon and 2 1/2 cups water to skillet; bring water to boiling; add livers; cover; cook 14 minutes, or until rice is tender and most of the water absorbed. Makes 4 to 6 servings.

DEVONSHIRE DEVILED CRAB (low-residue diet)

1 cup milk
2 tablespoons flour
1 chicken-bouillon cube
2 hard-cooked eggs, chopped
3 slices day-old bread, finely
  cubed
1 cup grated raw carrots
2 61/2**- to 7**1/2**-ounce cans King**
  crab, drained (or 2 6-ounce
  packages frozen King crab,
  thawed, drained)
1 tablespoon butter or margarine

About 50 minutes before serving: Preheat oven to 350°F. In medium saucepan, slowly stir milk into flour to form a smooth paste; add chicken bouillon. Cook, stirring constantly, until thickened. Stir in eggs, 2 slices cubed bread, carrots and crab. Turn mixture into 1-quart casserole; sprinkle with remaining cubed bread; dot with butter or margarine. Bake 30 to 35 minutes, or until bread crumbs are dark golden-brown. Makes 4 servings of about 1 cup each.

CRAB AND DUMPLINGS (bland and low-residue diets)

2 tablespoons butter or mar-
  garine
2 tablespoons flour
1/2 **teaspoon salt**
11/2 **cups milk**
11/4 **cups shredded American**
  cheese
1 61/2**- to 7**1/2**-ounce can King**
  crab, drained and flaked (or
  1 6-ounce package frozen
  King crab, thawed and
  drained)
1 cup sifted all-purpose flour
2 teaspoons double-acting
  baking powder
1/2 **teaspoon salt**
2 tablespoons shortening

About 1 hour before serving: Preheat oven to 450°F. In double boiler over boiling water, melt butter or margarine. Stir in 2 tablespoons flour and salt until blended; add 1 cup milk and cook, stirring, until thickened. Stir in 1 cup cheese until melted; add crabmeat. Pour mixture into 1 1/2-quart casserole. Sift together 1 cup flour, baking powder and salt; with pastry blender, or 2 knives used scissor-fashion, cut in shortening until mixture resembles coarse crumbs. Stir in remaining 1/4 cup cheese. Add 1/2 cup milk and mix, just until moistened. Drop mixture by teaspoonfuls on top of crab mixture. Bake 25 minutes, or until dumplings are dark golden-brown. Makes 6 to 8 servings.

SALMON BALLS (bland and low-residue diets)

1 cup instant potato flakes
1 73/4**-ounce can salmon,**
  drained, boned and flaked
2 eggs
1 teaspoon salt
1/2 **teaspoon ground thyme**
1/4 **cup unseasoned packaged**
  dried-bread crumbs

About 45 minutes before serving: Preheat oven to 375°F. Lightly grease medium baking pan. In medium bowl, combine potato flakes with 3/4 cup boiling water. Stir in salmon, then beat in eggs, salt and thyme until fluffy. Shape mixture in 4 to 6 balls (mixture may be sticky). Roll in bread crumbs until well coated. Place in pan; bake 30 minutes, or until light brown. Makes 4 servings.

NEPTUNE KABOBS (bland and low-residue diets)

1 pint shucked oysters (about
one dozen)
1 pound fresh large shrimp,
shelled and deveined
1/2 pound bacon
1/2 pound small mushrooms
salad oil
2 cups hot buttered rice

About 45 minutes before serving: Wash oysters, removing sand and pieces of shell; rinse shrimp. Cook bacon until almost crisp; cut in half crosswise. Wrap some shrimp and oysters with bacon; hold in place with toothpicks.

Preheat broiler 10 minutes if manufacturer directs. Thread six 8-inch skewers alternately with wrapped shrimp, mushrooms and oysters. (For non-dieters in family, also include cherry tomatoes and small canned onions on kabobs, if desired.) Brush generously with salad oil.

Broil, 3 to 4 inches from heat, 4 to 5 minutes; turn; brush again with oil and broil other side for 4 minutes more, or until oysters are tender but still moist, shrimp have turned pink and bacon is crisp; remove toothpicks. Serve on rice. Makes 3 to 4 servings.

BAKED FLOUNDER, SOUTHERN STYLE (bland and low-residue diets)

8 strips bacon
4 small fresh flounder fillets
(about 1 1/2 pounds)*
salt
lemon juice

About 40 minutes before serving: Preheat oven to 375°F. Cook bacon until almost crisp; drain. Place two strips bacon along length of each flounder fillet. Roll up; place, seam side down, in medium baking dish. Cover; bake 20 to 25 minutes, or until fish flakes easily with fork. Sprinkle with salt and lemon juice to taste. Makes 4 servings.

*Or use 1 16-ounce package frozen fillets. Thaw as label directs; roll each fillet with bacon and bake as directed above.

BAKED FISH WITH SOUR CREAM (bland, low-residue and gall bladder* diets)

1 16-ounce package frozen
fish fillets, thawed
1/2 teaspoon salt
1/2 cup sour cream
1 teaspoon parsley flakes
1/4 teaspoon paprika

About 40 minutes before serving: Preheat oven to 350°F. Grease medium baking pan. Sprinkle fish fillets with salt; place in single layer in baking pan. Spread with sour cream; sprinkle with parsley and paprika. Bake, covered, 30 minutes, or till fish flakes easily with fork. Makes 3 to 4 servings.

*Prepare as directed but use vanilla yogurt instead of sour cream. 2 grams fat per serving.

BREADED CHEESE SOUFFLÉ (bland and low-residue diets)

1 cup milk
1 tablespoon butter or margarine
1/4 teaspoon salt
1 1/2 cups fresh bread crumbs
1 1/2 cups (about 6 ounces) shredded process Cheddar cheese
3 eggs, separated

About 1 hour and 5 minutes before serving: Preheat oven to 375°F. Place large pan, filled 1/2-inch deep with hot water, in oven.

In medium saucepan, scald milk; add butter and salt; stir to melt butter. Remove from heat; stir in bread crumbs and cheese until melted; stir in egg yolks.

In medium bowl, beat egg whites until stiff peaks form. Fold milk-bread mixture into whites. Pour into 2-quart casserole. Bake, in pan of hot water, 45 minutes, or until nicely browned. Serve immediately. Makes 4 servings.

EGGS MORNAY (bland and low-residue diets)

2 tablespoons butter or margarine
2 tablespoons flour
1/2 teaspoon salt
1/2 teaspoon paprika
1 1/2 cups milk
1 cup shredded pasteurized process American cheese (4 ounces)
8 eggs

About 1 hour before serving: Preheat oven to 350°F. Grease four 10-ounce custard cups. In double boiler, over boiling water, melt butter; stir in flour, salt and paprika until blended; stir in milk. Stirring constantly, cook until thickened. Add cheese; stir until melted and well blended. In each custard cup, pour thin layer of sauce; top with 2 eggs. Add remaining sauce, leaving yolks partially uncovered. Bake 20 to 25 minutes, or until eggs are of desired doneness. Makes 4 servings.

LINGUINE ALFREDO (Alfred's linguine) (bland and low-residue diets)

1 8-ounce package linguine (very thin, flat spaghetti)
1/4 pound butter or margarine, softened
3 tablespoons heavy or whipping cream
1/2 cup grated Parmesan cheese
salt to taste

About 30 minutes before serving: Cook linguine as label directs; drain; keep warm. Meanwhile, cream butter with heavy cream and Parmesan cheese until light, fluffy and smooth.

To serve: Toss linguine with butter mixture. Sprinkle with salt to taste. Makes 6 appetizer servings or 3 main-dish servings.

DIABETIC DIET

The meal plan used by diabetics is a typical diet grounded on the Basic Four building blocks (see page 37), with the following exceptions: pure sugar is reduced to a minimum; other forms of carbohydrate are divided among the three meals and one or two snacks; the diet is restricted in fat content to 25 to 30 percent of the calories from fat.

The American Dietetic Association, American Diabetes Association and the Public Health Service developed the exchange system, a simplified form of diet calculation which virtually eliminated the need to weigh foods. This system is based on the fact that similar foods (the fruits as a group, for example), in varying amounts, are virtually identical in calories and the other nutrients calculated in the diabetic's diet—protein, fat and carbohydrate—and can therefore be exchanged for one another. The system is built on the six food categories listed below. One serving in each category contains approximately the same number of calories and the same amount of protein, fat or carbohydrate. Foods that are high in saturated fat and contain cholesterol should be restricted.

Milk:	8 grams protein, a trace of fat, 12 grams carbohydrate
Vegetables:	2 grams protein, 5 grams carbohydrate
Fruit:	10 grams carbohydrate
Bread, cereal and starchy vegetables:	2 grams protein, 15 grams carbohydrate
Meat:	
Lean:	7 grams protein, 3 grams fat
Medium fat:	omit 1/2 fat exchange
High-fat:	omit 1 fat exchange
Fat:	5 grams fat
"Free":	Contain too few nutrients to need to be counted.

The diabetic's diet prescription is determined by taking the estimated number of calories he needs each day, based on sex, age, activity and current weight, and dividing them among the three nutrient groups, allowing 15 to 20 percent for protein, 25 to 30 percent for fat, and 45 to 55 percent for carbohydrate. This gives a diet prescription which might look like this: Calories 1800, protein 90 grams, fat 50 grams, carbohydrate 250 grams. The dietitian takes this prescription, and after discussing the individual's food preferences, devises a meal plan which allows the patient to enjoy his regular foods as much as possible, yet keep a good nutritional balance. A typical meal plan might look like this:

Breakfast:
  1 fruit, 1 meat, 1 bread, 1 fat and 1 milk exchange.
Lunch:
  2 meat, 2 vegetables, 2 bread, 1 fat, 1 fruit and 1/2 milk exchange.
Dinner:
  3 meat, 2 vegetables, 2 bread, 1 fat and 1 fruit exchange.
Snack:
  1/2 milk, 1 bread exchange and 1 fat.

The next step is to go to the lists of foods in each "exchange" group and choose the meals for the day. A typical simple menu might include:

Breakfast:
  1/2 cup orange juice (1 fruit), 1 poached egg (1 meat) on 1 slice toast (1 bread), 2 strips bacon (1 fat) and 1 cup skim milk (1 milk). (Coffee or tea sweetened with non-nutritive sweetner).

Lunch:
  Sandwich: 1 slice ham (1 meat) and 1 slice cheese (1 meat) on 2 slices rye bread (2 bread) spread with 1 teaspoon butter or margarine (1 fat), lettuce (1 free vegetable), 1 small cucumber and 1 green pepper (2 vegetables), 1 apple (1 fruit) and 1/2 cup skim milk (1/2 milk).

Dinner:
  3 ounces broiled halibut (3 meat) topped with lemon and tomato slices (1 "free" and 1 vegetable), 1 large baked potato (2 bread) with 1 tablespoon sour cream (1 fat), carrot sticks (1 vegetable) and dietetic gelatin dessert with 1/2 banana (1 fruit).

Snack:
  2 slices bread (2 bread), 1 ounce cheddar cheese (1 meat and 1 fat), and 1/2 cup skim milk (1/2 milk)

Unfortuantely, far too many diabetics limit their meal planning to very basic meals of this type. With a good collection of recipes like those that follow, and no more effort, the variety of meals can be infinite. Each of the "diabetic" exchanges per serving is marked. Use them to fit the recipes into your diet outline.

To add full variety to the recipes allowed on the diet, the exchanges for the recipes have been calculated to allow full accuracy in the exchange system with a minimum of restriction in foods used in recipes. The protein, fat and carbohydrate values for all the ingredient foods are totaled, and divided by the number of servings (fractional amounts are ignored). Then the exchanges are assigned, keeping in mind the classifications of the ingredient foods. For example:

POTATO SOUP WITH OREGANO	protein (grams)	fat (grams)	carbohydrate (grams)
1 10¹/₄-ounce can frozen cream-of-potato soup	8	13	30
1¹/₄ cups skim milk	11	—	15
total	19	13	45
divided by 3 servings	6	4	15
Exchanges: ¹/₂ milk	4	5	6
¹/₂ bread	1	—	7
	5	5	13

There are 2 grams of carbohydrate left over, but this small amount is not significant. The individual food items that go into the bread exchanges vary from about 12 grams carbohydrate (1 slice bread) to 22 (¹/₂ cup rice) per serving. The system assumes that the highs and lows balance one another out by the end of the day.

How to use saccharin

To determine the amount of saccharin or non–nutritive sweetener to use in a recipe, check the label for the amount equivalent to 1 cup of sugar. Then calculate, by proportions, the amount to use. For example, if a recipe calls for saccharin equivalent to 1¹/₂ cups sugar and 1 tablespoon of saccharin is equivalent to ¹/₂ cup sugar, three times as much (3 tablespoons) would be needed for sweetness equal to 1¹/₂ cups sugar.

Saccharin, like cyclamates, which were banned by the Food and Drug Administration because it was found that large amounts possibly increase the risk of developing bladder cancer, has been under attack. To date, its fate is still uncertain. Warning labels on saccharin-containing food products will remain until Congress completes its review of U.S. food-safety-laws. Presently, these laws state that substances in foods are to be banned if animal studies suggest they might cause cancer. The law pertains to a risk in any amount of the substance, not just to normal consumption. Saccharin is 375 times as sweet as sucrose.

The Food and Drug Administration has recently approved the use of a low-calorie sweetener called "aspartame." Made from two amino acids (constituents of proteins) L-aspartic acid and phenylalanine, it is 180 times as sweet as sucrose (table sugar). Although aspartame does supply calories, the amount that is used per serving of food would supply almost none. Persons with phenylketonuria, or PKU, who must avoid protein foods that contain phenylalanine are warned against use of this product.

CUES FOR COOKING AND PLANNING MEALS

Planning Meals:

- Plan meals several days at a time to assure variety, and to make shopping easier. One way to do this is to prepare homemade TV dinners containing the meat, vegetables and bread exchanges called for on the menu outline, then freeze them. Also, have treats ready to serve in a few minutes by freezing extra servings of sugar-free cake or cookies.
- Follow your physician's or dietician's advice in using convenience foods. Don't assume a "dietetic" food is fine for a diabetic.
- In addition to the recipes in this book, make use of the recipe booklets published by the manufacturers of non-nutritive sweetners and of sugar-free products. These include exchanges per serving.
- Exchanges are based on accurate servings. Divide recipes carefully into the exact number of servings specified. To simplify the problem, try preparing casserole dishes in individual serving casseroles.
- As a rule, meat, fish and poultry shrink about 25 percent during cooking, so 4 ounces of uncooked meat gives 3 ounces of cooked.

Vegetables:
- For a richer flavor, with no added fat, add a bouillon cube to cooking water for vegetables and pastas.
- Try vegetable- as well as beef- and chicken-flavored bouillon cubes or powder. Count as a "free" exchange.

Milk:
- If diet plan calls for whole milk, substitute skimmed milk, and then add 2 fat exchanges to meal.
- Use evaporated skimmed milk in place of regular evaporated milk in cooking. Count $1/2$ cup (undiluted) as 1 skimmed-milk exchange.

Desserts:
- Try unsweetened canned pineapple packed in juice rather than water—the flavor is fuller and delightfully tart.
- Make homemade rennet custard pudding by using plain rennet tablets (not pudding mix); prepare as directed, but instead of sugar, try non-nutritive sweetner equivalent to $1/4$ cup sugar for each 2 cups milk.
- Look for unsweetened frozen strawberries, cherries, raspberries and blackberries. They thaw to form their own syrup.

Miscellaneous:
- Flavor plain yogurt with dietetic jams or jellies, or coffee powder or vanilla extract and non-nutritive sweetener to taste. One cup (8 ounces) equals 1 skimmed milk exchange.
- Count $1 1/2$ tablespoons reduced-calorie mayonnaise as 1 fat exchange.
- Diet margarine has half the fat of regular margarine—2 teaspoons equal 1 fat exchange.
- Use the reduced-calorie pourable dressings (up to 2 tablespoons) as a "free" exchange.
- Try the aromatic teas. They don't need sweetening to have a full, mellow flavor.

DIABETIC DIET: 23 Recipes for Sugar-Free Desserts, Jams and Jellies

BIG ORANGE-CHIFFON CAKE (exchanges per serving = 1 bread and 1 fat)

8 egg whites
5 egg yolks
2¼ cups sifted flour
3 teaspoons double-acting
   baking powder
1 teaspoon salt
3 tablespoons orange peel
orange juice
non-nutritive sweetener
   equivalent to 1½ cups sugar
½ teaspoon cream of tartar
½ cup salad oil

At least 3 hours before serving: Place egg whites in large bowl, yolks in small bowl; let warm to room temperature. Meanwhile, in medium bowl, sift together flour, baking powder and salt. Finely grate 3 tablespoons orange peel. Squeeze enough orange juice to mix with non-nutritive sweetener to make ³/₄ cup of liquid.

When ready to bake cake: Preheat oven to 325°F. Rinse 9-inch square cake pan; shake out excess water. Add cream of tartar to egg whites in large bowl and beat, with electric mixer at highest speed, until very stiff peaks form. (They should be stiffer than for angel-food cake or meringue.) Then make well in center of sifted dry ingredients; add salad oil, egg yolks, juice–non-nutritive sweetener mixture and orange peel. Stir to blend; beat, with mixer at medium speed, 1 minute. Slowly add yolk-orange mixture to whites; fold together until smooth. Pour into cake pan. Bake 35 minutes, or until cake tester, inserted in center, comes out clean. Invert pan to cool cake.

After 20 minutes, remove cake from pan by cutting around edge with knife. With fingertips, gently pull cake away from edge of pan, lifting slightly to loosen bottom. Turn onto rack to cool completely. Makes 16 servings.

ORANGE NUT COOKIES (exchanges for 2 cookies = ¹/₂ bread and 1 fat)

¼ cup butter or margarine
granulated non-nutritive
   sweetener equivalent to ¼
   cup sugar
½ teaspoon orange extract
½ teaspoon vanilla extract
1 cup sifted cake flour
½ teaspoon double-acting
   baking powder
¼ teaspoon salt
¼ cup finely chopped pecans
1 tablespoon finely grated
   orange peel

About 6 hours before serving: In medium bowl, cream butter with non-nutritive sweetener, 2 tablespoons hot water, orange and vanilla extracts until fluffy. Combine flour, baking powder and salt, then add pecans and orange peel; blend with butter mixture until smooth. Shape dough into long roll about 5″ by 1¹/₂″; wrap in waxed paper and refrigerate until well chilled.

About 1 hour before serving: Preheat oven to 400°F. Lightly grease cookie sheet. Cut roll into 24 cookies, each about ¹/₈-inch thick. Bake, on cookie sheet, 12 to 15 minutes, or until brown around edges. Makes about 2 dozen.

CHOCOLATE-SPICE COOKIES (exchanges for 3 cookies = ¹/₂ bread and 1 fat)

¹/₃ cup butter or margarine
1 cup sifted cake flour
¼ teaspoon double-acting
   baking powder
2 tablespoons cocoa
¼ teaspoon salt
1 tablespoon water
granulated non-nutritive
   sweetener equivalent to ¹/₃
   cup sugar
½ teaspoon cinnamon
1 teaspoon vanilla extract

At least 2 hours before serving: Preheat oven to 375°F. In medium bowl, with electric mixer, cream butter until light and fluffy. Stir together cake flour, baking powder, cocoa and salt; blend into butter until smooth. Mix water, non-nutritive sweetener, cinnamon and vanilla; beat into flour-butter mixture until smooth. (Dough will be very stiff.) Shape into balls a scant ³/₄ inch in diameter. Place on cookie sheet and flatten with fork that has been dipped into cold water. Bake 15 minutes, or until cookies seem "set." Remove from sheet; cool. Makes about 2 dozen.

BROWNIES (exchanges per brownie = ¹/₂ bread and 2 fat)

¹/₂ cup butter or margarine
non-nutritive sweetener
  equivalent to ³/₄ cup sugar
2 squares unsweetened
  chocolate, melted
2 eggs
¹/₂ teaspoon vanilla extract
³/₄ cup sifted all-purpose flour
1 teaspoon double-acting
  baking powder
¹/₂ cup chopped walnuts

About 1 hour before serving: Preheat oven to 350°F. In large bowl, cream butter and non-nutritive sweetener until light and fluffy; add chocolate; beat until smooth. Beat in eggs and vanilla; beat in flour, baking powder and walnuts. Spread batter in greased 8-inch square pan. Bake 30 minutes, or until surface is shiny. Cool in pan; cut into 16 pieces.

BANANA CREAM CAKE (exchanges per serving = 1 bread and 3 fat)

Big Orange-Chiffon Cake batter
  (see recipe above)
1 cup heavy cream
liquid non-nutritive sweetener
  equivalent to 2 tablespoons
  sugar
2 medium bananas
juice of half a lemon

At least 4 hours before serving: Prepare cake batter as directed, but bake for 30 minutes at 325°F. in 2 rinsed 8-inch round layer-cake pans. Cool and remove from pans as directed.

About 30 minutes before serving: In chilled bowl, whip cream and non-nutritive sweetener. Into medium bowl, peel and thinly slice bananas; add lemon juice and enough water to cover completely. Thoroughly drain banana slices on paper toweling. Place cake layer on cake plate; **lightly** frost with whipped cream; cover with single layer of sliced bananas. Add second cake layer; frost sides, then top, with remaining whipped cream. Circle top of cake with rest of banana slices; refrigerate until serving time. Makes 16 servings.

STRAWBERRY-GLAZED CHEESECAKE (exchanges per serving = 2 meat, 1 fruit and 2 fat)

Cornflake Crust (see recipe
  below)
3 envelopes unflavored gelatin
non-nutritive sweetener
1 cup orange juice
1 teaspoon grated lemon peel
2 tablespoons lemon juice
2 8-ounce containers creamed
  cottage cheese
³/₄ cup heavy cream
3 egg whites
¹/₄ teaspoon salt
2 cups hulled fresh
  strawberries, partially
  crushed (or 2 cups frozen
  unsweetened whole
  strawberries, thawed, then
  crushed slightly)

At least 6 hours before serving: Prepare Cornflake Crust as directed but press in bottom of 8-inch square cake pan; bake and cool as directed. In medium saucepan, mix 2 envelopes gelatin, granulated or liquid non-nutritive sweetener equivalent to ¹/₂ cup sugar, orange juice, lemon peel and juice; let stand 5 minutes to soften gelatin. Meanwhile, sieve cottage cheese. Heat mixture until gelatin is dissolved; beat in cottage cheese and heavy cream. Refrigerate until the consistency of soft pudding.

In medium bowl, beat egg whites with salt until stiff peaks form. Fold in gelatin mixture. Turn into cooled crumb mixture; smooth surface. Refrigerate until set.

While cheesecake is setting, prepare strawberry glaze. In medium saucepan, mix 1¹/₂ teaspoons gelatin with ¹/₄ cup water and non-nutritive sweetener equivalent to 2 tablespoons sugar. Let stand 5 minutes, then bring just to simmer. Stir in crushed strawberries. Pour glaze over cake and gently spread with spatula to edges. Refrigerate until completely set—about 3 hours. Makes 9 servings.

CORNFLAKE CRUST (exchanges per ¹/₈ crust = ¹/₂ bread and 1 fat)

3 tablespoons butter or
  margarine
liquid non-nutritive sweetener
  equivalent to 1 tablespoon
  sugar
³/₄ cup packaged cornflake
  crumbs

At least 1 hour before filling: Preheat oven to 375°F. In 9-inch pie plate, mix all ingredients, then press on sides and up edges of pie plate. Bake 8 minutes; cool, then fill as desired.

CHOCOLATE CHIFFON PIE (exchanges per serving = 1 meat, 1 bread and 2 fat)

Cornflake Crust (see recipe page 271)
1 4-serving envelope low-calorie chocolate pudding mix
1/3 cup cocoa
2 envelopes unflavored gelatin
13/4 cups skimmed milk or reliquefied nonfat dry milk
non-nutritive sweetener equivalent to 1/2 cup sugar
3 egg whites
1 cup heavy cream

About 4 hours before serving: Mix, bake and cool Cornflake Crust as recipe directs. In medium saucepan, mix pudding mix, cocoa and gelatin. Stirring constantly, slowly stir in enough milk to form a smooth paste. Add remaining milk and non-nutritive sweetener. Stir until smooth; let stand 5 minutes to soften gelatin. Heat, stirring constantly, until mixture boils. Cool slightly, then cover pudding with waxed paper. Refrigerate until cold. Beat until consistency of soft whipped cream.

In medium bowl, beat egg whites until stiff peaks form. Whip cream; fold 1 cup into chocolate mixture. Then fold in beaten egg whites. Pour into crumb shell. Refrigerate until firm—about 2 hours. Spread remaining whipped cream attractively on top of pie. Refrigerate until serving time. Makes 8 servings.

PUMPKIN PIE (exchanges per serving = 1 fruit, 1 fat and 1 milk)

9-inch single crust Flaky Piecrust (see recipe page 292)
non-nutritive sweetener equivalent to 1 cup sugar
1/2 teaspoon salt
11/2 teaspoon cinnamon
1/2 teaspoon ginger
1/2 teaspoon nutmeg
1/2 teaspoon allspice
1/2 teaspoon ground cloves
11/2 cups canned pumpkin
12/3 cups evaporated milk
2 eggs, well beaten

At least 4 hours before serving: Prepare Flaky Piecrust as directed. Preheat oven to 425°F. In medium bowl, combine non-nutritive sweetener, salt, cinnamon, ginger, nutmeg, allspice and cloves; beat in pumpkin, milk and eggs until smooth. Pour mixture into pie shell. Bake at 425°F. for 15 minutes; then reduce heat to 350°F. and bake 35 minutes, or until silver knife, inserted in center, comes out clean. Cool; refrigerate. Makes 8 servings.

APPLE PIE (exchanges per serving = 11/2 bread, 3 fat and 1 fruit)

8-inch double-crust Flaky Piecrust (see recipe page 292)
1 quart (about 2 pounds) thinly sliced tart cooking apples
liquid non-nutritive sweetener equivalent to 3/4 cup sugar
2 tablespoons cornstarch
1/4 finely grated lemon peel
1 to 2 teaspoons lemon juice
1/4 teaspoon nutmeg
1/2 teaspoon cinnamon

At least 4 hours before serving: Prepare double-crust Flaky Piecrust; use half to line 8-inch pie plate. Preheat oven to 425°F. In large bowl, toss together remaining ingredients. Fill crust with apple mixture; top with second crust. Flute edges; cut air vents. To prevent excessive browning of crust, lightly cover fluted edges with foil. Bake 40 to 50 minutes, or until apples are tender. Remove foil after 30 minutes baking time. Cool. Makes 8 servings.

BLUEBERRY PIE (exchanges per serving = 11/2 bread, 3 fat and 1 fruit)
Substitute 1 quart fresh blueberries for apples; prepare and bake pie as directed for Apple Pie, above. Makes 8 servings.

FRUIT-COCKTAIL PIE (exchanges per serving = 11/2 bread, 3 fat and 1 fruit)
Substitute 1 quart mixed sliced fresh fruit (choose from pears, peaches, seedless grapes, apples and pineapple) for apples; prepare and bake pie as directed for Apple Pie, above. Makes 8 servings.

FRUITFUL COBBLER (exchanges per serving 1 bread, 1 fat and 1 fruit)

1/2 teaspoon salt
1/2 tablespoon cornstarch
non-nutritive sweetener
1 quart sliced fresh peaches
1 cup packaged biscuit mix
1/2 cup light cream
1/2 teaspoon vanilla extract
1 teaspoon grated lemon peel

At least 1 1/2 hours before serving: Preheat oven to 425°F. In 1 1/2 quart casserole, combine salt, cornstarch, non-nutritive sweetener equivalent to 1/2 cup sugar and 1/2 cup water; add peach slices. In medium bowl, mix biscuit mix, light cream, vanilla, saccharin equivalent to 2 tablespoons sugar and lemon peel. Spread mixture over peaches. Bake, uncovered, 40 minutes, or until topping is golden-brown and peaches are bubbly and tender. Serve warm or cold. Makes 8 servings.

BLUEBERRY MUFFINS (exchanges per serving = 1 bread and 1 fat)

1/3 cup butter or margarine, melted
non-nutritive sweetener equivalent to 1/3 cup sugar, plus water to make 1/4 cup
2 eggs
1 1/4 cups cornmeal
3/4 cup sifted all-purpose flour
2 1/2 teaspoons double-acting baking powder
3/4 teaspoon salt
3/4 cup skimmed milk or reliquefied nonfat dry milk
1/2 cup fresh blueberries (or 1/2 cup unsweetened frozen blueberries, thawed and drained)

About 35 minutes before serving: Preheat oven to 400°F. Grease 15 cups of muffin pans. In medium bowl, beat butter, non-nutritive sweetener dissolved in water, and eggs; stir in cornmeal. Sift flour, baking powder and salt; stir a third of this mixture into cornmeal mixture; stir in half of milk; repeat, then stir in remaining third of flour mixture. Gently fold in blueberries. Place scant 1/4 cup of batter in each muffin cup. Bake 20 to 25 minutes, or until muffins are golden-brown. Makes 15.

CREAMY RICE PUDDING (exchanges per serving = 1 bread, 1 fat and 1/2 milk)

2/3 cup packaged precooked rice
1/3 cup raisins
2 cups milk
non-nutritive sweetener equivalent to 1/3 cup sugar
1 teaspoon vanilla extract
1/2 teaspoon salt
1/8 teaspoon nutmeg
1/8 teaspoon cinnamon
1/2 cup heavy cream, whipped

About 3 hours before serving: In medium saucepan, combine rice, raisins and milk; bring to boiling; simmer, loosely covered 15 minutes, fluffing rice occasionally with fork. Stir in non-nutritive sweetener, vanilla, salt, nutmeg and cinnamon. Refrigerate, covered, until cold. Fold in whipped cream. Makes 6 servings.

BAKED CUSTARD (exchanges per serving = 1/2 milk)

4 eggs
non-nutritive sweetener equivalent to 1/4 cup sugar
1/4 teaspoon salt
2 cups milk
1 teaspoon vanilla extract
nutmeg

At least 4 hours before serving: Preheat oven to 300°F. Butter six 3/4-cup custard cups. In medium bowl, beat eggs, non-nutritive sweetener, 1/4 cup water and salt until smooth. Scald milk, then slowly stir hot milk and vanilla into egg mixture. Divide among custard cups; sprinkle with nutmeg. Set custard cups in baking pan; place in oven and fill pan with hot water to 3/4 inch from top of cups. Bake about 1 1/2 hours, or until custard leaves thick coating on knife inserted in center. Cool; refrigerate. Makes 6 servings.

BUTTERMILK-OAT CRISPS (exchanges for 4 crisps = 1 bread and 1 fat)

1 cup sifted all-purpose flour
1/2 teaspoon salt
1/4 teaspoon baking soda
1/2 cup uncooked rolled oats
non-nutritive sweetener equivalent to 3 tablespoons sugar
1/4 cup buttermilk
1/4 cup butter or margarine, melted

At least 1 hour before serving: Preheat oven to 400° F. In medium bowl, stir flour, salt, baking soda and oatmeal. Stir non-nutritive sweetener, buttermilk and butter into flour-oat mixture until dry ingredients are just moistened. On well-floured pastry board or cloth, knead dough lightly for a few seconds. Then roll out into rectangle 10″ by 12″. Cut into 2″ by 2″ squares. Bake on ungreased cookie sheets 10 to 12 minutes, or until crisps are golden-brown. Serve hot or cold. Makes 30.

CHOCOLATE-CHIP-MINT ICE CREAM (exchanges per serving = 1/2 milk)

1 square unsweetened chocolate
1 tablespoon cornstarch
1 1/2 teaspoons spearmint or peppermint extract
1 tablespoon lemon juice
non-nutritive sweetener equivalent to 1/2 cup sugar
1/2 teaspoon vanilla extract
dash salt
green food color
3/4 cup evaporated skimmed milk

At least 6 hours before serving: Refrigerate square of chocolate. In small saucepan, stir 1/2 cup water into cornstarch to form a smooth paste. Add spearmint or peppermint extract, lemon juice, non-nutritive sweetener, vanilla and salt. Stir in enough food color to turn mixture kelly-green. Cook, stirring constantly, until mixture boils and thickens. (Mixture will then be forest-green.) Refrigerate, stirring occasionally.

Place milk (in medium bowl) and electric mixer beaters in freezer until ice crystals form 1/2 to 1 inch from edge of bowl. Shave or grate chilled chocolate. With electric mixer at highest speed, beat milk until consistency of whipped cream. Gradually beat cornstarch mixture into whipped milk; mix in chocolate. Turn into baking dish; smooth surface; cover with waxed paper. Freeze hard—3 to 4 hours. About 15 to 20 minutes before serving, remove ice cream from freezer; let warm to good spooning temperature. Makes 6 servings.

PEACH AND ORANGE SHERBET (exchanges per serving = 1 fruit)

2 16-ounce cans peach slices packed in water
non-nutritive sweetener equivalent to 1/2 cup sugar
1/4 teaspoon grapefruit juice
1/2 cup orange juice
1 tablespoon lemon juice
2 egg whites

About 6 hours before serving: Drain juice from peaches. In electric-blender container at low speed, blend enough peaches to make 1 3/4 cups puree. In medium bowl, mix this puree, non-nutritive sweetener, 1/4 cup water, grapefruit juice, orange juice and lemon juice. (Or press peaches through sieve and mix with other ingredients.) Freeze until firm about 1 inch from edge of bowl—about 30 minutes. Then, with electric mixer, beat egg whites until stiff peaks form. Beat fruit mixture until smooth. Fold egg whites into fruit. Freeze until just firm. If sherbet gets too hard to serve, let soften slightly, then beat with electric mixer until smooth. Makes 1 quart or six 2/3-cup servings.

FROSTY POP (exchanges per serving = 1 "free")

2 4-serving envelopes dietetic-packed cherry-, orange-, or lemon-flavor gelatin
1 cup boiling water
1 cup cold water

About 4 to 6 hours before serving: In medium bowl, stir together gelatin and boiling water until all gelatin is dissolved. Stir in cold water. Divide mixture among six 3-ounce paper cups. Freeze until firm. (If desired, wooden sticks may be added when mixture is semifirm.)

To serve: Let stand at room temperature for 5 minutes; peel paper cup down from pop to eat. Makes 6 servings.

ORANGE BAGATELLE (exchanges per serving = 1 fruit and 1 fat)

**1 4-serving envelope
orange-flavored low-calorie
gelatin
1 16-ounce jar unsweetened
applesauce
nutmeg
dash salt
coarsely grated orange peel
heavy cream, whipped and
seasoned to taste with liquid
non-nutritive sweetener and
vanilla**

About 4 hours before serving: In medium bowl, dissolve gelatin in
$1/2$ cup boiling water. Stir in applesauce, $1/8$ teaspoon nutmeg, salt
and 2 tablespoons grated orange peel. Pour into 9" by 5" by 3"
pan; refrigerate.

A few minutes before serving: Cut jelly into 1-inch squares;
heap into 4 sherbet glasses; sprinkle with more grated orange
peel and nutmeg, if desired. Top each serving with 2-tablespoon
dab whipped cream. Makes 4 servings.

SUGAR-FREE JAMS AND JELLIES (General Instructions)

- Sterilize jelly jars as follows:
  1. Boil, completely covered with water, for 15 minutes.
  2. Remove from water with tongs that have been held in boiling
  water at least one minute.
  3. Let drain, upside down, on clean paper toweling until
  immediately before using, then turn right-side up.
- Sweeten jam or jelly with liquid or granulated non-nutritive
  sweetener or if tablets are used, pulverize to a fine powder.
- Carefully calculate the amount of saccharin or other
  non-nutritive sweetner to use.* Stir into hot fruit until
  completely mixed and dissolved. Do not boil again.
- Melt paraffin in top of double boiler or in saucepan, over **very
  low heat**—paraffin burns easily.
- Pour jam or jelly into jars without smearing sides. Wipe away
  any dribbles.
- Pour on melted paraffin, covering jam or jelly with layer about
  $1/8$- to $1/4$-inch thick. Set to one side to cool, then refrigerate.
- After jam or jelly has been opened the first time, store, covered
  with lid or foil.
- Keep refrigerated. Use within 3 to 4 weeks, then prepare fresh
  batch.

*The first time, use the sweetening levels suggested. Later you may
want to adjust them to your personal taste.

BLUEBERRY JELLY-JAM (exchanges per tablespoon = 1 "free")

**1 tablespoon lemon juice
$1^1/2$ teaspoons cornstarch
$1^1/2$ teaspoons unflavored
gelatin
dash salt (optional)
1 10-ounce package frozen
unsweetened blueberries,
partially thawed
non-nutritive sweetner
equivalent to $3/4$ cup sugar**

Prepare two 1-cup jelly jars as directed in General Instructions
(above). In medium saucepan, mix lemon juice, cornstarch,
gelatin and salt; add blueberries. Stirring constantly, heat to
boiling; boil gently 3 minutes, or until blueberry syrup thickens
slightly and turns a rich shade of royal blue.

In electric-blender container at low speed (keep lid ajar to allow
steam to escape), blend blueberry mixture until smooth. (Or
mixture may be strained through food mill.) Return to saucepan;
stirring constantly, bring to boiling; boil 2 minutes. Stir in
non-nutritive sweetener. Fill jelly jars; seal and store as directed in
General Instructions. Makes slightly more than 1 cup of jelly-jam.

PINEAPPLE-APRICOT PRESERVES (exchanges per tablespoon = 1/2 fruit)

1/2 8-ounce package dried apricots
1 cup pineapple (from 15 1/4-ounce can pineapple tidbits packed in pineapple juice)
1 tablespoon lemon juice
dash salt (optional)
non-nutritive sweetener equivalent to 1/2 cup sugar

In medium saucepan, simmer apricots with 1 cup water 20 minutes, or until tender. Meanwhile, prepare two 1-cup jelly jars as directed in General Instructions (page 275). Drain pineapple tidbits and cut each, crosswise, into 3 pieces.

In electric-blender container, at low speed (cover ajar to allow steam to escape), blend apricots and cooking water with lemon juice and salt. (Mixture may also be strained through food mill.) Return to saucepan; stir in pineapple pieces. Simmer, stirring occasionally, 5 minutes. Remove from heat; stir in non-nutritive sweetener. Fill jelly jars; seal and store as directed in General Instructions. Makes generous cup of preserves.

PINEAPPLE-APRICOT CONSERVES
(exchanges per tablespoon = 1/2 fruit)
Prepare Pineapple-Apricot Preserves as directed above, but stir in 1/4 cup finely chopped, blanched almonds with pineapple pieces.

APPLE JELLY (exchanges per tablespoon = 1 "free")

1 tablespoon lemon juice
1 teaspoon unflavored gelatin
1 teaspoon cornstarch
dash salt (optional)
1 cup apple juice
non-nutritive sweetener equivalent to 3/4 cup sugar

Prepare one 1-cup jelly jar as directed in General Instructions (see page 275). In small saucepan, mix lemon juice, gelatin, cornstarch and salt; stir in apple juice. Stirring constantly, heat to boiling; boil 2 minutes. Remove from heat; stir in non-nutritive sweetener. Fill jelly jar; seal and store as directed in General Instructions. Makes full cup of jelly.

SUGAR-FREE CANNING

Canning fruits can be done successfully in water or unsweetened fruit juice, rather than the traditional sugar syrup, if you use proper techniques and adequate processing times. To assure good results, get one of the complete booklets on canning published by canning-equipment manufacturers or the U.S. Department of Agriculture,* and follow directions explicitly. These booklets give instructions for both water-bath and pressure-cooker methods of canning. When serving, count fruit exchanges as you would for fresh or commercially prepared sugar-free fruit.

If only one family member is eating sugar-free fruits, cut waste by using pint, or even half-pint, jars for canning. To keep fruit from darkening as you prepare it (apples, pears, peaches), soak it in an ascorbic-acid or lemon-juice solution.†

*For Home Canning of Fruits and Vegetables, send $1.75 to: Superintendent of Documents, U.S. Government Printing Office, Washington, D.C. 20402. Include your ZIP code.
†Ascorbic-acid solution: 1 teaspoon crystalline ascorbic acid for each quart of water or fruit juice. Lemon juice solution: 2 tablespoons lemon juice for each quart of water or fruit juice.

You'll need much less sweetener than would be equivalent to the amount of sugar used in a traditional sugar syrup. We recommend non–nutritive sweetener equivalent to 2 to 4 cups of sugar for every 2 to 3 quarts of liquid. Try this proportion first, then make any adjustments necessary to suit your taste. You can add non-nutritive sweetener during canning, but the sweetness seems more natural when added at serving time.

In canned fruit or vegetable relishes, unlike canned fruits, sugar does contribute to the texture and preservation of the ingredients. Experiment with recipes, but don't be too discouraged if some prove disappointing. (Fruits or vegetables can turn mushy, or have an unsuitable flavor.) Relishes aren't as suited to sugar-free canning as plain fruits are. To preserve sugar-free relishes, use the water-bath method of canning—you can't depend on open-kettle heating.

Pears or Peaches: Vary the pieces (halves, quarters or slices) so you'll have some variety. Small pieces pack best in small jars; halves in quart jars.

Use unsweetened orange or pineapple juice as the canning liquid to gain unusual flavor. *Note:* These juices will settle to the bottom of the jar. Before you serve, shake the jar to mix. For delicious variation, blend a 50-50 mixture of peaches and pears.

Raspberries and Strawberries: Mash berries; strain off and save juice. Use mixture of juice and water as canning liquid. The fruit will retain a richer color.

Fruit Cocktail: Mix peaches, pears, pineapple, apples, seedless oranges and grapes. Beware of adding banana slices—they get too soft, and their flavor changes. Since juices of strawberries, raspberries, blueberries, plums and cherries "weep," avoid using them in fruit cocktails.

Plums: Most plums can well, but take the advice of your canning booklet when selecting varieties. Halve large plums, or only 2 or 3 will fit into a pint jar. A mixture of strained plum juice and water, used as the canning liquid, cuts down on loss of color.

HIGH-IRON DIET

A high-iron diet is used to treat iron-deficiency anemia. Anemia is a general term used to describe the condition of the body when there are too few functioning blood cells. There are at least six different types of anemia, but the most common is caused by too little iron in the diet.

Everyone needs iron for blood-cell formation and function. The need is greatest in women of child-bearing age, for some of the body's supply of iron is depleted during menstruation and pregnancy. The blood stream is the main storage house for iron, but iron is also stored in body tissue—liver, bone marrow and spleen. When iron levels in the blood are lowered, iron is pulled from the body's tissue stores.

Men must absorb 1 milligram of iron per day and women 1.8 milligrams to replace the iron lost through perspiration, urine, and in women, menstruation. However, relatively little—about 10 percent—of the iron in food eaten daily is absorbed, so the Recommended Dietary Allowance for iron is 10 milligrams a day for men, 18 for women of child-bearing age. Note that while a woman's iron needs are higher than a man's, her caloric needs are lower, making it necessary for her to get more iron for her calorie "dollar."

If your physician has warned you that you are anemic, carefully follow all his instructions about iron supplements, medication and meal planning. Avoid eating a meal with huge "doses" of iron, and then one with little or no iron. Keep your iron intake at a steady pace and you will absorb more of it.

The foods that follow are all good sources of iron. Unfortunately, the very richest sources are relatively unpopular (liver), expensive (oysters), or difficult to obtain (dandelion greens). So don't underestimate the importance of vegetables, fruits and enriched or whole-grain breads in adding iron to the diet. These old faithfuls do the job unobtrusively. See pages 337 to 338 for the specific iron content of various foods.

Apricots (dried)
Beans, baked
Beef (trimmed meat)
Beet greens
Blackberries
Blueberries
Bran cereal
Breads (enriched or whole grain)
Broccoli
Brussels sprouts
Chard
Chinese cabbage
Clams
Collards
Cowpeas (black-eyed peas)
Dandelion greens
Egg yolks
Kale
Kidney
Liver
Mushrooms
Mustard greens
Oysters
Pastas (enriched)
Peaches (dried)
Plums
Pork (trimmed meat)
Rice (enriched)
Spinach
Squash (winter)
Strawberries
Sweet potatoes
Tongue
Turnip greens
Veal

If you are taking special care to meet the Recommended Dietary Allowance for iron, some of the suggestions that follow will be helpful.

• Products with the words enriched, whole-grain and fortified on their labels are all good sources of iron. For example, enriched refrigerator biscuits, rolls and sweet bread;

enriched saltines; enriched or whole-grain bread; ready-to-eat cereals fortified with iron as well as vitamins; whole-grain crackers; enriched white rice (don't rinse the rice before or after cooking—the enrichment mixture is on the surface); biscuits and quick breads made from enriched biscuit mix; juice drinks and synthetic drinks fortified with iron.

- Use dried fruits. Add prunes, dates and dried apricots to fruit cocktails and salads; use dried fruits as condiments for curries; make raisin sauces for ham; add raisins to cookies.
- If you like fresh fruit, the berries—blackberries, blueberries, strawberries, etc.—are among the fruits highest in iron content (1 milligram iron per cup).
- Try "Southern" vegetables—kale, chard, collards, dandelion greens, okra. They are available frozen as well as fresh. (Don't overcook!) Other vegetable suggestions: Steam mushrooms in broth with a few onion slices; Mixed-Bean Salad (see recipe on page 283).
- If you hate liver (one of the highest sources of iron), try chicken livers—the flavor is mild. Cook them smothered in onions. Chopped chicken livers come frozen so no preparation is needed. Use as a salad or in sandwiches. And don't forget *pork* liver; it's higher in iron content than beef or calves' liver and *much cheaper.*
- If you love chocolate, you will be glad to know that the cocoa and chocolate (particularly unsweetened) are rich in iron, too. A cup of prepared cocoa will provide 1 milligram of iron. Make it with skimmed milk and the calories are about the same as plain whole milk.
- Snack on delicious instant breakfast made with skimmed milk (225 calories and $2^{1}/_{2}$ milligrams of iron per serving). Try it as a milkshake: Mix instant breakfast, 1 cup skimmed milk and 3 or 4 ice cubes; buzz in blender until smooth.
- When making turkey gravy, use the giblets. Cook the gizzard and heart until tender; add the liver for the last 15 minutes. Trim away the tough parts of the gizzard and heart, and chop with the liver. Make gravy as usual; add giblets.
- Try baked eggs on toast: Beat 2 egg whites until stiff; spread on a slice of enriched or whole-wheat bread; nest yolks into the whites. Bake at 350° F. until done as you like—about 10 minutes. (3 milligrams iron and 220 calories per serving.)

HIGH-IRON DIET: 24 Recipes

KASHMIR SPLIT-PEA SOUP (2 milligrams iron per serving)

1 medium onion, sliced
1 medium carrot, sliced
1 cup dried green split peas
3 chicken-bouillon cubes
1 teaspoon salt
generous dash cayenne
1 teaspoon curry (optional)
³/₄ cup packaged croutons

About 1 hour before serving: In medium saucepan, heat 5 cups water, onion, carrot, peas, bouillon cubes, salt and cayenne to boiling; cover; simmer 50 minutes, or until peas are soft. Stir in curry if desired.

Press mixture through sieve or food mill. Return puree to saucepan. Serve topped with croutons. Makes 4 servings.

OYSTER-CORN CHOWDER (9 milligrams iron per serving)

1 medium onion, thinly sliced
¹/₂ cup chopped celery
¹/₂ teaspoon salt
generous dash garlic salt
generous dash pepper
generous dash nutmeg
1 16-ounce can cream-style corn
1 10¹/₂-ounce can condensed chicken broth
1 soup-can liquid from oysters
2 hard-cooked eggs, thinly sliced
2 dozen shucked oysters

About 30 minutes before serving: In large saucepan, simmer, uncovered, all ingredients but hard-cooked eggs and oysters, for 20 minutes. Add egg slices and oysters; simmer 3 minutes, or until oysters curl and are just cooked. Makes 4 main-dish servings.

LINGUINE WITH CLAM SAUCE (9 milligrams iron per serving)

¹/₂ 16-ounce package enriched linguine
2 7¹/₂-ounce cans minced clams
about 1 cup bottled clam juice
¹/₄ cup butter or margarine
1 garlic clove, minced
2 tablespoons flour
about ¹/₄ cup chopped parsley
1¹/₂ teaspoons thyme leaves
salt and pepper to taste

About 30 minutes before serving: Cook linguine as label directs. Meanwhile, drain clams, reserving liquid. Add enough bottled clam juice to liquid to make 2 cups. In large skillet over medium heat, in butter, sauté garlic until golden. Blend flour into butter. Slowly stir in liquid and seasonings until smooth. Cover and simmer 10 minutes, stirring occasionally. Add clams to sauce and heat; season with salt and pepper. Pour over drained linguine; toss. Makes 4 servings.

CLAM FRITTERS (4.5 milligrams iron per serving)

oil or fat for deep frying
1¹/₂ cups sifted enriched all-purpose flour
2 teaspoons double-acting baking powder
³/₄ teaspoon salt
2 eggs, separated
1 cup milk
1 teaspoon lemon juice
2 7¹/₂-ounce cans minced clams, thoroughly drained
catchup (optional)

About 1 hour before serving: Preheat oil or fat in deep fat fryer to 375° F. Stir together flour, baking powder and salt. In small bowl, beat egg whites until stiff peaks form. In medium bowl, beat together flour mixture, egg yolks, milk and lemon juice. Fold in egg whites, then drained clams.

Drop batter, ¹/₄ cup per fritter, into hot oil and cook until golden brown and bubbles stop forming in top of batter; turn and brown on other side. Drain on paper toweling. Serve hot; pass catchup if desired. Makes 6 servings of 2 fritters each.

CLAM-AND-CHEESE SANDWICHES (3 milligrams iron per serving)

1 3-ounce package Neufchâtel
  cheese
1 7- or 7¹/₂-ounce can minced
  clams, drained
1 teaspoon soy sauce
1 teaspoon prepared mustard
¹/₄ teaspoon salt
2 teaspoons instant minced
  onion
8 square slices pumpernickel
  bread

About 1 hour before serving: In small bowl, mix all ingredients but bread. Use to fill bread slices making 4 sandwiches.

OYSTER-MUSHROOM KABOBS (8 milligrams iron per serving)

12 slices bacon (about ³/₄
  pound)
2 8-ounce cans large oysters
¹/₂ pound medium mushrooms

About 40 minutes before serving: Preheat broiler if manufacturer directs. In medium skillet, cook bacon until slices are slightly browned but not yet crisp.

Drain oysters; wrap slice of bacon around each. Alternating oysters with mushrooms, place on four skewers. Broil, turning once, until bacon is crisp. Makes 4 servings.

HAZEL'S OYSTERS ROCKEFELLER (8 milligrams iron per serving)

1 10-ounce package frozen,
  chopped spinach, thawed
¹/₂ cup chopped parsley leaves
¹/₂ cup chopped celery leaves
¹/₄ cup minced onion
1 bay leaf
salt
1 tablespoon Worcestershire
dash cayenne
butter or margarine
4 slices whole-wheat toast
1 cup shucked oysters (about 2
  dozen oysters), carefully
  washed, with any pieces of
  shell removed
1 cup large bread cubes made
  with enriched bread

About 1 hour before serving: In electric-blender container, at low speed, combine spinach, parsley, celery leaves, onion, bay leaf, ¹/₂ teaspoon salt, Worcestershire and cayenne. In medium saucepan, heat puree, with 1 tablespoon butter, just to boiling. Preheat oven to 350° F. Into 8-inch pie plate, press toast slices to form 4 wedges. Spread puree on toast; then arrange oysters over puree; sprinkle with salt, if desired. Top oysters with bread cubes, then dot with 2 tablespoons butter or margarine. Bake 25 minutes, or until bread cubes are a dark golden-brown and oysters are easily pierced with a fork. Makes 4 servings.

LIVER EMPANADAS (6 milligrams iron per serving)

1 9.5-ounce can enriched refrigerated flaky buttermilk biscuits
1 6-ounce container frozen, seasoned chopped chicken liver,
  thawed
1 8- or 10¹/₄-ounce jar spaghetti
  sauce with mushrooms

About 25 minutes before serving: Preheat oven to 450° F. Separate biscuits; roll or press each into oval about 3″ by 3¹/₂″. In center of each biscuit, place 1 tablespoon chopped liver. Moisten edges slightly with water, then fold long end over and press edges together with tines of fork. Shape ends toward each other, forming crescent. Bake on ungreased cookie sheet 10 minutes, or until golden. Meanwhile, heat spaghetti sauce. Serve empanadas with sauce. Makes 3 main-course servings.

LIVERBURGERS (6 milligrams iron per serving)

¹/₂ pound beef liver
¹/₂ pound ground beef
³/₄ cup enriched dried bread crumbs
2 eggs
1 teaspoon salt
¹/₂ teaspoon Tabasco
¹/₂ teaspoon celery salt
¹/₄ cup minced onion
bacon fat

About 1 hour and 45 minutes before serving: Remove skin and large veins from liver. Using a fine blade, grind liver. Thoroughly mix liver, chuck, bread crumbs, eggs, salt, Tabasco, celery salt and onion. Form mixture into 8 patties; refrigerate about one hour, or until ready to fry. In large skillet, in bacon fat, fry patties until done. Makes 4 servings of 2 patties each.

EGGS À LA RUSSE (3 milligrams iron per serving)

¹/₂ cup mayonnaise
2 tablespoons chili sauce
1 teaspoon chopped chives
few drops lemon juice
dash Tabasco
10 hard-cooked eggs
5 small lettuce cups

At serving time: In medium bowl, stir together mayonnaise, chili sauce, chives, lemon juice and Tabasco. Cut eggs with egg slicer and "fan" attractively; place on lettuce cups and spoon on dressing. Makes 5 servings.

MUSHROOM DEVILED EGGS (1.5 milligrams iron per egg)

2 tablespoons butter or margarine
¹/₄ pound mushrooms, minced
2 tablespoons minced onion
8 hard-cooked eggs
2 tablespoons mayonnaise
2 tablespoons prepared mustard
1 tablespoon lemon juice
¹/₂ teaspoon celery salt
¹/₈ teaspoon pepper
paprika for garnish

About 30 minutes before serving: In skillet, in butter, sauté mushrooms and onion until onion is transparent. Meanwhile, halve eggs lengthwise; remove yolks, keeping whites intact. Mash yolks with fork; combine with mushroom mixture and remaining ingredients except paprika. Use mixture to refill hollows in whites, rounding each. Sprinkle with paprika. Makes 16 halves.

MODERN-DAY KNISHES (.5 milligrams iron per knish)

1 8-ounce can enriched refrigerated crescent rolls
1 6-ounce container frozen seasoned chopped chicken liver, thawed
1 egg, lightly beaten

About 35 minutes before serving: Preheat oven to 375° F. Unroll rolls; separate into 4 rectangles; pinch diagonal seams together. Cut each rectangle in half lengthwise, then thirds crosswise. Fill each tiny rectangle with about 1 teaspoon chopped chicken liver; roll up and place, seam side down, on ungreased cookie sheet. Brush each knish with beaten egg, then bake 12 to 15 minutes, or until a rich golden-brown. Serve immediately. Makes 24.

BAKED-BEAN SURPRISE (2.5 milligrams iron per serving)

1 16-ounce can vegetarian baked beans
1 15¹/₄-ounce can pineapple chunks packed in pineapple juice, drained
¹/₃ cup chili sauce

About 10 minutes before serving: In medium saucepan, mix ingredients; simmer 5 minutes. Makes 4 servings.

QUICK BAKED BEANS (4 milligrams iron per serving)

1/4 pound sliced bacon, cut into
  1-inch pieces
1 large onion, thinly sliced
1 garlic clove, minced
1 tablespoon cornstarch
2 16-ounce cans kidney beans,
  drained
1 16-ounce can tomatoes
1/2 teaspoon salt
1/2 teaspoon dry mustard
1/2 teaspoon chili powder
generous dash pepper
1 1/2 teaspoons Worcestershire
1/2 cup dark molasses

About 1 hour before serving: Preheat oven to 375° F. In medium skillet, cook bacon until almost crisp; remove. In bacon fat, sauté onion and garlic until golden—do not brown. Pour most of fat from skillet, then stir in cornstarch; mix in 1 can drained kidney beans. In 2-quart casserole, stir together bacon, onion mixture, remaining kidney beans, tomatoes, salt, mustard, chili powder, pepper, Worcestershire and molasses. Bake 45 minutes, or until bubbly and lightly browned on top. Makes eight 1-cup servings.

MIXED BEAN SALAD (4 milligrams iron per serving)

1 cup drained canned red kidney beans
1 cup drained canned white kidney beans
1 cup drained canned chick
  peas
1 small green pepper, chopped
3/4 cup chopped onions
3 tablespoons wine vinegar
1/2 cup olive oil
1 teaspoon salt
1/2 teaspoon garlic powder
dash pepper
4 lettuce leaves

About 1 hour before serving: In medium bowl, toss together all ingredients but lettuce; refrigerate.
  To serve: Drain mixture, then spoon into lettuce leaves. Makes 4 servings.

SALAD—TIVOLI GARDEN (4 milligrams iron per serving)

3/4 pound fresh spinach, cut
  into bite-size pieces
1 small head red cabbage, cut
  into thin strips
3 scallions, chopped
2 6 1/2- or 7-ounce cans tuna,
  drained and separated into
  chunks
1/4 cup salad oil
1/2 teaspoon salt
1/4 teaspoon dry mustard
1/4 cup vinegar
2 tablespoons grated Parmesan
  cheese
2 hard-cooked eggs, sliced for
  garnish

About 30 minutes before serving: In large bowl, toss spinach, cabbage and scallions with tuna. Stir together oil, salt, mustard and vinegar until smooth; then toss with greens and tuna. Sprinkle with Parmesan and garnish with egg slices. Makes 6 servings.

SPINACH SPECIAL (2.5 milligrams iron per serving)

1 16-ounce bag spinach, washed
1¹/₂ teaspoons salt
1 large carrot, coarsely grated
1 apple, grated
¹/₂ teaspoon lemon juice

About 15 minutes before serving: In large kettle, cook spinach and salt, in water that still clings to leaves, 6 minutes, or until just tender-crisp. Drain; return to kettle; stir in grated carrot, apple and lemon juice. Simmer, covered, a few minutes, or until heated through. Makes 6 servings.

BROCCOLI WITH HOLLANDAISE (1 milligram iron per serving)

2 10-ounce packages frozen cut broccoli
¹/₂ cup butter or margarine
3 egg yolks
2 tablespoons lemon juice
¹/₄ teaspoon salt
¹/₄ teaspoon onion salt
dash cayenne

About 15 minutes before serving: Cook broccoli as label directs; drain. Meanwhile, in small pan, heat butter or margarine until just bubbling, but not brown. In electric-blender container, at low speed, blend remaining ingredients until mixed. Still at low speed, remove center of cover and slowly pour in all hot butter in low, steady stream; turn off immediately. Serve over broccoli. Makes 6 servings.

HOT CUCUMBERS WITH DILL (1 milligram iron per serving)

5 medium cucumbers, pared
salt
1 cup plain yogurt
¹/₂ cup mayonnaise
¹/₈ teaspoon white pepper
2 egg yolks, lightly beaten
1 tablespoon chopped fresh dill

About 30 minutes before serving: Cut cucumbers into 1-inch crosswise chunks; cook, uncovered, in boiling salted water, 7 minutes, or until just fork-tender; drain. In double-boiler, over simmering water, combine yogurt with mayonnaise, ¹/₄ teaspoon salt, pepper and beaten egg yolks. Stir constantly for about 10 minutes, or until slightly thickened; do not boil. Turn drained cucumbers into serving dish; top with sauce; sprinkle with the dill. Makes 6 servings.

SOFT MOLASSES COOKIES (.5 milligram iron per cookie)

2¹/₄ cups sifted enriched all-purpose flour
1 teaspoon ginger
1 teaspoon cinnamon
¹/₄ teaspoon salt
2 teaspoons baking soda
¹/₂ cup shortening
¹/₂ cup packed dark-brown sugar
¹/₂ cup dark molasses
1 egg
1¹/₂ cups raisins

About 2 hours before serving: Preheat oven to 400° F. Lightly grease cookie sheets. Stir together flour, ginger, cinnamon and salt. Dissolve soda in 2 tablespoons hot water.

In medium bowl, with electric mixer at medium speed, cream shortening, brown sugar, molasses and egg until fluffy and golden-brown. Beat in flour mixture alternately with 6 tablespoons cold water. Beat in soda mixture and raisins.

Drop, by rounded tablespoonfuls, 2 inches apart, onto greased cookie sheets. Bake 10 to 12 minutes, or until done. Makes about 3¹/₂ dozen.

APRICOT BROWN BETTY (3 milligrams iron per serving)

1 cup dried apricot halves
¹/₂ cup packed dark brown sugar
2 cups fresh bread cubes (made from enriched bread)
2 tablespoons butter or margarine
cinnamon
ginger
light cream or whipped cream

About 1¹/₂ hours before serving: In medium saucepan, simmer apricot halves, brown sugar and 1¹/₂ cups water, covered, 20 minutes. Preheat oven to 350° F. In 1-quart casserole, place half of bread cubes; dot with half of butter; top with several dashes of cinnamon and ginger to taste. Top with hot apricot halves, lightly drained. Add remaining bread cubes; top with butter, cinnamon and ginger as before. Pour syrup used to cook apricots over bread cubes. Bake 30 minutes, or until brown. Cool until serving time.

To serve: Pass light cream, or top each serving with dab of whipped cream. Makes 4 servings.

PRUNE-FILLED BRAID (2.5 milligrams iron per serving)

1/2 12-ounce package pitted prunes
1/4 cup orange marmalade
1/3 cup chopped walnuts
2 8-ounce cans enriched cres-cent dinner rolls
1/4 cup raisins
1/2 cup confectioners' sugar
1 tablespoon milk

About 1 1/2 hours before serving: In medium saucepan, heat prunes and 2 cups water to boiling. Cover and simmer 20 to 25 minutes; drain. In medium bowl, mash prunes with fork. Stir in orange marmalade and walnuts.

Preheat oven to 375° F. On ungreased large cookie sheet, unroll both cans crescent rolls; form into one large rectangle, about 14" by 12", overlapping edges slightly; press together seams and perforated edges.

Spread prune filling in 2-inch wide strip, lengthwise, down center of dough to about 1/2 inch from each end; sprinkle with raisins. Make cuts 2 inches apart diagonally along both sides of filling. Alternating sides, fold strips across filling. Fold ends under to seal. Bake 25 minutes, or until dark golden-brown. Combine sugar and milk. Drizzle over braid. Makes 8 servings.

SHOOFLY PIE (2.5 milligrams iron per serving)

1 cup sifted enriched all-pur-pose flour
1/2 cup packed dark brown sugar
1/2 teaspoon salt
1/2 teaspoon cinnamon
1/8 teaspoon nutmeg
1/8 teaspoon ground cloves
2 tablespoons butter or marga-rine
1/2 teaspoon baking soda
1/2 cup dark molasses
1 egg
unbaked 9-inch pie shell
vanilla ice cream or whipped cream (optional)

About 4 hours before serving: Preheat oven to 375° F. In small bowl, mix flour, brown sugar, salt, cinnamon, nutmeg, cloves and butter to make crumb mixture.

In small bowl, stir together baking soda and 3/4 cup hot water. Then beat in molasses and egg until smooth. Sprinkle one-quarter of crumb mixture in pie shell; carefully pour in one-third of molasses mixture. Repeat two more times, then top with remaining crumb mixture. Bake 35 minutes, or until pie is firm in center. Cool and serve warm, topped with dollops of ice cream. Or chill and serve cold, topped with whipped cream. Makes 8 servings.

APRICOT CHIFFON PIE (4 milligrams iron per serving)

1/2 pound dried apricots
2 teaspoons unflavored gelatin
granulated sugar
3 eggs, separated
2 tablespoons lemon juice
1/8 teaspoon salt
4 drops almond extract
1/2 cup heavy cream, whipped
1 9-inch pie shell

About 4 hours before serving: In medium saucepan, soak apricots in 1 cup water 1 hour; then cook, in same water, covered, 10 minutes, or until tender. In electric-blender container, at low speed, blend apricots and cooking liquid. Measure one cup of this puree. (Or press apricots through food mill.)

In top of double boiler, mix gelatin, 1/4 cup sugar, egg yolks, lemon juice, salt, almond extract and apricot puree; let stand 5 minutes to soften gelatin. Cook mixture over boiling water, stirring constantly for 5 minutes. Let cool to lukewarm.

About 2 hours before serving: In medium bowl, with electric mixer at high speed, beat egg whites until soft peaks form; then beat in, a tablespoon at a time, 1/2 cup sugar; continue to beat until stiff peaks form. Fold cooled apricot mixture into beaten whites; then fold whipped cream into apricot-egg mixture. Pour into prepared pie shell. Refrigerate until firm. Makes 6 servings.
PRUNE CHIFFON PIE: Prepare as directed above, but substitute 1/2 pound pitted prunes for apricots.

LOW-FAT, LOW-CHOLESTEROL DIET

Low-fat, low-cholesterol diet is the general term for a family of diets all designed to help prevent arteriosclerosis, embolisms or coronary thrombosis—in two words, "heart attacks."

It became apparent 40 years ago that Americans had an abnormally high rate of heart attacks and circulatory diseases. Studies also showed that we are more apt to be overweight, to eat more fat, to get less exercise and to live under more stressful conditions than virtually any other people. Then studies in experimental animals demonstrated that high blood-cholesterol levels (an indicator of abnormalities in the circulatory system) could be reduced by a diet rich in polyunsaturated fats.

Diets now being prescribed are based on this work plus later studies which showed that, for best results, total fat should not exceed 30 to 35 percent of the calories in the diet,* and that cholesterol from foods should also be limited. These diets:

1. Restrict the total amount of fat—particularly that from saturated fats
2. Increase the use of polyunsaturated fats
3. Restrict cholesterol-rich foods

Some also restrict the use of pure carbohydrates (i.e., sugar), but relatively few doctors add this restriction to a patient's diet. (See the Low-Fat, Low-Cholesterol Diet Outline that follows.)

The most restricted diet is used to treat those who have already had a heart attack. The emphasis is placed on reducing weight to normal by the restriction of total fat intake as well as over-all calories. Cholesterol-rich foods are also severely limited, and the polyunsaturated fats are used wherever possible. The doctor often recommends increased regular exercise such as walking, bowling or cycling. The same diet is also prescribed for the special-risk groups—those with a family history of heart disease, diabetes or high-blood pressure, or those who are overweight or are moderate to heavy smokers.

The American Heart Association has taken the diet one step further by recommending that everyone follow a fat-controlled diet, one which places less restriction on the total amount of fat in the diet but severely limits saturated fats and substitutes polyunsaturated fats. Cholesterol-rich foods and pure sugars are also limited.

Not all recognized authorities agree on the scientific relationship of diet to heart disease. They do agree that a calorie surplus leads to overweight, which is a major factor in heart disease. Since the easiest way to cut calories is to eliminate fat from the diet, any well-balanced diet will limit fat intake to a certain extent. In short, it makes sense for everyone to avoid too many overrich foods.

*An average diet obtains 40 to 45 percent of its calories from fat.

DIET OUTLINE

This diet is designed to limit fat to 45 to 50 grams a day, cholesterol to less than 300 milligrams. Polyunsaturated fats are substituted for saturated wherever possible.

FOODS ALLOWED	FOODS FORBIDDEN

MILK

Skimmed milk; modified skimmed milk; buttermilk made from skimmed milk; evaporated skimmed milk

MILK

Whole milk; evaporated milk; buttermilk or yogurt made from whole milk

CHEESE

Low-fat cottage cheese; Farmer, hoop, mozzarella cheese

CHEESE

Cream cheese; hard cheeses

FATS

(Up to 3 teaspoons—about 15 grams fat a day)
"Special" margarine (those with liquid oil listed first in ingredients)
Corn, safflower, cottonseed or soybean oils

FATS

Butter; cooking fat; lard; olive oil; coconut oil

EGGS

Egg whites allowed freely; egg yolks up to 3 a week; cholesterol-free, fat-reduced liquid egg substitute

EGGS

More than 3 yolks a week

MEAT AND POULTRY

(Up to 15 grams fat per serving)
Lean cooked meat only—one serving equals 3 ounces cooked meat. Use lean trimmed beef, pork, lamb and veal
Chicken and turkey—do not eat skin

MEAT AND POULTRY

Fatty cuts of meat such as short ribs, fatty hamburger, bacon, shoulder lamb chops
Frankfurters, luncheon meats
Duck and goose
Skin of poultry

FISH

Any of the following:
Cod, flounder, haddock, hake, halibut, ocean perch, pickerel, pollock, red snapper, sand dabs, sea bass, sole, tuna
Moderate amounts of: bluefish, brook trout, lake herring, smelt and swordfish

FISH

Herring, lake trout, mackerel, rainbow trout, salmon, shad

SHELLFISH

Other than those forbidden (see right), in moderation

SHELLFISH

Oysters, lobster, shrimp

VEGETABLES

All

VEGETABLES

No restrictions

FRUIT

All except olives and coconut

FRUIT

Olives and coconut

BREAD

Cracked wheat, French or Italian, rye, white and whole-wheat breads
Homemade quick breads made with allowed oil or margarine and no egg yolks
Angel-food cake

BREAD

Commercial quick breads, pastries, cakes and pies, most crackers and doughnuts

FOODS ALLOWED

CEREALS AND PASTAS
All

DESSERTS
Fruit; sherbet and Italian ices; puddings made with skimmed milk; gelatin; angel-food cake

BEVERAGES
Coffee; tea; carbonated beverages; beer and liquor as physician permits

MISCELLANEOUS
Herbs and spices
Condiments such as catchup, mustard, pickles
Sugar, honey, syrups, hard candy

FOODS FORBIDDEN

CEREALS AND PASTAS
No restrictions

DESSERTS
Ice cream and ice milk; others not specifically mentioned

BEVERAGES
Any containing forbidden foods

MISCELLANEOUS
Chocolate; olives; nuts

FAT-CONTROLLED DIET OUTLINE
Follow the low-fat, low-cholesterol diet as given above but:
1. Limit servings of meat to 3 times a week
2. Use fish, poultry or low-fat cottage cheese for remaining 11 lunch and dinner main dishes
3. Increase allowed fats to 2 to 4 tablespoons a day as allowed by doctor
4. Restrict starchy vegetables, breads and cereals as needed to adjust calories

QUESTIONS MOST OFTEN ASKED

Q. What is the difference between saturated fats and polyunsaturated fats?
A. The terms saturated and polyunsaturated describe the chemical structure of the fats. The names also give a clue to the form and origin of the fats. Saturated fats, usually solid at room temperature, are mainly fats of animal origin, such as those found in meat, cheese (except cottage cheese), egg yolk and butter, though coconut oil and hydrogenated vegetable oils are also relatively saturated. Polyunsaturated fats are generally of vegetable origin and are liquid at room temperature. These include corn, cottonseed, soybean and safflower oils.

Q. What is cholesterol? Where is it found?
A Cholesterol is a natural fat-like substance in cell tissue that plays a fundamental role in the body functions of both animals and man. It is manufactured in body tissue and can also be obtained from food we eat. It's not possible (except with medication) to control the amount the body manufactures, but the amount from food can be limited. Cholesterol is found only in animal food products. The foods highest in cholesterol include egg yolks, oysters, liver and other variety meats. Cholesterol is not found in plant foods such as vegetables, fruits, grain and cereal products and nuts.

Q. What is meant by the term "special margarine?"
A. See page 287 for the difference between regular and "special" margarine.

Q. May coffee lighteners and sour-cream substitutes be used on the low-fat, low-cholesterol diet?

A. No, they may not. Virtually all the coffee lighteners and sour-cream substitutes on the market today are made with saturated fat and so are forbidden. The fat content of these products is high enough to eliminate them for this reason also. Since they are made with vegetable fat, they do not contain any cholesterol.

Q. May filled milk or imitation milk be used on the diet?

A. Filled milks are made by substituting another fat (usually partially hydrogenated soybean or coconut oil) for butterfat. Since filled milks contain saturated fats, they are not allowed on the diet. Imitation milk does not have a skimmed-milk base but it does contain a relatively high fat content; saturated fats are ordinarily used. It is forbidden also.

Q. Which frozen desserts are suitable for low-fat, low-cholesterol diets?

A. On a strict low-fat, low-cholesterol diet, sherbets and fruit ices only. On a low-cholesterol diet with no restrictions in the total amount of fat, mellorine (ice cream made with other fats besides butterfat) is allowable. On a diet only slightly restricted in fat and cholesterol, moderate amounts of ice milk may be eaten if your doctor allows.

Q. What's the difference in fat and cholesterol content of an 8-ounce container of these cheeses: ricotta, unsalted, uncreamed, and creamed cottage cheese?

A. The fat content depends on the kind of milk from which the cheese is made. All of the above except ricotta are made with the curd of skimmed milk. Creamed cottage cheese does have some cream added; this makes it richer and the texture smoother. Creamed cottage cheese has 10 grams fat per 8-ounce container; uncreamed cottage cheese has negligible fat per 8-ounce container. Unsalted cottage cheese is usually uncreamed, but there may be some creamed, unsalted types on the market—

check the label. Ricotta cheese is produced from either partially skimmed or whole milk. Partially skimmed ricotta has 20 grams fat and whole-milk ricotta 30 grams fat per 8 ounces.

Uncreamed cottage cheese is allowed on all low-fat, low-cholesterol diets. Creamed cottage cheese is allowed on all but the most restricted; it provides 35 milligrams cholesterol per 8 ounces. Ricotta cheese is too high in cholesterol and fat to be recommended on the diet.

Q. Will mushrooms harm someone who is on an exceptionally low-cholesterol diet?

A. Actually, mushrooms are ideal for such a diet because they, like all fruits and vegetables, contain no cholesterol at all. Also, their fat and calorie content is very low.

Q. May cocoa and chocolate be used on a low-cholesterol diet?

A. Cocoa and chocolate do not contain cholesterol, but both are high in fat content. There are 6 grams of fat in 1/4 cup cocoa, 15 grams in 1 ounce of chocolate. All but the most restricted diets allow small amounts of cocoa and chocolate-pudding mixes; chocolate is usually forbidden.

Q. Are there any substitutes for sour-cream dips and gravies, bananas with sour cream, etc. for those on a low-fat, low-cholesterol diet?

A. Since the fat content of the diet is limited, sour cream (at 48 grams of fat per cup) is definitely out. However, the situation isn't hopeless. Try these ideas: In gravies calling for a small amount of sour cream, substitute buttermilk. Add it at the last minute to the gravy—never boil buttermilk or it will curdle. Serve sliced bananas in pineapple or orange juice. The flavor is a long way from that of sour cream, but it's delicious in its own way. Or enjoy fruits with cottage cheese instead of sour cream. A creamed cottage cheese (or uncreamed, if fat in a diet is extremely limited) can be whirled in a blender to become a base for dips or salad dressings ordinarily containing sour cream.

Q. Is it true that food preservatives are high in cholesterol?
A. Preservatives used in foods do not contain cholesterol. There is no reason to avoid foods with preservatives, if they are otherwise appropriate for the diet.

Q. My doctor has told me to avoid fatty fish, but I am allowed to have the leanest ones. Which fish are right for the diet?
A. The various fish fall into three main categories by fat content. Those containing up to 7 grams of fat per pound of flesh include cod, flounder, haddock, hake, halibut, ocean perch, pickerel, pollock, red snapper, sand dabs, sea bass, sole and water-packed tuna. At 10 to 20 grams per pound are bluefish, brook trout, lake herring, smelt, swordfish and fresh tuna. Fish with fat content of 45 grams per pound and up are herring, lake trout, mackerel, rainbow trout, Chinook (king) salmon and shad. Use the first two groups on your diet.

Q. Is it the white or the yolk of an egg that contains cholesterol? If egg yolks are not eaten, would any nutrients be missing from the diet?
A. The yolk has all the cholesterol. It also happens to have more iron, calcium and Vitamin A than the white. But don't worry if the doctor forbids yolks—you can get adequate amounts of the nutrients they contain from other foods.

Q. Can lecithin lower high cholesterol?
A. There is no scientific evidence to prove that lecithin can lower cholesterol or prevent heart disease. The body produces and uses lecithin, a fatlike substance, for various metabolic processes, such as manufacturing hormones. It is plentiful in a variety

of foods as well—egg yolk, beef liver, whole grains, legumes and milk. It's also added to many processed foods—chocolate candy, salad dressing, cake mixes—for smoother consistency.

Q. When polyunsaturated salad oil is used to fry foods, does it become saturated fat? If not, why are fried foods forbidden on fat-restricted diets?
A. No. Frying does not turn such oils into saturated fat. Fat-restricted diets limit the total intake of all fats, so naturally, fried foods are forbidden.

Q. If a doctor recommends a diet high in polyunsaturated oils, may olive oil be used in cooking rather than vegetable oils?
A. Use only the oils the doctor recommends. Experiments have shown that monounsaturated oils, of which olive oil is the best-known example, have no significant effect on lowering blood-cholesterol levels.

Q. Vegetable fats are stressed in my diet. May I always bake with oils?
A. If a small amount of melted shortening is called for in a recipe, you may use salad oil. But, in practically all baked goods, you will need special recipes calling for salad oil. Write salad-oil manufacturers for help along this line, and try the following recipes.

Q. Is it true that the easiest way to lose weight is to go on a low-cholesterol diet?
A. The cholesterol content of foods has nothing to do with gaining or losing weight. However, most individuals on low-cholesterol diets must also restrict the total fat and calories in their diet. But don't confuse the separate factors and assume that reducing cholesterol will also reduce the calories and fat content of the diet.

LOW-FAT, LOW-CHOLESTEROL DIET: 25 Recipes

CHERRY-GLAZED PINEAPPLE-CHEESE PIE (5 grams fat per serving)

Graham-Cracker Crust (see recipe below)
1 8-ounce container creamed cottage cheese
1 envelope unflavored gelatin
granulated sugar
1 cup canned pineapple juice
1 teaspoon grated lemon peel
lemon juice
3 egg whites
1/4 teaspoon salt
1 tablespoon cornstarch
1 16-ounce can pitted red sour cherries, drained (reserve liquid)
1/4 teaspoon almond extract
few drops red food color

About 5 hours before serving: Prepare and cool Graham-Cracker Crust. Press cottage cheese through fine sieve. In medium saucepan, stir together gelatin, 1/4 cup sugar, pineapple juice, lemon peel and 2 tablespoons lemon juice; let stand 5 minutes. Stirring constantly, heat mixture until gelatin just dissolves; stir in cottage cheese. Refrigerate until slightly thicker than consistency of unbeaten egg whites.

Beat egg whites and salt until whites form soft peaks; beating constantly, gradually add 1/4 cup sugar until stiff peaks form. Fold gelatin mixture into whites. Turn into Graham-Cracker Crust; refrigerate until set—1 to 2 hours.

While pie is setting, prepare cherry glaze. In small sauce pan, mix cornstarch with 2 tablespoons sugar; slowly stir in 1/2 cup liquid drained from canned cherries. Simmer mixture, stirring constantly, until clear and thickened. Stir in thoroughly drained cherries, 1 tablespoon lemon juice, almond extract and food color; cool to room temperature.

When pie has set, pour on glaze; spread to edges of pie; refrigerate at least 2 hours. Makes 10 servings.

SPRINGTIME STRAWBERRY PIE (3 grams fat per serving)

Graham-Cracker Crust (see recipe below)
2 10-ounce packages frozen sweetened strawberries, thawed
1 envelope unflavored gelatin
1/3 cup fresh lemon juice
2 egg whites

About 6 hours before serving: Prepare, bake and cool Graham-Cracker Crust. In small saucepan, drain syrup from thawed strawberries. Stir in gelatin; let stand 5 minutes. Heat, stirring constantly, until gelatin just dissolves; stir in lemon juice. Refrigerate, stirring occasionally, until thickened to consistency of unbeaten egg white; then stir in egg whites. With electric mixer at high speed, beat mixture until light and fluffy. Fold in drained strawberries. Heap in pie shell; refrigerate until serving time—at least 3 hours. Makes 8 servings.

GRAHAM-CRACKER CRUST (3 grams fat per 1/8 crust)

3/4 cup graham-cracker crumbs
1 tablespoon granulated sugar
2 tablespoons special margarine
1 tablespoon water
dash salt

About 1 hour before filling: Preheat oven to 350°F. In 9-inch pie plate. Bake 6 to 8 minutes. Cool before filling.

BAKED ALASKA (negligible fat per serving)

3 egg whites
6 tablespoons granulated sugar
1/4 teaspoon vanilla extract
dash salt
1 pint raspberry or lime sherbet
4 1-inch thick slices angel-food cake

About 15 minutes before serving: Preheat oven to 450°F. Line cookie sheet with double thickness of brown paper. In medium bowl, beat egg whites until soft peaks form. Gradually beat in sugar, then vanilla and salt until stiff peaks form. Cut sherbet into 4 pieces. Place cake slices on brown paper; top each with 1/4 sherbet. Cover with meringue, taking care to seal meringue all around edges of cake. Bake 4 to 5 minutes, or until golden-brown. Serve immediately. Makes 4 servings.

PUMPKIN CHIFFON PIE (5 grams fat per serving)

Graham-Cracker Crust (see recipe page 291)
dark brown sugar
1 envelope unflavored gelatin
1/2 teaspoon salt
1/2 teaspoon nutmeg
1/2 teaspoon cinnamon
1/4 teaspoon ginger
1 tablespoon cornstarch
1 cup evaporated milk
2 egg whites
1 1/4 cups canned mashed pumpkin

Early in day: Prepare, bake and cool Graham Cracker Crust. In top of double boiler, combine 1/2 cup brown sugar, gelatin, salt, nutmeg, cinnamon, ginger, cornstarch, evaporated skimmed milk and 1/2 cup water; beat smooth with an egg beater. Over boiling water, cook, stirring regularly, 10 minutes. Cool until consistency of thin pudding.

In medium bowl, with electric mixer at high speed, beat egg whites until soft peaks form. Beating constantly, gradually beat in 1/4 cup brown sugar until stiff peaks form. Beat pumpkin into gelatin mixture. Fold this mixture into meringue. Pour into pie shell; refrigerate untl firm—at least 2 hours. Makes 8 servings.

FLAKY PIECRUST (10 grams fat for 1/8 crust)

1 1/3 cups sifted all-purpose flour
1/2 teaspoon salt
1/3 cup salad oil
2 tablespoon cold water

About 1 hour before filling: Preheat oven to 450°F. In medium bowl, sift together flour and salt. Dribble salad oil over flour, then mix, with fork, until flour and oil are completely mixed. Dribble water over this mixture and stir to form smooth dough that can easily be formed into a ball. Dampen work surface, then press on sheet of waxed paper about 15-inches long. Place ball of dough in center of paper; cover with second sheet at right angles to first. Gently roll dough into 12-inch circle. Peel off top sheet of paper. Turn dough into 8- or 9-inch pie plate; peel off paper. Gently shape crust into plate; flute or finish edge. Prick bottom and sides of crust at least every 1/2 inch. Bake 12 to 15 minutes, or until light golden-brown. Cool before filling.

FLAKY PIECRUST FOR 2-CRUST PIE: Use 2 cups sifted all-purpose flour, 1 teaspoon salt, 1/2 cup salad oil and 3 tablespoons cold water. Prepare as above; divide in half and roll as directed. Bake according to instructions for filling.

LEMON-CHIFFON PIE (10 grams fat per serving)

single crust 9-inch Flaky Piecrust (see recipes above)
1 1/2 teaspoons unflavored gelatin
granulated sugar
1 tablespoon grated lemon peel
1/3 cup lemon juice
1/4 cup water
7 egg whites
1/4 teaspoon salt

About 6 hours before serving: Prepare, bake and cool Flaky Piecrust. In top of double boiler, combine gelatin, 1/3 cup sugar, lemon peel, lemon juice, water and 3 egg whites. Beat thoroughly; let stand 5 minutes to soften gelatin. Cook, over boiling water, 5 minutes, or until thickened. Remove from heat; cool slightly; refrigerate, stirring occasionally, until consistency of soft gelatin dessert.

In medium bowl, beat 4 egg whites until soft peaks form. Gradually beat in 1/2 cup granulated sugar and salt, then beat until soft peaks form. Beat gelatin mixture until smooth; fold into egg whites until smooth. Turn into pie shell; swirl topping. Refrigerate until firm—2 to 3 hours. Makes 8 servings.

CRANBERRY ANGEL CAKE (negligible fat per serving)

1 8-ounce can whole cranberry sauce
1/3 cup raisins
1/4 teaspoon vanilla extract
6 1-inch slices angel-food cake

Day before serving: In small saucepan, heat and stir whole-cranberry sauce with raisins until sauce has melted; stir in vanilla. Cover; refrigerate.

To serve: Top each slice of angel food with dab of sauce. If desired, sauce may be heated and served warm. Makes 6 servings.

BUTTERMILK-PINEAPPLE ICE MILK (negligible fat per serving)

2 envelopes unflavored gelatin
2 8¹/₂-ounce cans crushed pineapple
1 cup granulated sugar
1 quart buttermilk
¹/₄ cup lemon juice
2 teaspoons vanilla extract

About 2 hours before churning ice cream: In medium saucepan, soften gelatin in syrup drained from pineapple. Stir in sugar; heat until sugar and gelatin are just dissolved. Refrigerate in mixing bowl until lukewarm. Slowly stir in buttermilk, then lemon juice, vanilla and crushed pineapple. Refrigerate at least 1 hour. Churn and freeze in ice-cream maker as manufacturer directs. Makes 2 quarts or sixteen ¹/₂-cup servings.

CREAMY PEACH ICE CREAM (negligible fat per serving)

1 14¹/₂-ounce can evaporated
  skimmed milk
1 envelope unflavored gelatin
2 tablespoons lemon juice
2 cups sliced fresh peaches
1 cup granulated sugar
1 teaspoon vanilla extract

About 1 hour before churning ice cream: Pour evaporated skimmed milk into large bowl. Place bowl and electric-mixer beater blades in freezer until ice crystals have formed about 1 inch in from edge of bowl.

Meanwhile, in small saucepan, mix gelatin and lemon juice; let stand 5 minutes to soften. Stirring constantly, heat gently over low heat until gelatin has just dissolved. In electric-blender container at high speed, blend gelatin mixture and peaches to form smooth puree. Add sugar and vanilla; blend until sugar is dissolved. (Or peaches may be pureed with sieve or food mill, then mixed with gelatin mixture, sugar and vanilla.) With electric mixer at high speed, beat chilled milk until the consistency of whipped cream. Gently fold in peach mixture; refrigerate 1 hour.

Churn and freeze in ice-cream maker as manufacturer directs. Makes 1¹/₂ quarts or twelve ¹/₂-cup servings.

CREAMY STRAWBERRY ICE CREAM (negligible fat per serving)
Substitute 1 pint fresh strawberries for peaches; prepare as directed for Creamy Peach Ice Cream, above.

RAINBOW ROLLS (1 gram fat per serving)

2 pints raspberry sherbet, softened slightly
2 pints orange sherbet, softened slightly

Several days ahead, or up to 6 hours before serving: Line 15" by 10" jelly-roll pan with waxed paper, extending paper about 2 inches beyond each short side of pan. Refrigerate until cold. Spread raspberry sherbet evenly in bottom of chilled pan; freeze until firm—about 3 hours. Then spread orange sherbet evenly over raspberry; freeze until firm, but not solid—about 3 hours. (When frozen solid, sherbet does not roll well.)

To roll: With spatula, loosen long sides of sherbet from waxed paper. Working quickly start with narrow side of paper and roll sherbet tightly, "jelly-roll" fashion. Discard paper. Place roll, seam side down, on freezer-proof platter. Return to freezer until serving time. Make 10 servings.

APRICOT RICE PUDDING (negligible fat per serving)

1 16-ounce can peeled apricots
²/₃ cup packaged precooked
  rice
¹/₄ teaspoon salt
2 tablespoons lemon juice
cinnamon and nutmeg

About 45 minutes before serving: Preheat oven to 350°F. Pit, then quarter apricots. In 1-quart casserole, combine rice, salt, lemon juice and apricot pieces and syrup. Sprinkle with cinnamon and nutmeg. Bake 20 to 25 minutes, or until rice is tender. Serve warm. Makes 4 servings.

PINEAPPLE RICE PUDDING: Prepare as directed, but substitute 1 15³/₄-ounce can pineapple chunks packed in pineapple juice for apricots.

FRUIT-MERINGUE SURPRISE (negligible fat per serving)

1 large apple, thinly sliced
1 to 2 tablespoons lemon juice
1 16-ounce can freestone peach
    halves (8 halves),drained
1 13¹/₂-ounce can pineapple
    chunks, drained
2 tablespoons cornstarch
¹/₄ teaspoon cinnamon
dash nutmeg
2 cups orange juice
3 egg whites
6 tablespoons granulated sugar
¹/₄ teaspoon salt

About 20 minutes before serving: Toss apple slices with lemon juice; spread in bottom of cake pan. Preheat oven to 450°F. Place 6 peach halves, cut side down, in pan; distribute pineapple around peach halves.

In medium saucepan, mix cornstarch, cinnamon and nutmeg; stir in orange juice until smooth. Stirring constantly, simmer until juice thickens slightly. Pour over fruit.

In medium bowl, beat egg whites until frothy; beating constantly, gradually add sugar and salt until stiff peaks form. Spread meringue on top of fruit, taking care to seal it all around edges of pan. Bake 4 minutes, or until golden-brown. Serve warm or cold. Makes 6 servings.

BUTTERMILK WAFFLES (10 grams fat per 4-inch waffle)

1¹/₂ cups sifted all-purpose flour
3 teaspoons double-acting baking powder
2 tablespoons granulated sugar
¹/₂ teaspoon salt
1 cup buttermilk
3 egg whites
¹/₂ cup salad oil

About 30 minutes before serving: Preheat waffle iron if manufacturer directs. In medium bowl, sift together flour, baking powder, sugar and salt. In small bowl, beat buttermilk with egg whites and oil. Add to flour mixture, beating until flour is almost smooth. Bake as usual. Serve with syrup or jelly. Makes about twelve 4-inch waffles.

BANANA TEA BREAD (5 grams fat per serving)

1³/₄ cups sifted all-purpose flour
3 teaspoons double-acting baking powder
¹/₂ teaspoon salt
3 egg whites
²/₃ cup granulated sugar
¹/₃ cup salad oil
1 cup mashed ripe bananas (2
    to 3 medium bananas)

About 6 hours before serving: Preheat oven to 350°F. Grease and flour 9″ by 5″ by 3″ loaf pan. On sheet of waxed paper, stir together flour, baking powder and salt. In medium bowl, beat egg whites until soft peaks form. Beating continually, slowly add ¹/₃ cup sugar; beat until stiff peaks form. In medium bowl, blend salad oil and remaining ¹/₃ cup sugar. WIth mixer at low speed, beat half the dry ingredients into oil-sugar mixture. Beat in half the crushed bananas. Repeat; then beat batter at medium speed one minute. Pour batter over meringue; fold two together until smooth. Pour into prepared loaf pan; smooth surface. Bake 55 minutes, or until bread comes away from edge of pan. Cool 10 minutes on rack, then turn out of pan. Cool thoroughly before cutting. Makes 16 slices—bread will have compact texture.

SEEDED HERB TOAST (5 grams fat per serving)

1 slice day-old bread
1 teaspoon special margarine
¹/₂ teaspoon sesame seeds,
¹/₂ teaspoon poppy seeds,
¹/₄ teaspoon celery seeds;
    onion salt

About 5 minutes before serving: Spread bread with margarine. Then sprinkle evenly with sesame, poppy and celery seeds; sprinkle with onion salt. Heat under broiler until edges of bread are golden. Serve warm or cold.

EASY STIR-AND-ROLL BUTTERMILK BISCUITS (5 grams fat per biscuit)

2 cups sifted all-purpose flour
2 teaspoons double-acting baking powder
1/4 teaspoon baking soda
1 teaspoon salt
1/3 cup salad oil
2/3 cup buttermilk

About 30 minutes before serving: Preheat oven to 475°F. Mix together flour, baking powder, baking soda and salt. Measure salad oil, then buttermilk into measuring cup (don't stir together). Pour, all at once, over flour mixture. With fork, mix to form soft dough that rounds up into a ball. Turn dough onto sheet of waxed paper; knead lightly, without additional flour, 10 times, or until smooth. Between 2 sheets of waxed paper, pat or roll dough 1/4-inch thick. Remove top sheet of paper. Cut with unfloured biscuit cutter. Bake on ungreased cookie sheet 10 to 12 minutes, or until golden brown. Makes about 12 biscuits.

GRANNY'S FAVORITES (2 grams fat per cookie)

Flaky Piecrust (page 292)
1/4 cup granulated sugar
1/4 teaspoon cinnamon
1/8 teaspoon nutmeg

About 2 hours before serving: Preheat oven to 450°F. Prepare Flaky Piecrust as directed; roll between two sheets of waxed paper to form rectangle about 12" by 15" by 1/8". With 2-inch cookie cutter, cut out and transfer to ungreased cookie sheets. Starting with fresh sheets of waxed paper, reroll scraps and cut as above.

In small bowl, mix sugar, cinnamon and nutmeg. Sprinkle each cookie with 1/8 teaspoon of mixture; spread smoothly over surface. Bake 12 to 15 minutes, or until golden-brown around edges. Remove from cookie sheets; cool; store in airtight container. Makes about 4 dozen.

LACY ALMOND ROLLS (5 grams fat per cookie)

2/3 cup blanched almonds, finely ground
1/2 cup special margarine
1/2 cup granulated sugar
2 tablespoons water
1 tablespoon flour
confectioners' sugar

About 1 hour before serving: Preheat oven to 350°F. Grease and flour several cookie sheets. In large skillet, blend almonds, margarine, sugar, water, flour. Heat over low heat, stirring, until margarine is melted and mixture just boils. On prepared cookie sheets, drop batter, by teaspoonfuls, 3 inches apart. Bake, one sheet at a time, 5 to 6 minutes, or until golden. Let cool slightly; then remove cookies, one at a time, from cookie sheet. Quickly roll around handle of wooden spoon; cool. (If cookies become too hard, warm in oven a minute or so, then roll.)

To serve: Dust lightly with confectioners' sugar. Store tightly covered. Makes about 2 1/2 dozen.

"BUTTER" DIPS (2 grams fat per "dip")

1/3 cup special margarine
2 1/4 cups sifted all-purpose flour
1 tablespoon granulated sugar
3 1/2 teaspoons double-acting baking powder
1 teaspoon salt
1 cup skimmed milk or re-liquefied nonfat dry milk

About 35 minutes before serving: Preheat oven to 450°F. Heat margarine in 13" by 9" by 2" baking pan, in oven, until just melted. Mix together flour, sugar, baking powder and salt. Add milk; stir with fork until dough just clings together—about 30 strokes. Turn onto well-floured board. Roll over to coat with flour. Knead lightly about 10 times. Roll out 1/2-inch thick into rectangle 12" by 8". With floured knife, cut dough in half lengthwise, then crosswise into 16 strips. Dip each strip into melted margarine, then lay, close together, in 2 rows in pan. Bake 15 to 20 minutes, or until golden. Makes 32.

VANILLA COOKIES (2 grams fat per cookie)

2¹/₂ cups sifted all-purpose flour
1¹/₂ teaspoons double-acting
  baking powder
³/₄ teaspoon salt
1 cup granulated sugar
3 egg whites
1 teaspoon vanilla extract

Early in day: Preheat oven to 375°F. Grease cookie sheets. Mix together flour, baking powder, salt. In large mixing bowl, with electric mixer at medium speed, beat oil and sugar until blended. Add whites, one at a time, beating well after each addition. Gradually beat in vanilla and dry ingredients until smooth. With lightly flourerd hands, roll dough into balls, using a rounded measuring teaspoonful for each; place 2 inches apart on cookie sheets. Bake 10 to 12 minutes. Makes about 5 dozen.

RAISIN-GINGER BARS (1 gram fat per bar)

2¹/₄ cups all-purpose flour
¹/₂ teaspoon baking soda
¹/₄ teaspoon salt
1¹/₄ teaspoons pumpkin-pie
  spice
¹/₃ cup special margarine
²/₃ cup brown sugar, packed
¹/₂ cup dark molasses
¹/₂ cup raisins

At least 1 hour before serving: Preheat oven to 375°F. Grease a 15¹/₂″ by 10¹/₂″ jelly-roll pan. Sift together flour, baking soda, salt, pumpkin-pie spice; set aside. In large bowl, with electric mixer at medium speed, cream margarine and brown sugar until light and fluffy. Beat in molasses. Divide dry ingredients in half and beat in alternately with ¹/₂ cup water until blended. Fold in raisins. Spread dough evenly in pan. Bake 15 to 20 minutes. Cool in pan. Cut into 2¹/₂″ by 1¹/₄″ bars. Makes 4 dozen.

FRUIT FRENCH DRESSING (10 grams fat per tablespoon)

¹/₂ teaspoon salt
1 teaspoon granulated sugar
dashes pepper and paprika
¹/₃ cup salad oil
2 tablespoons milk vinegar
2 teaspoons honey
2 teaspoons lemon juice
¹/₄ teaspoon grated lemon peal

About 2 hours before serving: In small jar, shake together all ingredients. Refrigerate until serving time. Makes about ¹/₂ cup.

SIMPLE FRENCH DRESSING (10 grams fat per tablespoon)

³/₄ teaspoon salt
dash pepper
¹/₄ teaspoon granulated sugar
¹/₄ cup lemon juice or vinegar
³/₄ cup salad oil
1 garlic clove, minced
¹/₂ teaspoon caraway seeds
  (optional)

About 2 hours before serving: In pint jar, combine all ingredients. Shake well; cover; refrigerate until serving time. Makes about 1 cup.

EGGLESS MAYONNAISE (10 grams fat per tablespoon)

¹/₂ teaspoon salt
¹/₂ teaspoon dry mustard
¹/₄ teaspoon paprika
1 teaspoon granulated sugar
dash cayenne
¹/₄ cup nonfat dry-milk powder
2 tablespoons ice water
³/₄ cup salad oil
3 tablespoons lemon juice or 2
  tablespoons wine vinegar

About 1 hour before serving: Refrigerate deep medium bowl and electric-mixer beaters. In chilled bowl, mix salt, mustard, paprika, sugar, cayenne, dry-milk powder and water. With mixer at highest speed, add oil, drop by drop, until 2 tablespoons have been used. Still beating, continue to add oil, by half-teaspoonfuls, until 2 more tablespoons have been added. Still beating, add remaining oil by the teaspoonful. Reduce mixer speed; slowly beat in lemon juice or vinegar. Continue to beat until mayonnaise is thick and smooth. Makes about 1 cup.

LOW-PURINE DIET

A low-purine diet is used to treat both acute and chronic gout, which results when the body is unable to metabolize uric acid properly. Instead of being excreted through the kidneys, uric acid accumulates in the blood stream, forming sodium urate crystals in the joints—particularly in the fingers and toes.

Gout is primarily a disease of older adults—men more frequently than women. During the acute stages it is extremely painful; left untreated, it can cause changes in bone structure that lead to permanent crippling. Medical treatment attempts to accelerate the rate the urate crystals dissolve; dietary treatment attempts to eliminate those foods that are sources of uric acid, plus fats. The latter have a tendency to slow down the rate of excretion of uric acid through the kidneys.

Although the body manufactures its own supply of uric acid, the uric-acid level in the blood can be decreased significantly by eliminating purine-containing food from your diet. The cellular structure of meat (especially glandular meats), fish, poultry and some vegetables and legumes contain nucleo-proteins. These are broken down in the body to purines, which, in turn, form uric acid. Therefore, all protein-rich foods, except eggs, milk and cheese (which do not produce purines) are severely restricted on a low-purine diet. Some doctors also restrict the use of coffee, tea, chocolate, carbonated beverages, herbs and spices because they believe that these foods can also be converted to purine. Yet recent medical studies prove there is no scientific basis to support the exclusion of coffee, tea or cocoa. Since the stress on the joints produced by gout is greater and more painful for anyone who is overweight, the diet of such a patient is also restricted in calories.

MODERATE PURINE RESTRICTION

An outline for "Moderate Purine Restriction" follows; it is typical of the diet most often prescribed for chronic gout, and should be more restricted during acute attacks. As always, check with your doctor before using this diet.

ALLOWED

SOUPS

All except those containing forbidden foods

MEAT, FISH AND POULTRY

Limited to 4 ounces a week

EGGS AND CHEESE

Use as directed but cook with a minimum of added fat. Cottage cheese is particularly recommended

FORBIDDEN

SOUPS

Avoid all broths, consommés, gravies made from meat drippings

MEAT, FISH AND POULTRY

Avoid liver, sweetbreads, brains and kidney, shrimp and anchovies

EGGS AND CHEESE

None

ALLOWED

MILK

Skimmed milk; buttermilk; yogurt; evaporated skimmed milk. Whole milk and evaporated milk as allowed by physician

VEGETABLES

As desired except those forbidden

FRUITS

As desired

BREADS, CEREALS AND PASTAS

Enriched breads, cereals and pastas

DESSERTS

Any made with allowed foods

MISCELLANEOUS

Nuts; herbs and spices; condiments; sugar; gelatin

FORBIDDEN

MILK

Whole milk if fat is restricted

VEGETABLES

Dried beans and peas; lentils; asparagus; cauliflower; spinach; mushrooms

FRUITS

No restrictions

BREADS, CEREALS, AND PASTAS

Whole-grain breads and cereals. Quick breads high in fat

DESSERTS

Cakes, pastries, frozen desserts, etc. high in fat

MISCELLANEOUS

Alcoholic beverages. Gravies containing meat drippings, broth or bouillon

The limitation on the sources of protein to primarily eggs, milk and cheese, plus the limitation on fats, makes this a difficult diet to maintain. The cooking and planning aids that follow should be helpful:

- Break away from the habit of meat, potato and vegetable meals; try soup and sandwiches, casserole dishes, salads. (Main-dish salads fit fairly easily into a low-purine diet plan.)
- When possible, serve five or six "snacks" a day instead of three large meals. You'll find the lack of meat won't be quite so obvious. When meat is allowed, slice it thin to make the serving look more generous.
- Mix cottage cheese with apricots, peaches or pineapple for an appetizing off-beat breakfast.
- Try instant breakfast made with skimmed milk; crackers and a salad for lunch or dinner.
- For homemade fried rice: Stir and cook rice in a little butter until brown; add onion, cel-

ery, soy sauce and water; cook until fluffy. Stir in one or two scrambled eggs.

Check the infinite variety of cheese flavors and textures available at cheese shops; start to accumulate recipes. Avoid cream cheese—it's too high in fat and too low in protein to be a good choice.

Learn how to incorporate "milk-without-fat" into your diet: Substitute cottage cheese for sour cream in baked potatoes; try diet margarine, and make the fat allowance go farther; dilute canned or frozen cream-of-potato soup with half the usual skimmed milk for a hearty main-dish soup; use Mozzarella cheese made from partially skimmed milk.

For those important snacks: A milkshake made in a blender with ice milk, nonfat dry-milk powder and fruit flavorings; "sour cream dips" made with yogurt (or blend cottage cheese until smooth)—use vegetables as "dippers;" apple slices and cheese; flavored yogurts.

LOW-PURINE DIETS: 25 Recipes

YANKEE PASTA (15 grams fat per serving)

1 8-ounce package thin spaghetti
1 15¹/₂-ounce jar meatless spaghetti sauce
1 cup grated mild Cheddar cheese (or 1 4-ounce package shredded mild Cheddar cheese)
chopped parsley for garnish

About 30 minutes before serving: Cook spaghetti as label directs; drain. Meanwhile, heat spaghetti sauce to boiling. Toss hot spaghetti with cheese until cheese melts.

To serve: Pile spaghetti in center of serving dish; surround with sauce; top with parsley. Makes 3 servings.

PINEAPPLE-CHEESE SPREAD (5 grams fat per serving)

1 8¹/₂-ounce can crushed pineapple, thoroughly drained
1 8-ounce container small-curd creamed cottage cheese
dash salt
8 slices toast

About 10 minutes before serving: Stir together pineapple, cottage cheese and salt. Use as filling for 4 sandwiches.

WHITE-CAP STUFFED TOMATOES (10 grams fat per serving)

4 large tomatoes
salt
2 8-ounce containers small-curd, creamed cottage cheese
³/₄ cup packaged bread-stuffing mix
2 hard-cooked eggs, finely chopped
1 tablespoon butter or margarine
¹/₂ tablespoon flour
dash onion powder
¹/₂ cup skimmed milk or reliquefied nonfat dry milk
chopped parsley for garnish

About 45 minutes before serving: Preheat oven to 350°F. Wash tomatoes, then cut thin slice from stem end of each. Scoop out seeds and pulp, reserving pulp. Sprinkle insides with salt. Sieve ¹/₂ cup of the cottage cheese.

Chop ¹/₂ cup tomato pulp; mix with stuffing mix, eggs and unsieved cottage cheese. Use mixture to stuff tomatoes. Place in shallow baking dish; bake 30 minutes.

About 10 minutes before tomatoes are done: In small saucepan, melt butter; add flour and onion powder; stir until smooth and bubbly. Add milk; heat, stirring contantly, until smooth and thickened; stir in sieved cottage cheese; heat to boiling.

To serve: Top each tomato with cottage-cheese sauce; sprinkle with parsley. Makes 4 servings.

CHEDDAR-STUFFED POTATOES (10 grams fat per serving)

4 large baking potatoes
¹/₂ to ³/₄ cup milk or skimmed milk
1 4-ounce package shredded mild Cheddar cheese (or 1 cup grated milk Cheddar cheese)
2 tablespoons chopped parsley

About 1 hour and 20 minutes before serving: Preheat oven to 450°F. Prick skins of potatoes with fork. Bake 45 to 55 minutes, or until fork-tender. Turn oven to 325°F.

Cut thin slice from each potato and hollow out, leaving shell intact. In medium bowl, with electric mixer at high speed, mash potatoes. Beat in enough milk to make them creamy. Beat in cheese and parsley until cheese is melted. Refill potato shells, heaping them high. Bake, on cookie sheet, 30 minutes, or until potatoes are lightly browned. Makes 4 servings.

STUFFED TOMATOES PROVENÇALE (10 grams fat per serving)

4 large ripe tomatoes
salt
1 tablespoon butter or margarine
1 small onion, finely chopped
1½ cups cooked rice
1 cup grated mild Cheddar or Swiss cheese

About 30 minutes before serving: Preheat oven to 350°F. Cut thin slice from stem end of each tomato. Scoop out seeds and pulp, reserving pulp. Sprinkle insides with salt. Chop tomato pulp into small pieces.

In medium skillet over medium heat, in butter, sauté onion until golden. Add rice and tomato pulp; heat, stirring constantly, just to boiling. Remove from heat, then stir in cheese. Use mixture to fill tomato shells. Place in baking dish; bake 15 minutes, or until tomatoes are tender. Makes 4 servings.

OPEN-FACED TOAST AND EGGS (15 grams fat per serving)

4 slices bread
4 1-ounce slices Provolone cheese
4 poached eggs

About 15 minutes before serving: Preheat oven to 350°F. Toast bread, then top each with slice of cheese. Place on cookie sheet and heat in oven until cheese is just melted—about 3 minutes. Top each slice with poached egg. Makes 4 servings.

BLUE CHEESE AND MACARONI (15 grams fat per serving)

1 8-ounce package elbow macaroni
2 cups skimmed milk or reliquefied nonfat dry milk
¼ teaspoon salt
3 ounces blue cheese, crumbled
1 cup grated process Gruyère cheese
2 slices bread, cubed

About 1½ hours before serving: Cook macaroni as label directs but use minimum cooking time; drain. Preheat oven to 350°F. Scald milk; stir in salt. In 1½-quart casserole, layer one-third of hot drained macaroni; top wih crumbled blue cheese. Repeat, using macaroni and Gruyère. Top with remaining macaroni; then pour on hot milk. Top macaroni with bread cubes. Bake, covered, 20 minutes; uncover and bake 15 minutes more, or until cubes brown. Makes 4 servings.

BAKED EGGS ON TOAST (10 grams fat per serving)

butter or margarine
4 slices white bread
4 eggs, separated
salt or seasoned salt

About 20 minutes before serving: Preheat oven to 350°F. Lightly butter each slice of bread; place on cookie sheet. In medium bowl, beat egg whites until stiff peaks form. Heap beaten egg whites on slices of bread; make slight hollow in center of each; fill with yolk; sprinkle entire egg with bit of salt. Bake about 15 minutes, or until yolk is almost set and white is lightly browned. Makes 4 servings.

FAR-WEST FRIED RICE (20 grams fat per serving)

2 tablespoons butter or margarine
1 stalk green celery, finely chopped
¼ cup finely chopped onion
½ cup chopped walnuts
⅓ cup raisins
3 cups cold cooked rice
1 to 2 tablespoons soy sauce
4 poached eggs

About 20 minutes before serving: In large skillet, in butter, sauté celery, onion, walnuts and raisins until onion is golden. Stir in rice; stirring constantly, cook until it begins to brown very lightly. Stir in soy sauce to taste.

To serve: Divide rice among 4 plates, then top each serving with poached egg. Makes 4 servings.

CHEESE-AND-POTATO SOUP (25 grams fat per serving)

1 10¼-ounce can frozen condensed cream-of-potato soup
1 soup-can skimmed milk or
   reliquefied nonfat dry milk
1 4-ounce package shredded
   Cheddar cheese (or 1 cup
   grated Cheddar cheese)
1 carrot, grated
2 slices dry toast, quartered

About 20 minutes before serving: In medium saucepan, heat soup and milk until soup melts and mixture just boils. If desired, blend soup in electric blender or sieve to make a smooth puree. Add cheese; stir over low heat until melted. Serve, topped with grated carrot and accompanied by toast quarters, Makes two 1¼-cup servings.

ELEVEN-LAYERED CASSEROLE (15 grams fat per serving)

1 8-ounce package elbow macaroni
2 large tomatoes, sliced
2 cups grated process Cheddar
   cheese
¼ teaspoon oregano leaves
2 onions, thinly sliced
1 14½-ounce can evaporated
   skimmed milk
2 tablespoons shredded Parmesan cheese (optional)

About 1 hour before serving: Cook macaroni as label directs but use shortest recommended cooking time; drain. Butter 2-quart casserole; line sides with tomato slices. Preheat oven to 350°F.

Place half of macaroni in bottom of casserole; top with 1 cup cheese. Sprinkle oregano over cheese. Sprinkle with half of onion slices. Repeat this layering, then pour evaporated skimmed milk over mixture. Sprinkle with Parmesan cheese. Bake 30 minutes, or until lightly browned. Makes 6 servings.

CURRIED EGGS (15 grams fat per serving)

6 hard-cooked eggs
2 tablespoons butter or margarine
1 medium onion, finely chopped
1 large stalk green celery, finely
   chopped
3 tablespoons flour
1 teaspoon salt
1 to 2 teaspoons curry
2 cups skimmed milk or reliquefied nonfat dry milk
4 slices toast

About 30 minutes before serving: Shell and thinly slice or chop eggs. In skillet over medium heat, in butter, sauté onion and celery until onion is golden. Stir in flour, salt and curry. Slowly stir in milk; cook, stirring constantly, until thickened and smooth. Stir in chopped eggs; heat just to boiling.

To serve: Top toast with curried eggs. Makes 4 servings.

CALICO MACARONI AND CHEESE (20 grams fat per serving)

1 8-ounce package elbow macaroni
⅔ cup nonfat dry-milk powder
½ teaspoon dry mustard
1 teaspoon salt
2⅓ cups (1 13¾-ounce can
   plus 1 6-ounce can) evaporated milk, undiluted
1½ teaspoons Worcestershire
¼ cup minced canned pimento
⅓ cup minced green pepper
½ pound sharp Cheddar
   cheese, grated

About 1 hour and 10 minutes before serving: Cook macaroni as label directs, but use shortest recommended cooking time. Meanwhile, preheat oven to 350°F. In 2-quart casserole, mix dry-milk powder, mustard and salt; slowly stir in evaporated milk to form a smooth paste. Stir in Worcestershire, pimento and green pepper.

Thoroughly drain cooked macaroni; mix it and grated cheese with milk mixture in casserole. Bake 25 minutes, or until lightly browned on top. Let stand 10 minutes before serving. Makes 6 generous servings.

MOLDED COTTAGE-CHEESE SALAD (15 grams fat per serving)

1 8¹/₂-ounce can crushed pineapple, drained
1 16-ounce container creamed
   cottage cheese
1 cup grated mild Cheddar
   cheese
4 individual lettuce cups

At least 4 hours before serving: In medium bowl, stir together pineapple, cottage cheese and grated cheese. Pour into a rinsed 9″ by 5″ by 3″ loaf pan. Refrigerate at least 3 hours.

To serve: Spoon into lettuce cups. Makes 4 servings.

CORN FRITTERS (10 grams fat per serving)

3 eggs, separated
¹/₄ cup flour
1 teaspoon salt
1 16-ounce can whole-kernel
   corn, thoroughly drained
3 tablespoons salad oil

About 30 minutes before serving: In medium bowl, beat egg whites until stiff peaks form. In small bowl, beat egg yolks well; stir in flour and salt, then corn. Fold mixture into beaten egg whites.

In large skillet over medium heat, in oil, cook batter in ¹/₄-cup dollops until dark-golden brown; turn; brown on other side. Drain on paper toweling. Makes 4 servings of 3 fritters each.

HOT EGG-SALAD SANDWICH (10 grams fat per serving)

1 12-ounce loaf French bread
6 hard-cooked eggs, finely
   chopped
1¹/₂ cups chopped celery
¹/₄ cup minced onion
1 garlic clove, minced
³/₄ teaspoon salt
¹/₃ cup reduced-calorie mayonnaise
1 to 2 tablespoons prepared
   mustard
raw vegetable garnishes

About 50 minutes before serving: Preheat oven to 375°F. Cut bread in half horizontally. Remove most of soft part from center, leaving shell about ¹/₂-inch thick. Prepare one cup of crumbs from soft part.

In large bowl, toss together 1 cup soft bread crumbs, chopped eggs, celery, onion, garlic, salt, mayonnaise and mustard. Use to fill bottom half of bread shell; cover with top. Using double folds, wrap bread in wide foil. Bake 30 to 40 minutes.

To serve: Cut into quarters; garnish platter with raw vegetables. Make 4 servings.

FRIDAY'S LASAGNA (20 grams fat per serving)

1 tablespoon olive oil
1 cup minced onion
1 cup chopped green pepper
1 teaspoon salt
¹/₂ teaspoon oregano leaves
2 tablespoons chopped parsley
1 16-ounce can tomatoes
2 8-ounce can tomato sauce
1 tablespoon granulated sugar
9 wide lasagna noodles
3 8-ounce containers creamed
   cottage cheese
³/₄ pound grated Swiss cheese
¹/₂ cup grated Edam or Gouda
   cheese

About 1 hour and 45 minutes before serving: In large skillet, in olive oil, sauté onion and green pepper until onion is golden. Add salt, oregano, parsley, tomatoes, tomato sauce and sugar; simmer, uncovered, 30 minutes.

Meanwhile, cook noodles as label directs; drain. Preheat oven to 350°F. In bottom of 12″ by 8″ by 2″ shallow baking dish, spread one-quarter of hot tomato sauce. Cover with three wide noodles, one container of cottage cheese, one-third of grated Swiss cheese in that order; top with one-quarter of hot tomato sauce.

Repeat two more times. Top tomato sauce with Edam cheese. Bake 35 minutes; let stand 15 minutes before serving. Makes 8 servings.

ALICE'S HOT-EGG PATTIES (20 grams fat per serving)

butter or margarine
1 tablespoon chopped onion
1 tablespoon chopped parsley
1/4 cup flour
1 cup finely skimmed milk or
reliquefied nonfat dry milk
1 teaspoon salt
6 hard-cooked eggs
1 egg
packaged dried bread crumbs
Crushed-Pineapple Relish
(optional), see recipe at right,
below

About 4 hours before serving: In medium saucepan, in 2 tablespoons butter, sauté onion and parsley until onion is golden. Stir in flour and cook about one minute. Stirring constantly, add milk and salt; heat until thickened and smooth. In medium bowl, finely chop eggs. Stir in hot white sauce; cover; refrigerate.

About 20 minutes before serving: In shallow bowl, beat egg with a bit of water. Pour about 3/4 cup bread crumbs onto sheet of waxed paper. Stir cold egg mixture until smooth. Drop a dollop onto bread crumbs; turn over, dip other side, then flatten slightly with spatula. Dip patty into beaten egg; then again into bread crumbs. Repeat, making 8 patties.

In large skillet over medium heat, in 2 tablespoons butter, cook patties until brown—about 5 minutes on each side. Serve with Crushed Pineapple Relish. Makes 4 servings.

CRUSHED PINEAPPLE RELISH: In medium saucepan, place 1 8 1/2-ounce can crushed pineapple, drained; mix with 3 tablespoons brown sugar, 1 tablespoon vinegar and 1 tablespoon butter or margarine. Cook, stirring occasionally, 5 to 10 minutes. Makes about 1 cup.

EGGPLANT STEAKS À LA HOLSTEIN (25 grams fat per serving)

5 eggs
1 tablespoon milk
1/2 cup packaged dried bread
crumbs
1/3 cup grated Parmesan cheese
1 medium eggplant
2 tablespoons butter or margarine
1 cup grated Edam or Cheddar
cheese
seasoned salt

About 40 minutes before serving: Preheat oven to 350°F. In flat dish, beat together 1 egg and milk until smooth. On piece of waxed paper, stir together bread crumbs and Parmesan cheese. Cut stem from eggplant, then cut 4 lengthwise slices, 1/2- to 3/4-inch thick, from center of eggplant; pare slices. Taking care to completely coat both sides, dip slices, first into egg-milk mixture, then into crumb-cheese mixture. In large skillet, in butter, brown slices slowly until browned and almost tender; turn; brown other side. Place on cookie sheet; sprinkle with Edam cheese. Bake 10 to 15 minutes, or until cheese melts and eggplant is tender. Meanwhile, poach 4 eggs; sprinkle lightly with seasoned salt. Top each eggplant slice with an egg. Makes 4 servings.

CHEESE ONION SOUFFLÉ (20 grams fat per serving)

1 medium onion
1 tablespoon butter or margarine
2 tablespoons finely minced
onion
1/4 cup flour
1 cup skimmed milk or reliquified nonfat dried milk
1/2 teaspoon salt
1 cup grated sharp Cheddar
cheese (or 1 4-ounce package
shredded sharp Cheddar
cheese)
4 eggs, separated
seasoned pepper

About 1 hour before serving: Preheat oven to 350°F. Lightly butter 2-quart casserole. Cut onion into very thin slices, then separate rings.

In small saucepan over medium heat, in butter, sauté minced onion until golden. Mix in flour; stirring constantly, slowly add milk and salt until smooth. Cook, continuing to stir, until thickened and smooth. Remove from heat. Stir in cheese until melted, then egg yolks.

In medium bowl, beat egg whites until stiff peaks form. Carefully fold cheese mixture into whites. Turn into casserole; smooth surface. Arrange onion rings in attractive pattern on top; sprinkle to taste with seasoned pepper. Bake 45 minutes, or until a rich brown. Serve **immediately.** Makes 4 servings.

BROCCOLI IN CHEESE CUSTARD (20 grams fat per serving)

1 10-ounce package frozen
   chopped broccoli
3/4 cup nonfat dry-milk powder
1/2 cup grated Swiss cheese
2 eggs
2 tablespoons lemon juice
2 tablespoons butter or margarine, melted
1 teaspoon salt

About 1 hour before serving: Preheat oven to 350°F. Cook broc-coli as label directs; drain thoroughly. Meanwhile, in large bowl, beat remaining ingredients with 1¼ cups hot water until combined. Place broccoli in 1½-quart casserole; pour in custard mixture. Set casserole in shallow pan on oven rack; add enough hot water to pan to come up an inch around casserole. Bake 40 minutes or until knife inserted in center comes out clean. Makes 4 servings.

OEUFS À LA BERNADETTE (20 grams fat per serving)

butter or margarine
1/2 tablespoon flour
1/2 cup milk
1/2 cup grated Edam or Cheddar
   cheese
4 slices bread
1 large tomato
salt
4 eggs
paprika and chopped parsley
   for garnish

Abot 25 minutes before serving: Preheat broiler 10 minutes if manufacturer directs. In small saucepan, melt 1 tablespoon butter or margarine; stir in flour. Add milk; stirring constantly, heat until smooth and thickened; stir in grated cheese.

Lightly butter bread; cut tomato into 4 slices; place bread on cookie sheet; top each slice with tomato slice; sprinkle lightly with salt. Broil until edge of bread toasts lightly and tomato slices are hot.

Meanwhile, poach eggs. Top each tomato slice with poached egg; sprinkle with more salt; add dab of cheese sauce and sprinkle with paprika and parsley. Makes 4 servings.

GRANDMA'S VEGETABLE CUTLETS (15 grams fat per serving)

butter or margarine
1 cup chopped onion
1 cup grated carrots
1/2 cup shopped celery
1 8-ounce can cut green beans,
   drained
2 eggs
1 teaspoon salt
1/4 cup matzoh meal
chopped parsley for garnish

About 4 hours before serving: In large skillet over medium heat, in 2 tablespoons butter, sauté chopped onion, grated carrots and chopped celery until onion is golden; add green beans. Cool; grind mixture with food chopper. Mix ground vegetables, eggs, salt and matzoh meal; cover; refrigerate

About 39 minutes before serving: In large skillet, heat 2 tablespoons butter or margarine until bubbling. Drop vegetable mixture, by large dollops, into hot pan; spread until about 1/2- to 3/4-inch thick; cook, over medium heat 5 minutes on each side, or until browned. Serve, topped wth sprinkling of parsley. Makes 4 servings.

CHEESY SPAGHETTI OMELET (15 grams fat per serving)

3 eggs, separated
1/4 teaspoon salt
1 10¼-ounce can spaghetti in
   tomato sauce with cheese
2 tablespoons salad oil
1/4 cup grated process sharp
   Cheddar cheese

About 30 minutes before serving: Mix egg yolks with salt and canned spaghetti in tomato sauce. Beat 3 egg whites until stiff peaks form, then fold spaghetti mixture into whites.

Preheat oven to 375°F. In large skillet, heat oil; pour in spaghetti mixture and cook, over medium heat, 10 minutes, or until omelet is brown on the bottom.

Sprinkle omelet with cheese; bake 10 to 15 minutes, or until cheese is melted and top of omelet light brown and firm. Makes 4 servings.

MILANESE MINESTRONE (10 grams fat per serving)

2 tablespoons olive oil
1 medium onion, minced
1 teaspoon thyme leaves
2 tablespoons canned Italian
   tomato paste
2 16-ounce cans tomatoes
3 stalks celery, sliced
2 carrots, scraped and thinly
   sliced
2 small zucchini, sliced
2 medium potatoes, cut into
   ³/₄-inch cubes
1 very small head cabbage, cut
   into 8 wedges
1 tablespoon salt
2 tablespoons chopped parsley
¹/₃ cup uncooked long-grain rice
1 cup grated Parmesan cheese

About 1 hour and 15 minutes before serving: In large Dutch oven, in olive oil, sauté onion and thyme until onion is golden. Add tomato paste and ¹/₂ cup water; simmer gently for 10 minutes. Add 4 cups water and remaining ingredients except rice; simmer gently, covered, 20 minutes. Stir in rice; simmer 25 minutes longer. Serve with grated Parmesan cheese. Makes 6 servings.

LOW-SODIUM DIETS

Salt-free diet is the less accurate, but more descriptive, name for a low-sodium diet. Sodium is a chemical element that forms part of the compound sodium chloride—table salt. It is also present naturally in other forms, such as monosodium glutamate (a seasoning used as a flavor enhancer which also occurs naturally in foods), sodium caseinate (a protien fraction of milk) and sodium sulfite (used to prevent dried fruit from turning black).

Sodium is an essential nutrient which functions in the body primarily to maintain proper water balance. With too little sodium the body becomes dehydrated; with too much, swelling (edema) occurs. Under normal circumstances the body can handle large quantities of sodium by excreting the excesses through the kidneys. However, in cases of high blood pressure, and in some kidney diseases the body is unable to excrete the extra sodium. Edema occurs and high-blood pressure is aggravated.

Treatment is two-fold—medications called diuretics which accelerate the excretion of sodium are given, and the levels of sodium in the diet are restricted. Normal diets vary greatly in sodium content—5 to 10 grams a day is common. Sodium-restricted diets limit this intake from 2000 (2 grams) to as little as 200 milligrams daily. As the diet becomes more restricted, the need to limit the choice of foods and to depend on home-prepared foods increases. The outlines on pages 307-309 delineate the general restrictions for 2000-, 1000-, 500- and 250-milligram sodium diets.

If a low-sodium diet is used in treatment of high-blood pressure, it is usually combined with a low-fat, low-cholesterol diet. When used to treat kidney conditions such as glomerulonephritis and nephrosis the protein content of the diet may be normal *or* severely restricted. Because of the specialized nature of the low-sodium diet when combined with a low-protein diet, that particular problem is not treated in this book. Restrict sodium in the diet only with a physician's specific instructions.

Whether or not high-blood pressure is a concern, "low-sodium dieting" makes sense. Today, Americans misuse salt to the point that the National Research Council and various government agencies have recommended limiting salt intake to 1100–3300 milligrams a day. (Three grams, or 3,000 milligrams, is a little more than half a teaspoon.) Although minimal amounts of salt in your diet are not harmful, it is important to remember that you get all the salt you need naturally in foods. For more information on the sodium content of various foods, see pp. 339 to 343.

500-MILLIGRAM LOW-SODIUM DIET

Select foods from the following:

ALLOWED

FORBIDDEN

MEAT, FISH AND POULTRY

Up to 5 ounces cooked lean meat a day

Unsalted fresh, frozen or canned meat, fish or poultry

See exceptions to right

MEAT, FISH AND POULTRY

Omit all salted, smoked, corned, processed or koshered meat, fish or poultry

Organ meats (except liver and heart once every 2 weeks)

Frozen fish fillets

Shellfish: clams, crab, lobster, scallops, shrimp, etc.

Frozen dinners, meat pies and casseroles

EGGS AND CHEESE

Eggs are limited to one a day

Unsalted cottage or pot cheese may be used in place of meat—1/4 cup = 1 ounce meat

EGGS AND CHEESE

All cheeses except unsalted cottage or pot cheese

MILK

Up to 2 cups whole milk, skimmed milk, unsalted buttermilk

MILK

Salted buttermilk

VEGETABLES

All but exceptions listed at right

VEGETABLES

Canned vegetables except low-sodium packed

Frozen vegetables processed with salt— particularly lima beans and peas

These vegetables in any form: artichokes, beet greens, beets, carrots, celery, chard, dandelion greens, kale, mustard greens, sauerkraut, spinach, white turnips

Instant dehydrated potatoes

FRUITS

All but exceptions listed at right

FRUITS

Crystallized, glazed, or sulfur-dried fruit and maraschino cherries

Canned pie fillings which contain sodium benzoate as a preservative

BREADS, CEREALS AND PASTAS

Breads and rolls made without salt

Quick breads made with low-sodium baking powder (see page 310)

Low-sodium crackers

Farina, grits, oatmeal and rolled wheat cooked without salt

Puffed rice, puffed wheat and shredded wheat

Noodles, macaroni, spaghetti and rice cooked without added salt

BREADS, CEREALS AND PASTAS

Regular homemade and commercial yeast breads

Regular commercial and homemade quick breads

Self-rising flour

Regular commercial crackers

Quick-cooking and enriched cereals containing sodium compounds

All other dry cereals except special low-sodium packs

Potato chips and pretzels

FATS

Up to 1/3 cup cream a day

Unsalted (sweet) butter or margarine

Salad oil and cooking fat

Low-sodium salad dressings

Unsalted nuts and avocado

FATS

Salted butter or margarine

Bacon fat

Commercial and homemade dressings

Salted nuts

ALLOWED

DESSERTS

Fruit

Baked goods made without salt and with low-sodium baking powder

Homemade puddings made with allowed milk and no salt

Italian ices

Gelatin made with unflavored gelatin, sugar and fruit juices

Low-calorie gelatin (check package's nutrition panel for sodium listing)

BEVERAGES

Coffee, tea, decaffeinated coffee, cocoa (see right), carbonated beverages

CONDIMENTS

Herbs and spices

Vanilla and other extracts

Vinegar and lemon

Dry mustard

Tabasco

MISCELLANEOUS

Sugar, hard candy, honey, jams and jellies (not containing sodium benzoate), maple syrup

Low-sodium peanut butter (make your own in blender with roasted peanuts)

FORBIDDEN

DESSERTS

Regular commercial and homemade baked goods

Puddings made from mixes

Ice cream and sherbets

Gelatin made from mixes

BEVERAGES

Dutch-process cocoa and instant cocoa mixes

(Check labels on mineral waters)

CONDIMENTS

Salt; celery, onion and garlic salt; seasoned salt; monosodium glutamate

Catchup; chili and barbecue sauces

Soy sauce

Prepared mustard and horseradish

Worcestershire and A-1

Bouillon cubes and canned broth

Gravy mixes

Meat tenderizers

MISCELLANEOUS

Baking powder and soda

Pickles, olives and relishes

Molasses

Canned and frozen soups

Regular peanut butter

250-MILLIGRAM LOW-SODIUM DIET

Follow the 500 milligram diet, but substitute low-sodium milk for regular

1000-MILLIGRAM LOW-SODIUM DIET

Follow the 500 milligram diet, but use up to ¼ teaspoon salt each day to season food. Or substitute 4 slices regular salted bread for unsalted. Add carrots, celery, spinach in moderation. Yogurt may be substituted for an equal amount of milk.

1000-MILLIGRAM LOW-SODIUM DIET

Follow the 500 milligram diet, but add the following: fresh (instead of frozen or canned) shell-fish; regular breads, quick breads and crackers (except those with salted tops); salted butter or margarine; all cooked and ready-to-eat cereals; all vegetables except those prepared with brine, such as sauerkraut; cottage cream or any natural yellow cheese. Avoid adding salt to food at table.

Sodium content in food

If only the food itself is considered, and it is assumed that no sodium is added during processing, meat and milk are the highest natural source of sodium, fruits and vegetables the lowest. Breads are relatively high because they contain salt. If calories need not be restricted, the emphasis in a low-sodium diet, is placed on limiting the meat, fish and poultry intake to 5 ounces a day, milk to 2 glasses. Both the sodium and calorie levels can be adjusted by varying the amount of breads (regular or salt-free), butter (again regular or salt-free) and fruits and vegetables eaten.

The most important rule to follow in planning a low-sodium diet (and any of the other special diets) is to read labels. Foods which list salt, sodium (as in monosodium glutamate, sodium propionate or sodium alginate), brine, baking powder, or soda (as in bicarbonate of soda or baking soda) in ingredients are forbidden.

There is, however, a variety of low-sodium (unsalted) products on the market. Some are more widely distributed than others. If the items listed below are not available in your local supermarket, try gourmet shops or health-food stores.

tomatoes	meat tenderizers
tuna	salad dressings (or make your own
curry	—see page 317)
chili powder	prepared mustards
soups	unsalted butter or margarine
catchup	unsalted melba toast—plain and rye
bouillon cubes	

On a low-sodium diet, you may have to leave out salt, but there are other ways to add flavor and character to your cooking. Here are a few alternatives:

1. Add wine to sauces and use in gravies. (Do not use "cooking wines"—they contain salt.)
2. Experiment with fruit sauces and sweet-and-sour sauces for pork, chicken and fish.
3. Save cooking liquid from vegetables to substitute for broths as a base for sauces and gravies.
4. Use a wide variety of herbs and spices in your cooking as a substitute for salt. See chart on page 318.
5. Lemon juice and vinegar are the best all-purpose seasonings on a low-sodium diet. They can add tang to meat, vegetables and salads. Try lemon juice on fruit too.
6. Make homemade seasoned rice mixes, using herbs and spices, dried onion (not containing sodium compounds), curry or garlic or onion powder.
7. Consult your doctor for information about salt substitute products. Some substitutes have a much lower sodium content than regular salt, but contain an excessive amount of potassium.

If sodium is restricted in the diet, it is also important to avoid medicines and dentifrices containing it. Alkalizers for indigestion, laxatives, pain relievers, sedatives and cough medicines often contain sodium so don't take even nonprescription medications without your physician's approval. Also, some toothpastes and mouth washes contain sodium. As a precaution, don't swallow toothpaste, and rinse your mouth well after using mouth wash.

Water for drinking is another possible source of sodium. Do not drink water that has been softened by an ion exchange (zeolite) system. Ask your physician about the sodium content of the local water—does it contain high amounts of sodium? If there is any doubt, the Department of Health can provide you with the necessary information. If local water can't be used, you will have to drink and cook with distilled water.

Low-sodium baking powder

Commercial low-sodium baking-powder mixes are available in many drug stores or health-food stores. Follow the label instructions for using each brand. Or ask your druggist to prepare low-sodium baking powder using this formula:

potassium bicarbonate	79.5 grams
cornstarch	56.0 grams
tartaric acid	15.0 grams
potassium bitartrate	112.3 grams

Use 1$1/2$ teaspoons of this baking powder for each teaspoon of regular baking powder called for in a recipe. (This adjustment has already been made in the special low-sodium recipes that follow.)

LOW-SODIUM DIET: 25 Recipes (also to be used in Low-Fat, Low-Cholesterol Diet, where indicated)

BREAD OR ROLLS (5 milligrams sodium per slice or per roll)

1 teaspoon active dry yeast
1 cup minus 2 tablespoons
  warm water
2 tablespoons granulated sugar
1 tablespoon salad oil
2³/₄ cups sifted all-purpose flour
3 tablespoons wheat germ
  (optional)
¹/₄ cup skimmed milk or
  reliquefied nonfat dry milk
unsalted butter or margarine,
  melted (optional)*

At least 4 hours before serving: In large bowl, dissolve yeast in warm water. Add sugar, salad oil, flour, wheat germ and milk. Mix until dough comes away from bowl; turn out onto generously floured board; knead until smooth and satiny. Place in lightly oiled bowl; cover with damp towel, then let rise in warm place (about 85°F.) for 1 hour, or until double in bulk.

Return to floured board; knead 5 minutes, then form into loaf. Place in lightly oiled 8" by 4" by 3" loaf pan. Spread surface of loaf with butter, if desired.

Preheat oven to 400°F. Let bread rise in warm place until double in bulk—about 30 to 40 minutes. Bake 30 to 40 minutes, or until bread has hollow sound when top is tapped. Immediately remove from pan and cool, right side up, on cake rack. Makes 1 loaf.

For rolls: Mix, then let dough rise as directed; after second kneading, treat in one of ways below.

For crescents: Divide dough into 2 equal portions. Using pie plate as guide, roll dough into circle 10 to 11 inches in diameter; cut into 10 wedge-shaped sections; lightly brush surface with melted butter; roll each section into crescent, then place on greased cookie sheet. Repeat with remaining half of dough.

For pan rolls: Divide batter into 5 equal portions, then divide each portion into 4 equal parts. Roll each into ball; dip into butter and place, almost touching, in 2 greased 8-inch layer-cake pans.

For Vienna rolls: Divide dough as for pan rolls. With fingers, flatten each ball until it is a rectangle about 2¹/₂" by 1", then taper ends. Place on greased cookie sheet about 2 inches apart; brush each with mixture of egg white and 1 tablespoon water; sprinkle with sesame, caraway or poppy seed, if desired.

Prehet oven to 350°F. Let rolls rise until double in bulk—about 30 to 40 minutes; bake 12 to 15 minutes, or until golden-brown; remove from pan immediately. Serve warm or reheat to serve. Makes 20 rolls.

*For low-fat, low-cholesterol diet use unsalted special margarine.

MUFFINS (15 milligrams sodium per muffin)

1 cup sifted all-purpose flour
2 teaspoons low-sodium baking
  powder
1 tablespoon granulated sugar
¹/₂ cup milk*
1 egg*
2 tablespoons salad oil*

About 30 minutes before serving: Preheat oven to 400°F. Lightly grease 9 medium cups of muffin pans. In medium bowl, sift together flour, baking powder and sugar. Mix together milk, egg and oil; stir into dry ingredients until latter are just dampened. Fill each muffin cup about half full. Bake 18 to 22 minutes, or until muffins are light golden-brown. Makes 9.

*For low-fat, low-cholesterol diet use skimmed milk and only white of egg; increase salad oil to 3 tablespoons.

BAKING-POWDER BISCUITS (5 milligrams sodium per biscuit)

1 cup sifted all-purpose flour
2 teaspoons low-sodium baking powder
1 teaspoon sugar
2 tablespoons unsalted butter or margarine*
1/2 cup milk*

About 25 minutes before serving: Preheat oven to 450°F. In medium bowl, sift together flour, baking powder and sugar; cut butter into dry ingredients until mixture is like coarse cornmeal. Stir in milk; beat mixture until smooth. Drop, by rounded tablespoonfuls, onto greased cookie sheet. Bake 12 to 15 minutes, or until surface rebounds when touched; biscuits will be only very lightly browned. Serve warm. Makes 10.
Variations:
• Before baking, sprinkle each biscuit with about 1/4 teaspoon grated lemon or orange peel.
• Mix 2 tablespoons fresh chopped chives into batter.
• Before baking, sprinkle each biscuit with about 1/4 teaspoon sesame or 1/8 teaspoon poppy seed.
• Mix in 1/2 cup thoroughly drained, crushed pineapple and decrease milk to 1/3 cup.

*For low-fat, low-cholesterol diet use 3 tablespoons unsalted special margarine and skimmed milk in place of regular.

CORNBREAD (15 milligrams sodium per serving)

1/4 cup unsalted butter or margarine*
1/4 cup granulated sugar
1 egg*
1 cup milk*
1 1/3 cups sifted all-purpose flour
2/3 cup white or yellow cornmeal
4 teaspoons low-sodium baking powder

About 35 minutes before serving: Preheat oven to 400°F. Grease and lightly flour 9-inch square cake pan. In medium bowl, cream butter and sugar until light and fluffy; stir in egg, then milk. Sift together flour, cornmeal and baking powder; add to butter mixture, then beat until just moistened. Turn into baking pan; smooth surface; bake 20 to 25 minutes, or until bread pulls away from sides of pan. Serve warm, cool, or split and toast until brown. Makes 16 servings.

*For low-fat, low-cholesterol diet use 1/3 cup unsalted special margarine; use only white of egg; substitute skimmed milk for whole.

LEMON CRISPIES (1 milligram sodium per cookie)

1 cup unsalted butter or margarine*
1 cup granulated sugar
1 egg*
1 1/2 teaspoons lemon extract
1 1/2 cups sifted all-purpose flour

At least 1 hour before serving: Preheat oven to 375°F. In medium bowl, with electric mixer at medium speed, cream butter with sugar, then beat in egg and lemon extract until light and fluffy. At low speed, beat in flour until smooth. Drop batter, by level tablespoonfuls and at least 2 inches apart, onto an ungreased cookie sheet. Bake 10 minutes, or until golden-brown around edges. Let cool a minute or two, then remove from cookie sheet. Makes about 5 dozen.

*For low-fat, low-cholesterol diet use unsalted special margarine and only white of egg.

CARROT-POTATO PANCAKES (35 milligrams sodium per serving)

1 large or 2 small carrots, grated
2 medium potatoes, grated
1 medium onion, minced
1/3 cup flour
2 eggs*
dash cayenne

About 45 minutes before serving time: Spread griddle with a bit of oil. Heat until drop of water "dances" on griddle. In large bowl, toss together grated carrots, potatoes and onion. Mix in flour; then add eggs and cayenne. Drop batter, by rounded tablespoonfuls, on griddle; brown on one side at least 5 minutes, then turn. Flatten each pancake with spatula; cook 5 minutes more. Makes 5 servings.

*For low-fat, low-cholesterol diet use only whites of eggs.

PANCAKES (15 milligrams sodium per pancake)

3/4 cup skimmed milk or
  reliquified nonfat dry milk
1 tablespoon unsalted butter or
  margarine, melted*
1 egg, separated*
1 tablespoon sugar
1 cup sifted all-purpose flour
1 1/2 teaspoons low-sodium
  baking powder
1 tablespoon wheat germ
  (optional)

About 30 minutes before serving: Heat griddle until drop of water "dances" on it. In medium bowl, beat milk, melted butter and egg yolk until smooth. Add sugar, flour, baking powder and wheat germ; beat until just mixed. Pour batter, a scant 1/4 cup at a time, on heated griddle. When bubbles form on top, turn pancakes; brown on second side. Keep warm until serving time. Makes ten 4-inch pancakes.

*For low-fat, low-cholesterol diet use unsalted special margarine and only white of egg.

WAFFLES (25 milligrams sodium per waffle)

1 1/2 cups sifted all-purpose flour
4 1/2 teaspoons low-sodium
  baking powder
1 tablespoon granulated sugar
2 eggs*
1 cup plus 2 tablespoons
  skimmed milk or reliquified
  nonfat dry milk
1/4 cup melted unsalted butter
  or margarine or salad oil*

About 30 minutes before serving: Preheat waffle iron as manufacturer directs. In medium bowl, sift together flour, baking powder and sugar. In small bowl, beat eggs; add milk and butter, then beat until smooth. Add to flour mixture; beat with beater until all the flour is wet and batter is smooth. Using a scant 1/4 cup of batter for each 4-inch waffle, cook as directed by manufacturer. Makes about twelve 4-inch waffles.

*For low-fat, low-cholesterol diet use only whites of eggs; use special margarine or oil (not butter); increase margarine to 5 tablespoons.

WONDERFUL WHITE CAKE (25 milligrams sodium per serving)

2 1/2 cups sifted cake flour
3 teaspoons low-sodium baking
  powder
4 egg whites
1 1/2 cups granulated sugar
1/2 cup unsalted butter or
  margarine*
1 cup plus 2 tablespoons
  skimmed milk or reliquified
  nonfat dry milk
1 teaspoon vanilla extract
1/4 teaspoon almond extract
  (optional)
low-sodium frosting, if desired

At least 4 hours before serving: Preheat oven to 375°F. Grease, then line with waxed paper, bottoms of two 8-inch layer-cake pans. Sift flour with low-sodium baking powder.

In small bowl, with electric mixer at high speed, beat egg whites until foamy. Gradually add 1/2 cup sugar, beating only until mixture holds soft peaks. Set aside.

In large bowl, with mixer at medium speed, cream butter with 1 cup sugar until very light and fluffy—about 2 minutes altogether.

Next, at low speed, beat in alternately, just until smooth, flour mixture by fourths and milk and extracts by thirds. Then thoroughly beat egg-white mixture into batter. Turn into pans. Bake 25 minutes, or until cake tester, inserted in center, comes out clean. Cool 20 minutes on rack, then turn out of pans; peel off waxed paper. Cool thoroughly, then ice with your favorite low-sodium frosting. Makes 16 servings.

*For low-fat, low-cholesterol diet use unsalted special margarine.

SPONGECAKE (25 milligrams sodium per serving)

3 eggs
1 cup sifted cake flour
1¹/₂ teaspoons low-sodium
   baking powder
1 cup granulated sugar
¹/₂ teaspoon grated lemon peel
2 teaspoons lemon juice
6 tablespoons hot milk
confectioners' sugar

At least 6 hours before serving: Set out eggs to warm to room temperature. When ready to make cake, preheat oven to 350°F. In large bowl, with electric mixer at high speed, beat eggs until very thick and light—about 5 minutes. Sift together flour and baking powder. Gradually add sugar to eggs, beating constantly, then beat in lemon peel and juice. Fold flour mixture into egg mixture. Stir in hot milk. Immediately turn batter into ungreased 9″ by 5″ by 3″ loaf pan. Bake 35 minutes, or until cake tester, inserted in center, comes out clean. To cool cake, invert pan and let hang for 1 hour. Remove from pan and serve sprinkled with powdered sugar. Makes 10 servings.

COD FILLETS WITH CUCUMBER SAUCE (120 milligrams sodium per serving)

3 fresh small cod fillets (about 1
   pound)
2 tablespoons melted unsalted
   butter or margarine*
¹/₈ teaspoon pepper
2 tablespoons unsalted butter
   or margarine*
1 teaspoon vinegar
dash cayenne
¹/₃ cup pared, seeded and
   grated cucumber
1 tablespoon chopped parsley

About 35 minutes before serving: Preheat broiler 10 minutes if manufacturer directs. Arrange fillets in large shallow pan. Brush with melted butter, then sprinkle with pepper. Broil 5 to 8 minutes, or until fillets flake easily when tested with fork.

Meanwhile, in small saucepan, combine remaining ingredients; cook, over medium heat, until just boiling.

To serve: Transfer fillets to platter; pour cucumber sauce over them. Makes 3 servings.

*For low-fat, low-cholesterol diet use unsalted special margarine.

CURRIED HADDOCK FILLETS (130 milligrams sodium per serving)

2 tablespoons salad oil
¹/₂ cup sliced celery
2 medium onions, thinly sliced
4 small fresh haddock fillets
   (about 1¹/₄ pounds)
dash pepper
1 teaspoon curry*
1 cup milk†

About 45 minutes before serving: Preheat oven to 350°F. In medium skillet, in oil, sauté celery and onions until golden—do not brown. Place fillets in large (about 13″ by 9″ by 2″) baking dish. Top with sautéed celery and onions. Mix pepper, curry and milk and pour over fillets. Bake 20 to 30 minutes, or until fish flakes easily when tested with fork.

*Use curry not containing salt—check label.
†For low-fat, low-cholesterol diet use skimmed milk.

HALIBUT STEAK HAWAIIAN (85 milligrams sodium per serving)

2 cups unsalted cooked rice
4 teaspoons lemon juice
¹/₄ cup melted unsalted butter
   or margarine*
¹/₂ teaspoon curry†
1 8-ounce can pineapple tidbits,
   drained
2 1-pound fresh halibut steaks
1 lemon, cut into wedges for
   garnish

About 1 hour before serving: Preheat oven to 350°F. In medium bowl, combine rice with 3 teaspoons lemon juice, 2 tablespoons melted butter, curry and all but 10 pineapple tidbits (reserve these for garnish).

Sprinkle each halibut steak with 1 teaspoon lemon juice. Place one steak in large shallow open baking pan; brush with 1 tablespoon melted butter. Press rice filling on top. (Spoon any extra filling alongside.) Top with other halibut steak; brush with remaining butter. Secure in place with metal skewers. Bake 40 minutes, or until fish flakes easily with fork. Remove skewers; garnish with reserved pineapple tidbits and lemon wedges. Makes 6 servings.

*For low-fat, low-cholesterol diet use unsalted special margarine.
†Use curry containing salt—check label.

PINEAPPLE-MEAT LOAF (120 milligrams sodium per serving)

1 pound lean ground beef
1 8¹/₂-ounce can crushed
   pineapple, undrained
2 slices unsalted bread, finely
   cubed*
1 egg †
¹/₄ cup finely chopped onion
¹/₄ teaspoon dry mustard
¹/₈ teaspoon pepper

About 1 hour and 15 minutes before serving: Preheat oven to 350°F. In medium baking pan, mix all ingredients; shape into loaf. Bake 60 minutes. Makes 4 servings.

*If regular bread is used, count meat loaf at 170 milligrams sodium per serving.
†For low-fat, low-cholesterol diet use 2 egg whites in place of whole egg.

SWISS STEAK (100 milligrams sodium per serving)

1¹/₂ pounds beef round rump
   roast, cut about 1-inch thick
¹/₄ cup flour
¹/₈ teaspoon pepper
1 tablespoon parsley flakes
2 tablespoons salad oil
1 16-ounce can
   low-sodium-pack tomatoes*
3 large onions, thinly sliced
1 stalk green celery, sliced
1 garlic clove, minced
1 1¹/₂-ounce package (¹/₃ cup)
   raisins

About 1¹/₂ hours before serving: Trim fat from meat, then cut into serving pieces. Toss together flour, pepper and parsley flakes. Use to coat meat. In large skillet, in oil, brown meat thoroughly on both sides. Pour off oil. Add remaining ingredients. Cover; simmer 1 hour and 15 minutes (adding some water, if needed), or until meat is tender and gravy thickens slightly. Makes 6 servings.

*Or substitute 6 peeled fresh medium tomatoes and ¹/₂ cup water. Fine for low-fat, low-cholesterol diets.

RHINE CARAWAY MEATBALLS (95 milligrams sodium per serving)

1 cup coarsely grated raw
   potato
1 pound lean ground beef
¹/₄ teaspoon pepper
1 tablespoon parsley flakes
1 small onion, finely grated
lemon peel
1 egg*
4 low-sodium beef-bouillon
   cubes (optional)
¹/₂ teaspoon caraway seeds
2 teaspoons cornstarch
chopped parsley for garnish

About 1 hour before serving: In medium bowl, mix potato, meat, pepper, parsley flakes, onion, lemon peel and egg; form into 12 meatballs.
   In medium skillet, heat 2¹/₂ cups water and bouillon cubes to boiling; add meatballs; cover; simmer 30 minutes. Remove meatballs to warm platter. Add caraway seeds and cornstarch dissolved in 1 tablespoon water; stir until thickened and smooth. Pour a bit of the gravy over meatballs; garnish with chopped parsley. Pass remaining gravy. Makes 4 servings.

*For low-fat, low-cholesterol diet use only egg white.

TANGY POTTED BEEF (90 milligrams sodium per serving)

1¹/₂ pounds beef round rump,
   cut about 1-inch thick
¹/₄ cup flour
¹/₂ teaspoon onion powder
¹/₂ teaspoon garlic powder
¹/₂ teaspoon celery seed
¹/₄ teaspoon pepper
2 tablespoons salad oil
4 thin lemon slices
2 low-sodium beef-bouillon
   cubes (optional)
1 tablespoon cornstarch
   (optional)

About 2 hours before serving: Trim fat from meat, then cut into serving pieces. Toss together flour, onion powder, garlic powder, celery seed and pepper. Use to coat meat. In large skillet, in oil, brown meat on both sides. Add lemon slices, bouillon cubes and 1 cup water; cover; simmer 1¹/₂ hours, or until meat is tender. If desired, mix enough water with cornstarch to form a smooth paste; stir into hot gravy; cook until thickened. Makes 6 servings.

Fine for low-fat, low-cholesterol diets.

HAMBURGER PLUS (90 milligrams sodium per serving)

1 pound lean ground beef
1/8 teaspoon pepper
1/4 cup chopped parsley
1/4 cup finely chopped onion
1 egg*
1 tablespoon salad oil

About 30 minutes before serving: Thoroughly mix beef, pepper, parsley, onion and egg. Form into 4 patties. In skillet, in oil, cook patties until done as you like. Makes 4 servings.

*For low-fat, low-cholesterol diet use only white of egg.

MEAL-IN-A-DISH CHICKEN (100 milligrams sodium per serving)

1/4 cup flour
1/2 teaspoon onion powder
1 teaspoon curry*
1 teaspoon tarragon or parsley flakes
2 whole chicken breasts (about 1 1/2 pounds), split and skinned
2 tablespoons salad oil
1 cup pineapple juice
2 tablespoons brown sugar
2 tablespoons vinegar
1 teaspoon chopped chives
8 small new potatoes
8 carrots, cut into 1-inch slices

About 1 hour before serving: Mix flour, onion powder, curry and tarragon; use to coat chicken completely. In large skillet, in oil, brown chicken thoroughly. Add pineapple juice, brown sugar, vinegar, chives, potatoes and carrots. Cover; simmer 45 minutes (adding water, if needed), or until vegetables are tender and chicken done. Makes 4 servings.

*Use curry not containing salt—check label.
Fine for low-fat, low-cholesterol diet.

CHICKEN MARENGO (90 milligrams sodium per serving)

1/4 cup flour
1/2 teaspoon garlic powder
1/2 teaspoon onion powder
1/2 teaspoon celery seed
1/4 teaspoon pepper
2 whole chicken breasts (about 1 1/2 pounds), split and skinned
2 tablespoons salad oil
12 small white onions
1/2 pound fresh mushrooms
2 garlic cloves, minced
1 16-ounce can low-sodium-pack canned tomatoes*
1/2 cup dry sherry (optional)

About 1 hour before serving: Mix flour, garlic powder, onion powder, celery seed and pepper. Use to coat chicken. In skillet, in oil, brown chicken thoroughly. Remove chicken, then quickly sauté onions, mushrooms and garlic until golden. Add tomatoes, sherry and chicken. Cover; simmer 40 minutes, or until onions are tender. Makes 4 servings.

*Or substitute 6 peeled fresh medium tomatoes and 1/2 cup water.
Fine for low-fat, low-cholesterol diet.

APPLE-ACORN SQUASH (5 milligrams sodium per serving)

2 small acorn squash, halved and seeded
1 cup applesauce
1/4 teaspoon nutmeg

About 1 hour before serving: Preheat oven to 425°F. Lightly oil large baking dish. Place squash, cut side down, in baking dish; bake 30 minutes; turn right side up. Meanwhile, mix applesauce and nutmeg. Use to fill squash. Return to oven and bake 20 minutes more, or until tender. Makes 4 servings.

Fine for low-fat, low-cholesterol diet.

CREAMED CAULIFLOWER (20 milligrams sodium per serving)

1 small to medium head
  cauliflower
1 low-sodium chicken-bouillon
  cube (optional)*
milk (to make 1 cup)†
1 tablespoon unsalted butter or
  margarine†
1 tablespoon plus 2 teaspoons
  flour
1 teaspoon parsley flakes
generous dash nutmeg
paprika

About 25 minutes before serving: Separate cauliflower into small flowerets; wash; drain. In medium saucepan, bring 1 cup water to boiling; in it dissolve bouillon cube. Add cauliflower; cover; simmer 10 minutes, or until just tender-crisp. Drain cauliflower, reserving cooking liquid. Keep cauliflower warm. Add enough milk to reserved liquid to make 1 cup. In saucepan, melt butter, then stir in flour, parsley flakes and nutmeg. Stirring constantly, slowly add water-milk mixture; cook until thickened.

    To serve: Top cauliflower with sauce; sprinkle with paprika. Makes 6 servings.

*Available in many specialty-food stores.
†For low-fat, low-cholesterol diet use skimmed milk and unsalted special margarine.

POTATOES ROSEMARY (5 milligrams sodium per serving)

1 16-ounce can whole potatoes*
1 medium onion, thinly sliced
1/2 teaspoon rosemary, crushed
2 teaspoons salad oil

About 25 minutes before serving: In medium saucepan over medium heat, simmer potatoes, onion and rosemary 10 minutes, or until onion is tender; drain off water. In medium skillet, in salad oil, sauté potatoes and onion, stirring occasionally, about 10 minutes until potatoes are golden. Makes 4 servings.

*Use potatoes not containing added salt—check label.
Fine for low-fat, low-cholesterol diet.

MAYONNAISE (3 milligrams sodium per tablespoon)

1 cup salad oil
1 egg
1 teaspoon granulated sugar
1/2 teaspoon dry mustard
1 1/2 teaspoons lemon juice
1/2 to 1 tablespoon vinegar, as
  desired
pepper to taste

At least 2 hours before serving: Refrigerate oil, deep medium bowl and electric-mixer beaters. When bowl is chilled, break egg into it; add sugar, mustard and 1/2 teaspoon lemon juice, beat until well blended and egg is beginning to thicken. With mixer at highest speed, add oil, drop by drop, until 2 tablespoons have been used. Beat in 1/2 teaspoon lemon juice; still beating, continue to add oil by half teaspoonfuls until 2 more tablespoons have been added. Still beating, add 1/2 teaspoon lemon juice and vinegar; then add remaining oil by teaspoonfuls. If desired, beat in additional 1/2 tablespoon vinegar and pepper to taste. Continue to beat until mayonnaise has thickened. Store in warmest part of refrigerator. Makes 1 1/3 cups.

PIQUANT SALAD DRESSING (3 milligrams sodium per tablespoon)

1 1/2 teaspoons unflavored
  gelatin
2 cups low-sodium-pack canned
  tomato juice
2 tablespoons vinegar
1/4 teaspoon onion powder
1/4 teaspoon garlic powder
1/2 teaspoon pepper
2 tablespoons salad oil

At least 2 hours before serving: In medium saucepan, soften gelatin on 2 tablespoons water; heat to dissolve gelatin. Stir in remaining ingredients. Refrigerate, covered, until serving time.

    To serve: Stir until smooth. Makes 2 1/2 cups.

Fine for low-fat, low-cholesterol diet.

HOW TO USE HERBS AND SPICES ON A LOW-SODIUM DIET

Whether or not you are following a low-sodium diet, it behooves you to use less salt. Next time instead of reaching for the salt shaker, turn to the herb and spice shelf. A variety of herbs and spices can enhance food flavors, without adversely affecting your health or "artificially" flavoring your food. The chart below offers a list of flavorful combinations.

Herb/Spice	Use it in	Herb/Spice	Use it in
Allspice	gravies, meat and fish dishes, cakes puddings, tomato sauces	Nutmeg	cakes, breads, green beans, custard, sauces
Basil	green beans, lamb, peas, potatoes, soups, tomato dishes	Oregano	hamburger, omelet, stews, vegetables
Bay Leaf	fish, sauces and gravies, stews and soups	Paprika	fish, gravies, meats, salad dressings, vegetables
Caraway seeds	asparagus, noodles, soups, cookies, breads and rolls, liver, meat loaf	Pepper	soups, vegetables, meat, eggs
		Poppy seed	breads, rolls, cookies, noodles, salad dressings
Chervil	fish and poultry dishes, salad dressings, sauces, stews	Poultry seasoning	biscuit dough, poultry dishes
Chili powder*	chili con carne, gravies, fish, stew	Rosemary	biscuit dough, potatoes, roasts, sauce for meat and poultry, orange or pear salad
Cinnamon	fruits, mashed sweet potatoes, toast, cookies, cakes, biscuits	Sage	fish, pork, veal and poultry, tomato dishes
		Saffron	baked goods, rice
Cloves	port, peaches, stews, puddings, broiled grapefruit	Savory	vegetable soup, mushrooms, peas, poultry and tomato dishes
Curry*	sauce for eggs, fish, meat, poultry, vegetables	Tarragon	salads, sauces, seafood, tomato dishes
Ginger	stewed fruit, applesauce, gingerbread, pumpkin pie, melon	Thyme	veal, pork, eggplant, peas, tomatoes, chowders, fish dishes
Mace	cherries, jellies, canned fruit, gingerbread, fish sauces	Turmeric	curries, chicken, eggs, fish
Marjoram	lamb, meat pies, stews, stuffings, asparagus, squash, fish sauces		

* Use a brand not containing salt.

Mean Heights and Weights/Recommended Energy Intake

Category	Age (yr)	Weight (kg)	Weight (lb)	Height (cm)	Height (in.)	Energy needs (with range) (kcal)
Infants	0.0–0.5	6	13	60	24	kg × 115 (95–145)
	0.05–1.0	9	20	71	28	kg × 105 (80–135)
Children	1–3	13	29	90	35	1300 (900–1800)
	4–6	20	44	112	44	1700 (1300–2300)
	7–10	28	62	132	52	2400 (1650–3300)
Males	11–14	45	99	157	62	2700 (2000–3700)
	15–18	66	145	176	69	2800 (2100–3900)
	19–22	70	154	177	70	2900 (2500–3300)
	23–50	70	154	178	70	2700 (2300–3100)
	51–75	70	154	178	70	2400 (2000–2800)
	76 +	70	154	178	70	2050 (1650–2450)
Females	11–14	46	101	157	62	2200 (1500–3000)
	15–18	55	120	163	64	2100 (1200–3000)
	19–22	55	120	163	64	2100 (1700–2500)
	23–50	55	120	163	64	2000 (1600–2400)
	51–75	55	120	163	64	1800 (1400–2200)
	76 +	55	120	163	64	1600 (1200–2000)
Pregnancy						+300
Lactation						+500

The data in this table have been assembled from the observed median heights and weights of children, together with desirable weights for adults given here for the mean heights of men (70 inches) and women (64 inches) between the ages of 18 and 34 years as surveyed in the U.S. population (HEW/NCHS data).

The energy allowances for the young adults are for men and women doing light work. The allowances for the two older age groups represent mean energy needs over these age spans, allowing for a 2% decrease in basal (resting) metabolic rate per decade and a reduction in activity of 200 kcal/day for men and women between 51 and 75 years, 500 kcal for men over 75 years and 400 kcal for women over 75. The customary range of daily energy output is shown for adults in parentheses, and is based on a variation in energy needs of ± 400 kcal at any one age, emphasizing the wide range of energy intakes appropriate for any group of people.

Energy allowances for children through age 18 are based on median energy intakes of children of these ages followed in longitudinal growth studies. The values in parentheses are 10th and 90th percentiles of energy intake, to indicate the range of energy consumption among children of these ages.

Source: Recommended Dietary Allowances, Revised 1980. Food and Nutrition Board National Academy of Sciences—National Research Council, Washington, D.C.

Suggested Desirable Weights for Heights and Ranges for Adult Males and Females

		Weight[b]							
Height[a] (in)	(cm)	Men (lb)		Men (kg)		Women (lb)		Women (kg)	
58	147	—		—		102	(92–119)	46	(42–54)
60	152	—		—		107	(96–125)	49	(44–57)
62	158	123	(112–141)	56	(51–64)	113	(102–131)	51	(46–59)
64	163	130	(118–148)	59	(54–67)	120	(108–138)	55	(49–63)
66	168	136	(124–156)	62	(56–71)	128	(114–146)	58	(52–66)
68	173	145	(132–166)	66	(60–75)	136	(122–154)	62	(55–70)
70	178	154	(140–174)	70	(64–79)	144	(130–163)	65	(59–74)
72	183	162	(148–184)	74	(67–84)	152	(138–173)	69	(63–79)
74	188	171	(156–194)	78	(71–88)	—		—	
76	193	181	(164–204)	82	(74–93)	—		—	

[a]Without shoes.
[b]Without clothes.

Source: Bray, 1975.

Food and Nutrition Board National Academy of Sciences–National Research Council
Recommended Daily Dietary Allowances,[a] Revised 1980

	Age (yrs)	Weight (kg)	Weight (lb)	Height (cm)	Height (in)	Protein (g)	Fat-Soluble Vitamins			Water Soluble Vitamins							Minerals					
							Vita- min A (µg RE)[b]	Vita- min D (µg)[c]	Vita- min E (mg α-TE)[d]	Vita- min C (mg)	Thia- min (mg)	Ribo- flavin (mg)	Niacin (mg NE)[e]	Vita- min B-6 (mg)	Fola- cin[f] (µg)	Vitamin B-12 (µg)	Cal- cium (mg)	Phos- phorous (mg)	Mag- nesium (mg)	Iron (mg)	Zinc (mg)	Iodine (µg)
Infants	0.0-0.5	6	13	60	24	kg × 2.2	420	10	3	35	0.3	0.4	6	0.3	30	0.5[g]	360	240	50	10	3	40
	0.5-1.0	9	20	71	28	kg × 2.0	400	10	4	35	0.5	0.6	8	0.6	45	1.5	540	360	70	15	5	50
Children	1-3	13	29	90	35	23	400	10	5	45	0.7	0.8	9	0.9	100	2.0	800	800	150	15	10	70
	4-6	20	44	112	44	30	500	10	6	45	0.9	1.0	11	1.3	200	2.5	800	800	200	10	10	90
	7-10	28	62	132	52	34	700	10	7	45	1.2	1.4	16	1.6	300	3.0	800	800	250	10	10	120
Males	11-14	45	99	157	62	45	1000	10	8	50	1.4	1.6	18	1.8	400	3.0	1200	1200	350	18	15	150
	15-18	66	145	176	69	56	1000	10	10	60	1.4	1.7	18	2.0	400	3.0	1200	1200	400	18	15	150
	19-22	70	154	177	70	56	1000	7.5	10	60	1.5	1.7	19	2.2	400	3.0	800	800	350	10	15	150
	23-50	70	154	178	70	56	1000	5	10	60	1.4	1.6	18	2.2	400	3.0	800	800	350	10	15	150
	51+	70	154	178	70	56	1000	5	10	60	1.2	1.4	16	2.2	400	3.0	800	800	350	10	15	150
Females	11-14	46	101	157	62	46	800	10	8	50	1.1	1.3	15	1.8	400	3.0	1200	1200	300	18	15	150
	15-18	55	120	163	64	46	800	10	8	60	1.1	1.3	14	2.0	400	3.0	1200	1200	300	18	15	150
	19-22	55	120	163	64	44	800	7.5	8	60	1.1	1.3	14	2.0	400	3.0	800	800	300	18	15	150
	23-50	55	120	163	64	44	800	5	8	60	1.0	1.2	13	2.0	400	3.0	800	800	300	18	15	150
	51+	55	120	163	64	44	800	5	8	60	1.0	1.2	13	2.0	400	3.0	800	800	300	10	15	150
Pregnant						+30	+200	+5	+2	+20	+0.4	+0.3	+2	+0.6	+400	+1.0	+400	+400	+150	h	+5	+25
Lactating						+20	+400	+5	+3	+40	+0.5	+0.5	+5	+0.5	+100	+1.0	+400	+400	+150	h	+10	+50

a The allowances are intended to provide for individual variations among most normal persons as they live in the United States under usual environmental stresses. Diets should be based on a variety of common foods in order to provide other nutrients for which human requirements have been less well defined.

b Retinol equivalents. 1 retinol equivalent = 1 µg retinol or 6 µg β carotene. See text for calculation of vitamin A activity of diets as retinol equivalents.

c As cholecalciferol. 10 µg cholecalciferol = 400 IU of vitamin D.

d α-tocopherol equivalents. 1 mg d-α tocopherol = 1 α-TE.

e 1 NE (niacin equivalent is equal to 1 mg of niacin or 60 mg of dietary tryptophan.

f The folacin allowances refer to dietary sources as determined by Lactobacillus casei assay after treatment with enzymes (conjugases) to make polyglutamyl forms of the vitamin available to the test organism.

g The recommended dietary allowance for vitamin B-12 in infants is based on average concentration of the vitamin in human milk. The allowances after weaning are based on energy intake (as recommended by the American Academy of Pediatrics) and consideration of other factors, such as intestinal absorption; see text.

h The increased requirement during pregnancy cannot be met by the iron content of habitual American diets nor by the existing iron stores of many women; therefore the use of 30-60 mg of supplemental iron is recommended. Iron needs during lactation are not substantially different from those of nonpregnant women, but continued supplementation of the mother for 2-3 months after parturition is advisable in order to replenish stores depleted by pregnancy.

Estimated Safe and Adequate Daily Dietary Intakes of Additional Selected Vitamins and Minerals[a]

	Age (yr)	Vitamins			Trace elements[b]						Electrolytes		
		Vitamin K (µg)	Biotin (µg)	Pantothenic acid (mg)	Copper (mg)	Manganese (mg)	Fluoride (mg)	Chromium (mg)	Selenium (mg)	Molybdenum (mg)	Sodium (mg)	Potassium (mg)	Chloride (mg)
Infants	0-0.5	12	35	2	0.5-0.7	0.5-0.7	0.1-0.5	0.01-0.04	0.01-0.04	0.03-0.06	115-350	350-925	275-700
	0.5-1	10-20	50	3	0.7-1.0	0.7-1.0	0.2-1.0	0.02-0.06	0.02-0.06	0.04-0.08	250-750	425-1275	400-1200
Children	1-3	15-30	65	3	1.0-1.5	1.0-1.5	0.5-1.5	0.02-0.08	0.02-0.08	0.05-0.10	325-975	550-1650	500-1500
and	4-6	20-40	85	3-4	1.5-2.0	1.5-2.0	1.0-2.5	0.03-0.12	0.03-0.12	0.06-0.15	450-1350	775-2325	700-2100
adolescents	7-10	30-60	120	4-5	2.0-2.5	2.0-3.0	1.5-2.5	0.05-0.20	0.05-0.20	0.1-0.30	600-1800	1000-3000	925-2775
	11+	50-100	100-200	4-7	2.0-3.0	2.5-5.0	1.5-2.5	0.05-0.20	0.05-0.20	0.15-0.50	900-2700	1525-4575	1400-4200
Adults		70-140	100-200	4-7	2.0-3.0	2.5-5.0	1.5-4.0	0.05-0.20	0.05-0.20	0.15-0.50	1100-3300	1875-5625	1700-5100

[a] Because there is less information on which to base allowances, these figures are not given in the main table of the RDA and are provided here in the form of ranges of recommended intakes.

[b] Since the toxic levels for many trace elements may be ony several times usual intakes, the upper levels for the trace elements given in this table should not be habitually exceeded.

Source: Recommended Dietary Allowances, Revised 1980. Food and Nutrition Board National Academy of Sciences–National Research Council, Washington, D.C.

321

CALORIE, PROTEIN, FAT AND
CARBOHYDRATE VALUES OF FOODS

The following table lists calorie, protein, fat and carbohydrate values by common serving sizes. All calorie values have been rounded to the nearest five calories. Values for the remaining nutrients are rounded to the nearest gram. Values of 0.5 or less are listed as zero. A dash (—) means no values are available. This table has been abstracted from *Composition of Foods—Raw, Processed, Prepared* and the *Home and Gardens Bulletin Number 72,* both available from the Superintendent of Documents, U.S. Government Printing Office, Washington, D.C. 20402.

Food	Amount	Cal-ories	Pro-tein	Fat	Carbo-hydrate
Alcoholic Beverages*					
ale	1 bottle (12 ounces)	160	1	0	13
beer	1 bottle (12 ounces)	150	1	0	14
bourbon (100-proof)	1 jigger (1¹/₂ ounces)	125	0	0	0
brandy	1 jigger (1¹/₂ ounces)	75	0	0	0
champagne	1 glass (4 ounces)	85	0	0	5
daiquiri	1 average	120	0	0	9
gin (90-proof)	1 jigger (1¹/₂ ounces)	110	0	0	0
Manhattan	1 average	130	0	0	7
old-fashioned	1 average	130	0	0	7
rum (80-proof)	1 jigger (1¹/₂ ounces)	95	0	0	0
rye (90-proof)	1 jigger (1¹/₂ ounces)	110	0	0	0
Scotch (86-proof)	1 jigger (1¹/₂ ounces)	105	0	0	0
vodka (86-proof)	1 jigger (1¹/₂ ounces)	105	0	0	0
wine, dry	1 wineglass (3¹/₂ ounces)	85	0	0	4
sweet	1 wineglass (3¹/₂ ounces)	140	0	0	8
Almonds, shelled	12 to 14 (¹/₄ cup)	210	7	19	7
Apple	1 medium (2³/₄-inch diameter)	80	0	1	20
Apple Brown Betty	¹/₂ cup	160	2	4	32
Apple Butter	1 tablespoon	35	0	0	8
Apple Juice (Cider)	¹/₂ cup	60	0	0	15
Applesauce:					
sweetened	¹/₂ cup	115	0	0	30
unsweetened	¹/₂ cup	50	0	0	13
Apricot Nectar	¹/₂ cup	70	0	0	18
Apricots:					
canned in syrup	4 medium halves, 2 tablespoons syrup	110	1	0	29
dried	5 halves	50	1	0	13
fresh	3 medium	55	1	0	14
stewed and sweetened	¹/₂ cup	200	2	0	51
Asparagus, canned/fresh	4 medium stalks	10	1	0	2
Avocado	¹/₂ 10-ounce avocado	185	2	18	6

*Except as noted, alcoholic beverages do not contain protein, fat or carbohydrate. The calories come directly from the alcohol.

Food	Amount	Cal-ories	Pro-tein	Fat	Carbo-hydrate
Bacon:					
crisp, fried	2 slices	85	4	8	0
Canadian, uncooked	3 ounces	175	17	11	0
Banana	1 medium (6-inches long)	100	1	0	26
Bagel	1 large (1³/₄ ounces)	165	6	2	28
Barley, pearl	1 cup, raw	700	16	2	158
Bass, striped, uncooked	3 ounces	90	16	2	0
Beans:					
baked, canned, with pork and tomato sauce	1 cup	320	16	7	50
green, fresh	1 cup (1-inch pieces)	30	2	0	7
kidney, canned	1 cup	230	15	0	42
limas, fresh	¹/₂ cup	95	6	0	17
mung, sprouted seeds, uncooked	¹/₂ cup	20	2	0	4
wax, canned	1 cup	30	2	0	7
Beef:					
chuck, uncooked, lean meat only	4 ounces†	185	23	10	0
uncooked, as purchased, with bone	1 pound	985	72	75	0
flank, uncooked, lean meat only	4 ounces†	165	24	6	0
uncooked, as purchased	1 pound	655	98	26	0
porterhouse, uncooked, lean meat only	4 ounces†	185	24	9	0
uncooked, as purchased	1 pound	1,605	61	149	0
rib roast, uncooked, lean meat only	4 ounces†	220	23	13	0
uncooked, as purchased, no bone	1 pound	1,820	67	170	0
round, uncooked, lean meat only	4 ounces†	150	24	5	0
uncooked, as purchased, no bone	1 pound	895	92	56	0
rump, uncooked, lean meat only	4 ounces†	180	24	9	0
uncooked, as purchased, no bone	1 pound	1,375	79	115	0
sirloin, uncooked, lean meat only	4 ounces†	60	24	6	0
uncooked, as purchased, no bone	1 pound	1,510	74	132	0

† 4 ounces raw meat will make 3 ounces cooked.

Food	Amount	Cal-ories	Pro-tein	Fat	Carbo-hydrate
Beef, dried	2 ounces	115	19	4	0
Beef Stew, canned	1 serving (1 cup)	210	15	10	15
Beet Greens, cooked	¹/₂ cup	15	1	0	2
Beets	2 (¹/₂ cup, diced)	30	1	0	7
Biscuit Mix, enriched flour	1 cup	540	10	16	88
Biscuits:					
baking powder, enriched flour	1 (2-inch diameter)	105	2	5	13
refrigerated	1 biscuit	60 to 80 (varies according to brand)			
Blackberries, fresh	¹/₂ cup	40	1	0	9
Blueberries, fresh or frozen, unsweetened	¹/₂ cup	45	0	0	11
Bluefish:					
cooked, baked	4 ounces	180	29	6	0
uncooked fillets	1 pound	530	96	15	0
Bologna (all meat)	1 ounce	85	4	8	0
Bouillon cubes (all types)	1 cube	5	1	0	0
Brains, uncooked	3 ounces	105	9	7	1
Brazil Nuts	6–8	185	4	19	3
Breads, fresh or toasted:					
Boston brown	1 slice	100	3	1	22
cornbread, enriched	1 slice	185	6	5	30
cracked wheat	1 slice	65	2	1	13
French or Italian, unenriched	1 slice	85	3	0	17
Melba toast	1 slice	15	0	0	3
rye, light	1 slice	60	2	0	13
white, enriched	1 slice	70	2	1	13
white, raisin, un-enriched	1 slice	65	2	1	13
whole wheat	1 slice	65	3	1	14
Bread Crumbs:					
fresh, unbuttered	2 slices (1 cup)	140	4	2	26
packaged dry	¹/₄ cup	100	3	1	18
Broccoli, fresh, cooked	¹/₂ cup	20	2	0	4
Brownies, with nuts	1 square from mix	85	1	4	13
Brussels Sprouts	1 cup	55	7	1	10
Bulgar	¹/₂ cup uncooked (¹/₂ cup cooked)	300	10	1	65
Butter or Margarine	1 tablespoon	100	0	12	0
	1 cup	1,630	1	184	2
Buttermilk	1 cup (8 ounces)	100	8	2	12
Cabbage:					
boiled	¹/₂ cup	15	1	0	3
raw	1 cup shredded	20	1	0	5
	1 pound	100	5	1	22

Food	Amount	Cal-ories	Pro-tein	Fat	Carbo-hydrate
Cakes:					
angel-food	1/12 of 10-inch cake	160	4	0	36
cheesecake (cream-cheese base)	1 slice (1/8 of cake)	450	5	32	40
chiffon	10-inch cake (1/16 of cake)	215	4	9	31
chocolate cake, fudge frosting	2 9-inch layers (1/16 of cake)	235	3	9	40
cupcake, unfrosted	1 medium	90	1	3	14
fruitcake	1/30 of 8-inch loaf	55	1	2	9
poundcake	1/2-inch slice	160	2	10	16
spongecake	10-inch tube cake (1/12 of cake)	235	3	8	40
yellow cake, choco-late frosting	2 9-inch layers (1/16 of cake)	275	3	10	45
Candy:					
caramel, plain	1 small piece	40	0	1	8
chocolate cream	1 medium piece	50	—	—	—
chocolate, milk	1 ounce	145	2	9	16
fondant	1 ounce	105	0	1	25
fudge	1 ounce	115	1	4	21
gum drops	1 small	10	0	0	2
hard candy	1 large sour ball	35	0	0	9
life savers	1	10	0	0	2
peanut brittle	1 ounce	120	2	3	23
Cantaloupe	1/2 (5-inch diameter)	80	2	0	20
Carrots:					
cooked	1/2 cup, diced	25	1	0	11
raw	1 cup (grated)	45	1	0	11
	1 pound (tops trimmed)	155	4	1	36
Catchup, Chili Sauce	1 tablespoon	15	0	0	4
Catfish, uncooked	4 ounces	115	20	4	0
Cauliflower:					
cooked (boiled)	1 cup	30	3	0	5
raw	1 pound (fully trimmed)	120	12	1	12
Caviar, pressed	1 ounce	90	10	5	1
Celery, raw	1 cup, diced	20	1	0	5
	1 stalk	5	0	0	2
Cereals, cooked:					
cornmeal, enriched grits	1 cup	120	3	1	26
farina, enriched	1 cup	105	3	0	22
rolled oats	1 cup	130	5	2	23
Cereals, ready-to-eat:					
bran flakes	1 cup	105	4	1	28
corn flakes	1 cup (about 1 ounce)	95	2	0	21
oat cereal	1 cup (2/3 ounce)	100	3	1	19
puffed rice, wheat	1 cup (about 1/2 ounce)	60	1	0	13

Food	Amount	Cal-ories	Pro-tein	Fat	Carbo-hydrate
shredded wheat	1 medium biscuit	90	2	1	20
Cheese:					
American, processed or natural	1 slice (1 ounce)	105	6	9	1
Camembert	1 ounce	85	5	7	1
Cheddar	1 slice (1 ounce)	115	7	9	1
cheese spread	1 ounce	80	5	6	2
cottage, creamed	1/2 cup	117	14	5	3
uncreamed	1/2 cup	60	12	0	2
cream	2 tablespoons (1 ounce)	100	2	10	1
Mozzarella, whole milk	1 ounce	90	6	7	1
Neufchâtel	1 ounce	70	3	7	1
Parmesan or Romano, grated	2 tablespoons (1/3 ounce)	50	4	4	0
Ricotta, partially skimmed milk	1/3 cup	110	9	6	4
whole milk	1/3 cup	140	9	10	2
Roquefort or blue	1 ounce	100	6	8	1
Swiss, processed or natural	1 slice (1 ounce)	105	8	8	1
Cherries					
canned in syrup	1/2 cup, 3 tablespoons syrup	115	1	0	30
canned, red sour pitted	1 cup	105	2	0	26
fresh, sweet	1 cup	80	2	0	20
Chewing Gum	1 stick	10	0	0	3
Chicken, fryers, uncooked					
breast	1 whole, small (3/4 pound)	295	56	6	0
leg and thigh	1 small (1/2 pound)	190	28	7	0
roasted, no bone	average serving (4 ounces)	205	33	7	0
	5 ounces (1 cup diced)	225	41	9	0
Chicken Pot Pie	1 4-inch pie	535	23	31	42
Chili Con Carne, canned	1 cup	335	19	15	30
Chocolate:					
milk	1 cup	210	8	8	26
semi-sweet	1 ounce	145	1	10	16
unsweetened (baking)	1 ounce	145	3	15	8
Chocolate Syrup	1 tablespoon	50	0	1	10
Clams, uncooked	6 (4 ounces, meat only)	85	14	2	2
canned	3 ounces	45	7	1	2
Cocoa	1 tablespoon	20	1	2	3
Coconut, fresh, shredded	1/2 cup	225	3	23	6
Cod, uncooked	4 ounces	90	20	1	0
Coffee, without sugar and cream	1 cup	0	0	0	0
Coffee lighteners	1 tablespoon	20 to 30 (varies according to brand)			
Cola Drinks	6-ounce bottle	70	0	0	18
Collards, cooked	1/2 cup	30	3	0	5
Cookies:					
chocolate chip	1 (1-inch diameter)	50	1	3	6

Food	Amount	Cal-ories	Pro-tein	Fat	Carbo-hydrate
fig bar	1 square	50	1	1	11
gingersnap	1 small (2-inch diameter)	20	0	1	5
macaroon	1 (2¹/₂-inch diameter)	90	1	4	13
oatmeal	1 large (3-inch diameter)	65	1	2	11
sandwich-type	1 cookie	50	1	2	7
sugar	1 medium (3-inch diameter)	80	1	2	12
sugar wafer	1 2¹/₂″ × ³/₄″ rectangle	25	0	1	4
Corn					
canned, whole kernel	¹/₂ cup	85	3	1	20
	1 pound	300	9	3	71
fresh	1 ear (5-inches long)	70	3	1	16
Cornmeal, uncooked, degermed, enriched	1 cup	500	11	2	108
Cornstarch	1 tablespoon	30	0	0	7
Cornstarch pudding	¹/₂ cup	140	4	5	19
Crab, cooked	4 ounces	105	20	2	1
Crackers:					
graham	4 (2¹/₂-inch diameter)	110	2	2	20
oyster	10 crackers	45	1	1	7
saltine	4 squares	50	1	1	8
soda	2 (2¹/₂-inch square)	50	1	1	8
whole rye	1 double cracker	20	1	—	5
Cranberries, raw	1 cup	45	0	1	10
Cranberry Juice	¹/₂ cup	80	0	0	21
Cranberry Sauce, canned	1 tablespoon	20	0	0	5
	¹/₂ cup	200	0	0	52
Cream:					
half-and-half	1 tablespoon	20	1	2	1
heavy	1 tablespoon	80	0	6	1
	1 cup	820	5	90	7
light	1 tablespoon	45	0	5	1
	1 cup	700	5	74	7
sour, commercial	1 tablespoon	25	0	2	1
Cucumbers, raw	6 slices (¹/₈-inch thick)	5	0	0	2
Custard, baked	¹/₂ cup	150	7	7	14
Dandelion Greens, cooked	1 cup	35	2	0	7
Danish Pastry, plain	4¹/₂-inch piece	275	5	15	30
Dates, dried and pitted	¹/₄ cup (3)	110	1	0	29
Dessert Topping	1 tablespoon	10 to 25 (varies according to brand)			
Doughnuts (cake type)	1 medium	125	1	6	16
Duck, uncooked	1 average serving (4 ounces)	185	24	9	0
Eggs:					
fried	1 egg, 1 teaspoon butter	110	6	10	0
omelet	2 eggs, 2 teaspoons butter, milk	220	14	16	3

Food	Amount	Cal-ories	Pro-tein	Fat	Carbo-hydrate
raw:	1 large	80	6	6	1
white	1 large	15	3	0	0
yolk	1 large	65	3	6	0
scrambled	1 egg, milk and butter	95	6	7	1
shirred or poached	1 large	80	6	6	0
Eggplant, cooked, (boiled)	1 cup	40	12	0	8
	1 pound	90	4	1	18
Escarole, raw	4 leaves	5	0	0	1
Figs, dried	1 large	60	1	0	15
Finnan Haddie	4 ounces	120	25	0	0
Fish Sticks	1 breaded stick	50	5	3	2
Flounder, uncooked fillets	4 ounces	90	19	1	0
Flour:					
all-purpose, enriched	1 cup, sifted	455	13	1	95
cake, unenriched	1 cup, sifted	350	7	1	76
whole wheat	1 cup, sifted	400	16	2	85
Frankfurters	1 medium (8 per pound)	170	7	15	1
French Toast	1 slice (no syrup)	140	5	7	12
Fruit Cocktail, canned	1/2 cup fruit and syrup	95	0	0	25
Gelatin Dessert	1/2 cup prepared	70	2	0	17
Gelatin, unflavored, dry	1 envelope (1 scant tablespoon)	25	6	0	0
Ginger Ale	1 glass (8 ounces)	85	0	0	21
Gingerbread	3 × 3 × 2-inch unfrosted	370	4	13	60
Goose, cooked	4 ounces	260	38	11	0
Grapefruit	1/2 medium	45	1	0	12
Grapefruit Juice:					
sweetened, canned	1/2 cup	65	0	0	16
unsweetened	1/2 cup	50	0	0	12
Grapefruit Sections	1/2 cup, 1 tablespoon syrup	90	1	0	22
Grape Juice	1/2 cup	80	0	0	22
Grapes	1 cup	70	1	1	15
Gravy:					
canned beef	2 tablespoons	15	1	1	1
homemade (from drippings)	2 tablespoons	30	0	3	1
Griddlecakes	2 (4-inch diameter, no syrup)	120	4	4	18
Guavas	1 medium	50	1	0	12
Haddock:					
pan fried	1 filet (3 ounces)	140	17	5	5
uncooked fillets	1 pound	360	83	1	0
Halibut:					
broiled	1 steak (4 1/2 ounces)	240	36	10	0
uncooked fillets	1 pound	455	95	5	0

Food	Amount	Cal-ories	Pro-tein	Fat	Carbo-hydrate
Herring:					
pickled	3 ounces	185	16	13	0
smoked kippered	3 ounces	180	18	11	0
Honey	1 tablespoon	65	0	0	17
Honeydew Melon	2-inch wedge from 6½″ × 7″ melon	50	1	0	11
Ice Cream, vanilla	1 cup (10 percent butter-fat)	255	6	14	28
	1 cup (16 percent butter-fat)	330	4	24	27
Ice Milk	1 cup	200	6	7	29
Jam	1 tablespoon	55	0	0	14
Jelly	1 tablespoon	50	0	0	13
Junket	½ cup	105	4	4	14
Kale, cooked	½ cup	20	2	0	3
Kidneys, Beef, uncooked	3 ounces	110	13	5	1
Kohlrabi, cooked	½ cup	20	2	0	4
Lamb:					
rib chop, with bone, lean only	4 ounces, cooked	240	32	12	0
leg, lean meat only	1 pound, uncooked	845	68	61	0
roast, no bone, lean only	3 ounces, cooked	235	22	16	0
Lard	1 tablespoon	115	0	13	0
Lemon or Lime Juice	¼ cup (4 tablespoons)	15	0	0	5
Lemonade, concentrated, frozen	1 cup, prepared as directed	110	0	0	28
Lentils, whole, cooked	1 cup	210	16	0	39
Lettuce, raw	2 large leaves	10	1	0	2
	1 pound	55	4	0	13
Liver:					
beef, uncooked	4 ounces	155	22	4	6
calf, uncooked	4 ounces	155	22	5	5
chicken, uncooked	4 ounces	145	22	4	3
Liverwurst	2 ounces	175	9	15	1
Lobster, cooked meat	½ cup (3 ounces)	80	16	1	—
Loganberries	½ cup	45	1	0	11
Macaroni:					
cooked, enriched	½ cup	95	3	0	20
uncooked, enriched	1 pound	1,675	57	5	341
Mackerel, uncooked fillets	4 ounces	215	21	14	0
Mangos	1 medium	85	1	0	23
Margarine	1 tablespoon	100	0	12	0
	1 cup	1,630	2	184	2
Marmalade, Jam	1 tablespoon	55	0	0	14

Food	Amount	Calories	Protein	Fat	Carbohydrate
Matzoh:					
egg	1 regular	135	—	—	—
plain	1 regular	120	—	—	—
Meat Loaf	1 serving (1-inch slice)	370	24	27	8
Milk:					
buttermilk, cultured	1 glass (8 ounces)	100	8	2	12
condensed, sweetened	1/2 cup	490	12	13	83
evaporated	1/2 cup, undiluted	170	9	10	12
liquid, skimmed	1 glass (8 ounces)	90	9	0	12
liquid, 98% fat-free	1 glass (8 ounces)	135	10	5	14
liquid, whole	1 glass (8 ounces)	160	9	9	12
milk shake	1 glass (8 ounces)	400	—	—	—
nonfat dry milk, instant (dry powder)	1/3 cup	85	8	0	12
yogurt (made with partially skimmed milk):					
plain	1 cup (8 ounces)	120 to 150 (varies according to brand)			
coffee, vanilla	1 cup (8 ounces)	200 to 250 (varies according to brand)			
fruit flavored	1 cup (8 ounces)	230 to 290 (varies according to brand and flavor)			
Molasses, light	1 tablespoon	50	0	0	13
Muffins:					
blueberry	1 2³/₈-inch diameter	110	3	4	17
bran	1 2³/₈-inch diameter	105	3	4	17
corn	1 2³/₈-inch diameter	125	3	4	19
English	1 3¹/₂-inch diameter	145	—	—	—
plain	1 3-inch diameter	120	3	4	17
Mushrooms:					
canned	1 cup (solids and liquid)	40	5	0	6
fresh	1 pound	125	12	1	20
fresh	4 large	10	1	0	2
Noodles:					
cooked, enriched	1/2 cup	100	3	1	18
Chow-Mein, canned	1 cup	200	6	11	26
uncooked, enriched	1/2 pound	880	29	10	163
Oatmeal, uncooked	1 cup	310	11	6	54
Oils:					
corn, cottonseed, olive, peanut, soybean	1 tablespoon	125	0	14	0
	1/2 cup	960	0	109	0
Okra, cooked	10 pods	30	2	0	6
Olives:					
green, unstoned	4 medium	15	0	2	0
ripe, unstoned	3 small	15	0	2	0

Food	Amount	Cal-ories	Pro-tein	Fat	Carbo-hydrate
Onion, raw	1 medium	40	2	0	10
	1 pound	170	7	0	40
Orange	1 medium (2⁵/₈-inch diameter)	65	1	0	16
Orange Juice, fresh, frozen					
or canned	¹/₂ cup	60	1	0	14
Orange Sections	¹/₂ cup	45	1	0	11
Oysters, Eastern,					
uncooked	6 to 8 medium (4 ounces, meat only)	80	10	2	4
Pancakes, from mix	2 (4-inch diameter)	120	4	4	18
Papaya, raw	1 medium	120	2	0	30
Parsley, raw	5 tablespoons, chopped	5	0	0	1
Parsnips, cooked	¹/₂ cup	50	1	0	11
Peach Nectar	¹/₂ cup	60	0	0	15
Peaches:					
canned, syrup pack	¹/₂ cup halves with syrup	100	0	0	25
	1 pound, undrained	355	2	0	91
fresh, uncooked	1 medium	40	1	0	10
	1 pound	150	2	0	38
frozen, sweetened	¹/₂ cup	110	1	0	26
Peanuts, roasted	8 to 10	55	2	4	2
¹/₂ pound, shelled		1,320	59	110	46
Peanut Butter	1 tablespoon	95	4	8	3
Pear Nectar	¹/₂ cup	60	0	0	16
Pears:					
canned, syrup pack	¹/₂ cup halves with syrup	100	0	0	25
	1 pound, undrained	345	1	1	89
fresh, uncooked	1 medium	100	1	1	25
	1 pound	250	3	2	63
Peas:					
green, canned	¹/₂ cup	75	4	0	15
	1 pound	300	16	1	57
fresh, cooked	¹/₂ cup	60	4	0	10
fresh, shelled	1 pound, uncooked	380	29	2	65
split, dried, raw	¹/₂ cup	345	24	1	62
Pecans	9 medium nuts	70	1	8	2
	1 cup, halves	810	11	84	17
Peppers, green, raw	1 medium	15	1	0	4
Perch (ocean), uncooked	4 ounces	105	21	2	0
Pickles:					
dill	1 large	10	1	0	1
sour	1 large	15	1	0	3
sweet	1 small	20	0	0	6
Pie Crust:					
homemade, double-crust	1 9-inch shell	1,800	22	120	158

Food	Amount	Calories	Protein	Fat	Carbohydrate
homemade, single-crust	1 9-inch shell	900	11	60	79
packaged mix, double crust	1 (8- or 9-inch shell)	1,485	20	93	141
Pies:					
apple, double crust	4-inch wedge (¹/₇ of 9-inch pie)	345	3	15	51
cherry, double crust	4-inch wedge (¹/₇ of 9-inch pie)	350	4	15	52
custard	4-inch wedge (¹/₇ of 9-inch pie)	285	8	14	30
lemon meringue	4-inch wedge (¹/₇ of 9-inch pie)	305	4	12	45
mince	4-inch wedge (¹/₇ of 9-inch pie)	365	3	16	56
pecan	4-inch wedge (¹/₇ of 9-inch pie)	495	6	27	61
pumpkin	4-inch wedge (¹/₇ of 9-inch pie)	275	5	15	32
Pineapple:					
canned, crushed	¹/₂ cup	95	0	0	25
	1 pound	335	1	0	88
juice	¹/₂ cup	65	1	0	17
sliced	1 large or 2 small slices	80	0	0	27
fresh, sliced	1 cup, chopped	80	1	0	21
	1 pound, untrimmed	123	1	0	32
Pizza, cheese	¹/₈ of 14-inch pie	155	8	5	18
Plums:					
canned, syrup pack	¹/₂ cup plums with syrup	105	0	0	28
	1 pound (undrained)	360	2	0	94
fresh	1 (2-inch diameter)	25	0	0	7
Popcorn, popped, with oil	1 cup	40	1	2	5
plain	1 cup	25	1	0	5
Popover	1 medium	120	4	7	10
Pork:					
ham, boiled	1 slice (1 ounce)	70	5	5	0
ham, cured, roasted	3 ounces (lean meat only)	245	18	19	0
ham, fresh, uncooked	3 ounces (lean meat only)	130	17	7	0
loin chop, uncooked	4 ounces (lean meat only)	300	34	18	0
Potatoes:					
baked or boiled	1 medium (1 cup, diced)	90	3	0	0
French-fried	10 pieces (2″ × ¹/₂″ × ¹/₂″)	135	2	7	18
mashed	¹/₂ cup, milk and butter added	95	2	4	12
scalloped	¹/₂ cup	120	—	—	—
sweet, baked or boiled	1 medium (5″ × 2″)	155	2	1	36
sweet, candied	1 small (3¹/₂″ × 2¹/₄″)	295	2	6	60

Food	Amount	Cal-ories	Pro-tein	Fat	Carbo-hydrate
Potato Chips	10 medium (2-inch diameter)	115	1	8	10
Pretzels	10 2¹/₄-inch long sticks	10	0	0	2
Prune Juice, canned	¹/₂ cup	100	0	0	25
Prunes, uncooked	5 large	110	1	0	29
Pudding:					
chocolate	¹/₂ cup	175	5	6	32
cornstarch	¹/₂ cup	140	4	5	19
Pumpkin, canned	¹/₂ cup	40	1	0	9
Pumpkin Seeds:					
shelled	1 tablespoon	60	3	5	1
unshelled	¹/₄ cup	60	3	5	1
Rabbit, uncooked, no bones	4 ounces	180	24	9	0
Radishes, raw	4 small	5	0	0	1
Raisins, seedless	¹/₄ cup	120	1	0	32
Raspberries, red fresh	¹/₂ cup	35	0	0	9
Rhubarb:					
stewed and sweet-ened	¹/₂ cup	190	1	0	49
uncooked	1 pound	60	2	0	14
Rice:					
brown, uncooked	¹/₂ cup (1¹/₂ cups cooked)	300	6	2	63
precooked	1 cup cooked	180	4	0	40
white, enriched					
uncooked	¹/₂ cup	330	7	0	71
	1 pound	1,645	30	2	365
cooked	¹/₂ cup	110	2	0	25
wild, uncooked	¹/₂ cup	295	12	1	61
Rice Pudding	1 serving (³/₄ cup)	225	6	9	32
Rye Wafers	2 wafers	45	2	0	10
Salad Dressings:					
blue or Roquefort	1 tablespoon	75	1	8	1
French	1 tablespoon	65	0	6	3
Italian	1 tablespoon	80	0	9	0
mayonnaise	1 tablespoon	100	0	11	0
salad, cooked type	1 tablespoon	65	0	6	2
Thousand Island	1 tablespoon	80	0	8	3
Salmon:					
baked	1 steak (4 ounces)	210	30	8	0
canned (sockeye or red)	¹/₂ cup, flaked (3 ounces)	120	17	5	0
Sardines, canned in oil	4 medium (1¹/₂ onces)	85	10	5	0
Sauces:					
barbecue	¹/₄ cup	80	1	0	16
chocolate syrup	2 tablespoons	100	0	1	26
hard	2 tablespoons	140	0	7	16
Hollandaise	2 tablespoons	175	0	17	0
spaghetti, canned					

Food	Amount	Cal-ories	Pro-tein	Fat	Carbo-hydrate
meat sauce	1/2 cup	100	5	5	8
tomato puree, canned	1/2 cup	45	2	0	10
white, medium	1/2 cup	210	4	6	9
Sauerkraut	1/2 cup	20	1	0	4
Sausage, cooked	2 links (16 per pound)	125	5	11	0
brown and serve	4 ounces (before browning)	445	15	41	3
Scallops, uncooked	8 medium (4 ounces)	90	17	0	5
Sherbet	1/2 cup	130	1	1	30
Shortening, solid	1 tablespoon	110	0	13	0
	1 cup	1,770	0	200	0
Shrimp, shelled, uncooked	12 to 14 medium (3 1/2 ounces)	90	18	1	1
unshelled	1 pound	525	110	5	3
canned	4 ounces	75	15	0	0
Soups (canned soups are prepared according to label directions):					
beef broth	scant cup	30	5	0	3
beef-noodle	scant cup	65	4	3	7
chicken broth	scant cup	20	2	0	2
chicken, cream of (with milk)	scant cup	180	7	10	15
chicken-gumbo	scant cup	50	2	1	7
chicken-noodle	scant cup	55	2	1	8
chicken with rice	scant cup	45	3	1	5
clam chowder:					
Manhattan	scant cup	80	2	3	12
New England (frozen)	scant cup	145	7	6	14
consommé	scant cup	30	5	0	3
minestrone	scant cup	105	5	3	14
mushroom, cream of	scant cup	135	2	10	10
onion	scant cup	35	1	1	6
pea, split	scant cup	145	9	3	21
potato, cream of (frozen)	scant cup	160	6	8	15
tomato:	scant cup	90	2	3	16
clear cream of	scant cup	175	7	7	23
turkey noodle	scant cup	65	3	3	7
vegetable-beef	scant cup	80	5	2	10
Spaghetti, cooked	1 cup	155	5	1	32
Spaghetti Sauce:					
canned mushroom	1 cup	155	3	6	22
canned with cheese	1 cup	190	6	2	38
Spinach or other greens, cooked	1/2 cup	20	3	1	3

Food	Amount	Calories	Protein	Fat	Carbohydrate
Squash:					
summer, cooked	1/2 cup	15	1	0	3
winter, cooked	1/2 cup	65	2	0	16
Starch (arrowroot, corn, etc.)	1 tablespoon	30	0	0	7
Strawberries, fresh	1/2 cup	25	0	0	6
Sugar:					
brown	1 tablespoon	50	0	0	13
	1 cup	820	0	0	212
granulated	1 tablespoon	40	0	0	11
	1 cup	770	0	0	199
powdered (confectioners')	1 tablespoon	30	0	0	8
	1 cup	460	0	0	119
Sunflower Seeds:					
shelled	1 tablespoon	45	2	4	1
unshelled	1/4 cup	45	2	4	1
Sweetbreads, calves, cooked	3/4 cup (3 1/2 ounces)	170	33	3	0
Sweet Potatoes	**See** Potatoes				
Swordfish, cooked	1 steak (4 ounces)	195	31	7	0
Syrup:					
maple	1 tablespoon	50	0	0	13
table (corn)	1 tablespoon	60	0	0	15
Tangerine	1 (2 1/2-inch diameter)	40	1	0	10
Tapioca, quick-cooking	1/4-cup (4 tablespoons)	140	0	0	36
Tea without sugar or cream	1 cup	0	0	0	0
Tomato Juice	1/2 cup (4 ounces)	25	1	0	5
Tomatoes:					
canned	1/2 cup	25	1	0	5
	1 pound	95	4	1	20
fresh	1 medium	40	2	0	9
Tongue, uncooked	4 ounces	180	14	13	0
Tripe, cooked	4 ounces	115	22	2	0
Trout (rainbow), uncooked	4 ounces (fillets)	220	24	13	0
Tuna:					
canned in oil	2/3 cup, drained (3 ounces)	170	24	7	0
	7 ounces (undrained)	576	48	41	0
canned water pack	2/3 cup (3 ounces)	110	23	1	0
Turkey, roasted (white and dark meat)	3 ounces	160	27	5	0
	1 pound	855	143	28	0
Turnips, white, cooked	1/2 cup	15	0	0	4
Veal:					
cutlet, cooked, no bone	3 ounces	185	23	9	0
roast, cooked, no bone	1 slice (3 ounces)	180	23	10	0

Food	Amount	Calories	Protein	Fat	Carbohydrate
Vegetable Juice, canned	½ cup (4 ounces)	20	1	0	4
Vienna Sausage, canned	1 sausage	40	2	3	0
Vinegar	1 cup	30	0	0	7
Waffle	1 7-inch waffle	210	7	7	28
Walnuts, chopped,	1 tablespoon	50	2	5	1
English or black	1 cup halves, chopped	85	26	74	19
Watercress, raw	1 bunch, 3″ long	20	2	0	4
Watermelon	1 wedge, 4″ × 8″	115	2	1	27
Wheat Germ	1 tablespoon	15	1	0	2
Whipped Toppings:					
aerosol	1 tablespoon	10 (varies according to brand)			
frozen or mix	1 tablespoon	10 to 25 (varies according to brand)			
Whitefish, uncooked fillets	4 ounces	175	21	9	0
Yams, cooked	**See** Potatoes				
Yeast:					
dried brewer's	1 package active dry	25	3	0	3
regular	1 cake, compressed	20	3	0	3
Yogurt	**See** Milk				
Zwieback	1 cracker	30	0	0	5

IRON CONTENT OF FOODS

The following is a list of the iron content of some foods. The recommended dietary allowance for iron is 18 mg. for women and 10 mg. for men, daily. All values were obtained from *Nutritive Value of American Foods,* Agricultural Handbook No. 456, available from the Superintendent of Documents, U.S. Government Printing Office, Washington, D.C. 20402.

Food	Amount	Iron mg.
Apple juice (cider)	1/2 cup	7
Apricots:		
dried	5 large halves	1.0
fresh	3 medium	5
Asparagus canned	6 medium stalks	1.8
Bacon, Canadian, uncooked	3 ounces	2.2
Beans:		
baked, canned with pork and tomato sauce	1 cup	4.6
black	1 cup	7.9
garbanzo (chick peas)	1 cup	6.9
lima, fresh	1/2 cup	2.2
canned	1/2 cup	2.0
dry	1 cup	5.1
kidney, canned	1 cup	4.6
soy	1 cup	4.9
Beef (uncooked, trimmed lean meat only):		
chuck	4 ounces*	3.6
flank steak	4 ounces	3.6
sirloin	4 ounces	3.6
Beet greens, cooked	1/2 cup	1.4
Blueberries, fresh or frozen, unsweetened	1/2 cup	.7
Brussels sprouts, cooked fresh	1 cup	1.7
frozen	1 cup	1.7
Cantaloupe	1/2 (5-inch diameter)	1.1
Cereals:		
rolled oats, cooked	3/4 cup	1.1
wheat bran (100%), ready to eat	1/2 cup (1 ounce)	3.0
Chicken:		
fryers, breast	1 whole small (3/4 pound)	3.2
roaster, boneless	4 ounces	1.7
Clams, uncooked	6 (4 ounces, meat only)	6.9
Coconut, dried, shredded	1/2 cup	1.1
Collards, cooked	1/2 cup	.5
Cornmeal, uncooked (enriched)	1 cup	4.0
Dates	10 medium	2.4

Food	Amount	Iron mg.
Eggs:		
whole	1 medium	1.1
yolk	1 average	1.1
Flour:		
enriched all purpose	1 cup sifted	3.3
whole wheat	1 cup sifted	4.0
Halibut, cooked	4 ounces	1.1
Kale, cooked	1 cup	1.8
Lamb, cooked chop	4 ounces	1.5
Lentils	1 cup cooked	4.2
Liver:		
beef uncooked	4 ounces	7.4
calf uncooked	4 ounces	10.0
chicken, uncooked	4 ounces	8.9
Liverwurst	2 ounces	3.0
Lobster, fresh, cooked	3 ounces	.7
Molasses:		
light	1 tablespoon	.9
dark	1 tablespoon	1.2
Mushrooms, canned	1 cup	1.2
Oysters, raw	6-8 (4 ounces meat)	6.2
Peas:		
canned	1/2 cup	2.1
fresh, cooked	1/2 cup	1.4
frozen, cooked	1/2 cup	1.4
Prune juice	1 cup	10.5
Pumpkin seeds	2 tablespoons	2.0
Raisins	1/2 cup	2.6
Raspberries, fresh	1 cup	1.1
Scallops, raw	4 ounces	2.0
Shrimp, raw	4 ounces	1.8
Spinach:		
canned	1/2 cup	2.3
fresh, cooked	1/2 cup	2.0
cooked, frozen	1/2 cup	2.0
Strawberries, fresh	1 cup	1.5
Tofu (soybean curd)	4 ounces	2.3
Tomato juice	1 cup	2.2
Tuna, canned	4 ounces, drained	2.0
Turkey, roasted	4 ounces	2.0
Wheat germ	1/4 cup	1.9
Yams, cooked	1 medium	1.0

SODIUM CONTENT OF FOODS

The following table gives the sodium content of foods by common serving sizes. All values are taken from *The Sodium Content of Your Foods,* available for $2.25 from the Superintendent of Documents, U.S. Government Printing Office, Washington, D.C. 20402.

Food	Amount	Sodium mg.
Cheese, natural:		
blue	1 ounce	396
brie	1 ounce	178
Cheddar, regular	1 ounce	176
cottage, regular and lowfat	4 ounces	457
dry curd, unsalted	4 ounces	14
cream	1 ounce	84
gouda	1 ounce	232
mozzarella, from whole milk	1 ounce	106
part skim milk	1 ounce	132
Neufchâtel	1 ounce	113
Parmesan, grated	1 ounce	528
Swiss	1 ounce	74
pasteurized processed cheese, American	1 ounce	406
Cream, sweet, fluid, all types	1 tablespoon	6
Ice cream, chocolate	1 cup	75
Yogurt, plain:		
regular	8 ounces	105
lowfat	8 ounces	159
Eggs:		
whole	1 egg	59
substitute, frozen	1/4 cup	120
Fish:		
bass, black sea, raw	3 ounces	57
flounder (includes sole and other flat fish) baked with butter)	3 ounces	201
herring, smoked	3 ounces	5,234
mackerel, raw	3 ounces	40
salmon, broiled with butter	3 ounces	99
canned, salt added, pink	3 ounces	443
without salt added	3 ounces	41
snapper, raw	3 ounces	56
trout, lake, raw	3 ounces	67
tuna, canned, light meat, chunk, oil pack	3 ounces	303
water pack	3 ounces	288
Shellfish:		
mussels, raw	3 ounces	243
oysters, raw	3 ounces	113

Food	Amount	Sodium mg.
scallops, raw	3 ounces	217
shrimps, raw	3 ounces	137
Meat:		
beef, cooked, lean	3 ounces	55
lamb, cooked, lean	3 ounces	58
pork,		
cured bacon, cooked	2 slices	274
Canadian	1 slice	394
ham	3 ounces	1,114
fresh, cooked, lean	3 ounces	59
veal, cooked, lean	3 ounces	69
Poultry and game:		
chicken, roasted	1/2 breast	69
breast, with skin		
products, frankfurter	1 frankfurter	617
turkey, small, roasted, breast	1/2 breast	182
with skin		
Fruit:		
apples, raw or baked	1 apple	2
banana, raw	1 banana	2
blueberries, raw	1 cup	1
strawberries, raw	1 cup	2
cherries, raw	1 cup	1
citrus fruit		
grapefruit, raw	1/2 grapefruit	1
orange, raw	1 orange	1
cranberry sauce	1 cup	75
fruit cocktail, canned	1 cup	15
muskmelon:		
cantaloupe	1/2 melon	24
honeydew	1/5 melon	28
peaches, raw	1 peach	1
pears, raw	1 pear	1
pineapple, raw	1 cup	1
plums, raw	1 plum	1
prunes, dried	5 large	2
raisins, seedless	1 cup	17
Bread:		
cornbread, homemade	1 ounce	176
white, regular	1 slice	114
whole wheat	1 slice	132
Legumes and nuts:		
almonds, salted, roasted	1 cup	311
unsalted, slivered	1 cup	4
beans, dry, cooked:		
kidney	1 cup	4
lentils, cooked	1 cup	4

Food	Amount	Sodium mg.
lima	1 cup	4
peanuts, dry roasted, salted	1 cup	986
unsalted	1 cup	8
peanut butter, smooth or crunchy	1 tablespoon	81
pecans	1 cup	1
pinto	1 cup	4
kidney, canned	1 cup	844
soybeans, cooked	1 cup	4
curd (tofu)	1/4 block	9
walnuts, English	1 cup	3
Vegetables:		
asparagus, raw	1 spear	1
frozen	4 spears	4
canned, regular	4 spears	298
beets, cooked	1 cup	73
Canned, sliced	1 cup	479
broccoli, raw	1 stalk	23
frozen, cooked	1 cup	35
carrots, raw	1 carrot	34
frozen, cut or whole	3.3 ounces	43
in butter sauce	3.3 ounces	350
with brown sugar glaze	3.3 ounces	500
canned, regular	1 cup	386
cauliflower, raw	1 cup	17
cooked	1 cup	13
celery	1 stalk	25
corn, cooked	1 ear	1
frozen	1 cup	7
vacuum pack	1 cup	577
whole kernel, regular	1 cup	384
kale, cooked	1 cup	47
lettuce	1 cup	4
mushrooms, raw	1 cup	7
peas, green, cooked	1 cup	2
frozen, regular	3 ounces	80
in butter sauce	3.3 ounces	402
in cream sauce	2.6 ounces	420
with mushrooms	3.3 ounces	240
peppers, hot, raw	1 pod	7
sweet, raw or cooked	1 pod	9
sauerkraut, canned	1 cup	1,554
spinach, cooked	1 cup	94
frozen, regular	3.3 ounces	65
canned, regular	1 cup	910
squash, summer, cooked	1 cup	5
tomatoes, raw	1 tomato	14

Food	Amount	Sodium mg.
cooked	1 cup	10
whole	1 cup	390
tomato juice, regular	1 cup	878
low sodium	1 cup	9
tomato paste	1 cup	77
tomato sauce	1 cup	1,498
Condiments, fats and oils:		
baking powder	1 teaspoon	339
baking soda	1 teaspoon	821
garlic, powder	1 teaspoon	1
salt	1 teaspoon	1,850
horse radish, prepared	1 tablespoon	198
olives, green	4 olives	323
onion, powder	1 teaspoon	1
salt	1 teaspoon	1,620
salt	1 teaspoon	1,938
Sauces:		
soy	1 tablespoon	1,029
tabasco	1 teaspoon	24
Worcestershire	1 tablespoon	206
Vinegar	1/2 cup	1
Fats, oils and related products:		
butter, regular	1 tablespoon	116
unsalted	1 tablespoon	2
margarine, regular	1 tablespoon	140
unsalted	1 tablespoon	1
French dressing, home recipe	1 tablespoon	92
bottled	1 tablespoon	214
dry mix, prepared	1 tablespoon	172
Italian dressing, bottled	1 tablespoon	214
dry mix, prepared	1 tablespoon	172
Russian dressing	1 tablespoon	133
Beverages:		
alcoholic		
beer	12 fluid ounces	25
gin, rum, whiskey	2 fluid ounces	1
whiskey sour mix	2 fluid ounces	4
wine, dessert	3 1/2 fluid ounces	4
sherry	4 fluid ounces	4
table	3 1/2 fluid ounces	5
carbonated		
club soda	8 fluid ounces	60
cola, regular	12 fluid ounces	22
low-calorie	12 fluid ounces	25
fruit-flavored soda	12 fluid ounces	27
quinine	12 fluid ounces	16
coffee		
brewed	8 fluid ounces	2

Food	Amount	Sodium mg.
instant, decaffeinated	8 fluid ounces	1
regular	8 fluid ounces	1
fruit drinks		
grape (canned)	8 fluid ounces	1
lemonade, flavored drink from		
mix	8 fluid ounces	—
frozen, from concentrate,		
diluted	8 fluid ounces	—
orange (canned	8 fluid ounces	77
fruit juices		
apple cider or juice	8 fluid ounces	2
apricot nectar	8 fluid ounces	trace
cranberry juice cocktail	8 fluid ounces	2
grapefruit juice, canned,		
unsweetened	8 fluid ounces	2
frozen, diluted, unsweetened	8 fluid ounces	2
grape juice, bottled	8 fluid ounces	5
orange juice, frozen, diluted	8 fluid ounces	2
pear nectar	8 fluid ounces	3
pineapple juice, unsweetened	8 fluid ounces	3
prune juice	8 fluid ounces	5
tea		
hot, instant	8 fluid ounces	2
iced, canned, sweetened	12 fluid ounces	13
iced, powdered, lemon flavored,		
sweetened	8 fluid ounces	1
low-calorie	8 fluid ounces	15
Milk:		
canned-evaporated, whole	8 fluid ounces	236
skim	8 fluid ounces	280
dry-nonfat, instant	8 fluid ounces	373
regular, whole	8 fluid ounces	518
fluid, buttermilk, cultured	8 fluid ounces	319
skim	8 fluid ounces	128
whole and low-fat	8 fluid ounces	122
sweetened-condensed	8 fluid ounces	336
Milk beverages		
chocolate (with whole milk)	8 fluid ounces	149
cocoa hot chocolate (with whole		
milk)	8 fluid ounces	123
cocoa mix with water	8 fluid ounces	154
eggnog (non-alcoholic)	8 fluid ounces	138
vegetable juices		
tomato	8 fluid ounces	486
vegetable juice cocktail	8 fluid ounces	484

CHOLESTEROL VALUES OF FOODS

Foods of animal origin (meat, fish, poultry, eggs and dairy products) primarily contain cholesterol. The highest concentration is found in organ meats (liver, brain, etc.), egg yolk and shellfish. Vegetables, grains and fruits do not contain cholesterol. The amount of cholesterol in combination foods, breads and desserts depends upon the amount of cholesterol-containing ingredients (eggs, butter, milk).

Food	Amount	Cholesterol mg.
Cheese:		
American, pasteurized processed	1 ounce	27
blue	1 ounce	21
brie	1 ounce	28
Cheddar	1 ounce	30
cream	2 tablespoons	34
gouda	1 ounce	32
mozzarella	1 ounce	22
mozzarella, part skim	1 ounce	57
muenster	1 ounce	27
Neufchâtel	1 ounce	21
Parmesan, grated	1 tablespoon	4
ricotta	1/2 cup	63
Swiss	1 ounce	26
American, pasteurized processed cheese food	1 ounce	64
Eggs:		
whole, fresh, chicken	1 medium	264
whites, fresh	1 medium	0
yolks, fresh	1 medium	272
Fats and oils:		
butter	1 teaspoon	11
chicken fat	1 tablespoon	9
margarine, vegetable oil	1 teaspoon	0
mayonnaise	1 tablespoon	10
pork fat	1 ounce	20
vegetable oils and shortenings	1 tablespoon	0
Frozen desserts:		
ice cream, 10% fat	1 cup	53
16% fat	1 cup	84
ice milk, strawberry	1/6 quart	18
vanilla	1/6 quart	13
Fish and shellfish:		
caviar, sturgeon	1 teaspoon	25
clams, canned	1/2 cup	80
raw	3 1/2 ounces	50
crab, canned	1/2 ounce	86
lobster, raw	3 1/2 ounces	200
mussels, canned	3 1/2 ounces	150
oysters, raw	5–8 ounces	200

Food	Amount	Cholesterol mg.
salmon, broil/baked	3½ ounces	47
scallops, bay and sea		
cooked	3 ½ ounces	53
shrimp, raw	3 ½ ounces	150
tuna, canned in oil	½ ounce	63
canned in water	½ ounce	63
Meats:		
bacon, cured cooked	2 slices	13
beef, cooked	3 ounces	80
chicken, cooked	½ breast	63
pork, cooked	3 ounces	76
turkey, light, cooked	3 ounces	65
veal, cooked	3 ounces	86
frankfurter, cooked	1 average	35
organ meats		
kidney, calf raw	3 ½ ounces	375
liver, calf, raw	3 ½ ounces	300
liver, chicken, raw	3 ½ ounces	555
sweetbread, calf	3 ½ ounces	466
brains	3 ½ ounces	2100
Milk and cream:		
buttermilk	1 cup	10
low-fat, 1% fat	1 cup	10
low-fat, 2% fat	1 cup	20
skim	1 cup	5
whole, 3.7% fat	1 cup	34
cream, half and half	1 tablespoon	6
light	1 tablespoon	10
sour	1 tablespoon	5
heavy whip	1 tablespoon	20
Yogurt:		
low-fat with non-fat		
milk solids	1 cup	14
low-fat, fruit flavor with non-		
fat milk solids	1 cup	10
whole	1 cup	30

*Data from *Food Values of Portions Commonly Used,* 13th ed., by Jean A.T. Pennington and Helen Nichols Church. Copyright © 1980 by Helen Nichols Church, B.S. and Jean A.T. Pennington, Ph.D., R.D. Reprinted by permission of Harper & Row Publishers, Inc.

Index

ALLERGY DIETS

BLAND, LOW-RESIDUE AND GALL-BLADDER DIETS

DIABETIC DIETS

HIGH-IRON DIETS

LOW-FAT AND/OR LOW-CHOLESTEROL DIETS

LOW-PURINE DIETS

LOW-SODIUM DIETS